Quantitative Analysis for Management
Volume 2
Third Edition

We work with leading authors to develop the strongest educational materials bringing cutting-edge thinking and best learning practice to a global market.

Under a range of well-known imprints, including Financial Times/Prentice Hall, Addison Wesley and Longman, we craft high quality print and electronic publications which help readers to understand and apply their content, whether studying or at work.

Pearson Custom Publishing enables our customers to access a wide and expanding range of market-leading content from world-renowned authors and develop their own tailor-made book. You choose the content that meets your needs and Pearson Custom Publishing produces a high-quality printed book.

To find out more about custom publishing, visit www.pearsoncustom.co.uk

A Pearson Custom Publication

Quantitative Analysis for Management
Volume 2
Third Edition

Compiled from:

Quantitative Methods for Business and Economics
Second Edition
Glyn Burton, George Carrol and Stuart Wall

Statistics for Business and Economics
Sixth Edition
Paul Newbold, William L. Carlson and Betty Thorne

Introduction to Management Science
Ninth Edition
Bernard W. Taylor III

Essential Quantitative Methods for Business, Management and Finance
Third Edition
Les Oakshott

Pearson Education Limited
Edinburgh Gate
Harlow
Essex CM20 2JE

And associated companies throughout the world

Visit us on the World Wide Web at:
www.pearsoned.co.uk

First published 2006

This Custom Book Edition © 2009 Published by Pearson Education Limited

Compiled from:

Quantitative Methods for Business and Economics
Second Edition
Glyn Burton, George Carrol and Stuart Wall
ISBN978 0 273 65570 1

Statistics for Business and Economics
Sixth Edition
Paul Newbold, William L. Carlson and Betty Thorne
ISBN 978 0 13 188090 0

Introduction to Management Science
Ninth Edition
Bernard W. Taylor III
ISBN 978 0 13 196133 3

Essential Quantitative Methods for Business, Management and Finance
Third Edition
Les Oakshott
ISBN 978 1 4039 4991 2

ISBN 978 1 84776 208 5

Printed and bound in Great Britain by Henry Ling Limited at the Dorset Press, Dorchester, DT1 1HD.

Contents

Introduction

These two volumes have been compiled from selected chapters of texts in the Pearson range of academic books. This has been done so that you get all the necessary background reading for the Quantitative Analysis for Management modules (QAMI and QAMII) without having to consult, or buy, a variety of different texts. As such, these two volumes are unique and have been designed specifically for the QAMI and QAMII modules at Warwick Business School.

These two volumes are arranged such that the first volume corresponds to the QAMI module and the second volume to the QAMII module.

QAMI and QAMII are applied modules rather than theoretical ones and emphasis is placed on learning to use the material covered in both of the modules. Therefore you will find that you are supplied here with many worked examples. Similarly you will be asked to undertake examples on your own in order to practise the applications and you will be required to discuss your results in tutorials.

The Contents pages of each of these two volumes provide a list of topics where each topic represents a chapter from a source text. The Contents pages also indicate the exact source text of each topic. Note that when you consult a particular topic you will sometimes see that the front page lists the various sections of that topic. These sections are numbered using the original chapter numbers from the source text (and not the topic number here). This is also true with respect to the numbering of figures and diagrams within that topic. This should not cause any confusion since when reading material from a particular topic it is still numbered consistently within that topic.

Topic 13

Management Science

1 Management Science

Management science is the application of a scientific approach to solving management problems in order to help managers make better decisions. As implied by this definition, management science encompasses a number of mathematically oriented techniques that have either been developed within the field of management science or been adapted from other disciplines, such as the natural sciences, mathematics, statistics, and engineering. This text provides an introduction to the techniques that make up management science and demonstrates their applications to management problems.

__Management science__ is a scientific approach to solving management problems.

Management science is a recognized and established discipline in business. The applications of management science techniques are widespread, and they have been frequently credited with increasing the efficiency and productivity of business firms. In various surveys of businesses, many indicate that they use management science techniques, and most rate the results to be very good. Management science (also referred to as *operations research, quantitative methods, quantitative analysis*, and *decision sciences*) is part of the fundamental curriculum of most programs in business.

Management science can be used in a variety of organizations to solve many different types of problems.

As you proceed through the various management science models and techniques contained in this text, you should remember several things. First, most of the examples presented in this text are for business organizations because businesses represent the main users of management science. However, management science techniques can be applied to solve problems in different types of organizations, including services, government, military, business and industry, and health care.

Second, in this text all of the modeling techniques and solution methods are mathematically based. In some instances the manual, mathematical solution approach is shown because it helps to understand how the modeling techniques are applied to different problems. However, a computer solution is possible for each of the modeling techniques in this text, and in many cases the computer solution is emphasized. The more detailed mathematical solution procedures for many of the modeling techniques are included as supplemental modules on the CD that accompanies this text.

Management science encompasses a logical approach to problem solving.

Finally, as the various management science techniques are presented, keep in mind that management science is more than just a collection of techniques. Management science also involves the philosophy of approaching a problem in a logical manner (i.e., a scientific approach). The logical, consistent, and systematic approach to problem solving can be as useful (and valuable) as the knowledge of the mechanics of the mathematical techniques themselves. This understanding is especially important for those readers who do not always see the immediate benefit of studying mathematically oriented disciplines such as management science.

The Management Science Approach to Problem Solving

The steps of the scientific method are (1) observation, (2) problem definition, (3) model construction, (4) model solution, and (5) implementation.

As indicated in the previous section, management science encompasses a logical, systematic approach to problem solving, which closely parallels what is known as the **scientific method** for attacking problems. This approach, as shown in Figure 1.1, follows a generally recognized and ordered series of steps: (1) observation, (2) definition of the problem, (3) model construction, (4) model solution, and (5) implementation of solution results. We will analyze each of these steps individually.

Observation

The first step in the management science process is the identification of a problem that exists in the system (organization). The system must be continuously and closely observed so that problems can be identified as soon as they occur or are anticipated. Problems are

Figure 1.1
The management science process

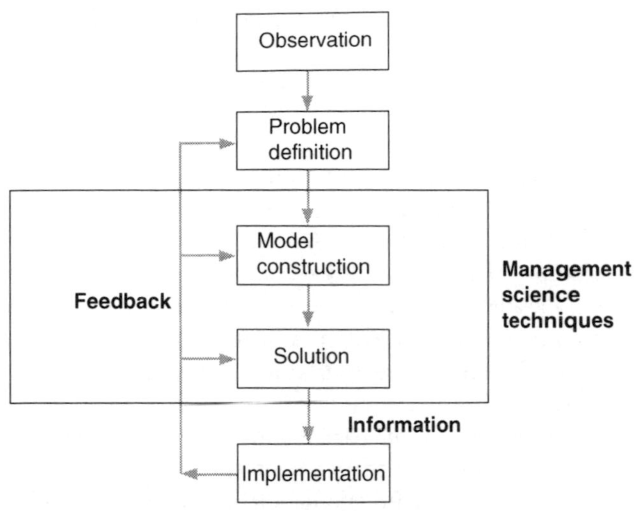

not always the result of a crisis that must be reacted to but, instead, frequently involve an anticipatory or planning situation. The person who normally identifies a problem is the manager because the managers work in places where problems might occur. However, problems can often be identified by a **management scientist**, a person skilled in the techniques of management science and trained to identify problems, who has been hired specifically to solve problems using management science techniques.

*A **management scientist** is a person skilled in the application of management science techniques.*

Definition of the Problem

Once it has been determined that a problem exists, the problem must be clearly and concisely *defined.* Improperly defining a problem can easily result in no solution or an inappropriate solution. Therefore, the limits of the problem and the degree to which it pervades other units of the organization must be included in the problem definition. Because the existence of a problem implies that the objectives of the firm are not being met in some way, the goals (or objectives) of the organization must also be clearly defined. A stated objective helps to focus attention on what the problem actually is.

Model Construction

*A **model** is an abstract mathematical representation of a problem situation.*

A management science **model** is an abstract representation of an existing problem situation. It can be in the form of a graph or chart, but most frequently a management science model consists of a set of mathematical relationships. These mathematical relationships are made up of numbers and symbols.

As an example, consider a business firm that sells a product. The product costs $5 to produce and sells for $20. A model that computes the total profit that will accrue from the items sold is

$$Z = \$20x - 5x$$

In this equation x represents the number of units of the product that are sold, and Z represents the total profit that results from the sale of the product. The *symbols* x and Z are *variables*. The term **variable** is used because no set numeric value has been specified for these items. The number of units sold, x, and the profit, Z, can be any amount (within limits); they can vary. These two variables can be further distinguished. Z is a *dependent variable* because its value is dependent on the number of units sold; x is an *independent*

*A **variable** is a symbol used to represent an item that can take on any value.*

variable because the number of units sold is *not* dependent on anything else (in this equation).

***Parameters** are known, constant values that are often coefficients of variables in equations.*

***Data** are pieces of information from the problem environment.*

The numbers \$20 and \$5 in the equation are referred to as **parameters**. Parameters are constant values that are generally coefficients of the variables (symbols) in an equation. Parameters usually remain constant during the process of solving a specific problem. The parameter values are derived from **data** (i.e., pieces of information) from the problem environment. Sometimes the data are readily available and quite accurate. For example, presumably the selling price of \$20 and product cost of \$5 could be obtained from the firm's accounting department and would be very accurate. However, sometimes data are not as readily available to the manager or firm, and the parameters must be either estimated or based on a combination of the available data and estimates. In such cases, the model is only as accurate as the data used in constructing the model.

*A model is a **functional relationship** that includes variables, parameters, and equations.*

The equation as a whole is known as a **functional relationship** (also called *function and relationship*). The term is derived from the fact that profit, Z, is a *function* of the number of units sold, x, and the equation *relates* profit to units sold.

Because only one functional relationship exists in this example, it is also the *model.* In this case the relationship is a model of the determination of profit for the firm. However, this model does not really replicate a problem. Therefore, we will expand our example to create a problem situation.

Let us assume that the product is made from steel and that the business firm has 100 pounds of steel available. If it takes 4 pounds of steel to make each unit of the product, we can develop an additional mathematical relationship to represent steel usage:

$$4x = 100 \text{ lb. of steel}$$

This equation indicates that for every unit produced, 4 of the available 100 pounds of steel will be used. Now our model consists of two relationships:

$$\begin{aligned} Z &= \$20x - 5x \\ 4x &= 100 \end{aligned}$$

We say that the profit equation in this new model is an **objective function**, and the resource equation is a **constraint.** In other words, the objective of the firm is to achieve as much profit, Z, as possible, but the firm is constrained from achieving an infinite profit by the limited amount of steel available. To signify this distinction between the two relationships in this model, we will add the following notations:

$$\begin{aligned} &\text{maximize } Z = \$20x - 5x \\ &\text{subject to} \\ &\qquad 4x = 100 \end{aligned}$$

This model now represents the manager's problem of determining the number of units to produce. You will recall that we defined the number of units to be produced as x. Thus, when we determine the value of x, it represents a potential (or recommended) *decision* for the manager. Therefore, x is also known as a **decision variable**. The next step in the management science process is to solve the model to determine the value of the decision variable.

Model Solution

A management science technique usually applies to a specific model type.

Once models have been constructed in management science, they are solved using the management science techniques presented in this text. A management science solution technique usually applies to a specific type of model. Thus, the model type and solution method are both part of the management science technique. We are able to say that *a model*

Time Out for Pioneers in Management Science

Throughout this text TIME OUT boxes introduce you to the individuals who developed the various techniques that are described in the chapters. This will provide a historical perspective on the development of the field of management science. In this first instance we will briefly outline the development of management science.

Although a number of the mathematical techniques that make up management science date to the turn of the twentieth century or before, the field of management science itself can trace its beginnings to military operations research (OR) groups formed during World War II in Great Britain circa 1939. These OR groups typically consisted of a team of about a dozen individuals from different fields of science, mathematics, and the military, brought together to find solutions to military-related problems. One of the most famous of these groups—called "Blackett's circus" after its leader, Nobel laureate P. M. S. Blackett of the University of Manchester and a former naval officer—included three physiologists, two mathematical physicists, one astrophysicist, one general physicist, two mathematicians, an Army officer, and a surveyor. Blackett's group and the other OR teams made significant contributions in improving Britain's early-warning radar system (which was instrumental in their victory in the Battle of Britain), aircraft gunnery, antisubmarine warfare, civilian defense, convoy size determination, and bombing raids over Germany.

The successes achieved by the British OR groups were observed by two Americans working for the U.S. military, Dr. James B. Conant and Dr. Vannevar Bush, who recommended that OR teams be established in the U.S. branches of the military. Subsequently, both the Air Force and Navy created OR groups.

After World War II the contributions of the OR groups were considered so valuable that the Army, Air Force, and Navy set up various agencies to continue research of military problems. Two of the more famous agencies were the Navy's Operations Evaluation Group at MIT and Project RAND, established by the Air Force to study aerial warfare. Many of the individuals who developed operations research and management science techniques did so while working at one of these agencies after World War II or as a result of their work there.

As the war ended and the mathematical models and techniques that were kept secret during the war began to be released, there was a natural inclination to test their applicability to business problems. At the same time, various consulting firms were established to apply these techniques to industrial and business problems, and courses in the use of quantitative techniques for business management began to surface in American universities. In the early 1950s the use of these quantitative techniques to solve management problems became known as management science, and it was popularized by a book of that name by Stafford Beer of Great Britain.

is solved because the model represents a problem. When we refer to model solution, we also mean problem solution.

For the example model developed in the previous section,

$$\text{maximize } Z = \$20x - 5x$$
$$\text{subject to}$$
$$4x = 100$$

the solution technique is simple algebra. Solving the constraint equation for x, we have

$$\begin{aligned} 4x &= 100 \\ x &= 100/4 \\ x &= 25 \text{ units} \end{aligned}$$

Substituting the value of 25 for x into the profit function results in the total profit:

$$\begin{aligned} Z &= \$20x - 5x \\ &= 20(25) - 5(25) \\ &= \$375 \end{aligned}$$

Thus, if the manager decides to produce 25 units of the product and all 25 units sell, the business firm will receive \$375 in profit. Note, however, that the value of the decision variable does not constitute an actual decision; rather, it is *information* that serves as a recommendation or guideline, helping the manager make a decision.

Management Science Application

Management Science at Taco Bell

Taco Bell, an international fast-food chain with annual sales of approximately $4.6 billion, operates more than 6,500 locations worldwide. In the fast-food business the operating objective is, in general, to provide quality food, good service, and a clean environment. Although Taco Bell sees these three attributes as equally important, good service, as measured by its speed, has the greatest impact on revenues.

The 3-hour lunch period 11:00 A.M. to 2:00 P.M. accounts for 52% of Taco Bell's daily sales. Most fast-food restaurants have lines of waiting customers during this period, and so speed of service determines sales capacity. If service time decreases, sales capacity increases, and vice versa. However, as speed of service increases, labor costs also increase. Because very few food items can be prepared in advance and inventoried, products must be prepared when they are ordered, making food preparation very labor intensive. Thus, speed of service depends on labor availability.

Taco Bell research studies showed that when customers are in line up to 5 minutes only, their perception of that waiting time is only a few minutes. However, after waiting time exceeds 5 minutes, customer perception of that waiting time increases exponentially. The longer the perceived waiting time, the more likely the customer is to leave the restaurant without ordering. The company determined that a 3-minute average waiting time would result in only 2.5% of customers leaving. The company believed this was an acceptable level of attrition, and it established this waiting time as its service goal.

To achieve this goal Taco Bell developed a labor-management system based on an integrated set of management science models to forecast customer traffic for every 15-minute interval during the day and to schedule employees accordingly to meet customer demand. This labor-management system includes a forecasting model to predict customer transactions; a simulation model to determine labor requirements based on these transactions; and an integer programming model to schedule employees and minimize payroll. From 1993 through 1997 the labor-management system using these models saved Taco Bell over $53 million.

Source: J. Heuter and W. Swart, "An Integrated Labor-Management System for Taco Bell," *Interfaces* 28, no. 1 (January–February 1998): 75–91.

A management science solution can be either a recommended decision or information that helps a manager make a decision.

Some management science techniques do not generate an answer or a recommended decision. Instead, they provide *descriptive results:* results that describe the system being modeled. For example, suppose the business firm in our example desires to know the average number of units sold each month during a year. The monthly *data* (i.e., sales) for the past year are as follows:

Month	*Sales*	*Month*	*Sales*
January	30	July	35
February	40	August	50
March	25	September	60
April	60	October	40
May	30	November	35
June	25	December	50
		Total	480 units

Monthly sales average 40 units (400 ÷ 12). This result is not a decision; it is information that describes what is happening in the system. The results of the management science techniques in this text are examples of the two types shown in this section: (1) solutions/decisions and (2) descriptive results.

Implementation

The final step in the management science process for problem solving described in Figure 1.1 is implementation. **Implementation** is the actual use of the model once it has been developed or the solution to the problem the model was developed to solve. This is a critical but often overlooked step in the process. It is not always a given that once a model is developed or a solution found, it is automatically used. Frequently the person responsible for putting the model or solution to use is not the same person who developed the model and, thus, the user may not fully understand how the model works or exactly what it is supposed to do. Individuals are also sometimes hesitant to change the normal way they do things or to try new things. In this situation the model and solution may get pushed to the side or ignored altogether if they are not carefully explained and their benefit fully demonstrated. If the management science model and solution are not implemented, then the effort and resources used in their development have been wasted.

Model Building: Break-Even Analysis

In the previous section we gave a brief, general description of how management science models are formulated and solved, using a simple algebraic example. In this section we will continue to explore the process of building and solving management science models, using **break-even analysis**, also called *profit analysis*. Break-even analysis is a good topic to expand our discussion of model building and solution because it is straightforward, relatively familiar to most people, and not overly complex. In addition, it provides a convenient means to demonstrate the different ways management science models can be solved—mathematically (by hand), graphically, and with a computer.

The purpose of break-even analysis is to determine the number of units of a product (i.e., the volume) to sell or produce that will equate total revenue with total cost. The point where total revenue equals total cost is called the break-even point, and at this point profit is zero. The break-even point gives a manager a point of reference in determining how many units will be needed to ensure a profit.

Components of Break-Even Analysis

The three components of break-even analysis are volume, cost, and profit. *Volume* is the level of sales or production by a company. It can be expressed as the number of units (i.e., quantity) produced and sold, as the dollar volume of sales, or as a percentage of total capacity available.

__Fixed costs__ are independent of volume and remain constant.

Two type of costs are typically incurred in the production of a product: fixed costs and variable costs. **Fixed costs** are generally independent of the volume of units produced and sold. That is, fixed costs remain constant, regardless of how many units of product are produced within a given range. Fixed costs can include such items as rent on plant and equipment, taxes, staff and management salaries, insurance, advertising, depreciation, heat and light, plant maintenance, and so on. Taken together, these items result in total fixed costs.

__Variable costs__ depend on the number of items produced.

Variable costs are determined on a per-unit basis. Thus, total variable costs depend on the number of units produced. Variable costs include such items as raw materials and resources, direct labor, packaging, material handling, and freight.

Total variable costs are a function of the *volume* and the *variable cost per unit*. This relationship can be expressed mathematically as

$$\text{total variable cost} = vc_v$$

where c_v = variable cost per unit and v = volume (number of units) sold.

***Total cost** (TC) equals the fixed cost (c_f) plus the variable cost per unit (c_v) multiplied by volume (v).*

The **total cost** of an operation is computed by summing total fixed cost and total variable cost, as follows:

$$\text{total cost} = \text{total fixed cost} + \text{total variable cost}$$

or

$$TC = c_f + vc_v$$

where c_f = fixed cost.

As an example, consider Western Clothing Company, which produces denim jeans. The company incurs the following monthly costs to produce denim jeans:

$$\text{fixed cost} = c_f = \$10{,}000$$
$$\text{variable cost} = c_v = \$8 \text{ per pair}$$

If we arbitrarily let the monthly sales volume, v, equal 400 pairs of denim jeans, the total cost is

$$TC = c_f + vc_v = \$10{,}000 + (400)(8) = \$13{,}200$$

***Profit** is the difference between total revenue (volume multiplied by price) and total cost.*

The third component in our break-even model is **profit**. Profit is the difference between **total revenue** and total cost. Total revenue is the volume multiplied by the price per unit,

$$\text{total revenue} = vp$$

where p = price per unit.

For our clothing company example, if denim jeans sell for \$23 per pair and we sell 400 pairs per month, then the total monthly revenue is

$$\text{total revenue} = vp = (400)(23) = \$9{,}200$$

Now that we have developed relationships for total revenue and total cost, profit (Z) can be computed as follows:

$$\begin{aligned} \text{total profit} &= \text{total revenue} - \text{total cost} \\ Z &= vp - (c_f + vc_v) \\ &= vp - c_f - vc_v \end{aligned}$$

Computing the Break-Even Point

For our clothing company example, we have determined total revenue and total cost to be \$9,200 and \$13,200, respectively. With these values, there is no profit but, instead, a loss of \$4,000:

$$\text{total profit} = \text{total revenue} - \text{total cost} = \$9{,}200 - 13{,}200 = -\$4{,}000$$

We can verify this result by using our total profit formula,

$$Z = vp - c_f - vc_v$$

and the values $v = 400$, $p = \$23$, $c_f = \$10{,}000$, and $c_v = \$8$:

$$\begin{aligned} Z &= vp - c_f - vc_v \\ &= \$(400)(23) - 10{,}000 - (400)(8) \\ &= \$9{,}200 - 10{,}000 - 3{,}200 \\ &= -\$4{,}000 \end{aligned}$$

Obviously, the clothing company does not want to operate with a monthly loss of \$4,000 because doing so might eventually result in bankruptcy. If we assume that price is static because of market conditions and that fixed costs and the variable cost per unit are not subject to change, then the only part of our model that can be varied is *volume*. Using the modeling terms we developed earlier in this chapter, price, fixed costs, and variable costs are parameters, whereas the volume, v, is a **decision variable**. In break-even analysis we want to compute the value of v that will result in zero profit.

*The **break-even point** is the volume (v) that equates total revenue with total cost where profit is zero.*

At the **break-even point**, where total revenue equals total cost, the profit, Z, equals zero. Thus, if we let profit, Z, equal zero in our total profit equation and solve for v, we can determine the break-even volume:

$$\begin{aligned} Z &= vp - c_f - vc_v \\ 0 &= v(23) - 10{,}000 - v(8) \\ 0 &= 23v - 10{,}000 - 8v \\ 15v &= 10{,}000 \\ v &= 666.7 \text{ pairs of jeans} \end{aligned}$$

In other words, if the company produces and sells 666.7 pairs of jeans, the profit (and loss) will be zero and the company will *break even*. This gives the company a point of reference from which to determine how many pairs of jeans it needs to produce and sell in order to gain a profit (subject to any capacity limitations). For example, a sales volume of 800 pairs of denim jeans will result in the following monthly profit:

$$\begin{aligned} Z &= vp - c_f - vc_v \\ &= \$(800)(23) - 10{,}000 - (800)(8) = \$2{,}000 \end{aligned}$$

In general, the break-even volume can be determined using the following formula:

$$\begin{aligned} Z &= vp - c_f - vc_v \\ 0 &= v(p - c_v) - c_f \\ v(p - c_v) &= c_f \\ v &= \frac{c_f}{p - c_v} \end{aligned}$$

For our example,

$$\begin{aligned} v &= \frac{c_f}{p - c_v} \\ &= \frac{10{,}000}{23 - 8} \\ &= 666.7 \text{ pairs of jeans} \end{aligned}$$

Graphical Solution

It is possible to represent many of the management science models in this text graphically and use these graphical models to solve problems. Graphical models also have the advantage of providing a "picture" of the model that can sometimes help us understand the modeling process better than the mathematics alone can. We can easily graph the break-even model for our Western Clothing Company example because the functions for total cost and total revenue are *linear*. That means we can graph each relationship as a straight line on a set of coordinates, as shown in Figure 1.2.

In Figure 1.2, the fixed cost, c_f, has a constant value of \$10,000, regardless of the volume. The total cost line, *TC*, represents the sum of variable cost and fixed cost. The total cost line

Figure 1.2
Break-even model

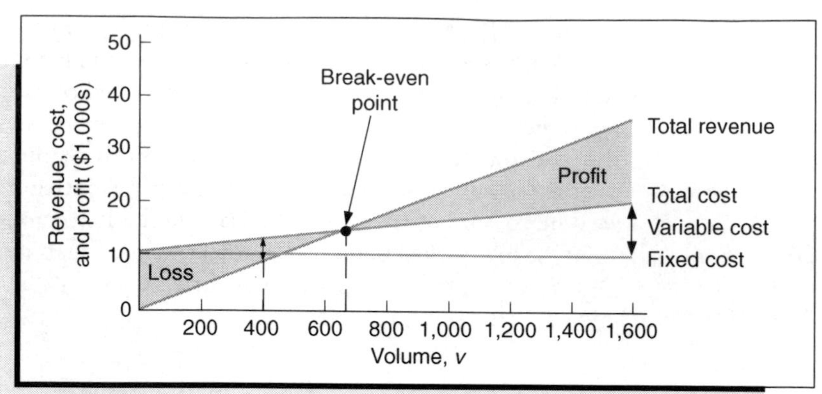

increases because variable cost increases as the volume increases. The total revenue line also increases as volume increases, but at a faster rate than total cost. The point where these two lines intersect indicates that total revenue equals total cost. The volume, v, that corresponds to this point is the *break-even volume*. The break-even volume in Figure 1.2 is 666.7 pairs of denim jeans.

Sensitivity Analysis

We have now developed a general relationship for determining the break-even volume, which was the objective of our modeling process. This relationship enables us to see how the level of profit (and loss) is directly affected by changes in volume. However, when we developed this model, we assumed that our parameters, fixed and variable costs and price, were constant. In reality such parameters are frequently uncertain and can rarely be assumed to be constant, and changes in any of the parameters can affect the model solution. The study of changes on a management science model is called **sensitivity analysis**—that is, seeing how sensitive the model is to changes.

Sensitivity analysis can be performed on all management science models in one form or another. In fact, sometimes companies develop models for the primary purpose of experimentation to see how the model will react to different changes the company is contemplating or that management might expect to occur in the future. As a demonstration of how sensitivity analysis works, we will look at the effects of some changes on our break-even model.

In general, an increase in price lowers the break-even point, all other things held constant.

The first thing we will analyze is price. As an example, we will increase the price for denim jeans from \$23 to \$30. As expected, this increases the total revenue, and it therefore reduces the break-even point from 666.7 pairs of jeans to 454.5 pairs of jeans:

$$v = \frac{c_f}{p - c_v}$$
$$= \frac{10{,}000}{30 - 8} = 454.5 \text{ pairs of denim jeans}$$

The effect of the price change on break-even volume is illustrated in Figure 1.3.

Although a decision to increase price looks inviting from a strictly analytical point of view, it must be remembered that the lower break-even volume and higher profit are *possible* but not guaranteed. A higher price can make it more difficult to sell the product. Thus, a change in price often must be accompanied by corresponding increases in costs, such as those for advertising, packaging, and possibly production (to enhance quality). However, even such direct changes as these may have little effect on product demand

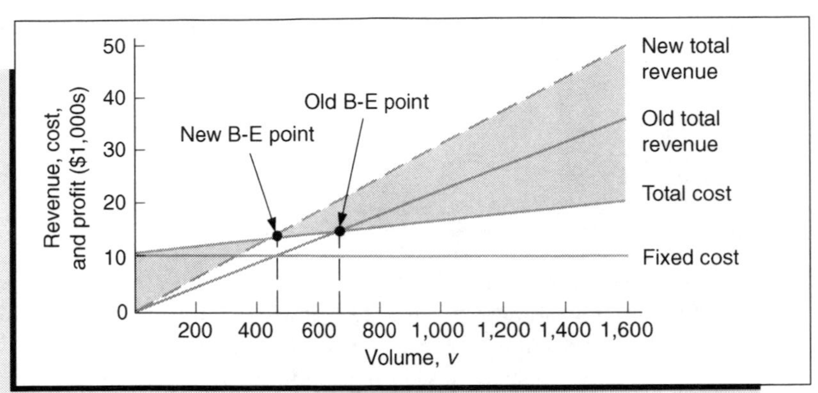

Figure 1.3

Break-even model with an increase in price

because price is often sensitive to numerous factors, such as the type of market, monopolistic elements, and product differentiation.

In general, an increase in variable costs will decrease the break-even point, all other things held constant.

When we increased price, we mentioned the possibility of raising the quality of the product to offset a potential loss of sales due to the price increase. For example, suppose the stitching on the denim jeans is changed to make the jeans more attractive and stronger. This change results in an increase in variable costs of $4 per pair of jeans, thus raising the variable cost per unit, c_v, to $12 per pair. This change (in conjunction with our previous price change to $30) results in a new break-even volume:

$$v = \frac{c_f}{p - c_v}$$
$$= \frac{10{,}000}{30 - 12} = 555.5 \text{ pairs of denim jeans}$$

This new break-even volume and the change in the total cost line that occurs as a result of the variable cost change are shown in Figure 1.4.

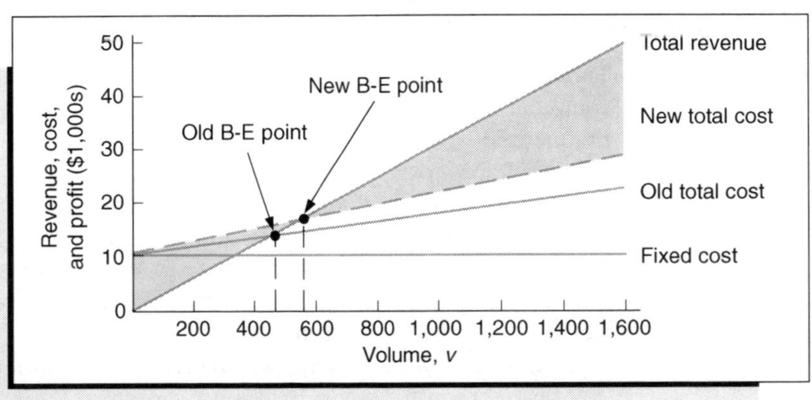

Figure 1.4

Break-even model with an increase in variable cost

Next let's consider an increase in advertising expenditures to offset the potential loss in sales resulting from a price increase. An increase in advertising expenditures is an addition to fixed costs. For example, if the clothing company increases its monthly advertising budget by $3,000, then the total fixed cost, c_f, becomes $13,000. Using this fixed cost, as well as the increased variable cost per unit of \$12 and the increased price of \$30, we compute the break-even volume as follows:

$$v = \frac{c_f}{p - c_v}$$
$$= \frac{13{,}000}{30 - 12}$$
$$= 722.2 \text{ pairs of denim jeans}$$

In general, an increase in fixed costs will increase the break-even point, all other things held constant.

This new break-even volume, representing changes in price, fixed costs, and variable costs, is illustrated in Figure 1.5. Notice that the break-even volume is now higher than the original volume of 666.7 pairs of jeans, as a result of the increased costs necessary to offset the potential loss in sales. This indicates the necessity to analyze the effect of a change in one of the break-even components on the whole break-even model. In other words, generally it is not sufficient to consider a change in one model component without considering the overall effect.

Figure 1.5
Break-even model with a change in fixed cost

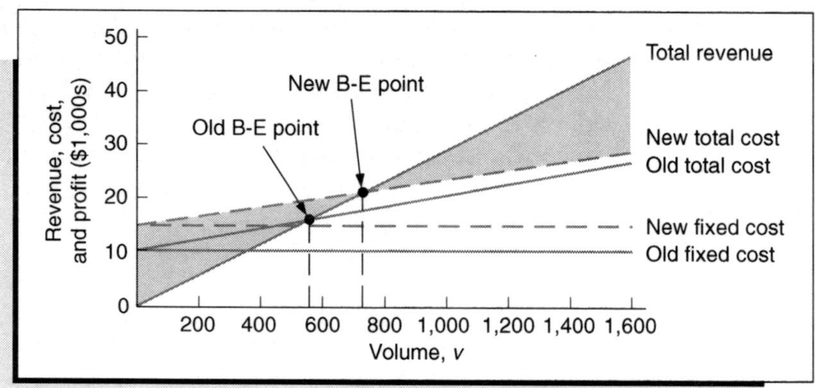

Computer Solution

Throughout the text we will demonstrate how to solve management science models on the computer by using Excel spreadsheets and QM for Windows, a general-purpose quantitative methods software package by Howard Weiss. QM for Windows has program modules to solve almost every type of management science problem you will encounter in this book. There are a number of similar quantitative methods software packages available on the market, with similar characteristics and capabilities as QM for Windows. In most cases you simply input problem data (i.e., model parameters) into a model template, click on a solve button, and the solution appears in a Windows format. QM for Windows is included on the CD that accompanies this text.

Spreadsheets are not always easy to use, and you cannot conveniently solve every type of management science model by using a spreadsheet. Most of the time you must not only input the model parameters but also set up the model mathematics, including formulas, as well as your own model template with headings to display your solution output. However, spreadsheets provide a powerful reporting tool in which you can present your model and results in any format you choose. Spreadsheets such as Excel have become almost universally available to anyone who owns a computer. In addition, spreadsheets have become very popular as a teaching tool because they tend to guide the student through a modeling procedure, and they can be interesting and fun to use. However, because spreadsheets are somewhat more difficult to set up and apply than is QM for Windows, we will spend more time explaining their use to solve various types of problems in this text.

One of the difficult aspects of using spreadsheets to solve management science problems is setting up a spreadsheet with some of the more complex models and formulas. For the most complex models in the text we will show how to use Excel QM, a supplemental spreadsheet macro that is included on the CD that accompanies this text. A *macro* is a template or an overlay that already has the model format with the necessary formulas set up on the spreadsheet so that the user only has to input the model parameters. We will demonstrate Excel QM in six chapters, including this chapter, Chapter 6 ("Transportation, Transshipment, and Assignment Problems"), Chapter 12 ("Decision Analysis"), Chapter 13 ("Queuing Analysis"), Chapter 15 ("Forecasting"), and Chapter 16 ("Inventory Management").

Later in this text we will also demonstrate two spreadsheet add-ins, TreePlan and Crystal Ball. TreePlan is a program for setting up and solving decision trees that we use in Chapter 12 ("Decision Analysis"), whereas Crystal Ball is a simulation package that we use in Chapter 14 ("Simulation"). Also, in Chapter 8 ("Project Management") we will demonstrate Microsoft Project.

In this section we will demonstrate how to use Excel, Excel QM, and QM for Windows, using our break-even model example for Western Clothing Company.

Excel Spreadsheets

To solve the break-even model using Excel, you must set up a spreadsheet with headings to identify your model parameters and variables and then input the appropriate mathematical formulas into the cells where you want to display your solution. Exhibit 1.1 shows the spreadsheet for the Western Clothing Company example. Setting up the different headings to describe the parameters and the solution is not difficult, but it does require that you know your way around Excel a little. Appendix B provides a brief tutorial titled "Setting Up and Editing a Spreadsheet" for solving management science problems.

Exhibit 1.1

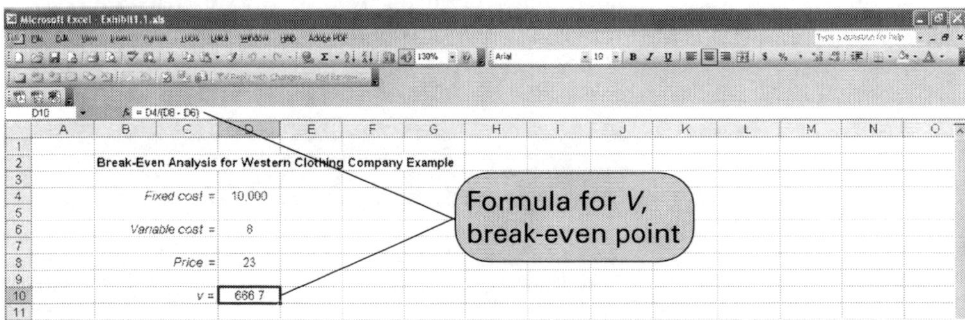

Notice that cell D10 contains the break-even formula, which is displayed on the toolbar near the top of the screen. The fixed cost of $10,000 is typed in cell D4, the variable cost of $8 is in cell D6, and the price of $23 is in cell D8.

As we present more complex models and problems in the chapters to come, the spreadsheets we will develop to solve these problems will become more involved and will enable us to demonstrate different features of Excel and spreadsheet modeling.

The Excel QM Macro for Spreadsheets

Excel QM is included on the CD that accompanies this text. You can install Excel QM onto your computer by following a brief series of steps displayed when the program is first accessed.

After Excel is started, Excel QM is normally accessed from the computer's program files, where it is usually loaded. When Excel QM is activated, "QM" will appear at the top of the spreadsheet (as indicated in Exhibit 1.3). Clicking on "QM" will pull down a menu of the topics in Excel QM, one of which is break-even analysis. Clicking on "Break-Even Analysis" will result in the window for spreadsheet initialization shown in Exhibit 1.2. Every Excel QM macro listed on the menu will start with a "Spreadsheet Initialization" window similar to this one.

Exhibit 1.2

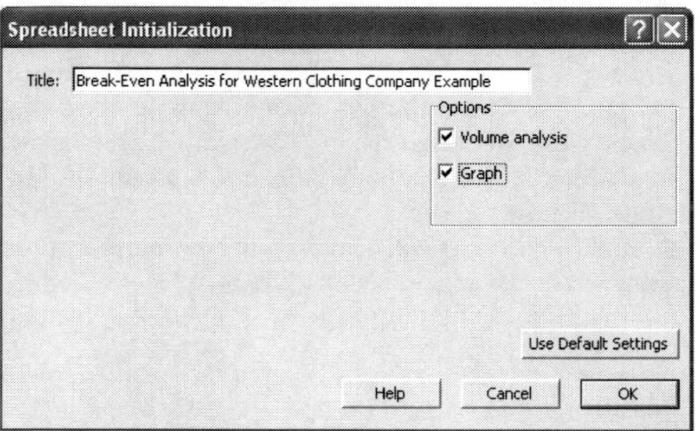

In the window in Exhibit 1.2 you can enter a spreadsheet title and choose under "Options" whether you also want volume analysis and a graph. Clicking on "OK" will result in the spreadsheet shown in Exhibit 1.3. The first step is to input the values for the Western Clothing Company example in cells B10 to B13, as shown in Exhibit 1.3. The spreadsheet shows the break-even volume in cell B17. However, notice that we have also chosen to perform some volume analysis by entering a hypothetical volume of 800 units in cell B13, which results in the volume analysis in cells B20 to B23.

Exhibit 1.3

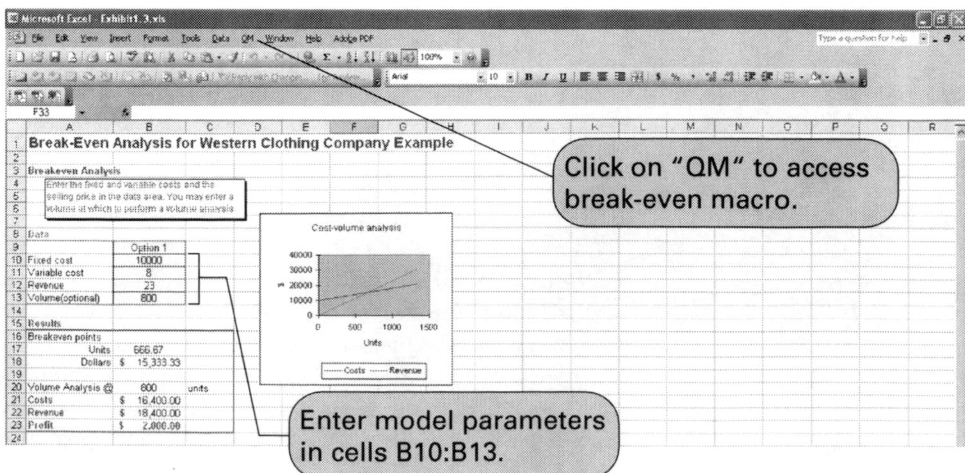

QM for Windows

You begin using QM for Windows by clicking on the "Module" button on the toolbar at the top of the main window that appears when you start the program. This will pull down a window with a list of all the model solution modules available in QM for Windows. Clicking on the "Break-even Analysis" module will access a new screen for typing in the problem title. Clicking again will access a screen with input cells for the model parameters—that is, fixed cost, variable cost, and price (or revenue). Next, clicking on the "Solve" button at the top of the screen will provide the solution to the Western Clothing Company example, as shown in Exhibit 1.4.

Exhibit 1.4

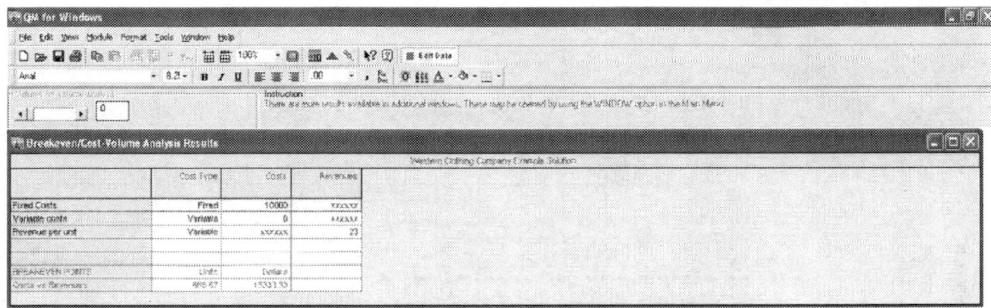

You can also get the graphical model and solution for this problem by clicking on "Window" at the top of the solution screen and selecting the menu item for a graph of the problem. The break-even graph for the Western Clothing example is shown in Exhibit 1.5.

Exhibit 1.5

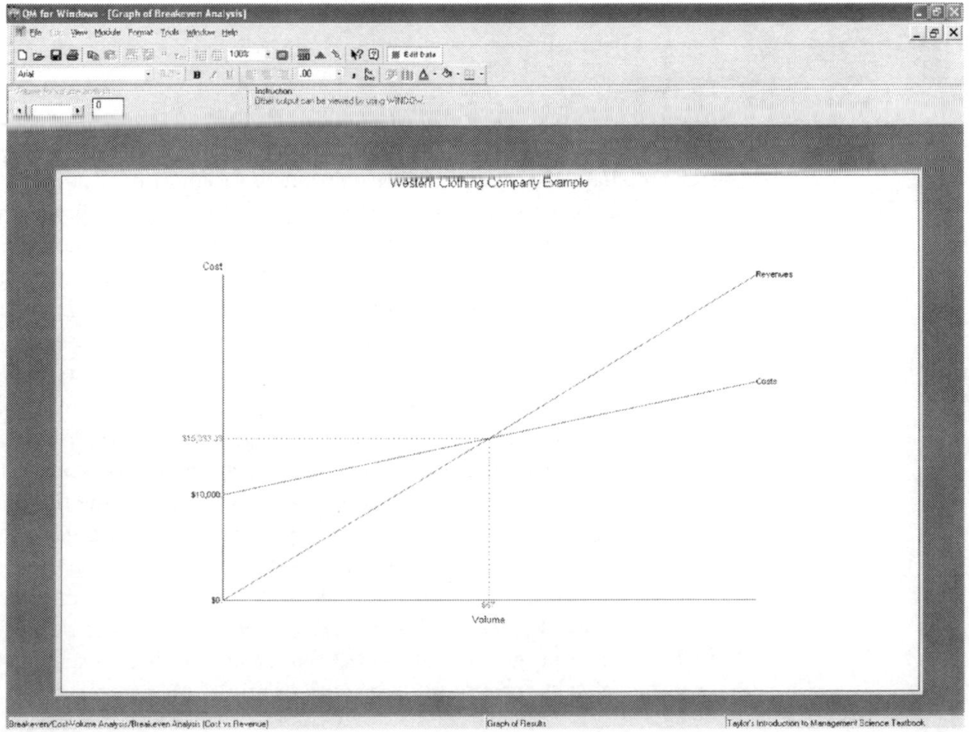

Management Science Modeling Techniques

This text focuses primarily on two of the five steps of the management science process described in Figure 1.1—model construction and solution. These are the two steps that use the management science technique. In a textbook, it is difficult to show how an unstructured real-world problem is identified and defined because the problem must be written out. However, once a problem statement has been given, we can show how a model is constructed and a solution is derived. The techniques presented in this text can be loosely classified into four categories, as shown in Figure 1.6.

Figure 1.6
Classification of management science techniques

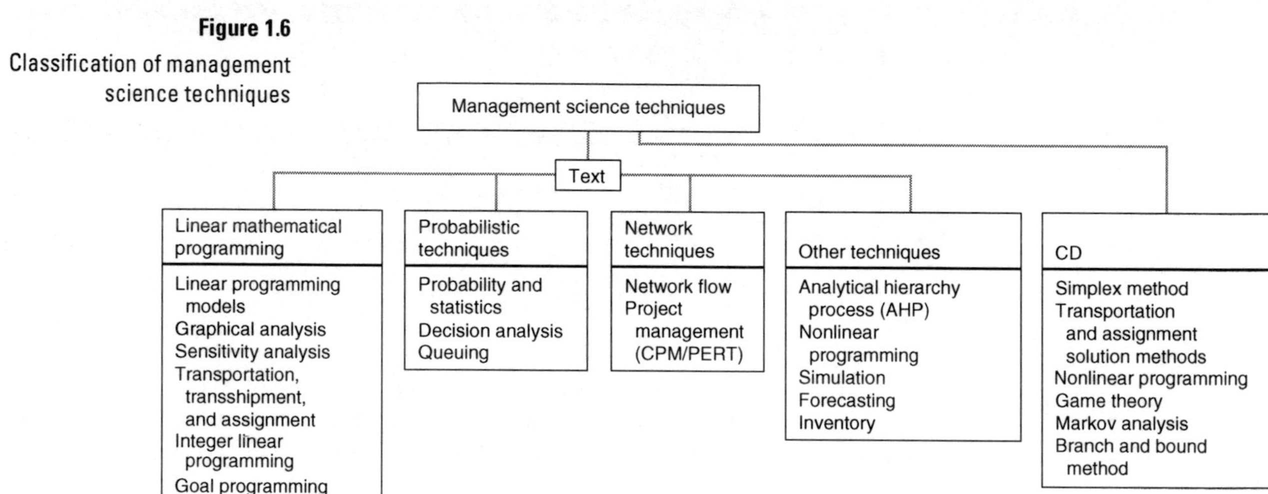

Linear Mathematical Programming Techniques

Chapters 2 through 6 and 9 present techniques that together make up **linear mathematical programming.** (The first example used to demonstrate model construction earlier in this chapter is a very rudimentary linear programming model.) The term *programming* used to identify this technique does not refer to computer programming but rather to a predetermined set of mathematical steps used to solve a problem. This particular class of techniques holds a predominant position in this text because it includes some of the more frequently used and popular techniques in management science.

In general, linear programming models help managers determine solutions (i.e., make decisions) for problems that will achieve some objective in which there are restrictions, such as limited resources or a recipe or perhaps production guidelines. For example, you could actually develop a linear programming model to help determine a breakfast menu for yourself that would meet dietary guidelines you may have set, such as number of calories, fat content, and vitamin level, while minimizing the cost of the breakfast. Manufacturing companies develop linear programming models to help decide how many units of different products they should produce to maximize their profit (or minimize their cost), given scarce resources such as capital, labor, and facilities.

Six chapters in this text are devoted to this topic because there are several variations of linear programming models that can be applied to specific types of problems. Chapter 4 is devoted entirely to describing example linear programming models for several different types of problem scenarios. Chapter 6, for example, focuses on one particular type of linear programming application for transportation, transshipment, and assignment problems. An example of a transportation problem is a manager trying to determine the lowest-cost routes to use to ship goods from several sources (such as plants or warehouses) to several destinations (such as retail stores), given that each source may have limited goods available and each destination may have limited demand for the goods. Also, Chapter 9 includes the topic of goal programming, which is a form of linear programming that addresses problems with more than one objective or goal.

As mentioned previously in this chapter, some of the more mathematical topics in the text are included as supplementary modules on the CD that accompanies the text. Among the linear programming topics included on the CD are modules on the simplex method; the transportation, transshipment, and assignment solution methods; and the branch and bound solution method for integer programming models. Also included on the CD are modules on nonlinear programming, game theory, and Markov analysis.

Probabilistic Techniques

Probabilistic techniques are presented in Chapters 11 through 13. These techniques are distinguished from mathematical programming techniques in that the results are probabilistic. Mathematical programming techniques assume that all parameters in the models are known with *certainty*. Therefore, the solution results are assumed to be known with certainty, with no probability that other solutions might exist. A technique that assumes certainty in its solution is referred to as **deterministic**. In contrast, the results from a probabilistic technique *do* contain uncertainty, with some possibility that alternative solutions might exist. In the model solution presented earlier in this chapter, the result of the first example ($x = 25$ units to produce) is deterministic, whereas the result of the second example (estimating an average of 40 units sold each month) is probabilistic.

An example of a probabilistic technique is decision analysis, the subject of Chapter 12. In decision analysis it is shown how to select among several different decision alternatives, given uncertain (i.e., probabilistic) future conditions. For example, a developer may want to decide whether to build a shopping mall, build an office complex, build condominiums, or not build anything at all, given future economic conditions that might be good, fair, or poor, each with a probability of occurrence. Chapter 13, on queuing analysis, presents probabilistic techniques for analyzing waiting lines that might occur, for example, at the grocery store, at a bank, or at a movie. The results of waiting line analysis are statistical averages showing, among other things, the average number of customers in line waiting to be served or the average time a customer might have to wait for service.

Network Techniques

Networks, the topic of Chapters 7 and 8, consist of models that are represented as diagrams rather than as strictly mathematical relationships. As such, these models offer a pictorial representation of the system under analysis. These models represent either probabilistic or deterministic systems.

For example, in shortest route problems, one of the topics in Chapter 7 ("Network Flow Models"), a network diagram can be drawn to help a manager determine the shortest route among a number of different routes from a source to a destination. For example, you could use this technique to determine the shortest or quickest car route from St. Louis to Daytona Beach for a spring break vacation. In Chapter 8 ("Project Management"), a network is drawn that shows the relationships of all the tasks and activities for a project, such as building a house or developing a new computer system. This type of network can help a manager plan the best way to accomplish each of the tasks in the project so that it will take the shortest amount of time possible. You could use this type of technique to plan for a concert or an intramural volleyball tournament on your campus.

Other Techniques

Some topics in the text are not easily categorized; they may overlap between several categories, or they may be unique. The analytical hierarchy process (AHP) in Chapter 9 is such a topic that is not easily classified. It is a mathematical technique for helping the decision maker choose between several alternative decisions, given more than one objective; however, it is not a form of linear programming, as is goal programming, the shared topic in Chapter 9, on multicriteria decision making. The structure of the mathematical models for nonlinear programming problems in Chapter 10 is similar to the linear programming problems in Chapters 2 through 6; however, the mathematical equations and functions in nonlinear programming can be nonlinear instead of linear, thus requiring the use of calculus to solve them. Simulation, the subject of Chapter 14, is probably the single most unique topic in the text. It has the capability to solve probabilistic and deterministic problems and is often the technique of last resort when no other management science technique will work. In simulation a mathematical model is constructed (typically using a computer) that replicates a real-world system under analysis, and then that simulation model is used to solve problems in the "simulated" real-world system. For example, with simulation you could build a model to simulate the traffic patterns of vehicles at a busy intersection to determine how to set the traffic light signals.

Forecasting, the subject of Chapter 15, and inventory management, in Chapter 16, are topics traditionally considered to be part of the field of operations management. However, because they are both important business functions that also rely heavily on quantitative models for their analysis, they are typically considered important topics in the study of management science as well. Both topics also include probabilistic as well as deterministic aspects. In Chapter 15 we will look at several different quantitative models that help managers predict what the future demand for products and services will look like. In general, historical sales and demand data are used to build a mathematical function or formula that can be used to estimate product demand in the future. In Chapter 16 we will look at several different quantitative models that help organizations determine how much inventory to keep on hand in order to minimize inventory costs, which can be significant.

Business Usage of Management Science Techniques

Not all management science techniques are equally useful or equally used by business firms and other organizations. Some techniques are used quite frequently by business practitioners and managers; others are used less often. The most frequently used techniques are linear and integer programming, simulation, network analysis (including critical path method/project evaluation and review technique [CPM/PERT]), inventory control, decision analysis, and queuing theory, as well as probability and statistics. An attempt has been made in this text to provide a comprehensive treatment of all the topics generally considered within the field of management science, regardless of how frequently they are used. Although some topics may have limited direct applicability, their study can reveal informative and unique means of approaching a problem and can often enhance one's understanding of the decision-making process.

Management Science Application

Management Science at FedEx

In 1973 Frederick W. Smith started Federal Express Corporation to provide overnight delivery of small, high-value items, such as pharmaceuticals, aerospace components, and computer parts. The company began operation on March 12, 1973, in 11 cities in the south with a fleet of 22 twin-engine executive jets, each with a payload of about 3 tons. That first day the company delivered only 6 packages, and three days later FedEx discontinued air delivery service because of a lack of business. At that point FedEx took stock of its situation and began using management science techniques and models to help solve its problems and redefine its operation. Since that time, management science has been an integral part of the company's spectacular success. Initially FedEx used quantitative techniques to analyze its original choice of cities, and a month after it shut down service, a rejuvenated FedEx began servicing a new 26-city system based on quantitative analysis of markets and cities. FedEx is now an $8 billion plus corporation and the world's largest express transportation company, delivering more than 2 million items to over 200 countries each day. Its transportation system includes more than 500 aircraft and 35,000 vehicles. The management science applications the company has conducted over the years include simulation models to develop economical flight schedules and determine resource requirements at its hub terminals; planning models to evaluate alternative routes and evaluate expansion plans; forecasting models to forecast aircraft maintenance requirements and develop maintenance schedules and to forecast when new terminal hubs would be needed to increase capacity for an expanding business; Markov models to plan for pilot requirements in the future and to show pilots their expected career path with the company; queuing analysis to develop and analyze the company's computerized call centers for customer orders and dispatching; and integer linear programming to help the company develop its SuperHub system instead of a less economical series of smaller hubs. All these techniques, plus others, are presented in this text. From its beginning, management science applications and models have been used in many of FedEx's crucial business-shaping decisions.

Source: R. O. Maxon, J. L. McKenney, W. Carlson, and D. Copeland, "Absolutely, Positively Operations Research: The Federal Express Story," *Interfaces* 27, no. 2 (March–April 1997): 17–36.

The variety and breadth of management science applications and of the potential for applying management science, not only in business and industry but also in government, health care, and service organizations, are extensive. Areas of application include project planning, capital budgeting, production planning, inventory analysis, scheduling, marketing planning, quality control, plant location, maintenance policy, personnel management, and product demand forecasting, among others. In this text the applicability of management science to a variety of problem areas is demonstrated via individual chapter examples and the problems that accompany each chapter.

A small portion of the thousands of applications of management science that occur each year are recorded in various academic and professional journals. Frequently, these journal articles are as complex as the applications themselves and are very difficult to read. However, one particular journal, *Interfaces*, is devoted specifically to the application of management science and is written not just for college professors but for businesspeople, practitioners, and students as well. *Interfaces* is published by INFORMS (Institute for Operations Research and Management Sciences), an international professional organization whose members include college professors, businesspeople, scientists, students, and a variety of professional people interested in the practice and application of management science and operations research.

Interfaces regularly publishes articles that report on the application of management science to a wide variety of problems. The chapters that follow present examples of applications of management science from *Interfaces* and other professional journals. These examples, as presented here, do not detail the actual models and the model components. Instead, they briefly indicate the type of problem the company or organization faced, the objective of the solution approach developed to solve the problem, and the benefits derived from the model or technique (i.e., what was accomplished). The interested reader who desires more detailed information about these and other management science applications is encouraged to go to the library and peruse *Interfaces* and the many other journals that contain articles on the application of management science.

Management Science Models in Decision Support Systems

Historically management science models have been applied to the solution of specific types of problems; for example, a waiting line model is used to analyze a specific waiting line system at a store or bank. However, the evolution of computer and information technology has enabled the development of expansive computer systems that combine several management science models and solution techniques in order to address more complex, interrelated organizational problems. A **decision support system (DSS)** is a computer-based system that helps decision makers address complex problems that cut across different parts of an organization and operations.

A DSS is normally *interactive*, combining various databases and different management science models and solution techniques with a user interface that enables the decision maker to ask questions and receive answers. In its simplest form any computer-based software program that helps a decision maker make a decision can be referred to as a DSS. For example, an Excel spreadsheet like the one shown for break-even analysis in Exhibit 1.1 or the QM for Windows model shown in Exhibit 1.4 can realistically be called a DSS. Alternatively enterprisewide DSSs can encompass many different types of models and large data warehouses, and they can serve many decision makers in an organization. They can provide decision makers with interrelated information and analyses about almost anything in a company.

Figure 1.7 illustrates the basic structure of a DSS with a database component, a modeling component, and a user interface with the decision maker. As noted earlier, each of these components can be small and singular, with one analytical model linked to a database, or they can be very large and complex, linking many models and large databases. A DSS can be primarily a data-oriented system, or it can be a model-oriented system. A new type of DSS, called an *online analytical processing* system, or *OLAP*, focuses on the use of analytical techniques such as management science models and statistics for decision making. A desktop DSS for a single user can be a spreadsheet program such as Excel to develop specific solutions to individual problems. Exhibit 1.1 includes all the components of a DSS—cost, volume, and price data, a break-even model, and the opportunity for the user to manipulate the data and see the results (i.e., a user interface). Expert Choice is another example of a desktop DSS that uses the analytical hierarchy process (AHP) described in Chapter 9 to structure complex problems by establishing decision criteria, developing priorities, and ranking decision alternatives.

On the other end of the DSS spectrum, an enterprise resource planning (ERP) system is software that can connect the components and functions of an entire company. It can transform data, such as individual daily sales, directly into information that supports

Figure 1.7
A decision support system

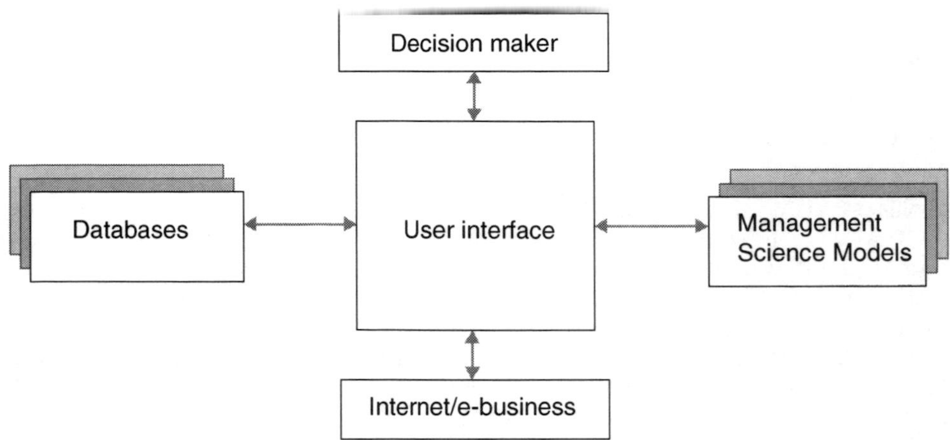

immediate decisions in other parts of the company, such as ordering, manufacturing, inventory, and distribution. A large-scale DSS such as an ERP system in a company might include a forecasting model (Chapter 15) to analyze sales data and help determine future product demand; an inventory model (Chapter 16) to determine how much inventory to keep on hand; a linear programming model (Chapters 2–5) to determine how much material to order and product to produce, and when to produce it; a transportation model (Chapter 6) to determine the most cost-effective method of distributing a product to customers; and a network flow model (Chapter 7) to determine the best delivery routes. All these different management science models and the data necessary to support them can be linked in a single enterprisewide DSS that can provide many decisions to many different decision makers.

In addition to helping managers answer specific questions and make decisions, a DSS may be most useful in answering what-if? questions and performing sensitivity analysis. In other words, a DSS provides a computer-based laboratory to perform experiments. By linking various management science models together with different databases, a user can change a parameter in one model related to one company function and see what the effect will be in a model related to a different operation in the company. For example, by changing the data in a forecasting model, a manager could see the impact of a hypothetical change in product demand on the production schedule, as determined by a linear programming model.

Advances in information and computer technology have provided the opportunity to apply management science models to a broad array of complex organizational problems by linking different models to databases in a DSS. These advances have also made the application of management science models more readily available to individual users in the form of desktop DSSs that can help managers make better decisions relative to their day-to-day operations. In the future it will undoubtedly become even easier to apply management science to the solution of problems with the development of newer software, and management science will become even more important and pervasive as an aid to decision makers as managers are linked within companies with sophisticated computer systems and between companies via the Internet.

Many companies now interface with new types of DSS over the Internet. In e-business applications companies can link to other business units around the world through computer systems called *intranets*, with other companies through systems called *extranets*, and over the Internet. For example, electronic data interchange (EDI) and point-of-sale data (through bar codes) can provide companies with instantaneous records of business transactions and sales at retail stores that are immediately entered into a company's DSS to

Management Science Application

A Decision Support System for Aluminum Can Production at Coors

Valley Metal Container (VMC), a joint venture between Coors Brewing Company and American National Can, operates the largest single facility for aluminum can production in the world in Golden, Colorado. The plant, encompassing six production lines, manufactures over 4 billion cans per year for seven Coors beer labels produced at Coors breweries in Colorado, Virginia, and Tennessee. The breweries' weekly production schedules are unpredictable, and if sufficient cans are not available, brewery fill lines can be shut down, at a cost of $65 per minute. In order to cope with variable brewery demand, VMC builds up inventories of cans for all seven Coors labels during winter and spring, when beer demand is lower, in order to meet higher demand in the summer. Each production line at the can production plant produces multiple labels, and when a line is switched from one label to another, a label change occurs. Finished cans go into either short-term inventory (in trailers), from which they are shipped to a brewery within a day, or two types of longer-term inventory, in which cans are stored on pallets for future delivery.

VMC developed a DSS to determine the weekly production schedule for cans that would meet brewery demand while minimizing the number of costly label changes and associated inventory costs. The DSS includes an Excel-based user interface for data entry. The Excel spreadsheets are linked to a linear programming model that develops the optimal production schedule that minimizes the costs associated with label changes while meeting demand. The spreadsheet format allows data to be entered and adjusted easily on one worksheet, and the production schedule is developed on another worksheet. The production schedule is then reported on another specially formatted spreadsheet, which the user can view, print, and edit. Costs savings with this DSS average about $3,000 per week and annual savings of over $160,000.

Source: E. Katok and D. Ott, "Using Mixed-Integer Programming to Reduce Label Changes in the Coors Aluminum Can Plant," *Interfaces* 30, no. 2 (March–April 2000): 1–12.

update inventory and production scheduling, using management science models. Internet transportation exchanges enable companies to arrange cost-effective transportation of their products at Web sites that match shipping loads with available trucks at the lowest cost and fastest delivery speed, using sophisticated management science models.

Summary

Management science is an art.

In the chapters that follow, the model construction and solutions that constitute each management science technique are presented in detail and illustrated with examples. In fact, the primary method of presenting the techniques is through examples. Thus, the text offers you a broad spectrum of knowledge of the mechanics of management science techniques and the types of problems to which these techniques are applied. However, the ultimate test of a management scientist or a manager who uses management science techniques is the ability to transfer textbook knowledge to the business world. In such instances there is an *art* to the application of management science, but it is an art predicated on practical experience and sound textbook knowledge. Providing the first of these necessities is beyond the scope of textbooks; providing the second is the objective of this text.

References

Ackoff, Russell L., and Sasieni, Maurice W. *Fundamentals of Operations Research*. New York: John Wiley & Sons, 1968.

Beer, Stafford. *Management Sciences: The Business Use of Operations Research*. New York: Doubleday, 1967.

Churchman, C. W., Ackoff, R. L., and Arnoff, E. L. *Introduction to Operations Research*. New York: John Wiley & Sons, 1957.

Fabrycky, W. J., and Torgersen, P. E. *Operations Economy: Industrial Applications of Operations Research*. Upper Saddle River, NJ: Prentice Hall, 1966.

Hillier, F. S., and Lieberman, G. J. *Operations Research*, 4th ed. San Francisco: Holden-Day, 1987.

Taha, Hamdy A. *Operations Research, An Introduction*, 4th ed. New York: Macmillan, 1987.

Teichroew, P. *An Introduction to Management Science*. New York: John Wiley & Sons, 1964.

Wagner, Harvey M. *Principles of Management Science*. Upper Saddle River, NJ: Prentice Hall, 1975.

———. *Principles of Operations Research*. 2d ed. Upper Saddle River, NJ: Prentice Hall, 1975.

Problems

1. The Willow Furniture Company produces tables. The fixed monthly cost of production is $8,000, and the variable cost per table is $65. The tables sell for $180 apiece.
   a. For a monthly volume of 300 tables, determine the total cost, total revenue, and profit.
   b. Determine the monthly break-even volume for the Willow Furniture Company.

2. The Retread Tire Company recaps tires. The fixed annual cost of the recapping operation is $60,000. The variable cost of recapping a tire is $9. The company charges $25 to recap a tire.
   a. For an annual volume of 12,000 tires, determine the total cost, total revenue, and profit.
   b. Determine the annual break-even volume for the Retread Tire Company operation.

3. The Rolling Creek Textile Mill produces denim. The fixed monthly cost is $21,000, and the variable cost per yard of denim is $0.45. The mill sells a yard of denim for $1.30.
   a. For a monthly volume of 18,000 yards of denim, determine the total cost, total revenue, and profit.
   b. Determine the annual break-even volume for the Rolling Creek Textile Mill.

4. Evergreen Fertilizer Company produces fertilizer. The company's fixed monthly cost is $25,000, and its variable cost per pound of fertilizer is $0.15. Evergreen sells the fertilizer for $0.40 per pound. Determine the monthly break-even volume for the company.

5. Graphically illustrate the break-even volume for the Retread Tire Company determined in Problem 2.

6. Graphically illustrate the break-even volume for the Evergreen Fertilizer Company determined in Problem 4.

7. Andy Mendoza makes handcrafted dolls, which he sells at craft fairs. He is considering mass-producing the dolls to sell in stores. He estimates that the initial investment for plant and equipment will be $25,000, whereas labor, material, packaging, and shipping will be about $10 per doll. If the dolls are sold for $30 each, what sales volume is necessary for Andy to break even?

8. If the maximum operating capacity of the Retread Tire Company, as described in Problem 2, is 8,000 tires annually, determine the break-even volume as a percentage of that capacity.

9. If the maximum operating capacity of the Rolling Creek Textile Mill described in Problem 3 is 25,000 yards of denim per month, determine the break-even volume as a percentage of capacity.

10. If the maximum operating capacity of Evergreen Fertilizer Company described in Problem 4 is 120,000 pounds of fertilizer per month, determine the break-even volume as a percentage of capacity.

11. If the Retread Tire Company in Problem 2 changes its pricing for recapping a tire from \$25 to \$31, what effect will the change have on the break-even volume?

12. If Evergreen Fertilizer Company in Problem 4 changes the price of its fertilizer from \$0.40 per pound to \$0.60 per pound, what effect will the change have on the break-even volume?

13. If Evergreen Fertilizer Company changes its production process to add a weed killer to the fertilizer in order to increase sales, the variable cost per pound will increase from \$0.15 to \$0.22. What effect will this change have on the break-even volume computed in Problem 12?

14. If Evergreen Fertilizer Company increases its advertising expenditures by \$14,000 per year, what effect will the increase have on the break-even volume computed in Problem 13?

15. Pastureland Dairy makes cheese, which it sells at local supermarkets. The fixed monthly cost of production is \$4,000, and the variable cost per pound of cheese is \$0.21. The cheese sells for \$0.75 per pound; however, the dairy is considering raising the price to \$0.95 per pound. The dairy currently produces and sells 9,000 pounds of cheese per month, but if it raises its price per pound, sales will decrease to 5,700 pounds per month. Should the dairy raise the price?

16. For the doll-manufacturing enterprise described in Problem 7, Andy Mendoza has determined that \$10,000 worth of advertising will increase sales volume by 400 dolls. Should he spend the extra amount for advertising?

17. Andy Mendoza in Problem 7 is concerned that the demand for his dolls will not exceed the break-even point. He believes he can reduce his initial investment by purchasing used sewing machines and fewer machines. This will reduce his initial investment from \$25,000 to \$17,000. However, it will also require his employees to work more slowly and perform more operations by hand, thus increasing variable cost from \$10 to \$14 per doll. Will these changes reduce his break-even point?

18. The General Store at State University is an auxiliary bookstore located near the dormitories that sells academic supplies, toiletries, sweatshirts and T-shirts, magazines, packaged food items, and canned soft drinks and fruit drinks. The manager of the store has noticed that several pizza delivery services near campus make frequent deliveries. The manager is therefore considering selling pizza at the store. She could buy premade frozen pizzas and heat them in an oven. The cost of the oven and freezer would be \$27,000. The frozen pizzas cost \$3.75 each to buy from a distributor and to prepare (including labor and a box). To be competitive with the local delivery services, the manager believes she should sell the pizzas for \$8.95 apiece. The manager needs to write up a proposal for the university's director of auxiliary services.
    a. Determine how many pizzas would have to be sold to break even.
    b. If The General Store sells 20 pizzas per day, how many days would it take to break even?
    c. The manager of the store anticipates that once the local pizza delivery services start losing business, they will react by cutting prices. If after a month (30 days) the manager has to lower the price of a pizza to \$7.95 to keep demand at 20 pizzas per day, as she expects, what will the new break-even point be, and how long will it take the store to break even?

19. Kim Davis has decided to purchase a cellular phone, but she is unsure about which rate plan to select. The "regular" plan charges a fixed fee of \$55 per month for 1,000 minutes of airtime plus \$0.33 per minute for any time over 1,000 minutes. The "executive" plan charges a fixed fee of \$100 per month for 1,200 minutes of airtime plus \$0.25 per minute over 1,200 minutes.

a. If Kim expects to use the phone for 21 hours per month, which plan should she select?
b. At what level of use would Kim be indifferent between the two plans?

20. Annie McCoy, a student at Tech, plans to open a hot dog stand inside Tech's football stadium during home games. There are seven home games scheduled for the upcoming season. She must pay the Tech athletic department a vendor's fee of \$3,000 for the season. Her stand and other equipment will cost her \$4,500 for the season. She estimates that each hot dog she sells will cost her \$0.35. She has talked to friends at other universities who sell hot dogs at games. Based on their information and the athletic department's forecast that each game will sell out, she anticipates that she will sell approximately 2,000 hot dogs during each game.
    a. What price should she charge for a hot dog in order to break even?
    b. What factors might occur during the season that would alter the volume sold and thus the break-even price Annie might charge?
    c. What price would you suggest that Annie charge for a hot dog to provide her with a reasonable profit while remaining competitive with other food vendors?

21. Molly Dymond and Kathleen Taylor are considering the possibility of teaching swimming to kids during the summer. A local swim club opens its pool at noon each day, so it is available to rent during the morning. The cost of renting the pool during the 10-week period for which Molly and Kathleen would need it is \$1,700. The pool would also charge Molly and Kathleen an admission, towel service, and life guarding fee of \$7 per pupil, and Molly and Kathleen estimate an additional \$5 cost per student to hire several assistants. Molly and Kathleen plan to charge \$75 per student for the 10-week swimming class.
    a. How many pupils do Molly and Kathleen need to enroll in their class to break even?
    b. If Molly and Kathleen want to make a profit of \$5,000 for the summer, how many pupils do they need to enroll?
    c. Molly and Kathleen estimate that they might not be able to enroll more than 60 pupils. If they enroll this many pupils, how much would they need to charge per pupil in order to realize their profit goal of \$5,000?

22. The College of Business at Tech is planning to begin an online MBA program. The initial start-up cost for computing equipment, facilities, course development, and staff recruitment and development is \$350,000. The college plans to charge tuition of \$18,000 per student per year. However, the university administration will charge the college \$12,000 per student for the first 100 students enrolled each year for administrative costs and its share of the tuition payments.
    a. How many students does the college need to enroll in the first year to break even?
    b. If the college can enroll 75 students the first year, how much profit will it make?
    c. The college believes it can increase tuition to \$24,000, but doing so would reduce enrollment to 35. Should the college consider doing this?

23. The Star Youth Soccer Club helps to support its 20 boys' and girls' teams financially, primarily through the payment of coaches. The club puts on a tournament each fall to help pay its expenses. The cost of putting on the tournament is \$8,000, mainly for development, printing, and mailing of the tournament brochures. The tournament entry fee is \$400 per team. For every team that enters, it costs the club about \$75 to pay referees for the three-game minimum each team is guaranteed. If the club needs to clear \$60,000 from the tournament, how many teams should it invite?

24. In the example used to demonstrate model construction in this chapter (p. 4), a firm sells a product, x, for \$20 that costs \$5 to make, it has 100 pounds of steel to make the product, and it takes 4 pounds of steel to make each unit. The model that was constructed is

$$\begin{aligned}&\text{maximize } Z = 15x\\&\text{subject to}\\&\qquad 4x = 100\end{aligned}$$

Now suppose that there is a second product, y, that has a profit of \$10 and requires 2 pounds of steel to make, such that the model becomes

$$\begin{aligned}&\text{maximize } Z = 15x + 10y\\&\text{subject to}\\&\qquad 4x + 2y = 100\end{aligned}$$

Can you determine a solution to this new model that will achieve the objective? Explain your answer.

25. Consider a model in which two products, x and y, are produced. There are 100 pounds of material and 80 hours of labor available. It requires 2 pounds of material and 1 hour of labor to produce a unit of x, and 4 pounds of material and 5 hours of labor to produce a unit of y. The profit for x is \$30 per unit, and the profit for y is \$50 per unit. If we want to know how many units of x and y to produce to maximize profit, the model is

$$\begin{aligned}&\text{maximize } Z = 30x + 50y\\&\text{subject to}\\&\qquad 2x + 4y = 100\\&\qquad x + 5y = 80\end{aligned}$$

Determine the solution to this problem and explain your answer.

26. The Easy Drive Car Rental Agency needs 500 new cars in its Nashville operation and 300 new cars in Jacksonville, and it currently has 400 new cars in both Atlanta and Birmingham. It costs \$30 to move a car from Atlanta to Nashville, \$70 to move a car from Atlanta to Jacksonville, \$40 to move a car from Birmingham to Nashville, and \$60 to move a car from Birmingham to Jacksonville. The agency wants to determine how many cars should be transported from the agencies in Atlanta and Birmingham to the agencies in Nashville and Jacksonville in order to meet demand while minimizing the transport costs. Develop a mathematical model for this problem and use logic to determine a solution.

27. Ed Norris has developed a Web site for his used textbook business at State University. To sell advertising he needs to forecast the number of site visits he expects in the future. For the past 6 months he has had the following number of site visits:

Month	1	2	3	4	5	6
Site visits	6,300	10,200	14,700	18,500	25,100	30,500

Determine a forecast for Ed to use for month 7 and explain the logic used to develop your forecast.

28. When Marie McCoy wakes up on Saturday morning, she remembers that she had promised the PTA she would make some cakes and/or homemade bread for its bake sale that afternoon. However, she does not have time to go to the store and get ingredients, and she has only a short time to bake things in her oven. Because cakes and breads require different baking temperatures, she cannot bake them simultaneously, and she has only 3 hours available to bake. A cake requires 3 cups of flour, and a loaf of bread requires 8 cups; Marie has 20 cups of flour. A cake requires 45 minutes to bake, and a loaf of bread requires 30 minutes. The PTA will sell a cake for \$10 and a loaf of bread for \$6. Marie wants to decide how many cakes and loaves of bread she should make. Identify all the possible solutions to this problem (i.e., combinations of cakes and loaves of bread Marie has the time and flour to bake) and select the best one.

Case Problem

The Clean Clothes Corner Laundry

When Molly Lai purchased the Clean Clothes Corner Laundry, she thought that because it was in a good location near several high-income neighborhoods, she would automatically generate good business if she improved the laundry's physical appearance. Thus, she initially invested a lot of her cash reserves in remodeling the exterior and interior of the laundry. However, she just about broke even in the year following her acquisition of the laundry, which she didn't feel was a sufficient return, given how hard she had worked. Molly didn't realize that the dry-cleaning business is very competitive and that success is based more on price and quality service, including quickness of service, than on the laundry's appearance.

In order to improve her service, Molly is considering purchasing new dry-cleaning equipment, including a pressing machine that could substantially increase the speed at which she can dry-clean clothes and improve their appearance. The new machinery costs $16,200 installed and can clean 40 clothes items per hour (or 320 items per day). Molly estimates her variable costs to be $0.25 per item dry-cleaned, which will not change if she purchases the new equipment. Her current fixed costs are $1,700 per month. She charges customers $1.10 per clothing item.

A. What is Molly's current monthly volume?

B. If Molly purchases the new equipment, how many additional items will she have to dry-clean each month to break even?

C. Molly estimates that with the new equipment she can increase her volume to 4,300 items per month. What monthly profit would she realize with that level of business during the next 3 years? After 3 years?

D. Molly believes that if she doesn't buy the new equipment but lowers her price to $0.99 per item, she will increase her business volume. If she lowers her price, what will her new break-even volume be? If her price reduction results in a monthly volume of 3,800 items, what will her monthly profit be?

E. Molly estimates that if she purchases the new equipment and lowers her price to $0.99 per item, her volume will increase to about 4,700 units per month. Based on the local market, that is the largest volume she can realistically expect. What should Molly do?

Case Problem

The Ocobee River Rafting Company

Vicki Smith, Penny Miller, and Darryl Davis are students at State University. In the summer they often go rafting with other students down the Ocobee River in the nearby Blue Ridge Mountain foothills. The river has a number of minor rapids but is not generally dangerous. The students' rafts basically consist of large rubber tubes, sometimes joined together with ski rope. They have noticed that a number of students who come to the river don't have rubber rafts and often ask to borrow theirs, which can be very annoying. In discussing this nuisance, it occurred to Vicki, Penny, and Darryl that the problem might provide an opportunity to make some extra money. They considered starting a new enterprise, the Ocobee River Rafting Company, to sell rubber rafts at the river. They determined that their initial investment would be about $3,000 to rent a small parcel of land next to the river on which to make and sell the rafts; to purchase a tent to operate out of; and to buy some small equipment such as air pumps and a rope cutter. They estimated that the labor and material cost per raft will be about $12, including the purchase and shipping costs for the rubber tubes and rope. They plan to sell the rafts for $20 apiece, which they think is about the maximum price students will pay for a preassembled raft.

Soon after they determined these cost estimates, the newly formed company learned about another rafting company in North Carolina that was doing essentially what they planned to do. Vicki got in touch with one of the operators of that company, and he told her the company would be willing to supply rafts to the Ocobee River Rafting Company for an initial fixed fee of $9,000 plus $8 per raft, including shipping. (The Ocobee River Rafting Company would still have to rent the parcel of riverside land and tent for $1,000.) The rafts would already be inflated and assembled. This alternative appealed to Vicki, Penny, and Darryl because it would reduce the amount of time they would have to work pumping up the tubes and putting the rafts together, and it would increase time for their schoolwork.

Although the students prefer the alternative of purchasing the rafts from the North Carolina company, they are concerned about the large initial cost and worried about whether they will lose money. Of course, Vicki, Penny, and Darryl realize that their profit, if any, will be determined by how many rafts they sell. As such, they believe that they first need to determine how many rafts they must sell with each alternative in order to make a profit and which alternative would be best given different levels of demand. Furthermore, Penny has conducted a brief sample survey of people at the river and estimates that demand for rafts for the summer will be around 1,000 rafts.

Perform an analysis for the Ocobee River Rafting Company to determine which alternative would be best for different levels of demand. Indicate which alternative should be selected if demand is approximately 1,000 rafts and how much profit the company would make.

Case Problem

Constructing a Downtown Parking Lot in Draper

The town of Draper, with a population of 20,000, sits adjacent to State University, which has an enrollment of 27,000 students. Downtown Draper merchants have long complained about the lack of parking available to their customers. This is one primary reason for the steady migration of downtown businesses to a mall several miles outside town. The local chamber of commerce has finally convinced the town council to consider the construction of a new multilevel indoor parking facility downtown. Kelly Mattingly, the town's public works director, has developed plans for a facility that would cost $4.5 million to construct. To pay for the project, the town would sell municipal bonds with a duration of 30 years at 8% interest. Kelly also estimates that five employees would be required to operate the lot on a daily basis, at a total annual cost of $140,000. It is estimated that each car that enters the lot would park for an average of 2.5 hours and pay an average fee of $3.20. Further, it is estimated that each car that parks in the lot would (on average) cost the town $0.60 in annual maintenance for cleaning and repairs to the facility. Most of the downtown businesses (which includes a number of restaurants) are open 7 days per week.

A. Using break-even analysis, determine the number of cars that would have to park in the lot on an annual basis to pay off the project in the 30-year time frame.
B. From the results in (A), determine the approximate number of cars that would have to park in the lot on a daily basis. Does this seem to be a reasonable number to achieve, given the size of the town and college population?

Topic 14

Linear Programming: Model Formulation and Graphical Solution

2

Linear Programming: Model Formulation and Graphical Solution

Objectives of a business frequently are to maximize profit or minimize cost.

Many major decisions faced by a manager of a business focus on the best way to achieve the objectives of the firm, subject to the restrictions placed on the manager by the operating environment. These restrictions can take the form of limited resources, such as time, labor, energy, material, or money; or they can be in the form of restrictive guidelines, such as a recipe for making cereal or engineering specifications. One of the most frequent objectives of business firms is to gain the most profit possible or, in other words, to *maximize* profit. The objective of individual organizational units within a firm (such as a production or packaging department) is often to *minimize* cost. When a manager attempts to solve a general type of problem by seeking an objective that is subject to restrictions, the management science technique called **linear programming** is frequently used.

__Linear programming__ is a model that consists of linear relationships representing a firm's decision(s), given an objective and resource constraints.

There are three steps in applying the linear programming technique. First, the problem must be identified as being solvable by linear programming. Second, the unstructured problem must be formulated as a mathematical model. Third, the model must be solved by using established mathematical techniques. The linear programming technique derives its name from the fact that the functional relationships in the mathematical model are *linear*, and the solution technique consists of predetermined mathematical steps—that is, a *program*. In this chapter we will concern ourselves with the formulation of the mathematical model that represents the problem and then with solving this model by using a graph.

Model Formulation

A linear programming model consists of certain common components and characteristics. The model components include decision variables, an objective function, and model constraints, which consist of decision variables and parameters. **Decision variables** are mathematical symbols that represent levels of activity by the firm. For example, an electrical manufacturing firm desires to produce x_1 radios, x_2 toasters, and x_3 clocks, where x_1, x_2, and x_3 are symbols representing unknown variable quantities of each item. The final values of x_1, x_2, and x_3, as determined by the firm, constitute a *decision* (e.g., the equation $x_1 = 100$ radios is a decision by the firm to produce 100 radios).

__Decision variables__ are mathematical symbols that represent levels of activity.

The **objective function** is a linear mathematical relationship that describes the objective of the firm in terms of the decision variables. The objective function always consists of either *maximizing* or *minimizing* some value (e.g., maximize the profit or minimize the cost of producing radios).

The __objective function__ is a linear relationship that reflects the objective of an operation.

The *model constraints* are also linear relationships of the decision variables; they represent the restrictions placed on the firm by the operating environment. The restrictions can be in the form of limited resources or restrictive guidelines. For example, only 40 hours of labor may be available to produce radios during production. The actual numeric values in the objective function and the constraints, such as the 40 hours of available labor, are **parameters**.

A __constraint__ is a linear relationship that represents a restriction on decision making.

__Parameters__ are numerical values that are included in the objective functions and constraints.

The next section presents an example of how a linear programming model is formulated. Although this example is simplified, it is realistic and represents the type of problem to which linear programming can be applied. In the example, the model components are distinctly identified and described. By carefully studying this example, you can become familiar with the process of formulating linear programming models.

A Maximization Model Example

Beaver Creek Pottery Company is a small crafts operation run by a Native American tribal council. The company employs skilled artisans to produce clay bowls and mugs with authentic Native American designs and colors. The two primary resources used by the company are

Time Out for George B. Dantzig

Linear programming, as it is known today, was conceived in 1947 by George B. Dantzig while he was the head of the Air Force Statistical Control's Combat Analysis Branch at the Pentagon. The military referred to its plans for training, supplying, and deploying combat units as "programs." When Dantzig analyzed Air Force planning problems, he realized that they could be formulated as a system of linear inequalities—hence his original name for the technique, "programming in a linear structure," which was later shortened to "linear programming."

special pottery clay and skilled labor. Given these limited resources, the company desires to know how many bowls and mugs to produce each day in order to maximize profit. This is generally referred to as a *product mix* problem type. This scenario is illustrated in Figure 2.1.

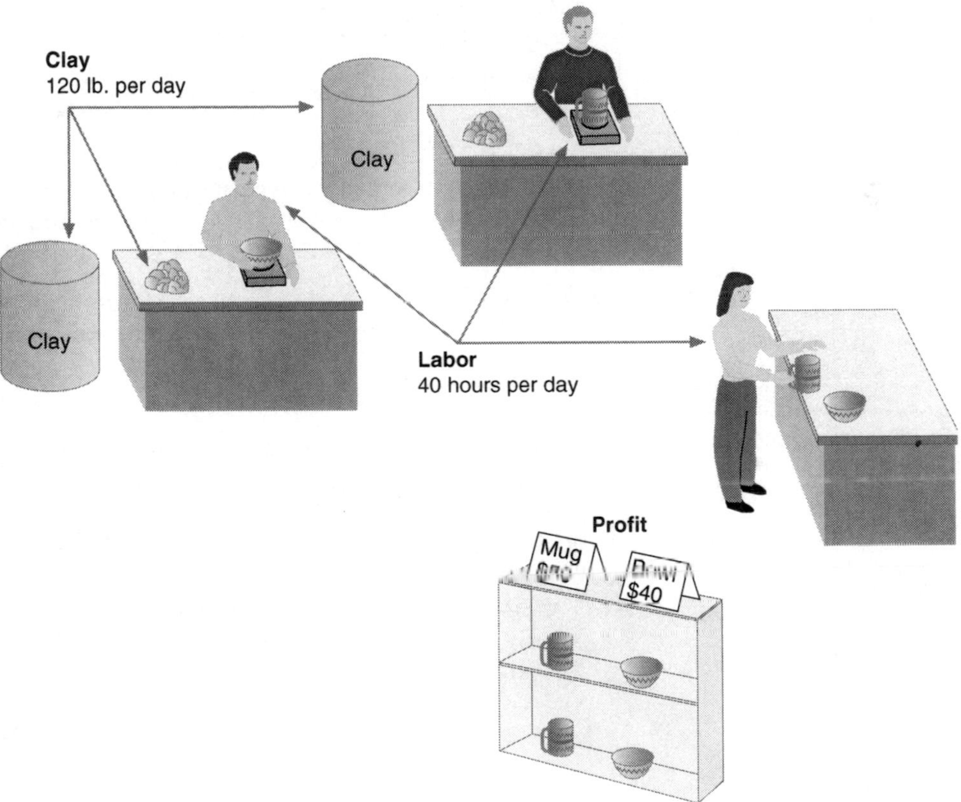

Figure 2.1
Beaver Creek Pottery Company

The two products have the following resource requirements for production and profit per item produced (i.e., the model parameters):

	Resource Requirements		
Product	LABOR (HR./UNIT)	CLAY (LB./UNIT)	PROFIT ($/UNIT)
Bowl	1	4	40
Mug	2	3	50

A linear programming model consists of decision variables, an objective function, and constraints.

There are 40 hours of labor and 120 pounds of clay available each day for production. We will formulate this problem as a linear programming model by defining each component of the model separately and then combining the components into a single model. The steps in this formulation process are summarized as follows:

> ### *Summary of LP Model Formulation Steps*
>
> ***Step 1: Define the decision variables***
>
> How many bowls and mugs to produce
>
> ***Step 2: Define the objective function***
>
> Maximize profit
>
> ***Step 3: Define the constraints***
>
> The resources (clay and labor) available

Decision Variables

The decision confronting management in this problem is how many bowls and mugs to produce. The two decision variables represent the number of bowls and mugs to be produced on a daily basis. The quantities to be produced can be represented symbolically as

$$x_1 = \text{number of bowls to produce}$$
$$x_2 = \text{number of mugs to produce}$$

The Objective Function

The objective of the company is to maximize total profit. The company's profit is the sum of the individual profits gained from each bowl and mug. Profit derived from bowls is determined by multiplying the unit profit of each bowl, \$40, by the number of bowls produced, x_1. Likewise, profit derived from mugs is derived from the unit profit of a mug, \$50, multiplied by the number of mugs produced, x_2. Thus, total profit, which we will define symbolically as Z, can be expressed mathematically as $\$40x_1 + \$50x_2$. By placing the term *maximize* in front of the profit function, we express the objective of the firm—to maximize total profit:

$$\text{maximize } Z = \$40x_1 + 50x_2$$

where

$$Z = \text{total profit per day}$$
$$\$40x_1 = \text{profit from bowls}$$
$$\$50x_2 = \text{profit from mugs}$$

Model Constraints

In this problem two resources are used for production—labor and clay—both of which are limited. Production of bowls and mugs requires both labor and clay. For each bowl produced, 1 hour of labor is required. Therefore, the labor used for the production of bowls is $1x_1$ hours. Similarly, each mug requires 2 hours of labor; thus, the labor used to produce mugs every day is $2x_2$ hours. The total labor used by the company is the sum of the individual amounts of labor used for each product:

$$1x_1 + 2x_2$$

However, the amount of labor represented by $1x_1 + 2x_2$ is limited to 40 hours per day; thus, the complete labor constraint is

$$1x_1 + 2x_2 \leq 40 \text{ hr.}$$

The "less than or equal to" (≤) inequality is employed instead of an equality (=) because the 40 hours of labor is a maximum limitation that *can be used*, not an amount that *must be used*. This constraint allows the company some flexibility; the company is not restricted to using exactly 40 hours but can use whatever amount is necessary to maximize profit, up to and including 40 hours. This means that it is possible to have idle, or excess, capacity (i.e., some of the 40 hours may not be used).

The constraint for clay is formulated in the same way as the labor constraint. Because each bowl requires 4 pounds of clay, the amount of clay used daily for the production of bowls is $4x_1$ pounds; and because each mug requires 3 pounds of clay, the amount of clay used daily for mugs is $3x_2$. Given that the amount of clay available for production each day is 120 pounds, the material constraint can be formulated as

$$4x_1 + 3x_2 \leq 120 \text{ lb.}$$

A final restriction is that the number of bowls and mugs produced must be either zero or a positive value because it is impossible to produce negative items. These restrictions are referred to as **nonnegativity constraints** and are expressed mathematically as

Nonnegativity constraints *restrict the decision variables to zero or positive values.*

$$x_1 \geq 0, x_2 \geq 0$$

The complete linear programming model for this problem can now be summarized as follows:

$$\begin{aligned} &\text{maximize } Z = \$40x_1 + 50x_2 \\ &\text{subject to} \\ &\quad 1x_1 + 2x_2 \leq 40 \\ &\quad 4x_1 + 3x_2 \leq 120 \\ &\quad x_1, x_2 \geq 0 \end{aligned}$$

The solution of this model will result in numeric values for x_1 and x_2 that will maximize total profit, Z. As *one possible* solution, consider $x_1 = 5$ bowls and $x_2 = 10$ mugs. First, we will substitute this hypothetical solution into each of the constraints in order to make sure that the solution does not require more resources than the constraints show are available:

$$\begin{aligned} 1(5) + 2(10) &\leq 40 \\ 25 &\leq 40 \end{aligned}$$

and

$$\begin{aligned} 4(5) + 3(10) &\leq 120 \\ 50 &\leq 120 \end{aligned}$$

Because neither of the constraints is violated by this hypothetical solution, we say the solution is **feasible** (i.e., it is possible). Substituting these solution values in the objective function gives $Z = 40(5) + 50(10) = \$700$. However, for the time being, we do not have any way of knowing whether \$700 is the *maximum* profit.

*A **feasible solution** does not violate any of the constraints.*

Now consider a solution of $x_1 = 10$ bowls and $x_2 = 20$ mugs. This solution results in a profit of

$$\begin{aligned} Z &= \$40(10) + 50(20) \\ &= 400 + 1{,}000 \\ &= \$1{,}400 \end{aligned}$$

*An **infeasible problem** violates at least one of the constraints.*

Although this is certainly a better solution in terms of profit, it is **infeasible** (i.e., not possible) because it violates the resource constraint for labor:

$$1(10) + 2(20) \leq 40$$
$$50 \not\leq 40$$

The solution to this problem must maximize profit without violating the constraints. The solution that achieves this objective is $x_1 = 24$ bowls and $x_2 = 8$ mugs, with a corresponding profit of $1,360. The determination of this solution is shown using the graphical solution approach in the following section.

Graphical Solutions of Linear Programming Models

Graphical solutions are limited to linear programming problems with only two decision variables.

Following the formulation of a mathematical model, the next stage in the application of linear programming to a decision-making problem is to find the solution of the model. A common solution approach is to solve algebraically the set of mathematical relationships that form the model either manually or using a computer program, thus determining the values for the decision variables. However, because the relationships are *linear*, some models and solutions can be illustrated *graphically.*

The graphical method is realistically limited to models with only two decision variables, which can be represented on a graph of two dimensions. Models with three decision variables can be graphed in three dimensions, but the process is quite cumbersome, and models of four or more decision variables cannot be graphed at all.

The graphical method provides a picture of how a solution is obtained for a linear programming problem.

Although the graphical method is limited as a solution approach, it is very useful at this point in our presentation of linear programming in that it gives a picture of how a solution is derived. Graphs can provide a clearer understanding of how the computer and mathematical solution approaches presented in subsequent chapters work and, thus, a better understanding of the solutions.

Graphical Solution of a Maximization Model

The product mix model will be used to demonstrate the graphical interpretation of a linear programming problem. Recall that the problem describes Beaver Creek Pottery Company's attempt to decide how many bowls and mugs to produce daily, given limited amounts of labor and clay. The complete linear programming model was formulated as

$$\text{maximize } Z = \$40x_1 + 50x_2$$
subject to
$$x_1 + 2x_2 \leq 40 \text{ hr. of labor}$$
$$4x_1 + 3x_2 \leq 120 \text{ lb. of clay}$$
$$x_1, x_2 \geq 0$$
where
x_1 = number of bowls produced
x_2 = number of mugs produced

Figure 2.2 is a set of coordinates for the decision variables x_1 and x_2, on which the graph of our model will be drawn. Note that only the positive quadrant is drawn (i.e., the quadrant where x_1 and x_2 will always be positive) because of the nonnegativity constraints, $x_1 \geq 0$ and $x_2 \geq 0$.

Management Science Application

Operational Cost Control at Kellogg

Kellogg is the world's largest cereal producer and a leading producer of convenience foods, with worldwide sales in 1999 of almost $7 billion. The company started with a single product, Kellogg's Corn Flakes, in 1906 and over the years developed a product line of other cereals, including Rice Krispies and Corn Pops, and convenience foods such as Pop-Tarts and Nutri-Grain cereal bars. Kellogg operates 5 plants in the United States and Canada and 7 distribution centers, and it contracts with 15 co-packers to produce or pack some of the Kellogg products. Kellogg must coordinate the production, packaging, inventory, and distribution of roughly 80 cereal products alone at these various facilities.

For more than a decade Kellogg has been using a large-scale linear programming model called the Kellogg Planning System (KPS) to plan its weekly production, inventory, and distribution decisions. The model decision variables include the amount of each product produced in a production process at each plant, the units of product packaged, the amount of inventory held, and the shipments of products to other plants and distribution centers. Model constraints include production processing time, packaging capacity, balancing constraints that make sure that all products produced are also packaged during the week, inventory balancing constraints, and inventory safety stock requirements. The model objective is cost minimization. Kellogg has also developed a tactical version of this basic operational linear programming model for long-range planning for 12 to 24 months into the future. The KPS model is credited with saving Kellogg $4.5 million in reduced production, inventory, and distribution costs in 1995, and it is estimated that KPS has saved Kellogg many more millions of dollars since the mid-1990s. The tactical version of KPS recently helped the company consolidate production capacity with estimated projected savings of almost $40 million.

Source: G. Brown, J. Keegan, B. Vigus, and K. Wood, "The Kellogg Company Optimizes Production, Inventory, and Distribution," *Interfaces* 31, no. 6 (November–December 2001): 1–15.

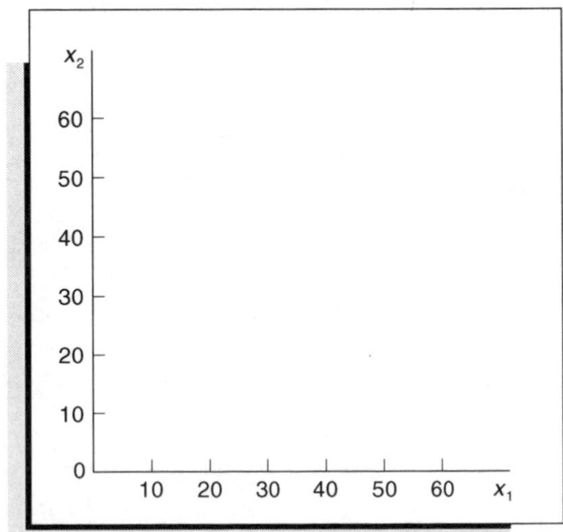

Figure 2.2
Coordinates for graphical analysis

Constraint lines are plotted as equations.

The first step in drawing the graph of the model is to plot the constraints on the graph. This is done by treating both constraints as equations (or straight lines) and plotting each line on the graph. Let's consider the labor constraint line first:

$$x_1 + 2x_2 = 40$$

A simple procedure for plotting this line is to determine two points that are on the line and then draw a straight line through the points. One point can be found by letting $x_1 = 0$ and solving for x_2:

$$(0) + 2x_2 = 40$$
$$x_2 = 20$$

Thus, one point is at the coordinates $x_1 = 0$ and $x_2 = 20$. A second point can be found by letting $x_2 = 0$ and solving for x_1:

$$x_1 + 2(0) = 40$$
$$x_1 = 40$$

Now we have a second point, $x_1 = 40$, $x_2 = 0$. The line on the graph representing this equation is drawn by connecting these two points, as shown in Figure 2.3. However, this is only the graph of the constraint *line* and does not reflect the entire constraint, which also includes the values that are less than or equal to (≤) this line. The *area* representing the entire constraint is shown in Figure 2.4.

Figure 2.3
Graph of the labor constraint line

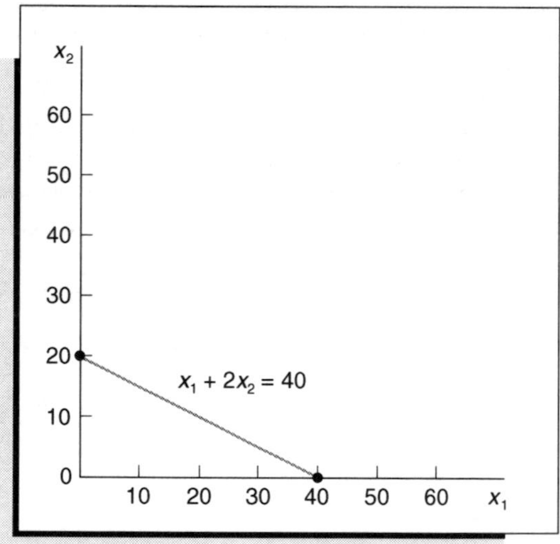

To test the correctness of the constraint area, we check any two points—one inside the constraint area and one outside. For example, check point *A* in Figure 2.4, which is at the intersection of $x_1 = 10$ and $x_2 = 10$. Substituting these values into the following labor constraint,

$$10 + 2(10) \leq 40$$
$$30 \leq 40 \text{ hr.}$$

Figure 2.4
The labor constraint area

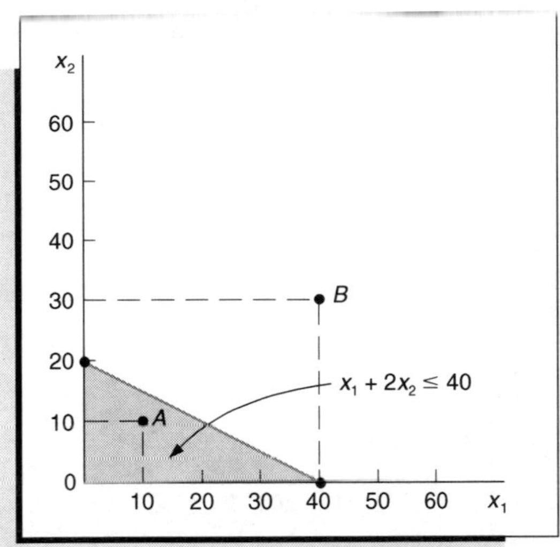

shows that point A is indeed within the constraint area, as these values for x_1 and x_2 yield a quantity that does not exceed the limit of 40 hours. Next, we check point B at $x_1 = 40$ and $x_2 = 30$:

$$40 + 2(30) \leq 40$$
$$100 \nleq 40 \text{ hr.}$$

Point B is obviously outside the constraint area because the values for x_1 and x_2 yield a quantity (100) that exceeds the limit of 40 hours.

We draw the line for the clay constraint the same way as the one for the labor constraint—by finding two points on the constraint line and connecting them with a straight line. First, let $x_1 = 0$ and solve for x_2:

$$4(0) + 3x_2 = 120$$
$$x_2 = 40$$

Performing this operation results in a point, $x_1 = 0$, $x_2 = 40$. Next, we let $x_2 = 0$ and then solve for x_1:

$$4x_1 + 3(0) = 120$$
$$x_1 = 30$$

This operation yields a second point, $x_1 = 30$, $x_2 = 0$. Plotting these points on the graph and connecting them with a line gives the constraint line and area for clay, as shown in Figure 2.5.

Combining the two individual graphs for both labor and clay (Figures 2.4 and 2.5) produces a graph of the model constraints, as shown in Figure 2.6. The shaded area in Figure 2.6 is the area that is common to both model constraints. Therefore, this is the only area on the graph that contains points (i.e., values for x_1 and x_2) that will satisfy both constraints simultaneously. For example, consider the points R, S, and T in Figure 2.7. Point R satisfies both constraints; thus, we say it is a *feasible* solution point. Point S satisfies the clay constraint ($4x_1 + 3x_2 \leq 120$) but exceeds the labor constraint; thus, it is infeasible. Point T satisfies neither constraint; thus, it is also infeasible.

Figure 2.5
The constraint area for clay

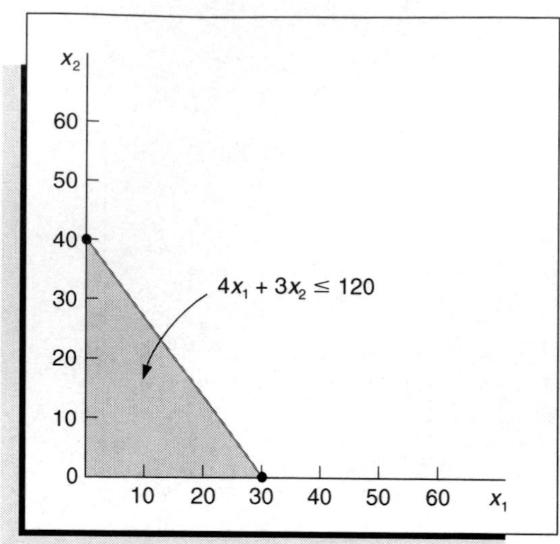

Figure 2.6
Graph of both model constraints

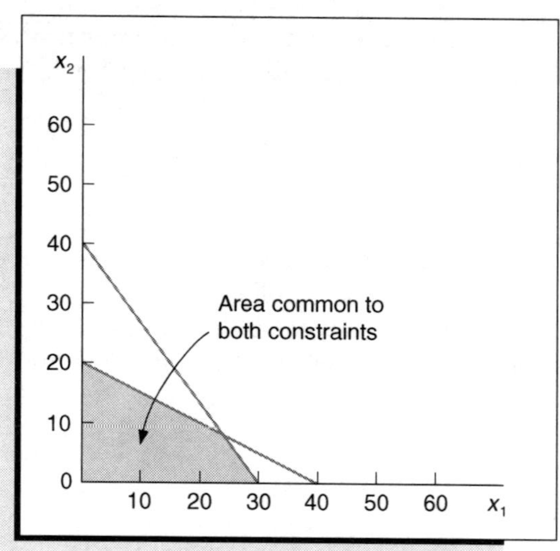

The feasible solution area is an area on the graph that is bounded by the constraint equations.

The shaded area in Figure 2.7 is referred to as the *feasible solution area* because all the points in this area satisfy both constraints. Some point within this feasible solution area will result in *maximum profit* for Beaver Creek Pottery Company. The next step in the graphical solution approach is to locate this point.

The Optimal Solution Point

The second step in the graphical solution method is to locate the point in the feasible solution area that will result in the greatest total profit. To begin the solution analysis, we first plot the objective function line for an *arbitrarily* selected level of profit. For example, if we say profit, Z, is \$800, the objective function is

$$\$800 = 40x_1 + 50x_2$$

Plotting this line just as we plotted the constraint lines results in the graph shown in Figure 2.8. Every point on this line is in the feasible solution area and will result in a profit

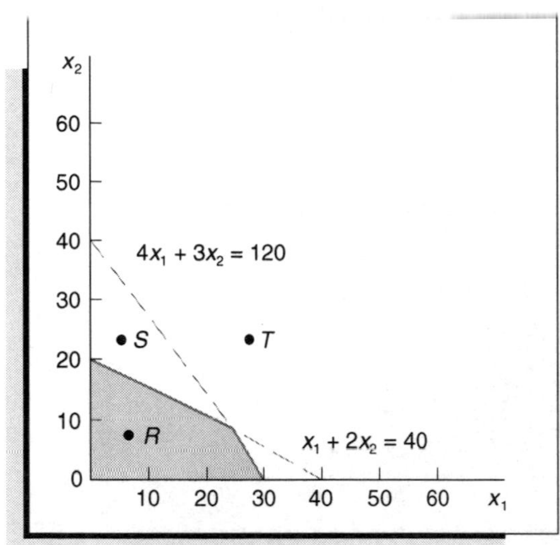

Figure 2.7
The feasible solution area constraints

of \$800 (i.e., every combination of x_1 and x_2 on this line will give a Z value of \$800). However, let us see whether an even greater profit will still provide a feasible solution. For example, consider profits of \$1,200 and \$1,600, as shown in Figure 2.9.

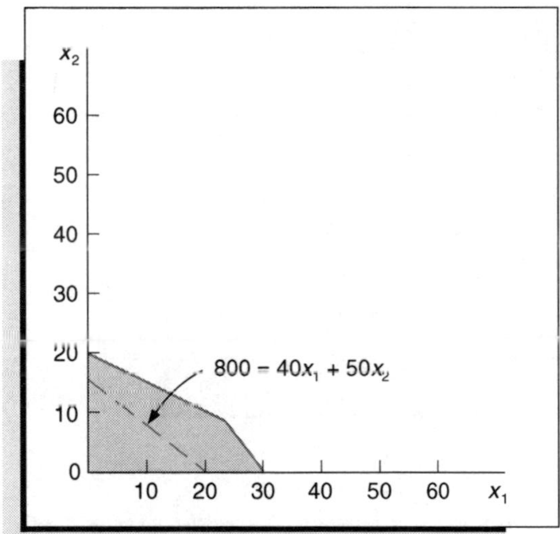

Figure 2.8
Objective function line for $Z = \$800$

A portion of the objective function line for a profit of \$1,200 is outside the feasible solution area, but part of the line remains within the feasible area. Therefore, this profit line indicates that there are feasible solution points that give a profit greater than \$800. Now let us increase profit again, to \$1,600. This profit line, also shown in Figure 2.9, is completely outside the feasible solution area. The fact that no points on this line are feasible indicates that a profit of \$1,600 is not possible.

Because a profit of \$1,600 is too great for the constraint limitations, as shown in Figure 2.9, the question of the maximum profit value remains. We can see from Figure 2.9 that profit increases as the objective function line moves away from the origin (i.e., the point $x_1 = 0, x_2 = 0$). Given this characteristic, the maximum profit will be attained at the point where the objective function line is farthest from the origin *and* is still touching a point in the feasible solution area. This point is shown as point B in Figure 2.10.

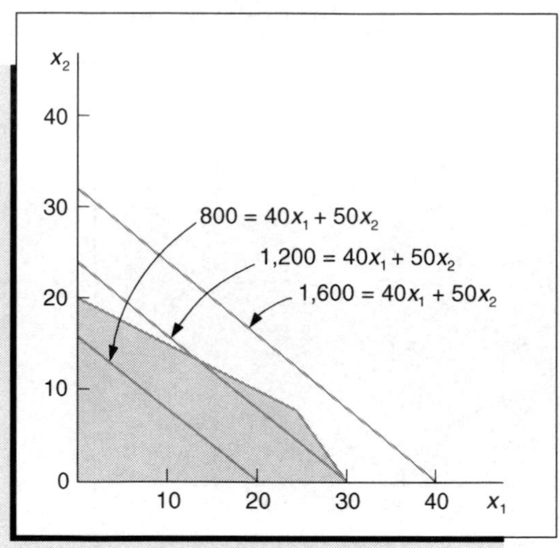

Figure 2.9
Alternative objective function lines for profits, *Z*, of \$800, \$1,200, and \$1,600

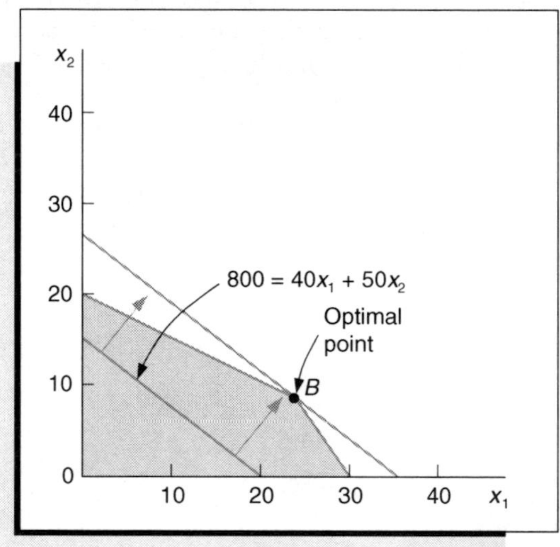

Figure 2.10
Identification of optimal solution point

*The **optimal solution** is the best feasible solution.*

To find point *B*, we place a straightedge parallel to the objective function line $\$800 = 40x_1 + 50x_2$ in Figure 2.10 and move it outward from the origin as far as we can without losing contact with the feasible solution area. Point *B* is referred to as the **optimal** (i.e., best) **solution**.

The Solution Values

The third step in the graphical solution approach is to solve for the values of x_1 and x_2 once the optimal solution point has been found. It is possible to determine the x_1 and x_2 coordinates of point *B* in Figure 2.10 directly from the graph, as shown in Figure 2.11. The graphical coordinates corresponding to point *B* in Figure 2.11 are $x_1 = 24$ and $x_2 = 8$. This is the optimal solution for the decision variables in the problem. However, unless an absolutely accurate graph is drawn, it is frequently difficult to determine the correct solution directly from the graph. A more exact approach is to determine the solution values mathematically once the optimal point on the graph has been determined. The mathematical approach for determining the solution is described in the following pages. First, however, we will consider a few characteristics of the solution.

Figure 2.11
Optimal solution coordinates

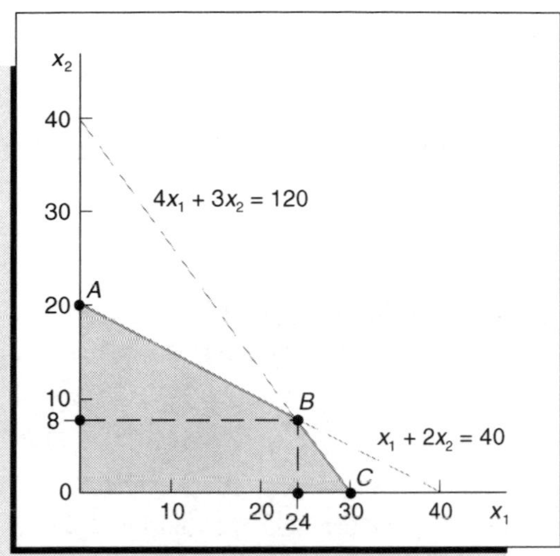

The optimal solution point is the last point the objective function touches as it leaves the feasible solution area.

In Figure 2.10, as the objective function was increased, the last point it touched in the feasible solution area was on the boundary of the feasible solution area. The solution point is always on this boundary because the boundary contains the points farthest from the origin (i.e., the points corresponding to the greatest profit). This characteristic of linear programming problems reduces the number of possible solution points considerably, from all points in the solution area to just those points on the boundary. However, the number of possible solution points is reduced even more by another characteristic of linear programming problems.

__Extreme points__ are corner points on the boundary of the feasible solution area.

The solution point will be on the boundary of the feasible solution area and at one of the *corners* of the boundary where two constraint lines intersect. (The graphical axes, you will recall, are also constraints because $x_1 \geq 0$ and $x_2 \geq 0$.) These corners (points *A*, *B*, and *C* in Figure 2.11) are protrusions, or *extremes*, in the feasible solution area; they are called **extreme points**. It has been proven mathematically that the optimal solution in a linear programming model will always occur at an extreme point. Therefore, in our sample problem the possible solution points are limited to the three extreme points, *A*, *B*, and *C*. The optimal extreme point is the extreme point the objective function touches last as it leaves the feasible solution area, as shown in Figure 2.10.

Constraint equations are solved simultaneously at the optimal extreme point to determine the variable solution values.

From the graph shown in Figure 2.10, we know that the optimal solution point is *B*. Because point *B* is formed by the intersection of two constraint lines, as shown in Figure 2.11, these two lines are *equal* at point *B*. Thus, the values of x_1 and x_2 at that intersection can be found by solving the two equations *simultaneously*.

First, we convert both equations to functions of x_1:

$$x_1 + 2x_2 = 40$$
$$x_1 = 40 - 2x_2$$

and

$$4x_1 + 3x_2 = 120$$
$$4x_1 = 120 - 3x_2$$
$$x_1 = 30 - (3x_2/4)$$

Now we let x_1 in the first equation equal x_1 in the second equation,

$$40 - 2x_2 = 30 - (3x_2/4)$$

and solve for x_2:

$$5x_2/4 = 10$$
$$x_2 = 8$$

Substituting $x_2 = 8$ into either one of the original equations gives a value for x_1:

$$x_1 = 40 - 2x_2$$
$$x_1 = 40 - 2(8)$$
$$= 24$$

Thus, the optimal solution at point B in Figure 2.11 is $x_1 = 24$ and $x_2 = 8$. Substituting these values into the objective function gives the maximum profit,

$$Z = \$40x_1 + 50x_2$$
$$Z = \$40(24) + 50(8)$$
$$= \$1{,}360$$

In terms of the original problem, the solution indicates that if the pottery company produces 24 bowls and 8 mugs, it will receive $1,360, the maximum daily profit possible (given the resource constraints).

Given that the optimal solution will be at one of the extreme corner points, A, B, or C, we can also find the solution by testing each of the three points to see which results in the greatest profit, rather than by graphing the objective function and seeing which point it last touches as it moves out of the feasible solution area. Figure 2.12 shows the solution values for all three points, A, B, and C, and the amount of profit, Z, at each point.

Figure 2.12
Solutions at all corner points

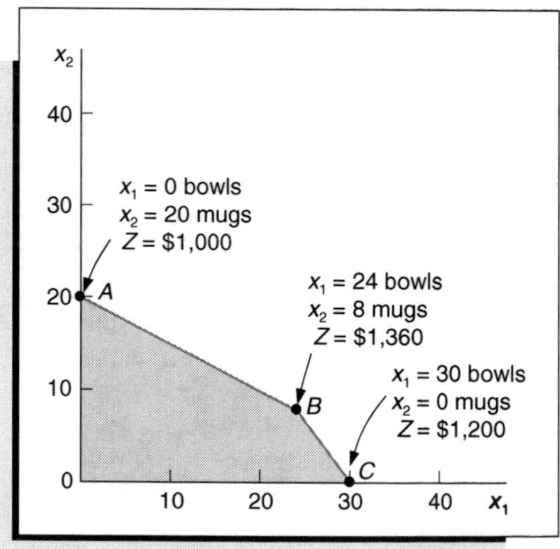

As indicated in the discussion of Figure 2.10, point B is the optimal solution point because it is the last point the objective function touches before it leaves the solution area. In other words, the objective function determines which extreme point is optimal. This is because the objective function designates the profit that will accrue from each combination of x_1 and x_2 values at the extreme points. If the objective function had had different coefficients (i.e., different x_1 and x_2 profit values), one of the extreme points other than B might have been optimal.

Let's assume for a moment that the profit for a bowl is \$70 instead of \$40, and the profit for a mug is \$20 instead of \$50. These values result in a new objective function, = \$$70x_1$ + $20x_2$. If the model constraints for labor or clay are not changed, the feasible solution area remains the same, as shown in Figure 2.13. However, the location of the objective function in Figure 2.13 is different from that of the original objective function in Figure 2.10. The reason for this change is that the new profit coefficients give the linear objective function a new *slope*.

Figure 2.13

The optimal solution with $Z = 70x_1 + 20x_2$

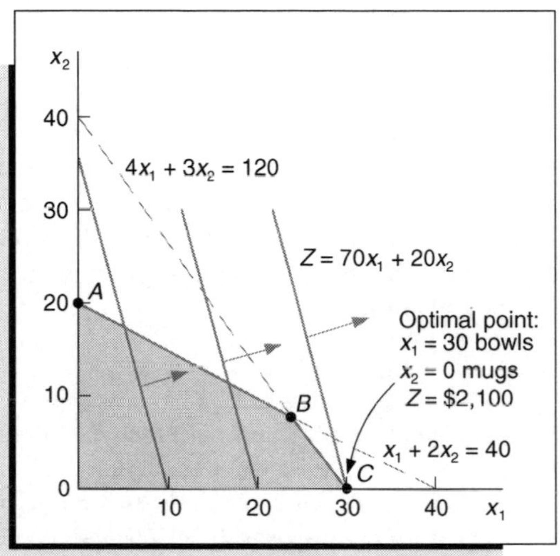

The ***slope*** *is computed as the "rise" over the "run."*

The **slope** can be determined by transforming the objective function into the general equation for a straight line, $y = a + bx$, where y is the dependent variable, a is the y intercept, b is the slope, and x is the independent variable. For our sample objective function, x_2 is the dependent variable corresponding to y (i.e., it is on the vertical axis), and x_1 is the independent variable. Thus, the objective function can be transformed into the general equation of a line as follows:

$$Z = 70x_1 + 20x_2$$
$$20x_2 = Z - 70x_1$$
$$\underset{\substack{\uparrow \\ y}}{x_2} = \underset{\substack{\uparrow \\ a}}{\frac{Z}{20}} - \underset{\substack{\uparrow \\ b}}{\frac{7}{2}}x_1$$

This transformation identifies the slope of the new objective function as −7/2 (the minus sign indicates that the line slopes downward). In contrast, the slope of the original objective function was −4/5.

If we move this new objective function out through the feasible solution area, the last extreme point it touches is point *C*. Simultaneously solving the constraint lines at point *C* results in the following solution:

$$x_1 = 30$$
$$4x_1 + 3x_2 = 120$$

and

$$x_2 = 40 - (4x_1/3)$$
$$x_2 = 40 - 4(30)/3$$
$$x_2 = 0$$

Thus, the optimal solution at point *C* in Figure 2.13 is x_1 = 30 bowls, x_2 = 0 mugs, and Z = \$2,100 profit. Altering the objective function coefficients results in a new solution.

This brief example of the effects of altering the objective function highlights two useful points. First, the optimal extreme point is determined by the objective function, and an extreme point on one axis of the graph is as likely to be the optimal solution as is an extreme point on a different axis. Second, the solution is sensitive to the values of the coefficients in the objective function. If the objective function coefficients are changed, as in our example, the solution may change. Likewise, if the constraint coefficients are changed, the solution space and solution points may change also. This information can be of consequence to the decision maker trying to determine how much of a product to produce. **Sensitivity analysis**—the use of linear programming to evaluate the effects of changes in model parameters—is discussed in Chapter 3.

__Sensitivity analysis__ is used to analyze changes in model parameters.

It should be noted that some problems do not have a single extreme point solution. For example, when the objective function line parallels one of the constraint lines, an entire line segment is bounded by two adjacent corner points that are optimal; there is no single extreme point on the objective function line. In this situation there are **multiple optimal solutions**. This and other irregular types of solution outcomes in linear programming are discussed at the end of this chapter.

__Multiple optimal solutions__ can occur when the objective function is parallel to a constraint line.

Slack Variables

Once the optimal solution was found at point B in Figure 2.12, simultaneous equations were solved to determine the values of x_1 and x_2. Recall that the solution occurs at an extreme point where constraint equation lines intersect with each other or with the axis. Thus, the model constraints are considered as *equations* (=) rather than ≤ or ≥ inequalities.

There is a standard procedure for transforming ≤ inequality constraints into equations. This transformation is achieved by adding a new variable, called a **slack variable**, to each constraint. For the pottery company example, the model constraints are

A slack variable is added to a ≤ constraint to convert it to an equation (=).

$$x_1 + 2x_2 \leq 40 \text{ hr. of labor}$$
$$4x_1 + 3x_2 \leq 120 \text{ lb. of clay}$$

The addition of a unique slack variable, s_1, to the labor constraint and s_2 to the constraint for clay results in the following equations:

A __slack variable__ represents unused resources.

$$x_1 + 2x_2 + s_1 = 40 \text{ hr. of labor}$$
$$4x_1 + 3x_2 + s_2 = 120 \text{ lb. of clay}$$

The slack variables in these equations, s_1 and s_2, will take on any value necessary to make the left-hand side of the equation equal to the right-hand side. For example, consider a hypothetical solution of $x_1 = 5$ and $x_2 = 10$. Substituting these values into the foregoing equations yields

$$x_1 + 2x_2 + s_1 = 40 \text{ hr. of labor}$$
$$5 + 2(10) + s_1 = 40 \text{ hr. of labor}$$
$$s_1 = 15 \text{ hr. of labor}$$

and

$$4x_1 + 3x_2 + s_2 = 120 \text{ lb. of clay}$$
$$4(5) + 3(10) + s_2 = 120 \text{ lb. of clay}$$
$$s_2 = 70 \text{ lb. of clay}$$

In this example, $x_1 = 5$ bowls and $x_2 = 10$ mugs represent a solution that does not make use of the total available amount of labor and clay. In the labor constraint, 5 bowls and 10 mugs require only 25 hours of labor. This leaves 15 hours that are not used. Thus, s_1 represents the amount of *unused* labor, or slack.

In the clay constraint, 5 bowls and 10 mugs require only 50 pounds of clay. This leaves 70 pounds of clay unused. Thus, s_2 represents the amount of *unused* clay. In general, slack variables represent the amount of *unused resources.*

The ultimate instance of unused resources occurs at the origin, where $x_1 = 0$ and $x_2 = 0$. Substituting these values into the equations yields

$$\begin{aligned} x_1 + 2x_2 + s_1 &= 40 \\ 0 + 2(0) + s_1 &= 40 \\ s_1 &= 40 \text{ hr. of labor} \end{aligned}$$

and

$$\begin{aligned} 4x_1 + 3x_2 + s_2 &= 120 \\ 4(0) + 3(0) + s_2 &= 120 \\ s_2 &= 120 \text{ lb. of clay} \end{aligned}$$

Because no production takes place at the origin, all the resources are unused; thus, the slack variables equal the total available amounts of each resource: $s_1 = 40$ hours of labor and $s_2 = 120$ pounds of clay.

What is the effect of these new slack variables on the objective function? The objective function for our example represents the profit gained from the production of bowls and mugs,

$$Z = \$40x_1 + \$50x_2$$

A slack variable contributes nothing to the objective function value.

The coefficient \$40 is the contribution to profit of each bowl; \$50 is the contribution to profit of each mug. What, then, do the slack variables s_1 and s_2 contribute? They contribute *nothing* to profit because they represent unused resources. Profit is made only after the resources are put to use in making bowls and mugs. Using slack variables, we can write the objective function as

$$\text{maximize } Z = \$40x_1 + \$50x_2 + 0s_1 + 0s_2$$

As in the case of decision variables (x_1 and x_2), slack variables can have only nonnegative values because negative resources are not possible. Therefore, for this model formulation, x_1, x_2, s_1, and $s_2 \geq 0$.

The complete linear programming model can be written in what is referred to as *standard form* with slack variables as follows:

$$\begin{aligned} &\text{maximize } Z = \$40x_1 + \$50x_2 + 0s_1 + 0s_2 \\ &\text{subject to} \\ &\qquad x_1 + 2x_2 + s_1 = 40 \\ &\qquad 4x_1 + 3x_2 + s_2 = 120 \\ &\qquad x_1, x_2, s_1, s_2 \geq 0 \end{aligned}$$

The solution values, including the slack at each solution point, are summarized as follows:

Solution Summary with Slack

Point	Solution Values	Z	Slack
A	$x_1 = 0$ bowls, $x_2 = 20$ mugs	\$1,000	$s_1 = 0$ hr.; $s_2 = 60$ lb.
B	$x_1 = 24$ bowls, $x_2 = 8$ mugs	\$1,360	$s_1 = 0$ hr.; $s_2 = 0$ lb.
C	$x_1 = 30$ bowls, $x_2 = 0$ mugs	\$1,200	$s_1 = 10$ hr.; $s_2 = 0$ lb.

Figure 2.14 shows the graphical solution of this example, with slack variables included at each solution point.

Management Science Application

Estimating Food Nutrient Values at Minnesota's Nutrition Coordinating Center

The Nutrition Coordinating Center (NCC) at the University of Minnesota maintains a food composition database used by institutions around the world. This database is used to calculate dietary material intake; to plan menus; to explore the relationships between diet and disease; to meet regulatory requirements; and to monitor the effects of education, intervention, and regulation. These calculations require an enormous amount of nutrient value data for different food products.

Every year, more than 12,000 new brand-name food products are introduced into the marketplace. However, it's not feasible to perform a chemical analysis on all foods for multiple nutrients, and so the NCC *estimates* thousands of nutrient values each year. The NCC has used a time-consuming trial-and-error approach to estimating these nutrient values. These estimates are a composite of the foods already in the database. The NCC developed a linear programming model that determines ingredient amounts in new food products. These estimated ingredient amounts are subsequently used to calculate nutrient amounts for a food product. The nutritionist normally uses the linear programming model to derive an initial estimate of ingredient amounts and then fine-tunes these amounts. The model has reduced the average time it takes to estimate a product formula from 8.3 minutes (using the trial-and-error approach) to 2.1 minutes of labor time and effort.

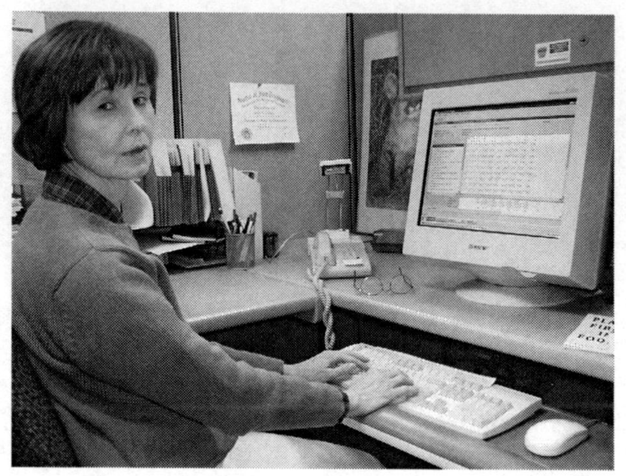

Source: B. J. Westrich, M. A. Altmann, and S. J. Potthoff, "Minnesota's Nutrition Coordinating Center Uses Mathematical Optimization to Estimate Food Nutrient Values," *Interfaces* 28, no. 5 (September–October 1998): 86–99.

Figure 2.14
Solutions at points *A*, *B*, and *C* with slack

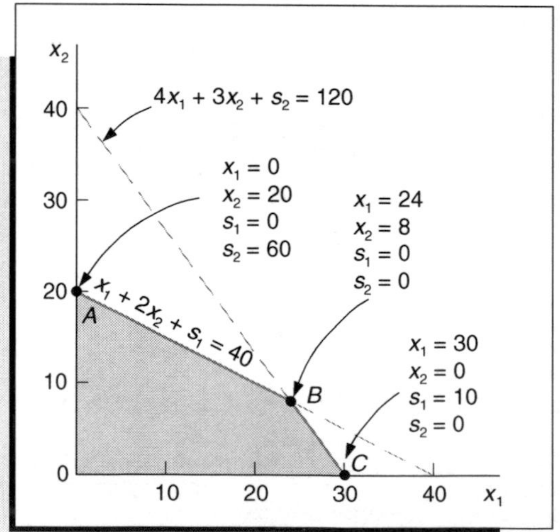

Summary of the Graphical Solution Steps

The steps for solving a graphical linear programming model are summarized here:

1. Plot the model constraints as equations on the graph; then, considering the inequalities of the constraints, indicate the feasible solution area.

2. Plot the objective function; then move this line out from the origin to locate the optimal solution point.
3. Solve simultaneous equations at the solution point to find the optimal solution values.

Or

2. Solve simultaneous equations at each corner point to find the solution values at each point.
3. Substitute these values into the objective function to find the set of values that results in the maximum Z value.

A Minimization Model Example

As mentioned at the beginning of this chapter, there are two types of linear programming problems: maximization problems (like the Beaver Creek Pottery Company example) and minimization problems. A minimization problem is formulated the same basic way as a maximization problem, except for a few minor differences. The following sample problem will demonstrate the formulation of a minimization model.

A farmer is preparing to plant a crop in the spring and needs to fertilize a field. There are two brands of fertilizer to choose from, Super-gro and Crop-quick. Each brand yields a specific amount of nitrogen and phosphate per bag, as follows:

	Chemical Contribution	
Brand	NITROGEN (LB./BAG)	PHOSPHATE (LB./BAG)
Super-gro	2	4
Crop-quick	4	3

The farmer's field requires at least 16 pounds of nitrogen and 24 pounds of phosphate. Super-gro costs \$6 per bag, and Crop-quick costs \$3. The farmer wants to know how many bags of each brand to purchase in order to minimize the total cost of fertilizing. This scenario is illustrated in Figure 2.15.

The steps in the linear programming model formulation process are summarized as follows:

Summary of LP Model Formulation Steps

Step 1: Define the decision variables

How many bags of Super-gro and Crop-quick to buy

Step 2: Define the objective function

Minimize cost

Step 3: Define the constraints

The field requirements for nitrogen and phosphate

Decision Variables

This problem contains two decision variables, representing the number of bags of each brand of fertilizer to purchase:

x_1 = bags of Super-gro
x_2 = bags of Crop-quick

Figure 2.15
Fertilizing farmer's field

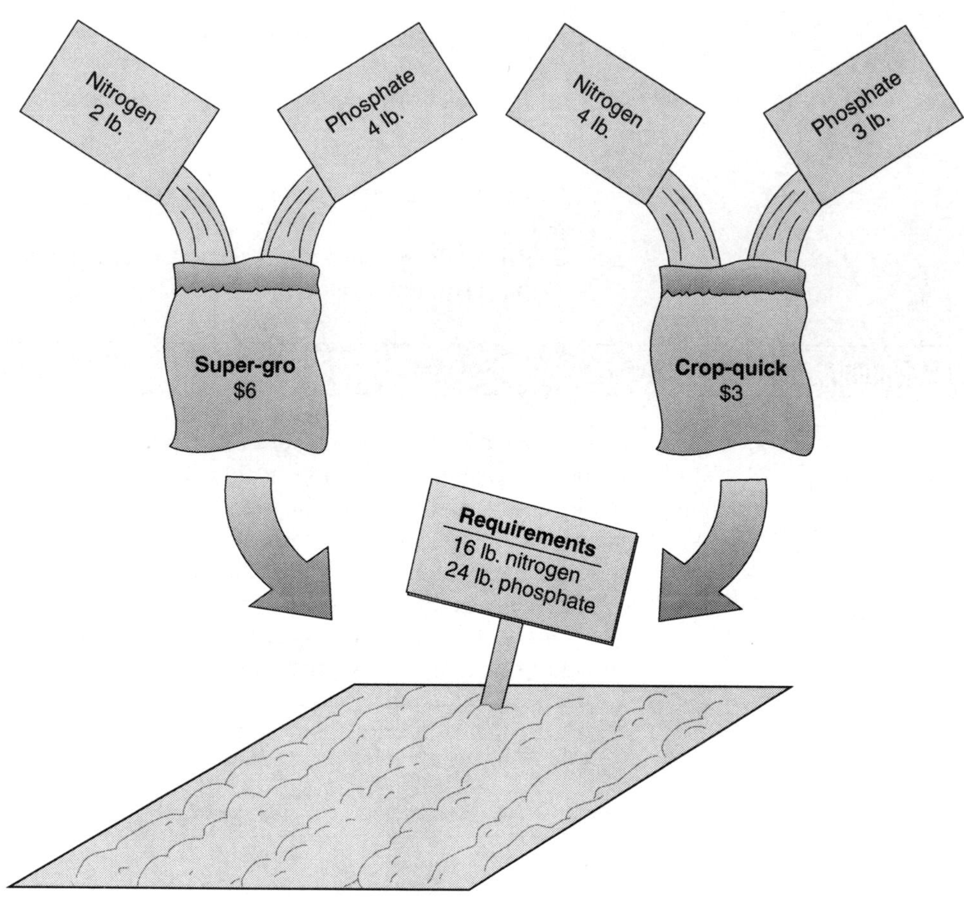

The Objective Function

The farmer's objective is to minimize the total cost of fertilizing. The total cost is the sum of the individual costs of each type of fertilizer purchased. The objective function that represents total cost is expressed as

$$\text{minimize } Z = \$6x_1 + 3x_2$$

where

$\$6x_1$ = cost of bags of Super-gro
$\$3x_2$ = cost of bags of Crop-quick

Model Constraints

The requirements for nitrogen and phosphate represent the constraints of the model. Each bag of fertilizer contributes a number of pounds of nitrogen and phosphate to the field. The constraint for nitrogen is

$$2x_1 + 4x_2 \geq 16 \text{ lb.}$$

where

$2x_1$ = the nitrogen contribution (lb.) per bag of Super-gro
$4x_2$ = the nitrogen contribution (lb.) per bag of Crop-quick

Rather than a ≤ (less than or equal to) inequality, as used in the Beaver Creek Pottery Company model, this constraint requires a ≥ (greater than or equal to) inequality. This is because the nitrogen content for the field is a minimum requirement specifying that at least 16 pounds of nitrogen be deposited on the farmer's field. If a minimum cost solution results in more than 16 pounds of nitrogen on the field, that is acceptable; however, the amount cannot be less than 16 pounds.

The constraint for phosphate is constructed like the constraint for nitrogen:

$$4x_1 + 3x_2 \geq 24 \text{ lb.}$$

The three types of linear programming constraints are ≤, =, and ≥.

With this example we have shown two of the three types of linear programming model constraints, ≤ and ≥. The third type is an exact equality, =. This type specifies that a constraint requirement must be exact. For example, if the farmer had said that the phosphate requirement for the field was exactly 24 pounds, the constraint would have been

$$4x_1 + 3x_2 = 24 \text{ lb.}$$

As in our maximization model, there are also nonnegativity constraints in this problem to indicate that negative bags of fertilizer cannot be purchased:

$$x_1, x_2 \geq 0$$

The complete model formulation for this minimization problem is

$$\begin{aligned}&\text{minimize } Z = \$6x_1 + 3x_2\\&\text{subject to}\\&2x_1 + 4x_2 \geq 16 \text{ lb. of nitrogen}\\&4x_1 + 3x_2 \geq 24 \text{ lb. of phosphate}\\&\quad x_1, x_2 \geq 0\end{aligned}$$

Graphical Solution of a Minimization Model

We follow the same basic steps in the graphical solution of a minimization model as in a maximization model. The fertilizer example will be used to demonstrate the graphical solution of a minimization model.

The first step is to graph the equations of the two model constraints, as shown in Figure 2.16. Next, the feasible solution area is chosen, to reflect the ≥ inequalities in the constraints, as shown in Figure 2.17.

Figure 2.16

Constraint lines for fertilizer model

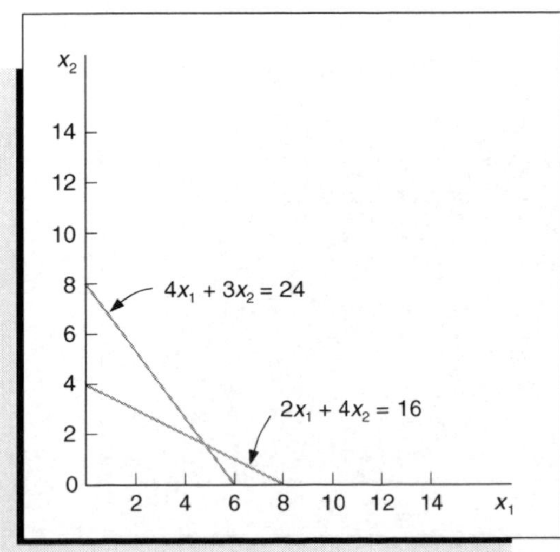

Figure 2.17
Feasible solution area

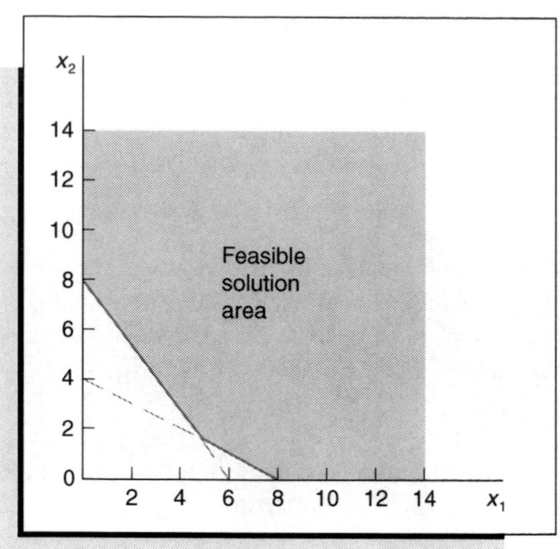

The optimal solution of a minimization problem is at the extreme point closest to the origin.

After the feasible solution area has been determined, the second step in the graphical solution approach is to locate the optimal point. Recall that in a maximization problem, the optimal solution is on the boundary of the feasible solution area that contains the point(s) farthest from the origin. The optimal solution point in a minimization problem is also on the boundary of the feasible solution area; however, the boundary contains the point(s) *closest* to the origin (zero being the lowest cost possible).

As in a maximization problem, the optimal solution is located at one of the extreme points of the boundary. In this case the corner points represent extremities in the boundary of the feasible solution area that are *closest* to the origin. Figure 2.18 shows the three corner points—*A*, *B*, and *C*—and the objective function line.

As the objective function edges *toward* the origin, the last point it touches in the feasible solution area is *A*. In other words, point *A* is the closest the objective function can get to the origin without encompassing infeasible points. Thus, it corresponds to the lowest cost that can be attained.

Figure 2.18
The optimal solution point

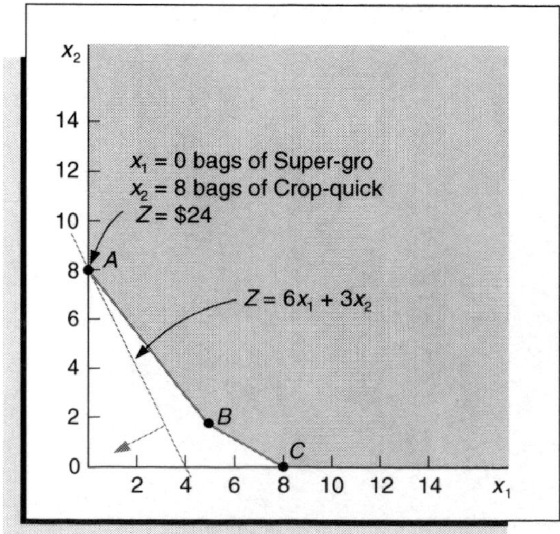

Management Science Application

Determining Optimal Fertilizer Mixes at Soquimich (South America)

Soquimich, a Chilean fertilizer manufacturer, is the leading producer and distributor of specialty fertilizers in the world, with revenues of almost US$0.5 billion in more than 80 countries. Soquimich produces four main specialty fertilizers and more than 200 fertilizer blends, depending on the needs of its customers. Farmers want the company to quickly recommend optimal fertilizer blends that will provide the appropriate quantity of ingredients for their particular crop at the lowest possible cost. A farmer will provide a company sales representative with information about previous crop yields and his or her target yields and then company representatives will visit the farm to obtain soil samples, which are analyzed in the company labs. A report is generated, which indicates the soil requirements for nutrients, including nitrogen, phosphorus, potassium, boron, magnesium, sulfur, and zinc. Given these soil requirements, company experts determine an optimal fertilizer blend, using a linear programming model that includes constraints for the nutrient quantities required by the soil (for a particular crop) and an objective function that minimizes production costs. Previously the company determined fertilizer blend recommendations by using a time-consuming manual procedure conducted by experts. The linear programming model enables the company to provide accurate, quick, low-cost (discounted) estimates to its customers, which has helped the company gain new customers and increase its market share.

Source: A. M. Angel, L. A. Taladriz, and R. Weber. "Soquimich Uses a System Based on Mixed-Integer Linear Programming and Expert Systems to Improve Customer Service," *Interfaces* 33, no. 4 (July–August 2003): 41–52.

The final step in the graphical solution approach is to solve for the values of x_1 and x_2 at point A. Because point A is on the x_2 axis, $x_1 = 0$; thus,

$$\begin{aligned} 4(0) + 3x_2 &= 24 \\ x_2 &= 8 \end{aligned}$$

Given that the optimal solution is $x_1 = 0, x_2 = 8$, the minimum cost, Z, is

$$\begin{aligned} Z &= \$6x_1 + \$3x_2 \\ Z &= 6(0) + 3(8) \\ &= \$24 \end{aligned}$$

This means the farmer should not purchase any Super-gro but, instead, should purchase eight bags of Crop-quick, at a total cost of $24.

Surplus Variables

Greater than or equal to constraints cannot be converted to equations by adding slack variables, as with $\leq$ constraints. Recall our fertilizer model, formulated as

$$\text{minimize } Z = \$6x_1 + \$3x_2$$

subject to

$$\begin{aligned} 2x_1 + 4x_2 &\geq 16 \text{ lb. of nitrogen} \\ 4x_1 + 3x_2 &\geq 24 \text{ lb. of phosphate} \\ x_1, x_2 &\geq 0 \end{aligned}$$

where
x_1 = bags of Super-gro fertilizer
x_2 = bags of Crop-quick fertilizer
Z = farmer's total cost ($) of purchasing fertilizer

A surplus variable is subtracted from a ≥ constraint to convert it to an equation (=).

*A **surplus variable** represents an excess above a constraint requirement level.*

Because this problem has ≥ constraints as opposed to the ≤ constraints of the Beaver Creek Pottery Company maximization example, the constraints are converted to equations a little differently.

Instead of adding a slack variable with a ≥ constraint, we subtract a **surplus variable.** Whereas a slack variable is added and reflects unused resources, a surplus variable is subtracted and reflects the excess above a minimum resource requirement level. Like a slack variable, a surplus variable is represented symbolically by s_1 and must be nonnegative.

For the nitrogen constraint, the subtraction of a surplus variable gives

$$2x_1 + 4x_2 - s_1 = 16$$

The surplus variable s_1 transforms the nitrogen constraint into an equation.

As an example, consider the hypothetical solution

$$x_1 = 0$$
$$x_2 = 10$$

Substituting these values into the previous equation yields

$$2(0) + 4(10) - s_1 = 16$$
$$-s_1 = 16 - 40$$
$$s_1 = 24 \text{ lb. of nitrogen}$$

In this equation s_1 can be interpreted as the *extra* amount of nitrogen above the minimum requirement of 16 pounds that would be obtained by purchasing 10 bags of Crop-quick fertilizer.

In a similar manner, the constraint for phosphate is converted to an equation by subtracting a surplus variable, s_2:

$$4x_1 + 3x_2 - s_2 = 24$$

Figure 2.19

Graph of the fertilizer example

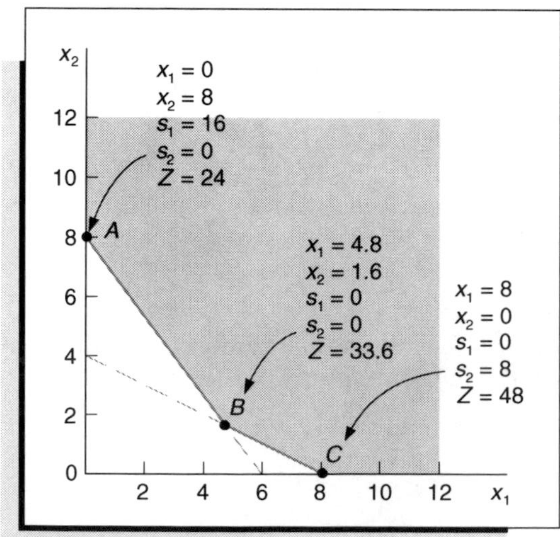

As is the case with slack variables, surplus variables contribute nothing to the overall cost of a model. For example, putting additional nitrogen or phosphate on the field will not affect the farmer's cost; the only thing affecting cost is the number of bags of fertilizer purchased. As such, the standard form of this linear programming model is summarized as

$$\begin{aligned}&\text{minimize } Z = \$6x_1 + 3x_2 + 0s_1 + 0s_2\\&\text{subject to}\\&\quad 2x_1 + 4x_2 - s_1 = 16\\&\quad 4x_1 + 3x_2 - s_2 = 24\\&\quad x_1, x_2, s_1, s_2 \geq 0\end{aligned}$$

Figure 2.19 shows the graphical solutions for our example, with surplus variables included at each solution point.

Irregular Types of Linear Programming Problems

For some linear programming models, the general rules do not always apply.

The basic forms of typical maximization and minimization problems have been shown in this chapter. However, there are several special types of atypical linear programming problems. Although these special cases do not occur frequently, they will be described so that you can recognize them when they arise. These special types include problems with more than one optimal solution, infeasible problems, and problems with unbounded solutions.

Multiple Optimal Solutions

Consider the Beaver Creek Pottery Company example, with the objective function changed from $Z = 40x_1 + 50x_2$ to $Z = 40x_1 + 30x_2$:

$$\begin{aligned}&\text{maximize } Z = 40x_1 + 30x_2\\&\text{subject to}\\&\quad x_1 + 2x_2 \leq 40 \text{ hr. of labor}\\&\quad 4x_1 + 3x_2 \leq 120 \text{ lb. of clay}\\&\quad x_1, x_2 \geq 0\\&\text{where}\\&\quad x_1 = \text{bowls produced}\\&\quad x_2 = \text{mugs produced}\end{aligned}$$

The graph of this model is shown in Figure 2.20. The slight change in the objective function makes it now *parallel* to the constraint line, $4x_1 + 3x_2 = 120$. Both lines now have the same slope of $-4/3$. Therefore, as the objective function edge moves outward from the origin, it touches the whole line segment *BC* rather than a single extreme corner point before it leaves the feasible solution area. This means that every point along this line segment is optimal (i.e., each point results in the same profit of $Z = \$1,200$). The endpoints of this line segment, *B* and *C*, are typically referred to as the **alternate optimal solutions**. It is understood that these points represent the endpoints of a range of optimal solutions.

Alternate optimal solutions are at the endpoints of the constraint line segment that the objective function parallels.

The pottery company, therefore, has several options in deciding on the number of bowls and mugs to produce. Multiple optimal solutions can benefit the decision maker because the number of decision options is enlarged. The multiple optimal solutions (along the line segment *BC* in Figure 2.20) allow the decision maker greater flexibility. For example, in the

Multiple optimal solutions provide greater flexibility to the decision maker.

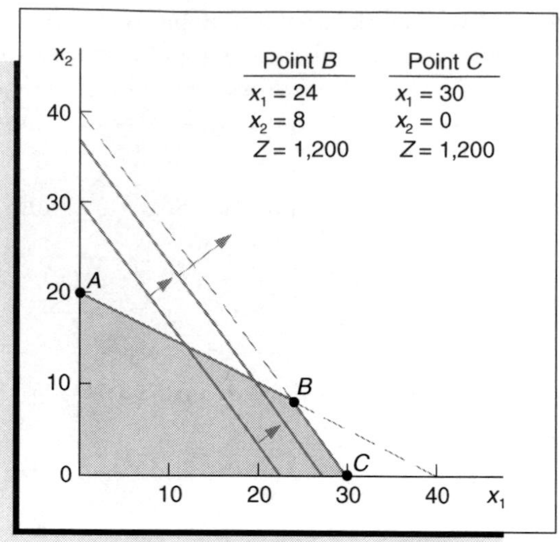

Figure 2.20
Graph of the Beaver Creek Pottery Company example with multiple optimal solutions

case of Beaver Creek Pottery Company, it may be easier to sell bowls than mugs; thus, the solution at point *C*, where only bowls are produced, would be more desirable than the solution at point *B*, where a mix of bowls and mugs is produced.

An Infeasible Problem

In some cases a linear programming problem has no feasible solution area; thus, there is no solution to the problem. An example of an infeasible problem is formulated next and depicted graphically in Figure 2.21:

$$\text{maximize } Z = 5x_1 + 3x_2$$
$$\text{subject to}$$
$$4x_1 + 2x_2 \leq 8$$
$$x_1 \geq 4$$
$$x_2 \geq 6$$
$$x_1, x_2 \geq 0$$

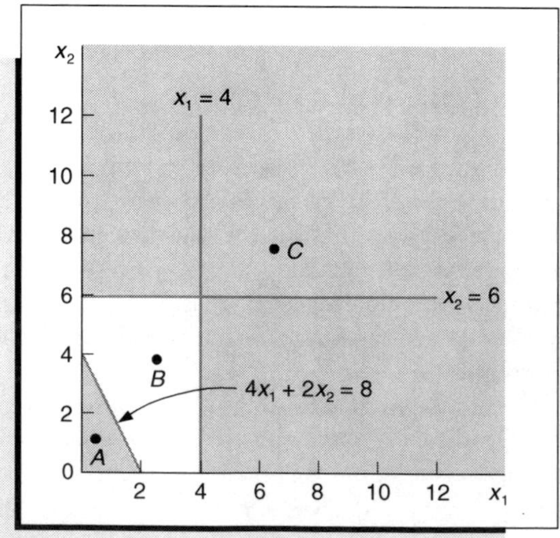

Figure 2.21
Graph of an infeasible problem

An ***infeasible problem*** *has no feasible solution area; every possible solution point violates one or more constraints.*

Point A in Figure 2.21 satisfies only the constraint $4x_1 + 2x_2 \leq 8$, whereas point C satisfies only the constraints $x_1 \geq 4$ and $x_2 \geq 6$. Point B satisfies none of the constraints. The three constraints do not overlap to form a feasible solution area. Because no point satisfies all three constraints simultaneously, there is no solution to the problem. Infeasible problems do not typically occur, but when they do, they are usually a result of errors in defining the problem or in formulating the linear programming model.

An Unbounded Problem

In an unbounded problem the objective function can increase indefinitely without reaching a maximum value.

In some problems the feasible solution area formed by the model constraints is not closed. In these cases it is possible for the objective function to increase indefinitely without ever reaching a maximum value because it never reaches the boundary of the feasible solution area.

An example of this type of problem is formulated next and shown graphically in Figure 2.22:

$$\begin{aligned}&\text{maximize } Z = 4x_1 + 2x_2\\&\text{subject to}\\&\qquad x_1 \geq 4\\&\qquad x_2 \leq 2\\&\qquad x_1, x_2 \geq 0\end{aligned}$$

Figure 2.22
An unbounded problem

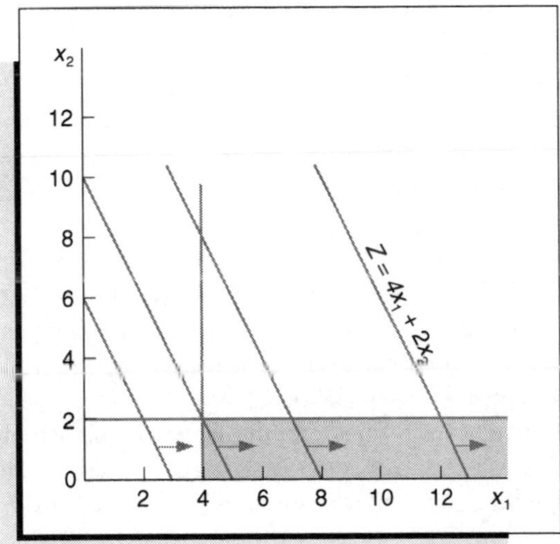

The solution space is not completely closed in.

In Figure 2.22 the objective function is shown to increase without bound; thus, a solution is never reached.

Unlimited profits are not possible in the real world; an unbounded solution, like an infeasible solution, typically reflects an error in defining the problem or in formulating the model.

Characteristics of Linear Programming Problems

The components of a linear programming model are an objective function, decision variables, and constraints.

Now that we have had the opportunity to construct several linear programming models, let's review the characteristics that identify a linear programming problem.

A linear programming problem requires a choice between alternative courses of action (i.e., a decision). The decision is represented in the model by decision variables. A typical choice task for a business firm is deciding how much of several different products to produce, as in the Beaver Creek Pottery Company example presented earlier in this chapter. Identifying the choice task and defining the decision variables is usually the first step in the formulation process because it is quite difficult to construct the objective function and constraints without first identifying the decision variables.

The problem encompasses an objective that the decision maker wants to achieve. The two most frequently encountered objectives for a business are maximizing profit and minimizing cost.

A third characteristic of a linear programming problem is that restrictions exist, making unlimited achievement of the objective function impossible. In a business firm these restrictions often take the form of limited resources, such as labor or material; however, the sample models in this chapter exhibit a variety of problem restrictions. These restrictions, as well as the objective, must be definable by mathematical functional relationships that are linear. Defining these relationships is typically the most difficult part of the formulation process.

Properties of Linear Programming Models

In addition to encompassing only linear relationships, a linear programming model also has several other implicit properties, which have been exhibited consistently throughout the examples in this chapter. The term *linear* not only means that the functions in the models are graphed as a straight line; it also means that the relationships exhibit **proportionality**. In other words, the rate of change, or slope, of the function is constant; therefore, changes of a given size in the value of a decision variable will result in exactly the same relative changes in the functional value.

Proportionality means the slope of a constraint or objective function line is constant.

Linear programming also requires that the objective function terms and the constraint terms be **additive**. For example, in the Beaver Creek Pottery Company model, the total profit (Z) must equal the sum of profits earned from making bowls ($\$40x_1$) and mugs ($\$50x_2$). Also, the total resources used must equal the sum of the resources used for each activity in a constraint (e.g., labor).

The terms in the objective function or constraints are additive.

Another property of linear programming models is that the solution values (of the decision variables) cannot be restricted to integer values; the decision variables can take on any fractional value. Thus, the variables are said to be *continuous* or **divisible**, as opposed to *integer* or *discrete*. For example, although decision variables representing bowls or mugs or airplanes or automobiles should realistically have integer (whole number) solutions, the solution methods for linear programming will not necessarily provide such solutions. This is a property that will be discussed further as solution methods are presented in subsequent chapters.

The values of decision variables are continuous or divisible.

The final property of linear programming models is that the values of all the model parameters are assumed to be constant and known with **certainty**. In real situations, however, model parameters are frequently uncertain because they reflect the future as well as the present, and future conditions are rarely known with certainty.

All model parameters are assumed to be known with certainty.

To summarize, a linear programming model has the following general properties: linearity, proportionality, additivity, divisibility, and certainty. As various linear programming solution methods are presented throughout this book, these properties will become more obvious, and their impact on problem solution will be discussed in greater detail.

Summary

The two example problems in this chapter were formulated as linear programming models in order to demonstrate the modeling process. These problems were similar in that they concerned achieving some objective subject to a set of restrictions or requirements. Linear programming models exhibit certain common characteristics:

- An objective function to be maximized or minimized
- A set of constraints
- Decision variables for measuring the level of activity
- Linearity among all constraint relationships and the objective function

The graphical approach to the solution of linear programming problems is not a very efficient means of solving problems. For one thing, drawing accurate graphs is tedious. Moreover, the graphical approach is limited to models with only two decision variables. However, the analysis of the graphical approach provides valuable insight into linear programming problems and their solutions.

In the graphical approach, once the feasible solution area and the optimal solution point have been determined from the graph, simultaneous equations are solved to determine the values of x_1 and x_2 at the solution point. In Chapter 3 we will show how linear programming solutions can be obtained using computer programs.

References

Baumol, W. J. *Economic Theory and Operations Analysis*, 4th ed. Upper Saddle River, NJ: Prentice Hall, 1977.

Charnes, A., and Cooper, W. W. *Management Models and Industrial Applications of Linear Programming*. New York: John Wiley & Sons, 1961.

Dantzig, G. B. *Linear Programming and Extensions*. Princeton, NJ: Princeton University Press, 1963.

Gass, S. *Linear Programming*, 4th ed. New York: McGraw-Hill, 1975.

Hadley, G. *Linear Programming*. Reading, MA: Addison-Wesley, 1962.

Hillier, F. S., and Lieberman, G. J. *Introduction to Operations Research*, 4th ed. San Francisco: Holden-Day, 1986.

Llewellyn, R. W. *Linear Programming*. New York: Holt, Rinehart and Winston, 1964.

Taha, H. A. *Operations Research, an Introduction*, 4th ed. New York: Macmillan, 1987.

Wagner, H. M. *Principles of Operations Research*, 2nd ed. Upper Saddle River, NJ: Prentice Hall, 1975.

Example Problem Solutions

As a prelude to the problems, this section presents example solutions to two linear programming problems.

Problem Statement

Moore's Meatpacking Company produces a hot dog mixture in 1,000-pound batches. The mixture contains two ingredients—chicken and beef. The cost per pound of each of these ingredients is as follows:

Ingredient	Cost/lb.
Chicken	$3
Beef	$5

Each batch has the following recipe requirements:

a. At least 500 pounds of chicken
b. At least 200 pounds of beef

The ratio of chicken to beef must be at least 2 to 1. The company wants to know the optimal mixture of ingredients that will minimize cost. Formulate a linear programming model for this problem.

Solution

Step 1: Identify Decision Variables

Recall that the problem should not be "swallowed whole." Identify each part of the model separately, starting with the decision variables:

$$x_1 = \text{lb. of chicken}$$
$$x_2 = \text{lb. of beef}$$

Step 2: Formulate the Objective Function

$$\text{minimize } Z = \$3x_1 + \$5x_2$$

where

$$Z = \text{cost per 1,000-lb batch}$$
$$\$3x_1 = \text{cost of chicken}$$
$$\$5x_2 = \text{cost of beef}$$

Step 3: Establish Model Constraints

The constraints of this problem are embodied in the recipe restrictions and (not to be overlooked) the fact that each batch must consist of 1,000 pounds of mixture:

$$x_1 + x_2 = 1{,}000 \text{ lb.}$$
$$x_1 \geq 500 \text{ lb. of chicken}$$
$$x_2 \geq 200 \text{ lb. of beef}$$
$$x_1/x_2 \geq 2/1 \text{ or } x_1 - 2x_2 \geq 0$$

and

$$x_1, x_2 \geq 0$$

The Model

$$\text{minimize } Z = \$3x_1 + \$5x_2$$

subject to

$$x_1 + x_2 = 1{,}000$$
$$x_1 \geq 500$$
$$x_2 \geq 200$$
$$x_1 - 2x_2 \geq 0$$
$$x_1, x_2 \geq 0$$

Problem Statement

Solve the following linear programming model graphically:

$$\text{maximize } Z = 4x_1 + 5x_2$$

subject to

$$x_1 + 2x_2 \leq 10$$
$$6x_1 + 6x_2 \leq 36$$
$$x_1 \leq 4$$
$$x_1, x_2 \geq 0$$

Solution

Step 1: Plot the Constraint Lines as Equations

A simple method for plotting constraint lines is to set one of the constraint variables equal to zero and solve for the other variable to establish a point on one of the axes. The three constraint lines are graphed in the following figure:

The constraint equations

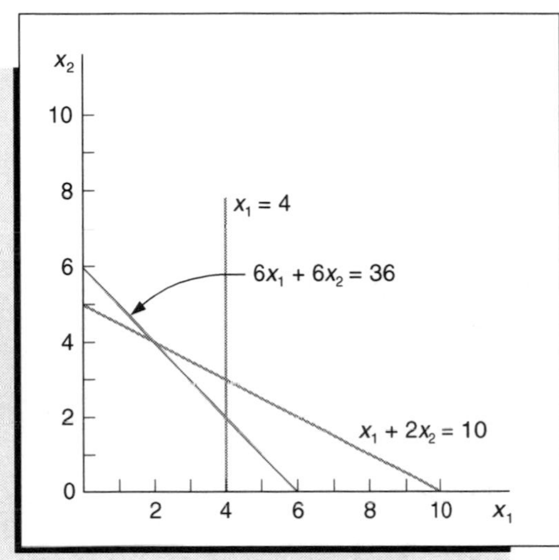

Step 2: Determine the Feasible Solution Area

The feasible solution area is determined by identifying the space that jointly satisfies the ≤ conditions of all three constraints, as shown in the following figure:

The feasible solution space and extreme points

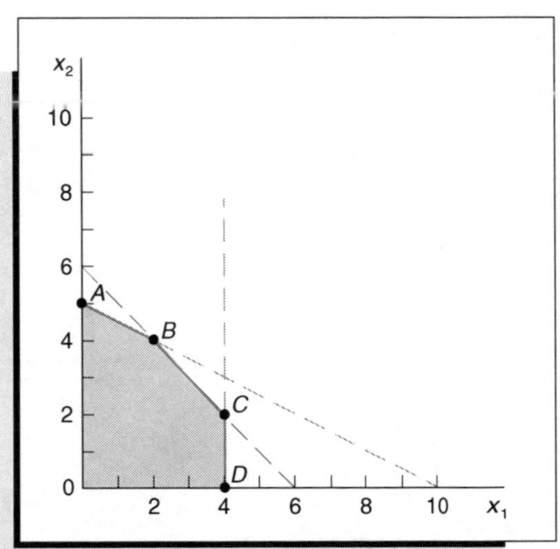

Step 3: Determine the Solution Points

The solution at point A can be determined by noting that the constraint line intersects the x_2 axis at 5; thus, $x_2 = 5, x_1 = 0$, and $Z = 25$. The solution at point D on the other axis can be determined similarly; the constraint intersects the axis at $x_1 = 4, x_2 = 0$, and $Z = 16$.

The values at points B and C must be found by solving simultaneous equations. Note that point B is formed by the intersection of the lines $x_1 + 2x_2 = 10$ and 6 $_1$ $_2 = 36$. First, convert both of these equations to functions of x_1:

$$x_1 + 2x_2 = 10$$
$$x_1 = 10 - 2x_2$$

and

$$6x_1 + 6x_2 = 36$$
$$6x_1 = 36 - 6x_2$$
$$x_1 = 6 - x_2$$

Now set the equations equal and solve for x_2:

$$10 - 2x_2 = 6 - x_2$$
$$-x_2 = -4$$
$$x_2 = 4$$

Substituting $x_2 = 4$ into either of the two equations gives a value for x_1:

$$x_1 = 6 - x_2$$
$$x_1 = 6 - (4)$$
$$x_1 = 2$$

Thus, at point B, $x_1 = 2$, $x_2 = 4$, and $Z = 28$.

At point C, $x_1 = 4$. Substituting $x_1 = 4$ into the equation $x_1 = 6 - x_2$ gives a value for x_2:

$$4 = 6 - x_2$$
$$x_2 = 2$$

Thus, $x_1 = 4$, $x_2 = 2$, and $Z = 26$.

Step 4: Determine the Optimal Solution

The optimal solution is at point B, where $x_1 = 2$, $x_2 = 4$, and $Z = 28$. The optimal solution and solutions at the other extreme points are summarized in the following figure:

Optimal solution point

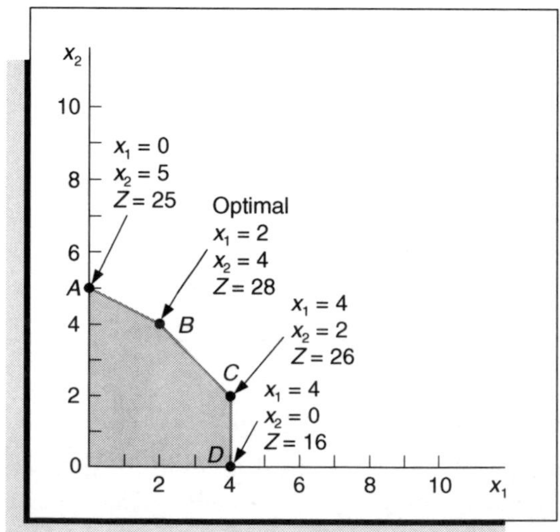

Problems

1. In Problem 28 in Chapter 1, when Marie McCoy wakes up Saturday morning, she remembers that she promised the PTA she would make some cakes and/or homemade bread for its bake sale that afternoon. However, she does not have time to go to the store to get ingredients, and she has only a short time to bake things in her oven. Because cakes and breads require different baking temperatures, she cannot bake them simultaneously, and she has only 3 hours available to bake. A cake requires 3 cups of flour, and a loaf of bread requires 8 cups; Marie has 20 cups of flour. A cake requires 45 minutes to bake, and a loaf of bread requires 30 minutes. The PTA will sell a cake for $10 and a loaf of bread for $6. Marie wants to decide how many cakes and loaves of bread she should make.
   a. Formulate a linear programming model for this problem.
   b. Solve this model by using graphical analysis.

2. A company produces two products that are processed on two assembly lines. Assembly line 1 has 100 available hours, and assembly line 2 has 42 available hours. Each product requires 10 hours of processing time on line 1, while on line 2 product 1 requires 7 hours and product 2 requires 3 hours. The profit for product 1 is $6 per unit, and the profit for product 2 is $4 per unit.
   a. Formulate a linear programming model for this problem.
   b. Solve this model by using graphical analysis.

3. The Munchies Cereal Company makes a cereal from several ingredients. Two of the ingredients, oats and rice, provide vitamins A and B. The company wants to know how many ounces of oats and rice it should include in each box of cereal to meet the minimum requirements of 48 milligrams of vitamin A and 12 milligrams of vitamin B while minimizing cost. An ounce of oats contributes 8 milligrams of vitamin A and 1 milligram of vitamin B, whereas an ounce of rice contributes 6 milligrams of A and 2 milligrams of B. An ounce of oats costs $0.05, and an ounce of rice costs $0.03.
   a. Formulate a linear programming model for this problem.
   b. Solve this model by using graphical analysis.

4. What would be the effect on the optimal solution in Problem 3 if the cost of rice increased from $0.03 per ounce to $0.06 per ounce?

5. The Kalo Fertilizer Company makes a fertilizer using two chemicals that provide nitrogen, phosphate, and potassium. A pound of ingredient 1 contributes 10 ounces of nitrogen and 6 ounces of phosphate, while a pound of ingredient 2 contributes 2 ounces of nitrogen, 6 ounces of phosphate, and 1 ounce of potassium. Ingredient 1 costs $3 per pound, and ingredient 2 costs $5 per pound. The company wants to know how many pounds of each chemical ingredient to put into a bag of fertilizer to meet the minimum requirements of 20 ounces of nitrogen, 36 ounces of phosphate, and 2 ounces of potassium while minimizing cost.
   a. Formulate a linear programming model for this problem.
   b. Solve this model by using graphical analysis.

6. The Pinewood Furniture Company produces chairs and tables from two resources—labor and wood. The company has 80 hours of labor and 36 pounds of wood available each day. Demand for chairs is limited to 6 per day. Each chair requires 8 hours of labor and 2 pounds of wood, whereas a table requires 10 hours of labor and 6 pounds of wood. The profit derived from each chair is $400 and from each table, $100. The company wants to determine the number of chairs and tables to produce each day in order to maximize profit.
   a. Formulate a linear programming model for this problem.
   b. Solve this model by using graphical analysis.

7. In Problem 6, how much labor and wood will be unused if the optimal numbers of chairs and tables are produced?

8. In Problem 6, explain the effect on the optimal solution of changing the profit on a table from $100 to $500.

9. The Crumb and Custard Bakery makes coffee cakes and Danish pastries in large pans. The main ingredients are flour and sugar. There are 25 pounds of flour and 16 pounds of sugar available, and the demand for coffee cakes is 5. Five pounds of flour and 2 pounds of sugar are required to make a pan of coffee cakes, and 5 pounds of flour and 4 pounds of sugar are required to make a pan of Danish. A pan of coffee cakes has a profit of $1, and a pan of Danish has a profit of $5. Determine the number of pans of cakes and Danish to produce each day so that profit will be maximized.
   a. Formulate a linear programming model for this problem.
   b. Solve this model by using graphical analysis.

10. In Problem 9, how much flour and sugar will be left unused if the optimal numbers of cakes and Danish are baked?

11. Solve the following linear programming model graphically:

$$\text{maximize } Z = 3x_1 + 6x_2$$

subject to

$$3x_1 + 2x_2 \leq 18$$
$$x_1 + x_2 \geq 5$$
$$x_1 \leq 4$$
$$x_1, x_2 \geq 0$$

12. The Elixer Drug Company produces a drug from two ingredients. Each ingredient contains the same three antibiotics, in different proportions. One gram of ingredient 1 contributes 3 units, and 1 gram of ingredient 2 contributes 1 unit of antibiotic 1; the drug requires 6 units. At least 4 units of antibiotic 2 are required, and the ingredients each contribute 1 unit per gram. At least 12 units of antibiotic 3 are required; a gram of ingredient 1 contributes 2 units, and a gram of ingredient 2 contributes 6 units. The cost for a gram of ingredient 1 is $80, and the cost for a gram of ingredient 2 is $50. The company wants to formulate a linear programming model to determine the number of grams of each ingredient that must go into the drug in order to meet the antibiotic requirements at the minimum cost.
   a. Formulate a linear programming model for this problem.
   b. Solve this model by using graphical analysis.

13. A jewelry store makes necklaces and bracelets from gold and platinum. The store has 18 ounces of gold and 20 ounces of platinum. Each necklace requires 3 ounces of gold and 2 ounces of platinum, whereas each bracelet requires 2 ounces of gold and 4 ounces of platinum. The demand for bracelets is no more than four. A necklace earns $300 in profit and a bracelet, $400. The store wants to determine the number of necklaces and bracelets to make in order to maximize profit.
   a. Formulate a linear programming model for this problem.
   b. Solve this model by using graphical analysis.

14. In Problem 13, explain the effect on the optimal solution of increasing the profit on a bracelet from $400 to $600. What will be the effect of changing the platinum requirement for a necklace from 2 ounces to 3 ounces?

15. In Problem 13:
    a. The maximum demand for bracelets is four. If the store produces the optimal number of bracelets and necklaces, will the maximum demand for bracelets be met? If not, by how much will it be missed?
    b. What profit for a necklace would result in no bracelets being produced, and what would be the optimal solution for this profit?

16. A clothier makes coats and slacks. The two resources required are wool cloth and labor. The clothier has 150 square yards of wool and 200 hours of labor available. Each coat requires 3 square yards of wool and 10 hours of labor, whereas each pair of slacks requires 5 square yards of wool and 4 hours of labor. The profit for a coat is $50, and the profit for slacks is $40. The clothier wants to determine the number of coats and pairs of slacks to make so that profit will be maximized.
    a. Formulate a linear programming model for this problem.
    b. Solve this model by using graphical analysis.

17. In Problem 16, what would be the effect on the optimal solution if the available labor were increased from 200 to 240 hours?

18. Solve the following linear programming model graphically:

$$\text{maximize } Z = 1.5x_1 + x_2$$

subject to

$$x_1 \leq 4$$
$$x_2 \leq 6$$
$$x_1 + x_2 \leq 5$$
$$x_1, x_2 \geq 0$$

19. Transform the model in Problem 18 into standard form and indicate the value of the slack variables at each corner point solution.

20. Solve the following linear programming model graphically:

$$\text{maximize } Z = 5x_1 + 8x_2$$

subject to

$$3x_1 + 5x_2 \leq 50$$
$$2x_1 + 4x_2 \leq 40$$
$$x_1 \leq 8$$
$$x_2 \leq 10$$
$$x_1, x_2 \geq 0$$

21. Transform the model in Problem 20 into standard form and indicate the value of the slack variables at each corner point solution.

22. Solve the following linear programming model graphically:

$$\text{maximize } Z = 6.5x_1 + 10x_2$$

subject to

$$2x_1 + 4x_2 \leq 40$$
$$x_1 + x_2 \leq 15$$
$$x_1 \geq 8$$
$$x_1, x_2 \geq 0$$

23. In Problem 22, if the constraint $x_1 \geq 8$ is changed to $x_1 \leq 8$, what effect does this have on the feasible solution space and the optimal solution?

24. Universal Claims Processors processes insurance claims for large national insurance companies. Most claim processing is done by a large pool of computer operators, some of whom are permanent and some of whom are temporary. A permanent operator can process 16 claims per day, whereas a temporary operator can process 12 per day, and on average the company processes at least 450 claims each day. The company has 40 computer workstations. A permanent operator generates about 0.5 claims with errors each day, whereas a temporary operator averages about 1.4 defective claims per day. The company wants to limit claims with errors to 25 per day. A permanent operator is paid $64 per day, and a temporary operator is paid $42 per day. The company wants to determine the number of permanent and temporary operators to hire in order to minimize costs.
    a. Formulate a linear programming model for this problem.
    b. Solve this model by using graphical analysis.

25. In Problem 24, explain the effect on the optimal solution of changing the daily pay for a permanent claims processor from $64 to $54. Explain the effect of changing the daily pay for a temporary claims processor from $42 to $36.

26. In Problem 24, what would be the effect on the optimal solution if Universal Claims Processors decided not to try to limit the number of defective claims each day?

27. In Problem 24, explain the effect on the optimal solution if the minimum number of claims the firm processes each day increased from 450 to at least 650.

28. Solve the following linear programming model graphically:

$$\text{minimize } Z = 8x_1 + 6x_2$$

$$\text{subject to}$$

$$\begin{aligned} 4x_1 + 2x_2 &\geq 20 \\ -6x_1 + 4x_2 &\leq 12 \\ x_1 + x_2 &\geq 6 \\ x_1, x_2 &\geq 0 \end{aligned}$$

29. Solve the following linear programming model graphically:

$$\text{minimize } Z = 3x_1 + 6x_2$$

$$\text{subject to}$$

$$\begin{aligned} 3x_1 + 2x_2 &\leq 18 \\ x_1 + x_2 &\geq 5 \\ x_1 &\leq 4 \\ x_2 &\leq 7 \\ x_2/x_1 &\leq 7/8 \\ x_1, x_2 &\geq 0 \end{aligned}$$

30. In Problem 29, what would be the effect on the solution if the constraint $x_2 \leq 7$ were changed to $x_2 \geq 7$?

31. Solve the following linear programming model graphically:

$$\text{minimize } Z = 5x_1 + x_2$$

$$\text{subject to}$$

$$\begin{aligned} 3x_1 + 4x_2 &= 24 \\ x_1 &\leq 6 \\ x_1 + 3x_2 &\leq 12 \\ x_1, x_2 &\geq 0 \end{aligned}$$

32. Solve the following linear programming model graphically:

$$\text{maximize } Z = 3x_1 + 2x_2$$

subject to

$$2x_1 + 4x_2 \leq 22$$
$$-x_1 + 4x_2 \leq 10$$
$$4x_1 - 2x_2 \leq 14$$
$$x_1 - 3x_2 \leq 1$$
$$x_1, x_2 \geq 0$$

33. Solve the following linear programming model graphically:

$$\text{minimize } Z = 8x_1 + 2x_2$$

subject to

$$2x_1 - 6x_2 \leq 12$$
$$5x_1 + 4x_2 \geq 40$$
$$x_1 + 2x_2 \geq 12$$
$$x_2 \leq 6$$
$$x_1, x_2 \geq 0$$

34. Gillian's Restaurant has an ice-cream counter where it sells two main products, ice cream and frozen yogurt, each in a variety of flavors. The restaurant makes one order for ice cream and yogurt each week, and the store has enough freezer space for 115 gallons total of both products. A gallon of frozen yogurt costs $0.75 and a gallon of ice cream costs $0.93, and the restaurant budgets $90 each week for these products. The manager estimates that each week the restaurant sells at least twice as much ice cream as frozen yogurt. Profit per gallon of ice cream is $4.15, and profit per gallon of yogurt is $3.60.
    a. Formulate a linear programming model for this problem.
    b. Solve this model by using graphical analysis.

35. In Problem 34, how much additional profit would the restaurant realize each week if it increased its freezer capacity to accommodate 20 extra gallons total of ice cream and yogurt?

36. Copperfield Mining Company owns two mines, each of which produces three grades of ore—high, medium, and low. The company has a contract to supply a smelting company with at least 12 tons of high-grade ore, 8 tons of medium-grade ore, and 24 tons of low-grade ore. Each mine produces a certain amount of each type of ore during each hour that it operates. Mine 1 produces 6 tons of high-grade ore, 2 tons of medium-grade ore, and 4 tons of low-grade ore per hour. Mine 2 produces 2, 2, and 12 tons, respectively, of high-, medium-, and low-grade ore per hour. It costs Copperfield $200 per hour to mine each ton of ore from mine 1, and it costs $160 per hour to mine each ton of ore from mine 2. The company wants to determine the number of hours it needs to operate each mine so that its contractual obligations can be met at the lowest cost.
    a. Formulate a linear programming model for this problem.
    b. Solve this model by using graphical analysis.

37. A canning company produces two sizes of cans—regular and large. The cans are produced in 10,000-can lots. The cans are processed through a stamping operation and a coating operation. The company has 30 days available for both stamping and coating. A lot of regular-size cans requires 2 days to stamp and 4 days to coat, whereas a lot of large cans requires 4 days to stamp and 2 days to coat. A lot of regular-size cans earns $800 profit, and a lot of large-size cans earns $900 profit. In order to fulfill its obligations under a shipping contract, the company must produce at least nine

lots. The company wants to determine the number of lots to produce of each size can (x_2) in order to maximize profit.

a. Formulate a linear programming model for this problem.
b. Solve this model by using graphical analysis.

38. A manufacturing firm produces two products. Each product must undergo an assembly process and a finishing process. It is then transferred to the warehouse, which has space for only a limited number of items. The firm has 80 hours available for assembly and 112 hours for finishing, and it can store a maximum of 10 units in the warehouse. Each unit of product 1 has a profit of \$30 and requires 4 hours to assemble and 14 hours to finish. Each unit of product 2 has a profit of \$70 and requires 10 hours to assemble and 8 hours to finish. The firm wants to determine the quantity of each product to produce in order to maximize profit.
    a. Formulate a linear programming model for this problem.
    b. Solve this model by using graphical analysis.

39. Assume that the objective function in Problem 38 has been changed from $Z = 30x_1 + 70x_2$ to $Z = 90x_1 + 70x_2$. Determine the slope of each objective function and discuss what effect these slopes have on the optimal solution.

40. The Valley Wine Company produces two kinds of wine—Valley Nectar and Valley Red. The wines are produced from 64 tons of grapes the company has acquired this season. A 1,000-gallon batch of Nectar requires 4 tons of grapes, and a batch of Red requires 8 tons. However, production is limited by the availability of only 50 cubic yards of storage space for aging and 120 hours of processing time. A batch of each type of wine requires 5 yd.^3 of storage space. The processing time for a batch of Nectar is 15 hours, and the processing time for a batch of Red is 8 hours. Demand for each type of wine is limited to seven batches. The profit for a batch of Nectar is \$9,000, and the profit for a batch of Red is \$12,000. The company wants to determine the number of 1,000-gallon batches of Nectar (x_1) and Red (x_2) to produce in order to maximize profit.
    a. Formulate a linear programming model for this problem.
    b. Solve this model by using graphical analysis.

41. In Problem 40:
    a. How much processing time will be left unused at the optimal solution?
    b. What would be the effect on the optimal solution of increasing the available storage space from 50 to 60 yd.^3?

42. Kroeger supermarket sells its own brand of canned peas as well as several national brands. The store makes a profit of \$0.28 per can for its own peas and a profit of \$0.19 for any of the national brands. The store has 6 square feet of shelf space available for canned peas, and each can of peas takes up 9 square inches of that space. Point-of-sale records show that each week the store never sells more than one-half as many cans of its own brand as it does of the national brands. The store wants to know how many cans of its own brand of peas and how many cans of the national brands to stock each week on the allocated shelf space in order to maximize profit.
    a. Formulate a linear programming model for this problem.
    b. Solve this model by using graphical analysis.

43. In Problem 42, if Kroeger discounts the price of its own brand of peas, the store will sell at least 1.5 times as much of the national brands as its own brand, but its profit margin on its own brand will be reduced to \$0.23 per can. What effect would the discount have on the optimal solution?

44. Shirtstop makes T-shirts with logos and sells them in its chain of retail stores. It contracts with two different plants—one in Puerto Rico and one in The Bahamas. The shirts from the plant in Puerto

Rico cost $0.46 apiece, and 9% of them are defective and can't be sold. The shirts from The Bahamas cost only $0.35 each, but they have an 18% defective rate. Shirtstop needs 3,500 shirts. To retain its relationship with the two plants, it wants to order at least 1,000 shirts from each. It would also like at least 88% of the shirts it receives to be salable.

a. Formulate a linear programming model for this problem.
b. Solve this model by using graphical analysis.

45. In Problem 44:
    a. Suppose Shirtstop decided it wanted to minimize the defective shirts while keeping costs below $2,000. Reformulate the problem with these changes and solve graphically.
    b. How many fewer defective items were achieved with the model in (a) than with the model in Problem 44?

46. Angela and Bob Ray keep a large garden in which they grow cabbage, tomatoes, and onions to make two kinds of relish—chow-chow and tomato. The chow-chow is made primarily of cabbage, whereas the tomato relish has more tomatoes than chow-chow. Both relishes include onions, and negligible amounts of bell peppers and spices. A jar of chow-chow contains 8 ounces of cabbage, 3 ounces of tomatoes, and 3 ounces of onions, whereas a jar of tomato relish contains 6 ounces of tomatoes, 6 ounces of cabbage, and 2 ounces of onions. The Rays grow 120 pounds of cabbage, 90 pounds of tomatoes, and 45 pounds of onions each summer. The Rays can produce no more than 24 dozen jars of relish. They make $2.25 in profit from a jar of chow-chow and $1.95 in profit from a jar of tomato relish. The Rays want to know how many jars of each kind of relish to produce to generate the most profit.
    a. Formulate a linear programming model for this problem.
    b. Solve this model graphically.

47. In Problem 46, the Rays have checked their sales records for the past five years and have found that they sell at least 50% more chow-chow than tomato relish. How will this additional information affect their model and solution?

48. A California grower has a 50-acre farm on which to plant strawberries and tomatoes. The grower has available 300 hours of labor per week and 800 tons of fertilizer, and he has contracted for shipping space for a maximum of 26 acres' worth of strawberries and 37 acres' worth of tomatoes. An acre of strawberries requires 10 hours of labor and 8 tons of fertilizer, whereas an acre of tomatoes requires 3 hours of labor and 20 tons of fertilizer. The profit from an acre of strawberries is $400, and the profit from an acre of tomatoes is $300. The farmer wants to know the number of acres of strawberries and tomatoes to plant to maximize profit.
    a. Formulate a linear programming model for this problem.
    b. Solve this model by using graphical analysis.

49. In Problem 48, if the amount of fertilizer required for each acre of strawberries were determined to be 20 tons instead of 8 tons, what would be the effect on the optimal solution?

50. The admissions office at Tech wants to determine how many in-state and how many out-of-state students to accept for next fall's entering freshman class. Tuition for an in-state student is $7,600 per year, whereas out-of-state tuition is $22,500 per year. A total of 12,800 in-state and 8,100 out-of-state freshmen have applied for next fall, and Tech does not want to accept more than 3,500 students. However, because Tech is a state institution, the state mandates that it can accept no more than 40% out-of-state students. From past experience the admissions office knows that 12% of in-state students and 24% of out-of-state students will drop out during their first year. Tech wants to maximize total tuition while limiting the total attrition to 600 first-year students.
    a. Formulate a linear programming model for this problem.
    b. Solve this model by using graphical analysis.

51. Janet Lopez is establishing an investment portfolio that will include stock and bond funds. She has \$720,000 to invest, and she does not want the portfolio to include more than 65% stocks. The average annual return for the stock fund she plans to invest in is 18%, whereas the average annual return for the bond fund is 6%. She further estimates that the most she could lose in the next year in the stock fund is 22%, whereas the most she could lose in the bond fund is 5%. To reduce her risk, she wants to limit her potential maximum losses to \$100,000.
    a. Formulate a linear programming model for this problem.
    b. Solve this model by using graphical analysis.

52. Professor Smith teaches two sections of business statistics, which combined will result in 120 final exams to be graded. Professor Smith has two graduate assistants. Brad and Sarah, who will grade the final exams. There is a 3-day period between the time the exam is administered and when final grades must be posted. During this period Brad has 12 hours available and Sarah has 10 hours available to grade the exams. It takes Brad an average of 7.2 minutes to grade an exam, and it takes Sarah 12 minutes to grade an exam; however, Brad's exams will have errors that will require Professor Smith to ultimately regrade 10% of the exams, while only 6% of Sarah's exams will require regrading. Professor Smith wants to know how many exams to assign to each graduate assistant to grade in order to minimize the number of exams to regrade.
    a. Formulate a linear programming model for this problem.
    b. Solve this model by using graphical analysis.

53. In Problem 52, if Professor Smith could hire Brad or Sarah to work 1 additional hour, which should she choose? What would be the effect of hiring the selected graduate assistant for 1 additional hour?

54. Starbright Coffee Shop at the Galleria Mall serves two coffee blends it brews on a daily basis, Pomona and Coastal. Each is a blend of three high-quality coffees from Colombia, Kenya, and Indonesia. The coffee shop has 10 pounds of each of these coffees available each day. Each pound of coffee will produce sixteen 16-ounce cups of coffee. The shop has enough brewing capacity to brew 30 gallons of these two coffee blends each day. Pomona is a blend of 20% Colombian, 35% Kenyan, and 45% Indonesian, while Coastal is a blend of 60% Colombian, 10% Kenyan, and 30% Indonesian. The shop sells 1.5 times more Pomona than Coastal each day. Pomona sells for \$2.05 per cup, and Coastal sells for \$1.85 per cup. The manager wants to know how many cups of each blend to sell each day in order to maximize sales.
    a. Formulate a linear programming model for this problem.
    b. Solve this model by using graphical analysis.

55. In Problem 54:
    a. If Starbright Coffee Shop could get 1 more pound of coffee, which one should it be? What would be the effect on sales of getting 1 more pound of this coffee? Would it benefit the shop to increase its brewing capacity from 30 gallons to 40 gallons?
    b. If the shop spent \$20 per day on advertising that would increase the relative demand for Pomona to twice that of Coastal, should it be done?

56. Solve the following linear programming model graphically and explain the solution result:

$$\text{minimize } Z = \$3{,}000x_1 + 1{,}000x_2$$

subject to

$$60x_1 + 20x_2 \geq 1{,}200$$
$$10x_1 + 10x_2 \geq 400$$
$$40x_1 + 160x_2 \geq 2{,}400$$
$$x_1, x_2 \geq 0$$

57. Solve the following linear programming model graphically and explain the solution result:

$$\text{maximize } Z = 60x_1 + 90x_2$$
subject to
$$60x_1 + 30x_2 \le 1{,}500$$
$$100x_1 + 100x_2 \ge 6{,}000$$
$$x_2 \ge 30$$
$$x_1, x_2 \ge 0$$

58. Solve the following linear programming model graphically and explain the solution result:

$$\text{maximize } Z = 110x_1 + 75x_2$$
subject to
$$2x_1 + x_2 \ge 40$$
$$-6x_1 + 8x_2 \le 120$$
$$70x_1 + 105x_2 \ge 2{,}100$$
$$x_1, x_2 \ge 0$$

Case Problem

Metropolitan Police Patrol

The Metropolitan Police Department had recently been criticized in the local media for not responding to police calls in the downtown area rapidly enough. In several recent cases, alarms had sounded for break-ins, but by the time the police car arrived, the perpetrators had left, and in one instance a store owner had been shot. Sergeant Joe Davis had been assigned by the chief as head of a task force to find a way to determine the optimal patrol area (dimensions) for their cars that would minimize the average time it took to respond to a call in the downtown area.

Sergeant Davis solicited help from Angela Maris, an analyst in the operations area for the police department. Together they began to work through the problem.

Joe noted to Angela that normal patrol sectors are laid out in rectangles, with each rectangle including a number of city blocks. For illustrative purposes he defined the dimensions of the sector as x in the horizontal direction and as y in the vertical direction. He explained to Angela that cars traveled in straight lines either horizontally or vertically and turned at right angles. Travel in a horizontal direction must be accompanied by travel in a vertical direction, and the total distance traveled is the sum of the horizontal and vertical segments. He further noted that past research on police patrolling in urban areas had shown that the average distance traveled by a patrol car responding to a call in either direction was one-third of the dimensions of the sector, or $x/3$ and $y/3$. He also explained that the travel time it took to respond to a call (assuming that a car left immediately upon receiving the call) is simply the average distance traveled divided by the average travel speed.

Angela told Joe that now that she understood how average travel time to a call was determined, she could see that it was closely related to the size of the patrol area. She asked Joe if there were any restrictions on the size of the area sectors that cars patrolled. He responded that for their city, the department believed that the perimeter of a patrol sector should not be less than 5 miles or exceed 12 miles. He noted several policy issues and staffing constraints that required these specifications. Angela wanted to know if any additional restrictions existed, and Joe indicated that the distance in the vertical direction must be at least 50% more than the horizontal distance for the sector. He explained that laying out sectors in that manner meant that the patrol areas would have a greater tendency to overlap different residential, income, and retail areas than if they ran the other way. He said that these areas were layered from north to south in the city. So if a sector area were laid out east to west, all of it would tend to be in one demographic layer.

Angela indicated that she had almost enough information to develop a model, except that she also needed to know the average travel speed the patrol cars could travel. Joe told her that cars moving vertically traveled an average of 15 miles per hour, whereas cars traveled horizontally an average of 20 miles per hour. He said that the difference was due to different traffic flows.

Develop a linear programming model for this problem and solve it by using the graphical method.

Case Problem

"The Possibility" Restaurant

Angela Fox and Zooey Caulfield were food and nutrition majors at State University, as well as close friends and roommates. Upon graduation Angela and Zooey decided to open a French restaurant in Draperton, the small town where the university was located. There were no other French restaurants in Draperton, and the possibility of doing something new and somewhat risky intrigued the two friends. They purchased an old Victorian home just off Main Street for their new restaurant, which they named "The Possibility."

Angela and Zooey knew in advance that at least initially they could not offer a full, varied menu of dishes. They had no idea what their local customers' tastes in French cuisine would be, so they decided to serve only two full-course meals each night, one with beef and the other with fish. Their chef, Pierre, was confident he could make each dish so exciting and unique that two meals would be sufficient, at least until they could assess which menu items were most popular. Pierre indicated that with each meal he could experiment with different appetizers, soups, salads, vegetable dishes, and desserts until they were able to identify a full selection of menu items.

The next problem for Angela and Zooey was to determine how many meals to prepare for each night so they could shop for ingredients and set up the work schedule. They could not afford too much waste. They estimated that they would sell a maximum of 60 meals each night. Each fish dinner, including all accompaniments, requires 15 minutes to prepare, and each beef dinner takes twice as long. There is a total of 20 hours of kitchen staff labor available each day. Angela and Zooey believe that because of the health consciousness of their potential clientele, they will sell at least three fish dinners for every two beef dinners. However, they also believe that at least 10% of their customers will order beef dinners. The profit from each fish dinner will be approximately $12, and the profit from a beef dinner will be about $16.

Formulate a linear programming model for Angela and Zooey that will help them estimate the number of meals they should prepare each night and solve this model graphically.

If Angela and Zooey increased the menu price on the fish dinner so that the profit for both dinners was the same, what effect would that have on their solution? Suppose Angela and Zooey reconsidered the demand for beef dinners and decided that at least 20% of their customers would purchase beef dinners. What effect would this have on their meal preparation plan?

Case Problem

Annabelle Invests in the Market

Annabelle Sizemore has cashed in some treasury bonds and a life insurance policy that her parents had accumulated over the years for her. She has also saved some money in certificates of deposit and savings bonds during the 10 years since she graduated from college. As a result, she has $120,000 available to invest. Given the recent rise in the stock market, she feels that she should invest all of this amount there. She has researched the market and has decided that she wants to invest in an index fund tied to S&P stocks and in an Internet stock fund. However, she is very concerned about the volatility of Internet stocks. Therefore, she wants to balance her risk to some degree.

She has decided to select an index fund from Shield Securities and an Internet stock fund from Madison Funds, Inc. She has also decided that the proportion of the dollar amount she invests in the index fund relative to the Internet fund should be at least one-third but that she should not invest more than twice the amount in the Internet fund that she invests in the index fund. The price per share of the index fund is $175, whereas the price per share of the Internet fund is $208. The average annual return during the last 3 years for the index fund has been 17%, and for the Internet stock fund it has been 28%. She anticipates that both mutual funds will realize the same average returns for the coming year that they have in the recent past; however, at the end of the year she is likely to reevaluate her investment strategy anyway. Thus, she wants to develop an investment strategy that will maximize her return for the coming year.

Formulate a linear programming model for Annabelle that will indicate how much money she should invest in each fund and solve this model by using the graphical method.

Suppose Annabelle decides to change her risk-balancing formula by eliminating the restriction that the proportion of the amount she invests in the index fund to the amount that she invests in the Internet fund must be at least one-third. What will the effect be on her solution? Suppose instead that she eliminates the restriction that the proportion of money she invests in the Internet fund relative to the stock fund not exceed a ratio of 2 to 1. How will this affect her solution?

If Annabelle can get $1 more to invest, how will that affect her solution? $2 more? $3 more? What can you say about her return on her investment strategy, given these successive changes?

Topic 15

Linear Programming: Computer Solution and Sensitivity Analysis

3

Linear Programming: Computer Solution and Sensitivity Analysis

Chapter 2 demonstrated how a linear programming model is formulated and how a solution can be derived from a graph of the model. Graphing can provide valuable insight into linear programming and linear programming solutions in general. However, the fact that this solution method is limited to problems with only two decision variables restricts its usefulness as a *general* solution technique.

In this chapter we will show how linear programming problems can be solved using several personal computer software packages. We will also describe how to use a computer solution result to experiment with a linear programming model to see what effect parameter changes have on the optimal solution, referred to as *sensitivity analysis.*

Computer Solution

*The **simplex method** is a procedure involving a set of mathematical steps to solve linear programming problems.*

When linear programming was first developed in the 1940s, virtually the only way to solve a problem was by using a lengthy manual mathematical solution procedure called the **simplex method**. However, during the next six decades, as computer technology evolved, the computer was used more and more to solve linear programming models. The mathematical steps of the simplex method were simply programmed in prewritten software packages designed for the solution of linear programming problems. The ability to solve linear programming problems quickly and cheaply on the computer, regardless of the size of the problem, popularized linear programming and expanded its use by businesses. There are currently dozens of software packages with linear programming capabilities. Many of these are general-purpose management science or quantitative methods packages with linear programming modules, among many other modules for other techniques. There are also numerous software packages that are devoted exclusively to linear programming and its derivatives. These packages are generally cheap, efficient, and easy to use.

As a result of the easy and low-cost availability of personal computers and linear programming software, the simplex method has become less of a focus in the teaching of linear programming. Thus, at this point in our presentation of linear programming, we focus exclusively on computer solution. However, knowledge of the simplex method is useful in gaining an overall, in-depth understanding of linear programming for those who are interested in this degree of understanding. As noted, computer solution itself is based on the simplex method. Thus, while we present linear programming in the text in a manner that does not require use of the simplex method, we also provide in-depth coverage of this topic on the CD that accompanies this text.

In the next few sections we demonstrate how to solve linear programming problems by using Excel spreadsheets and QM for Windows, a typical general-purpose quantitative methods software package.

Excel Spreadsheets

Excel can be used to solve linear programming problems, although the data input requirements can be more time-consuming and tedious than with a software package like QM for Windows that is specifically designed for the purpose. A spreadsheet requires that column and row headings for the specific model be set up and that constraint and objective function formulas be input in their entirety, as opposed to just the model parameters, as with QM for Windows. However, this is also an advantage of spreadsheets, in that it enables the problem to be set up in an attractive format for reporting and presentation purposes. In addition, once a spreadsheet is set up for one problem, it can often be used as a template for others. Exhibit 3.1 shows an Excel spreadsheet set up for our Beaver Creek Pottery Company example introduced in Chapter 2. Appendix B at the end of this text is the tutorial "Setting Up and Editing a Spreadsheet," using Exhibit 3.5 as an example.

Exhibit 3.1

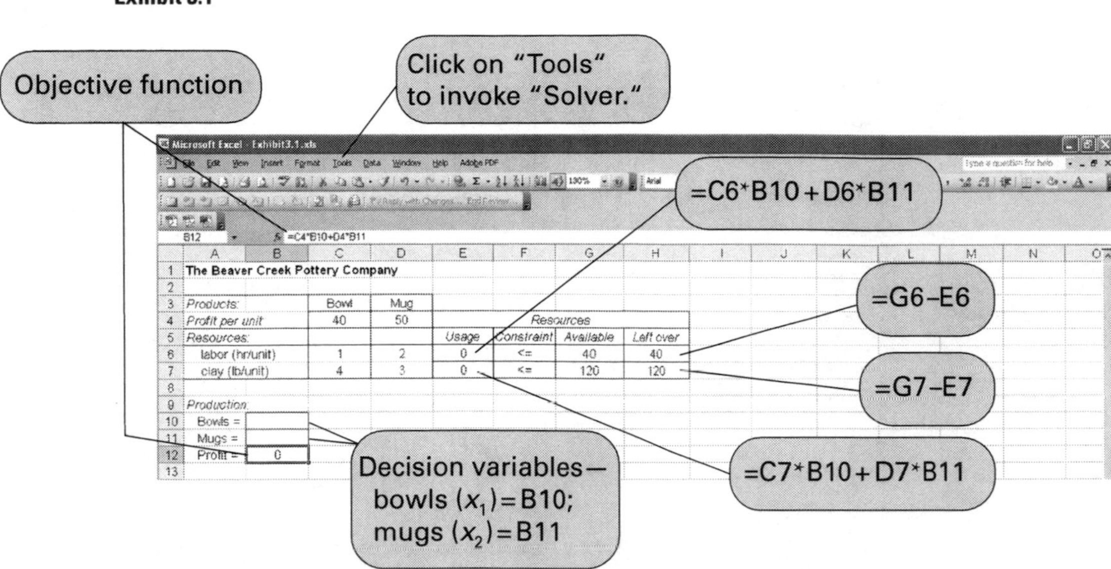

The values for bowls and mugs and for profit are contained in cells B10, B11, and B12, respectively. These cells are currently empty because the model has not yet been solved. The objective function for profit, **=C4*B10+D4*B11,** is embedded in cell B12 and shown on the formula bar at the top of the screen. This formula is essentially the same as $Z = 40x_1 + 50x_2$, where B10 and B11 represent x_1 and x_2, and B12 equals Z. The objective function coefficients, 40 and 50, are in cells C4 and D4. Similar formulas for the constraints for labor and clay are embedded in cells E6 and E7. For example, in cell E6 we input the formula **=C6*B10+D6*B11**. The <= signs in cells F6 and F7 are for cosmetic purposes only; they have no real effect.

To solve this problem, first bring down the "Tools" menu from the toolbar at the top of the screen and then select "Solver" from the list of menu items. (If "Solver" is not shown on the "Tools" menu, then it can be activated by clicking on "Add-ins" on the "Tools" menu and then "Solver." If Solver is not available from the "Add-ins" menu, it must be installed on the "Add-ins" menu directly from your Office or Excel software. For example, in Office you would access "Office Setup," then the "Office Applications" menu, then "Excel," then "Add-ins," and then activate "Solver.") The window Solver Parameters will appear, as shown in Exhibit 3.2. Initially all the windows on this screen are blank, and we must input the objective function cell, the cells representing the decision variables, and the cells that make up the model constraints.

When inputting the Solver parameters as shown in Exhibit 3.2, we first input the "target cell" that contains our objective function, which is B12 for our example. (Excel automatically inserts the $ sign next to cell addresses; you should not type it in.) Next we indicate that we want to maximize the target cell by clicking on "Max." We achieve our objective by changing cells B10 and B11, which represent our model decision variables. The designation "B10:B11" means all the cells between B10 and B11, inclusive. We next input our model constraints by clicking on "Add," which will access the screen shown in Exhibit 3.3.

Exhibit 3.3 shows our labor constraint. Cell E6 contains the constraint formula for labor (**=C6*B10+D6*B11**), whereas cell G6 contains the labor hours available (i.e., 40). We continue to add constraints until the model is complete. Note that we could have input our constraints by adding a single constraint formula, **E6:E7<=G6:G7**, which means that the constraints in

Exhibit 3.2

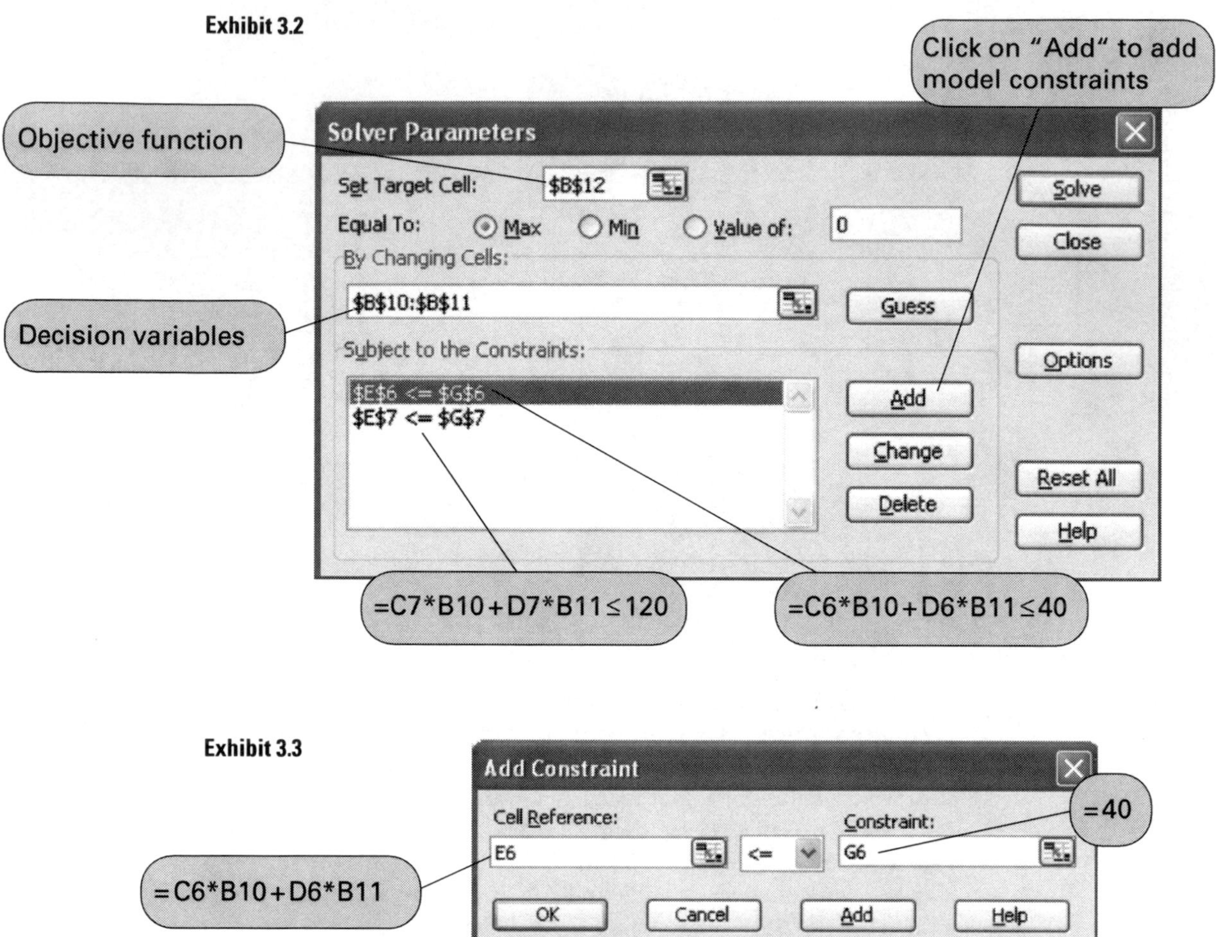

Exhibit 3.3

cells E6 and E7 are less than or equal to the values in cells G6 and G7, respectively. It is also not necessary to input the nonnegativity constraints for our decision variables, **B10:B11>=0**. This can be achieved in the Options screen, as explained next.

Click on "OK" on the Add Constraint window after all constraints have been added. This will return us to the Solver Parameters screen. There is one more necessary step before proceeding to solve the problem. Select "Options" from the Solver Parameters screen and then when the Options screen appears, as shown in Exhibit 3.4, click on "Assume Linear Models." This will ensure that Solver uses the simplex procedure to solve the model and not some other numeric method (which Excel has available). This is not too important for now, but later it will ensure that we get the right reports for sensitivity analysis, a topic we will take up next. Notice that the Options screen also enables you to establish the nonnegativity conditions by clicking on "Assume Non-Negative." Click on "OK" to return to Solver.

Once the complete model is input, click on "Solve" in the upper-right corner of the Solver Parameters screen (Exhibit 3.2). First, a screen will appear, titled Solver Results, which will provide you with the opportunity to select the reports you want and then when you click on "OK," the solution screen shown in Exhibit 3.5 will appear.

If there had been any extra, or *slack*, left over for labor or clay, it would have appeared in column H on our spreadsheet, under the heading "Left Over." In this case there are no slack resources left over.

Exhibit 3.4

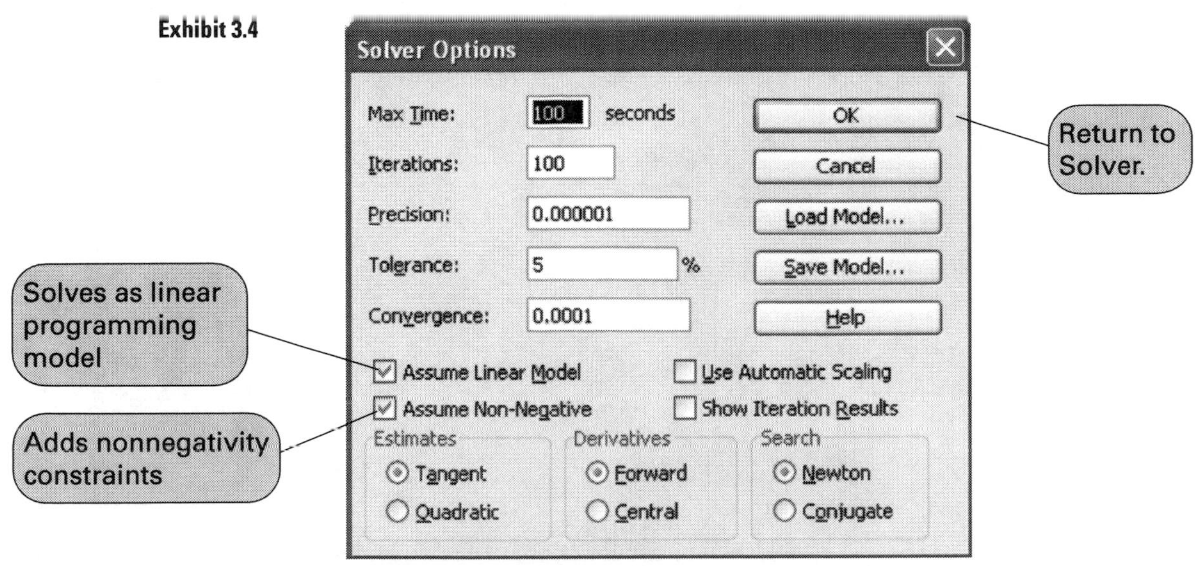

Exhibit 3.5

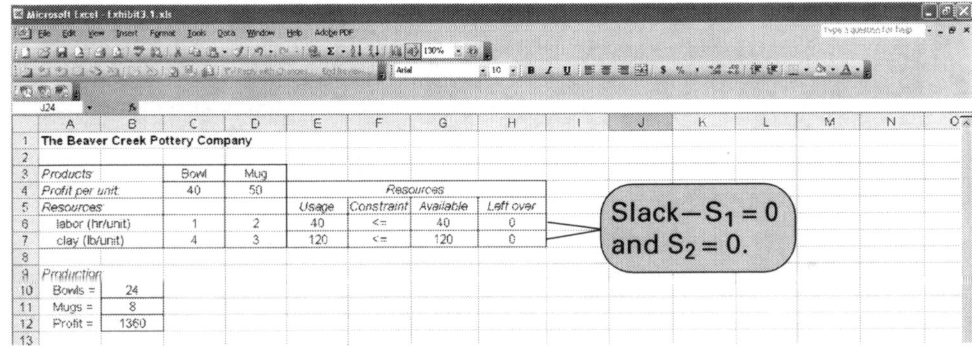

We can also generate several reports that summarize the model results. When you click on "OK" from the Solver screen, an intermediate screen will appear before the original spreadsheet, with the solution results. This screen is titled Solver Results, and it provides an opportunity for you to select several reports, including the answer report, shown in Exhibit 3.6. This report provides a summary of the solution results.

QM for Windows

Before demonstrating how to use QM for Windows, we must first make a few comments about the proper form that constraints must be in before a linear programming model can be solved with QM for Windows. The constraints formulated in the linear programming models presented in Chapter 2 and in this chapter have followed a consistent form. All the variables in the constraint have appeared to the left of the inequality, and all numerical values have been on the right-hand side of the inequality. For example, in the pottery company model, the constraint for labor is

$$x_1 + 2x_2 \leq 40$$

The value, 40, is referred to as the constraint quantity, or *right-hand-side*, value.

Exhibit 3.6

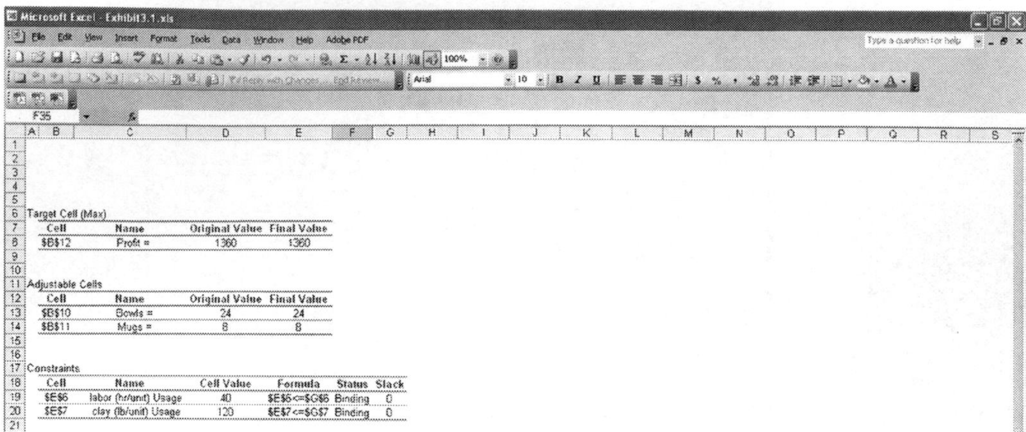

Target Cell (Max)

Cell	Name	Original Value	Final Value
$B$12	Profit =	1360	1360

Adjustable Cells

Cell	Name	Original Value	Final Value
$B$10	Bowls =	24	24
$B$11	Mugs =	8	8

Constraints

Cell	Name	Cell Value	Formula	Status	Slack
$E$6	labor (hr/unit) Usage	40	$E$6<=$G$6	Binding	0
$E$7	clay (lb/unit) Usage	120	$E$7<=$G$7	Binding	0

The standard form for a linear programming problem requires constraints to be in this form, with variables on the left side and numeric values to the right of the inequality or equality sign. This is a necessary condition to input problems into some computer programs, and specifically QM for Windows, for linear programming solution.

Management Science Application

Optimizing Production Quantities at GE Plastics

GE Plastics is a $5 billion global business that supplies plastics and raw materials from plants around the world to companies such as automotive, appliance, computer, and medical equipment companies. Among its seven major divisions, the High Performance Polymers (HPP) division is the fastest growing. HPP is a very heat-tolerant polymer that is used in the manufacture of microwave cookware, fire helmets, utensils, and aircraft. HPP has a supply chain that consists of two levels of manufacturing plants and distribution channels that is similar to all GE Plastics divisions. First-level plants convert feedstocks into resins and then ship them to finishing plants, where they are combined with additives to produce different grades of end products. The products are then shipped to GE Polymerland (a commercial front for GE plastics), which distributes them to customers. Each physical plant has multiple plant lines that operate as independent manufacturing facilities. HPP has 8 resin plant lines that feed 21 finishing plant lines, which produce 24 grades of HPP products. HPP uses a linear programming model to optimize production along this supply chain of manufacturing plant lines and distribution channels. The linear programming model objective function maximizes the total contribution margin, which consists of revenues minus the sum of manufacturing, additive, and distribution costs, subject to demand, manufacturing capacity, and flow constraints. The decision variables are the amount of each resin produced at each resin plant line that will be used at each finishing plant line and the amount of each product at each finishing plant line. The company uses the model to develop a four-year planning horizon by solving four single-year models; each single-year LP model has 3,100 variables and 1,100 constraints. The model is solved within an Excel framework, using LINGO, a commercial optimization solver.

Source: R. Tyagi, P. Kalish, K. Akbay, and G. Munshaw, "GE Plastics Optimizes the Two-Echelon Global Fulfillment Network at Its High Performance Polymers Division," *Interfaces* 34, no. 5 (September–October 2004): 359–366.

Consider a model requirement which states that the production of product 3 (x_3) must be as much as or more than the production of products 1 (x_1) and 2 (x_2). The model constraint for this requirement is formulated as

$$x_3 \geq x_1 + x_2$$

This constraint is not in proper form and could not be input into QM for Windows as it is. It must first be converted to

$$x_3 - x_1 - x_2 \geq 0$$

This constraint can now be input for computer solution.

Next consider a problem requirement that the ratio of the production of product 1 (x_1) to the production of products 2 (x_2) and 3 (x_3) must be at least 2 to 1. The model constraint for this requirement is formulated as

$$\frac{x_1}{x_2 + x_3} \geq 2$$

Fractional relationships between variables in constraints must be eliminated.

Although this constraint does meet the condition that variables be on the left side of the inequality and numeric values on the right, it is not in proper form. The fractional relationship of the variables, $x_1/(x_2 + x_3)$, cannot be input into the most commonly used linear programming computer programs in that form. It must be converted to

$$x_1 \geq 2(x_2 + x_3)$$

and

$$x_1 - 2x_2 - 2x_3 \geq 0$$

We will demonstrate how to use QM for Windows by solving our Beaver Creek Pottery Company example. The linear programming module in QM for Windows is accessed by clicking on "Module" at the top of the initial window. This will bring down a menu with all the program modules available in QM for Windows, as shown in Exhibit 3.7. By clicking on "Linear Programming," a window for this program will come up on the screen, and by clicking on "File" and then "New," a screen for inputting problem dimensions will appear. Exhibit 3.8 shows the data entry screen with the model type and the number of constraints and decision variables for our Beaver Creek Pottery Company example.

Exhibit 3.9 shows the data table for our example, with the model parameters, including the objective function and constraint coefficients, and the constraint quantity values.

Exhibit 3.7

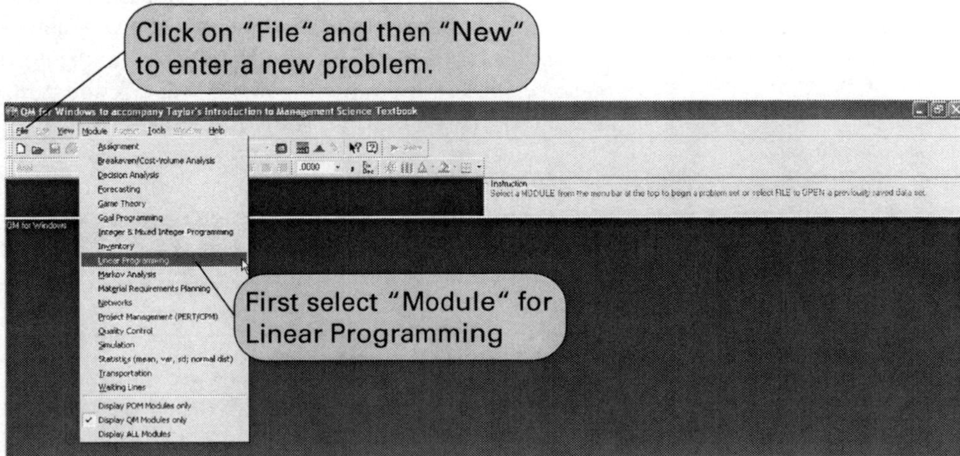

Exhibit 3.8

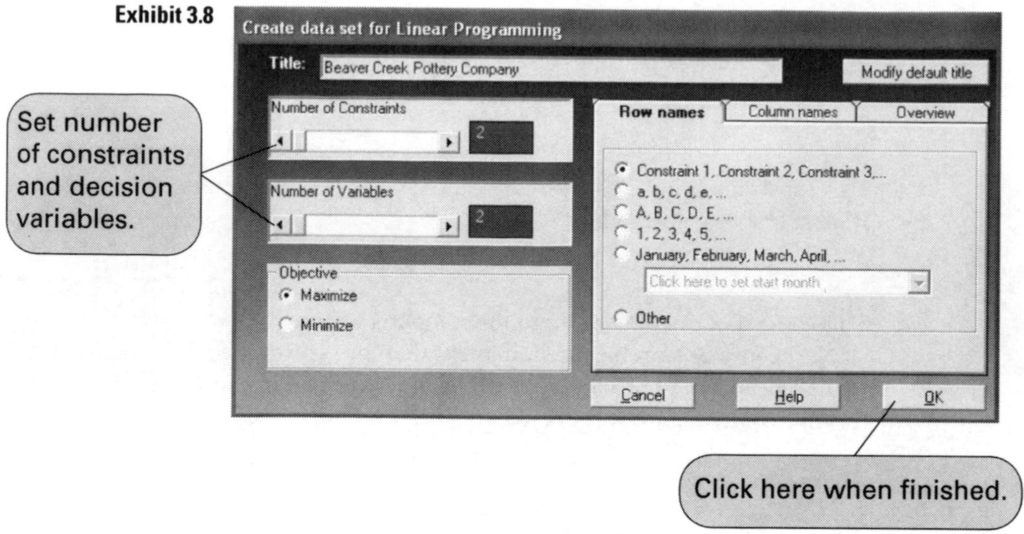

Exhibit 3.9

QM for Windows - [Data Table]

Objective: Maximize

Instruction: Enter the value for clay (lbs) for ths. Any non-negative value is permissible.

Beaver Creek Pottery Company

	X1	X2		RHS	Equation form
Maximize	40	50			Max 40X1 + 50X2
Labor (hrs)	1	2	<=	40	X1 + 2X2 <= 40
Clay (lbs)	4	3	<=	120	4X1 + 3X2 <= 0

Notice that we also customized the row headings for the constraints by typing in "Labor (hrs)" and "Clay (lbs)." Once the model parameters have been input, click on "Solve" to get the model solution, as shown in Exhibit 3.10. It is not necessary to put the model into standard form by adding slack variables.

The marginal value is the dollar amount one would be willing to pay for one additional resource unit.

Notice the values 16 and 6 under the column labeled "Dual" for the "Labor" and "Clay" rows. These dual values are the **marginal values** of labor and clay in our problem. This is useful information that is provided in addition to the normal model solution values when you solve a linear programming model. We talk about dual values in more detail later in this chapter, but for now it is sufficient to say that the marginal value is the dollar amount

Exhibit 3.10

Original Problem w/answers

Beaver Creek Pottery Company Solution

	X1	X2		RHS	Dual
Maximize	40	50			Max 40X1 +
Labor (hrs)	1	2	<=	40	16
Clay (lbs)	4	3	<=	120	6
Solution->	24	8	Optimal Z->	1360	4X1 + 3X2 <=

the company would be willing to pay for one additional unit of a resource. For example, the dual value of 16 for the labor constraint means that if 1 additional hour of labor could be obtained by the company, it would increase profit by \$16. Likewise, if 1 additional pound of clay could be obtained, it would increase profit by \$6. Thus, the company would be willing to pay up to \$16 for 1 more hour of labor and \$6 for 1 more pound of clay. The dual value is not the purchase price of one of these resources; it is the maximum amount the company would pay to get more of the resource. These dual values are helpful to the company in making decisions about acquiring additional resources.

QM for Windows provides solution results in several different formats, including a graphical solution by clicking on "Window" and then selecting "Graph." Exhibit 3.11 shows the graphical solution for our Beaver Creek Pottery Company example.

Exhibit 3.11

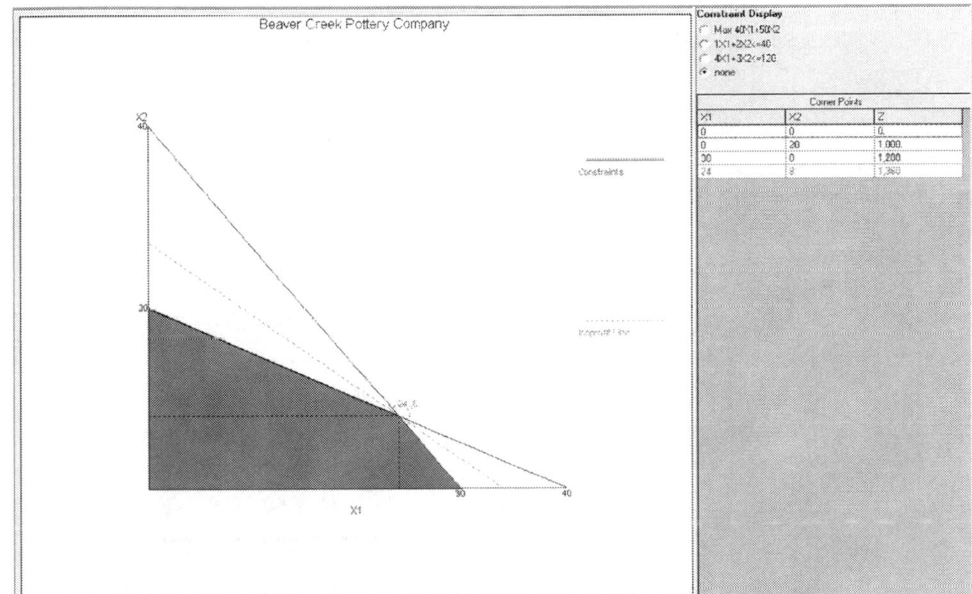

Sensitivity Analysis

Sensitivity analysis is the analysis of the effect of parameter changes on the optimal solution.

When linear programming models were formulated in Chapter 2, it was implicitly assumed that the *parameters* of the model were known with certainty. These parameters include the objective function coefficients, such as profit per bowl; model constraint quantity values, such as available hours of labor; and constraint coefficients, such as pounds of clay per bowl. In the examples presented so far, the models have been formulated as if these parameters are known exactly or with certainty. However, rarely does a manager know all these parameters exactly. In reality, the model parameters are simply estimates (or "best guesses") that are subject to change. For this reason, it is of interest to the manager to see what effect a change in a parameter will have on the solution to the model. Changes may be either reactions to anticipated uncertainties in the parameters or reactions to information. The analysis of parameter changes and their effects on the model solution is known as **sensitivity analysis**.

The most obvious way to ascertain the effect of a change in the parameter of a model is to make the change in the original model, *resolve* the model, and compare the solution results with the original. However, as we will demonstrate in this chapter, in some cases the effect of changes on the model can be determined without solving the problem again.

Changes in Objective Function Coefficients

The first model parameter change we will analyze is a change in an objective function coefficient. We will use our now-familiar Beaver Creek Pottery Company example to illustrate this change:

$$\begin{aligned}&\text{maximize } Z = \$40x_1 + 50x_2\\&\text{subject to}\\&\quad x_1 + 2x_2 \leq 40 \text{ hr. of labor}\\&\quad 4x_1 + 3x_2 \leq 120 \text{ lb. of clay}\\&\quad x_1, x_2 \geq 0\end{aligned}$$

The graphical solution for this problem is shown in Figure 3.1.

Figure 3.1
Optimal solution point

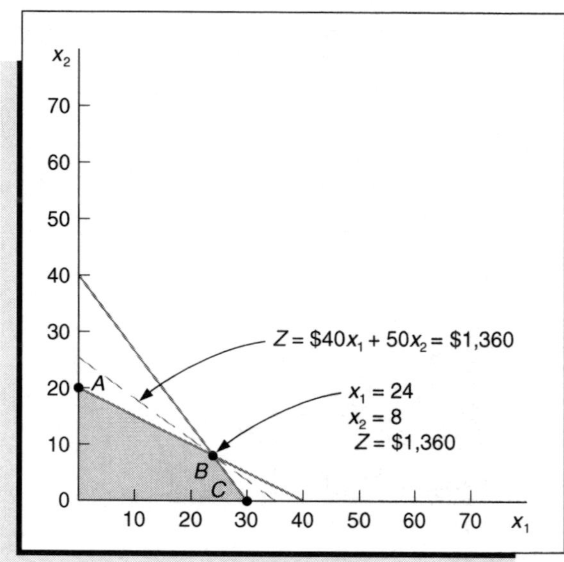

In Figure 3.1 the optimal solution point is shown to be at point B ($x_1 = 24$ and $x_2 = 8$), which is the last point the objective function, denoted by the dashed line, touches as it leaves the feasible solution area. However, what if we changed the profit of a bowl, x_1, from \$40 to \$100? How would that affect the solution identified in Figure 3.1? This change is shown in Figure 3.2.

Increasing profit for a bowl (i.e., the x_1 coefficient) from \$40 to \$100 makes the objective function line steeper, so much so that the optimal solution point changes from point B to point C. Alternatively, if we increased the profit for a mug, the x_2 coefficient, from \$50 to \$100, the objective function line would become flatter, to the extent that point A would become optimal, with

$$x_1 = 0, x_2 = 20, \text{and } Z = \$2,000$$

This is shown in Figure 3.3.

The sensitivity range for an objective coefficient is the range of values over which the current optimal solution point will remain optimal.

The objective of sensitivity analysis in this case is to determine the range of values for a specific objective function coefficient over which the optimal solution point, x_1 and x_2, will remain optimal. For example, the coefficient of x_1 in the objective function is originally \$40, but at some value greater than \$40, point C will become optimal, and at some value less than \$40, point A will become optimal. The focus of sensitivity analysis is to determine those two values, referred to as the sensitivity range for the x_1 coefficient, which we will designate as c_1.

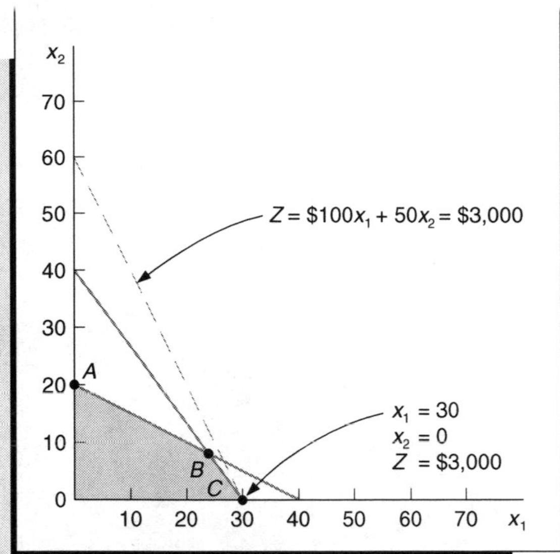

Figure 3.2
Changing the objective function x_1 coefficient

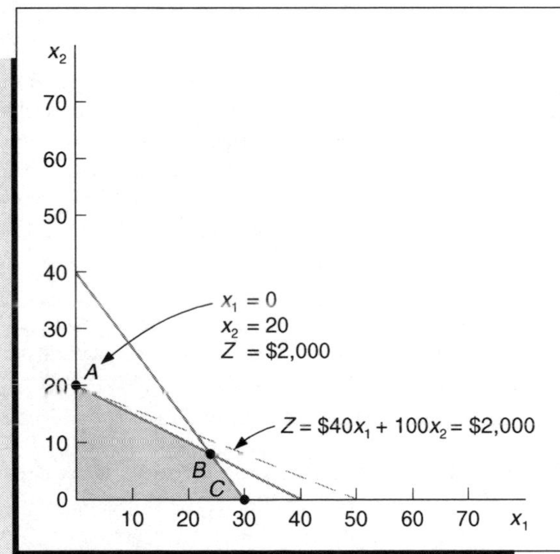

Figure 3.3
Changing the objective function x_2 coefficient

For our simple example, we can look at the graph in Figure 3.1 and determine the sensitivity range for the x_1 coefficient. The slope of the objective function is currently $-4/5$, determined as follows:

$$Z = 40x_1 + 50x_2$$

or

$$50x_2 = Z - 40x_1$$

and

$$x_2 = \frac{Z}{50} - \frac{4x_1}{5}$$

Management Science Application

Grape Juice Management at Welch's

With annual sales over \$550 million, Welch's is one of the world's largest grape-processing companies. Founded in 1869 by Dr. Thomas B. Welch, it processes raw grapes (nearly 300,000 tons per year) into juice, jellies, and frozen concentrates. Welch's is owned by the National Grape Cooperative Association (NGCA), which has a membership of 1,400 growers. Welch's is NGCA's production, distribution, and marketing organization. Welch's operates its grape-processing plants near its growers. Because of the dynamic nature of product demand and customer service, Welch's holds finished goods inventory as a buffer and maintains a large raw materials inventory, stored as grape juice in refrigerated tank farms. Packaging operations at each plant draw juice from the tank farms during the year as needed. The value of the stored grape juice often exceeds \$50 million. Harvest yields and grape quality vary between localities. In order to maintain national quality and consistency in its products, Welch's transfers juices between plants and adjusts product recipes. To do this Welch's uses a spreadsheet-based linear programming model. The juice logistics model (JLM) encompasses 324 decision variables and 361 constraints to minimize the combined costs of transporting grape juice between plants and the product recipes at each plant and the carrying cost of storing grape juice. The model decision variables include the grape juice shipped to customers for different product groups, the grape juice transferred between plants, and inventory levels at each plant. Constraints are for recipe requirements, inventories, and grape juice usage and transfers. During the first year the linear programming model was used, it saved Welch's between \$130,000 and \$170,000 in carrying costs alone by showing Welch's it did not need to purchase extra grapes that were then available. The model has enabled Welch's management to make quick decisions regarding inventories, purchasing grapes, and adjusting product recipes when grape harvests are higher or lower than expected and when demand changes, resulting in significant cost savings.

Source: E. W. Schuster and S. J. Allen, "Raw Material Management at Welch's, Inc.," *Interfaces* 28, no. 5 (September–October 1998): 13–24.

The objective function is now in the form of the equation of a straight line, $y = a + bx$, where the intercept, a, equals $Z/50$ and the slope, b, is $-4/5$.

If the slope of the objective function increases to $-4/3$, the objective function line becomes exactly parallel to the constraint line,

$$4x_1 + 3x_2 = 120$$

and point C becomes optimal (along with B). The slope of this constraint line is $-4/3$, so we ask ourselves what objective function coefficient for x_1 will make the objective function slope equal $-4/3$? The answer is determined as follows, where c_1 is the objective function coefficient for x_1:

$$\frac{-c_1}{50} = \frac{-4}{3}$$

$$-3c_1 = -200$$

$$c_1 = \$66.67$$

If the coefficient of x_1 is 66.67, then the objective function will have a slope of $-66.67/50$ or $-4/3$. This is illustrated in Figure 3.4(a).

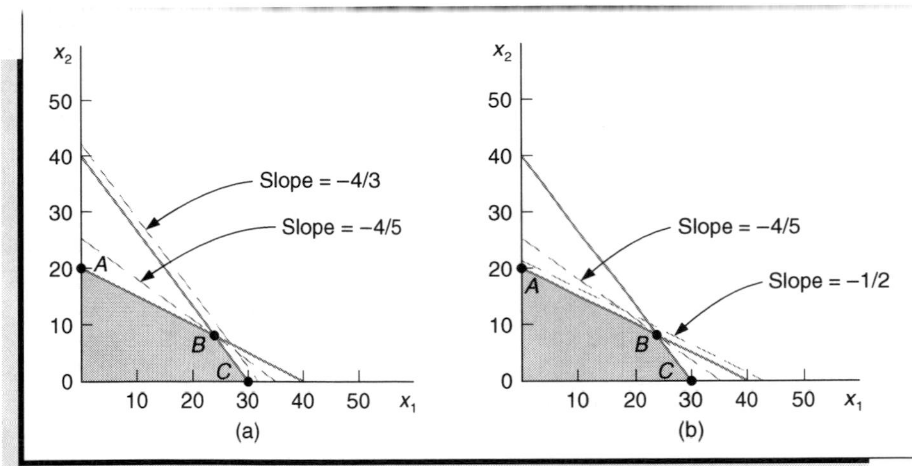

Figure 3.4 Determining the sensitivity range for c_1

We have determined that the upper limit of the sensitivity range for c_1, the x_1 coefficient, is 66.67. If profit for a bowl increases to exactly \$66.67, the solution points will be both *B* and *C*. If the profit for a bowl is more than \$66.67, point *C* will be the optimal solution point.

The lower limit for the sensitivity range can be determined by observing Figure 3.4(b). In this case, if the objective function line slope decreases (becomes flatter) from −4/5 to the same slope as the constraint line,

$$x_1 + 2x_2 = 40$$

then point *A* becomes optimal (along with *B*). The slope of this constraint line is −1/2, that is, $x_2 = 20 - (1/2)x_1$. In order to have an objective function slope of −1/2, the profit for a bowl would have to decrease to \$25, as follows:

$$\frac{-c_1}{50} = \frac{-1}{2}$$
$$-2c_1 = -50$$
$$c_1 = \$25$$

This is the lower limit of the sensitivity range for the x_1 coefficient.

The complete sensitivity range for the x_1 coefficient can be expressed as

$$25 \le c_1 \le 66.67$$

This means that the profit for a bowl can vary anywhere between \$25.00 and \$66.67, and the optimal solution point, $x_1 = 24$ and $x_2 = 8$, will not change. Of course, the total profit, or *Z* value, will change, depending on whatever value c_1 actually is.

For the manager this is useful information. Changing the production schedule in terms of how many items are produced can have a number of ramifications in an operation. Packaging, logistical, and marketing requirements for the product might need to be altered. However, with the preceding sensitivity range, the manager knows how much the profit, and hence the selling price and costs, can be altered without resulting in a change in production.

Performing the same type of graphical analysis will provide the sensitivity range for the x_2 objective function coefficient, c_2. This range is $30 \le c_2 \le 80$. This means that the profit for a mug can vary between \$30 and \$80, and the optimal solution point, *B*, will not change. However, for this case and the range for c_1, the sensitivity range generally applies only if one coefficient is varied and the other held constant. Thus, when we say that profit for a mug can vary between \$30 and \$80, this is true only if c_1 remains constant.

Simultaneous changes can be made in the objective function coefficients as long as the changes taken together do not change the optimal solution point. However, determining the effect of these simultaneous changes is overly complex and time-consuming using graphical analysis. In fact, using graphical analysis is a tedious way to perform sensitivity analysis in general, and it is impossible when the linear programming model contains three or more variables, thus requiring a three-dimensional graph. However, Excel and QM for Windows provide sensitivity analysis for linear programming problems as part of their standard solution output. Determining the effect of simultaneous changes in model parameters and performing sensitivity analysis in general are much easier and more practical using the computer. Later in this chapter we will show the sensitivity analysis output for Excel and QM for Windows.

However, before moving on to computer-generated sensitivity analysis, we want to look at one more aspect of the sensitivity ranges for objective function coefficients. Recall that the model for our fertilizer minimization model from Chapter 2 is

$$\begin{aligned}&\text{minimize } Z = \$6x_1 + 3x_2\\&\text{subject to}\\&\quad 2x_1 + 4x_2 \geq 16\\&\quad 4x_1 + 3x_2 \geq 24\\&\quad\quad x_1, x_2 \geq 0\end{aligned}$$

and the solution shown graphically in Figure 3.5 is $x_1 = 0, x_2 = 8$, and $Z = 24$.

The sensitivity ranges for the objective function coefficients are

$$4 \leq c_1 \leq \infty$$

$$0 \leq c_2 \leq 4.5$$

Notice that the upper bound for the x_1 coefficient range is infinity. The reason for this upper limit can be seen in the graphical solution of the problem shown in Figure 3.5.

As the objective function coefficient for x_1 decreases from \$6, the objective function slope of −2 decreases, and the objective function line gets flatter. When the coefficient, c_1,

Figure 3.5
Fertilizer example: sensitivity range for c_1

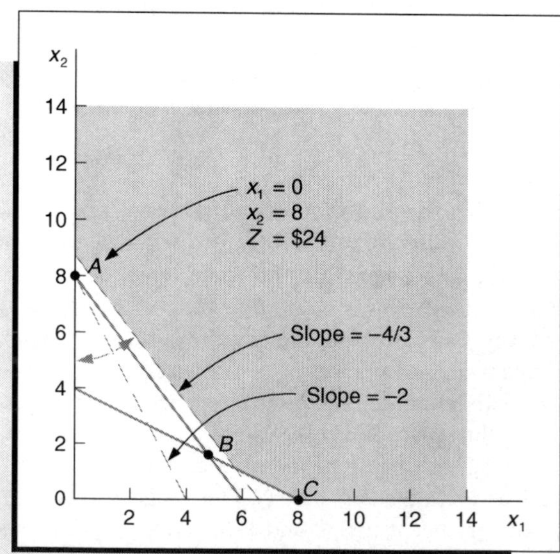

equals \$4, then the slope of the objective function is $-4/3$, which is the same as the constraint line, $4x_1 + 3x_2 = 24$. This makes point B optimal (as well as A). Thus, the lower limit of the sensitivity range for c_1 is \$4. However, notice that as c_1 increases from \$6, the objective function simply becomes steeper and steeper as it rotates toward the x_2 axis of the graph. The objective function will not come into contact with another feasible solution point. Thus, no matter how much we increase cost for Super-gro fertilizer (x_1), point A will always be optimal.

Objective Function Coefficient Ranges with the Computer

When we provided the Excel spreadsheet solution for the Beaver Creek Pottery Company example earlier in this chapter, we did not include sensitivity analysis. However, Excel will also generate a sensitivity report that provides the sensitivity ranges for the objective function coefficients. When you click on "Solve" from the Solver Parameters window, you will momentarily go to a Solver Results screen, shown in Exhibit 3.12, which provides you with an opportunity to select different reports before proceeding to the solution. This is how we selected our answer report earlier. The sensitivity report for our Beaver Creek Pottery Company example is shown in Exhibit 3.13. However, note that if you have not already clicked on "Assume Linear Models" from the Options screen, as we earlier warned, Excel will not generate this version of the sensitivity report.

Exhibit 3.12

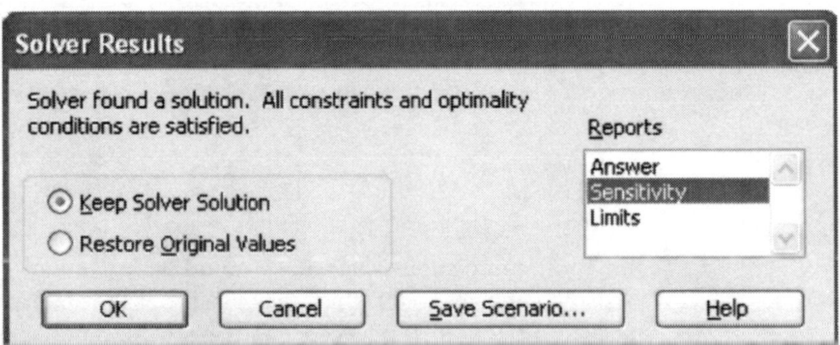

Exhibit 3.13

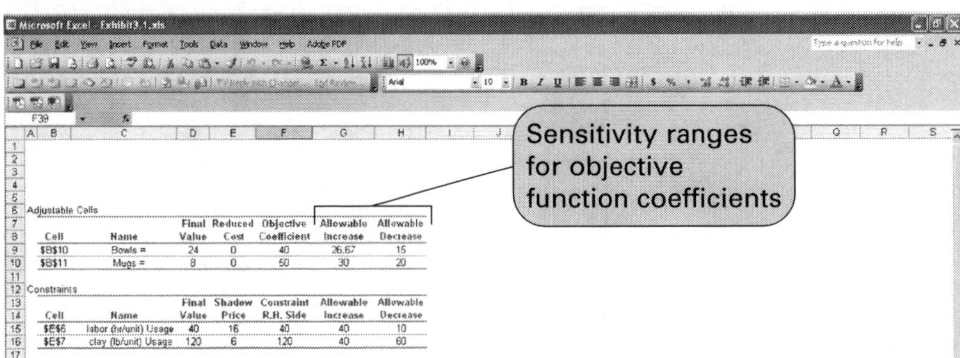

Adjustable Cells

Cell	Name	Final Value	Reduced Cost	Objective Coefficient	Allowable Increase	Allowable Decrease
\$B\$10	Bowls =	24	0	40	26.67	15
\$B\$11	Mugs =	8	0	50	30	20

Constraints

Cell	Name	Final Value	Shadow Price	Constraint R.H. Side	Allowable Increase	Allowable Decrease
\$E\$6	labor (hr/unit) Usage	40	16	40	40	10
\$E\$7	clay (lb/unit) Usage	120	6	120	40	60

Notice that the sensitivity ranges for the objective function coefficients (40 and 50) are not provided as an upper and lower limit but instead show an allowable increase and an allowable decrease. For example, for the coefficient \$40 for bowls (B10), the allowable increase of 26.667 results in an upper limit of 66.667, whereas the allowable decrease of 15 results in a lower limit of 25.

The sensitivity ranges for the objective function coefficients for our example are presented in QM for Windows in Exhibit 3.14. Notice that this output provides the upper and lower limits of the sensitivity ranges for both variables, x_1 and x_2.

Exhibit 3.14

Sensitivity ranges for objective function coefficients

Ranging

Beaver Creek Pottery Company Solution

Variable	Value	Reduced Cost	Original Val	Lower Bound	Upper Bound
X1	24	0	40	25	66.6667
X2	8	0	50	30	80
Constraint	Dual Value	Slack/Surplus	Original Val	Lower Bound	Upper Bound
Labor (hrs)	16	0	40	30	80
Clay (lbs)	6	0	120	60	160

Changes in Constraint Quantity Values

The second type of sensitivity analysis we will discuss is the sensitivity ranges for the constraint quantity values—that is, the values to the right of the inequality signs in the constraints. For our Beaver Creek Pottery Company model,

$$\text{maximize } Z = \$40x_1 + 50x_2$$
$$\text{subject to}$$
$$x_1 + 2x_2 + s_1 = 40 \text{ (labor, hr.)}$$
$$4x_1 + 3x_2 + s_2 = 120 \text{ (clay, lb.)}$$
$$x_1, x_2 \geq 0$$

the constraint quantity values are 40 and 120.

Consider a change in which the manager of the pottery company can increase the labor hours from 40 to 60. The effect of this change in the model is graphically displayed in Figure 3.6.

Figure 3.6
Increasing the labor constraint quantity

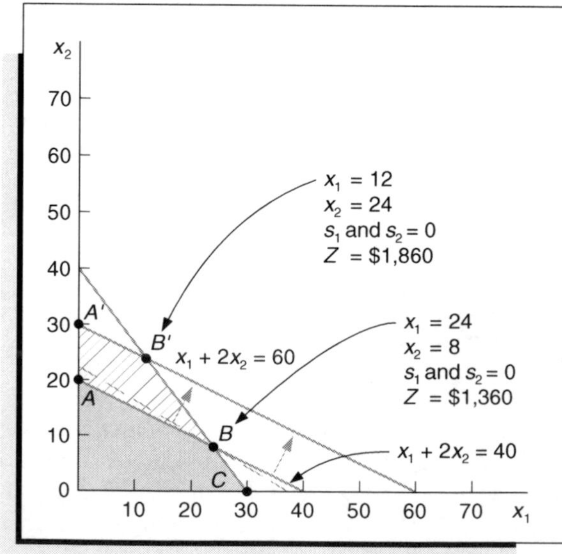

Increasing the available labor hours from 40 to 60 causes the feasible solution space to change. It was originally *OABC*, and now it is *OA'B'C*. *B'* is the new optimal solution, instead of *B*. However, the important consideration in this type of sensitivity analysis is that the solution *mix* (or variables that do not have zero values), including slack variables, did not change, even though the values of x_1 and x_2 did change (from $x_1 = 24, x_2 = 8$ to $x_1 = 12, x_2 = 24$). The focus of sensitivity analysis for constraint quantity values is to determine the range over which the constraint quantity values can change without changing the solution variable mix, specifically including the slack variables.

The sensitivity range for a right-hand-side value is the range of values over which the quantity values can change without changing the solution variable mix, including slack variables.

If the quantity value for the labor constraint is increased from 40 to 80 hours, the new solution space is *OA'C*, and a new solution variable mix occurs at *A'*, as shown in Figure 3.7(a). Whereas at the original optimal point, *B*, both x_1 and x_2 are in the solution, at the new optimal point, *A'*, only x_2 is produced (i.e., $x_1 = 0, x_2 = 40, s_1 = 0, s_2 = 0$).

Figure 3.7
Determining the sensitivity range for labor quantity

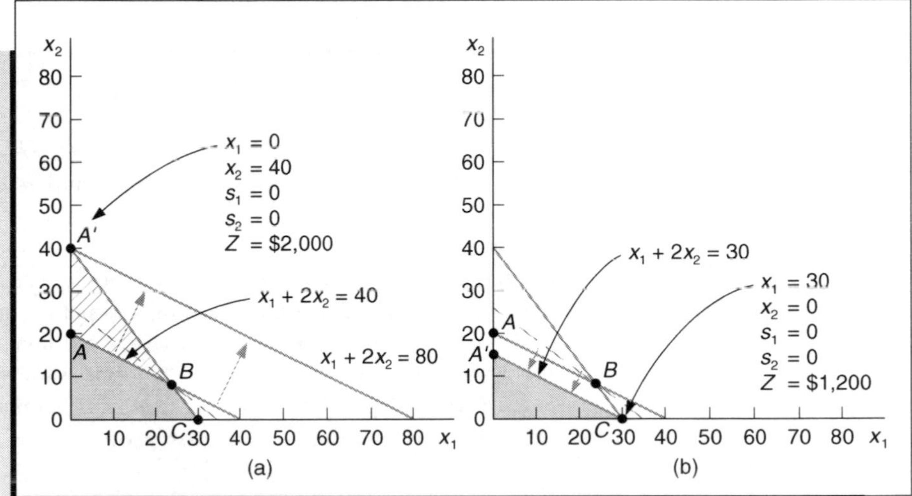

Thus, the upper limit of the sensitivity range for the quantity value for the first constraint, which we will refer to as q_1, is 80 hours. At this value the solution mix changes such that bowls are no longer produced. Furthermore, as q_1 increases past 80 hours, s_1 increases (i.e., slack hours are created). Similarly, if the value for q_1 is decreased to 30 hours, the new feasible solution space is *OA'C*, as shown in Figure 3.7(b). The new optimal point is at *C*, where no mugs (x_2) are produced. The new solution is $x_1 = 30, x_2 = 0, s_1 = 0, s_2 = 0$, and $Z =$ \$1,200. Again, the variable mix is changed. Summarizing, the sensitivity range for the constraint quantity value for labor hours is

$$30 \le q_1 \le 80 \text{ hr.}$$

The sensitivity range for clay can be determined graphically in a similar manner. If the quantity value for the clay constraint, $4x_1 + 3x_2 \le 120$, is increased from 120 to 160, shown in Figure 3.8(a), then a new solution space, *OAC'*, results, with a new optimal point, *C'*. Alternatively, if the quantity value is decreased from 120 to 60, as shown in Figure 3.8(b), the new solution space is *OAC'*, and the new optimal point is *A* ($x_1 = 0, x_2 = 20, s_1 = 0, s_2 = 0, Z =$ \$800).

Summarizing, the sensitivity ranges for q_1 and q_2 are

$$30 \le q_1 \le 80 \text{ hr.}$$

$$60 \le q_2 \le 160 \text{ lb.}$$

Figure 3.8
Determining the sensitivity range for clay quantity

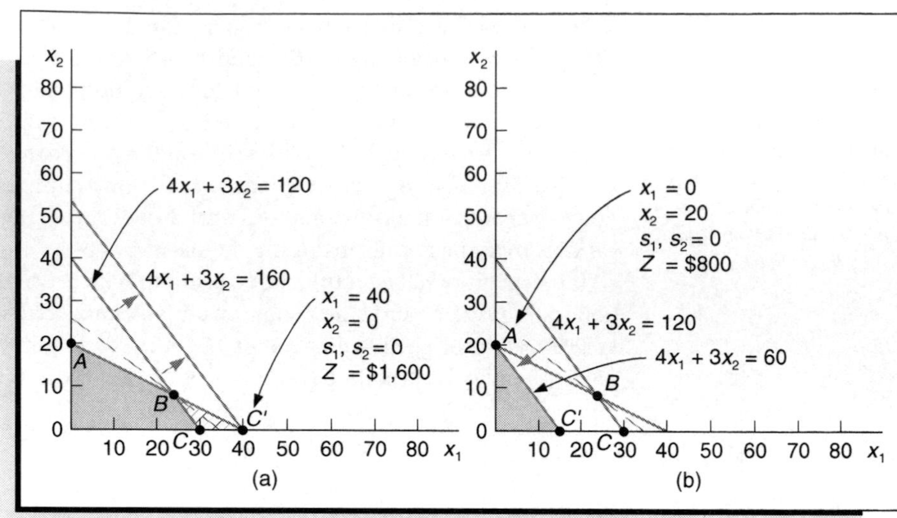

As was the case with the sensitivity ranges for the objective function coefficient, these sensitivity ranges are valid for only one q_i value and assumes all other q_i values are held constant. However, simultaneous changes can occur, as long as they do not change the variable mix.

These ranges for constraint quantity values provide useful information for the manager, especially regarding production scheduling and planning. If resources are reduced at the pottery company, then at some point one of the products will no longer be produced, and the support facilities and apparatus for that production will not be needed, or extra hours of resources will be created that are not needed. A similar result, albeit a better one, will occur if resources are increased because profit will be more than with a reduction in resources.

Constraint Quantity Value Ranges with Excel and QM for Windows

Previously we showed how to generate the sensitivity report for Excel, resulting in Exhibit 3.13. This report is shown again in Exhibit 3.15, with the sensitivity ranges for the constraint quantity values highlighted. As mentioned previously, the ranges are expressed in terms of an allowable increase and decrease instead of upper and lower limits.

The sensitivity ranges for the constraint quantity values with QM for Windows can be observed in Exhibit 3.16.

Exhibit 3.15

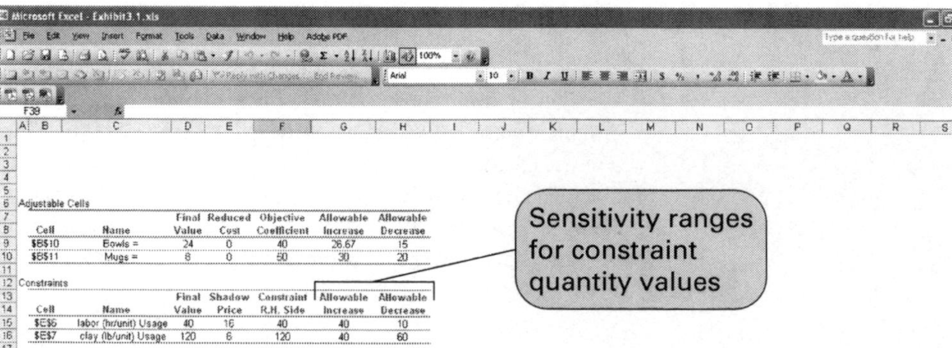

Adjustable Cells

Cell	Name	Final Value	Reduced Cost	Objective Coefficient	Allowable Increase	Allowable Decrease
$B$10	Bowls =	24	0	40	26.67	15
$B$11	Mugs =	8	0	50	30	20

Constraints

Cell	Name	Final Value	Shadow Price	Constraint R.H. Side	Allowable Increase	Allowable Decrease
$E$6	labor (hr/unit) Usage	40	16	40	40	10
$E$7	clay (lb/unit) Usage	120	6	120	40	60

Exhibit 3.16

Ranging

Beaver Creek Pottery Company Solution

Variable	Value	Reduced Cost	Original Val	Lower Bound	Upper Bound
X1	24	0	40	25	66.6667
X2	8	0	50	30	80
Constraint	Dual Value	Slack/Surplus	Original Val	Lower Bound	Upper Bound
Labor (hrs)	16	0	40	30	80
Clay (lbs)	6	0	120	60	160

Sensitivity ranges for constraint quantity values.

Other Forms of Sensitivity Analysis

Other forms of sensitivity analysis include changing constraint parameter values, adding new constraints, and adding new variables.

Excel and QM for Windows provide sensitivity analysis ranges for objective function coefficients and constraint quantity values as part of the standard solution output. However, there are other forms of sensitivity analysis, including changing individual constraint parameters, adding new constraints, and adding new variables.

For instance, in our Beaver Creek Pottery example, if a new, less-experienced artisan were hired to make pottery, it might take this individual 1.33 hours to produce a bowl instead of 1 hour. Thus, the labor constraint would change from $x_1 + 2x_2 \leq 40$ to $1.33x_1 + 2x_2 \leq 40$. This change is illustrated in Figure 3.9.

Figure 3.9

Changing the x_1 coefficient in the labor constraint

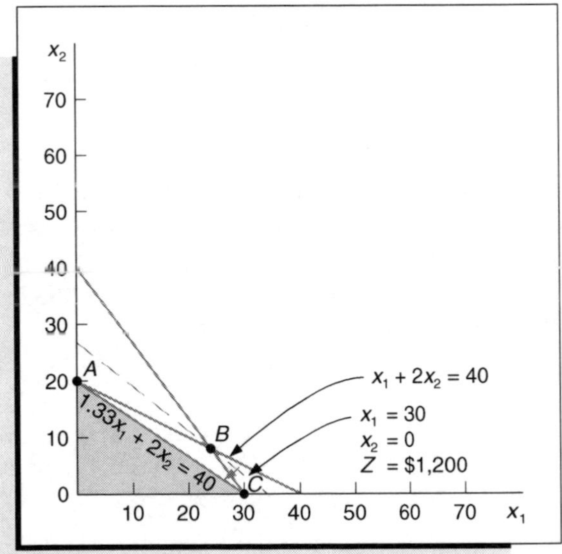

Note that a change in the coefficient for x_1 in the labor constraint rotates the constraint line, changing the solution space from *OABC* to *OAC*. It also results in a new optimal solution point, *C*, where $x_1 = 30$, $x_2 = 0$, and $Z = \$1,200$. Then 1.33 hours would be the logical upper limit for this constraint coefficient. However, as we pointed out, this type of sensitivity analysis for constraint variable coefficients is not typically provided in the standard linear programming computer output. As a result, the most logical way to ascertain the effect of this type of change is simply to run the computer program with different values.

Other types of sensitivity analysis are to add a new constraint to the model or to add a new variable. For example, suppose the Beaver Creek Pottery Company added a third constraint for packaging its pottery, as follows:

$$0.20x_1 + 0.10x_2 \leq 5 \text{ hr.}$$

This would require the model to be solved again with the new constraint. This new constraint does, in fact, change the optimal solution, as shown in the Excel spreadsheet in Exhibit 3.17. This spreadsheet requires a new row (8) added to the original spreadsheet (first shown in Exhibit 3.1) with our new constraint parameter values, and a new constraint, E8 ≤ G8, added to Solver. In the original model, the solution (shown in Exhibit 3.5) was 24 bowls and 8 mugs, with a profit of $1,360. With the new constraint for packaging added, the solution is now 20 bowls and 10 mugs, with a profit of $1,300.

Exhibit 3.17

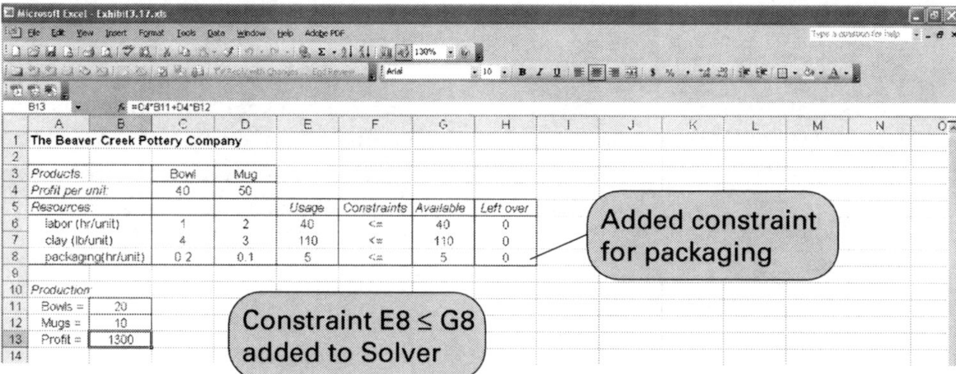

B13 =C4*B11+D4*B12

	A/B	C	D	E	F	G	H
1	The Beaver Creek Pottery Company						
2							
3	Products	Bowl	Mug				
4	Profit per unit	40	50				
5	Resources			Usage	Constraints	Available	Left over
6	labor (hr/unit)	1	2	40	<=	40	0
7	clay (lb/unit)	4	3	110	<=	110	0
8	packaging(hr/unit)	0.2	0.1	5	<=	5	0
9							
10	Production						
11	Bowls =	20					
12	Mugs =	10					
13	Profit =	1300					

If a new variable is added to the model, this would also require that the model be solved again to determine the effect of the change. For example, suppose the pottery company was contemplating producing a third product, cups. It can secure no additional resources, and the profit for a cup is estimated to be $30. This change is reflected in the following model reformulation:

$$\begin{aligned} &\text{maximize } Z = \$40x_1 + 50x_2 + 30x_3 \\ &\text{subject to} \\ &x_1 + 2x_2 + 1.2x_3 \leq 40 \text{ (labor, hr.)} \\ &4x_1 + 3x_2 + 2x_3 \leq 120 \text{ (clay, lb.)} \\ &x_1, x_2, x_3 \geq 0 \end{aligned}$$

Solving this new formulation with the computer will show that this prospective change will have no effect on the original solution—that is, the model is not sensitive to this change. The estimated profit from cups was not enough to offset the production of bowls and mugs, and the solution remained the same.

Shadow Prices

We briefly discussed dual values (also called *shadow prices*) earlier in this chapter, in our discussion of QM for Windows. You will recall that a dual value was defined as the marginal value of one additional unit of resource. We need to mention shadow prices again at this point in our discussion of sensitivity analysis because decisions are often made regarding resources by considering the marginal value of resources in conjunction with their sensitivity ranges.

Consider again the Excel sensitivity report for the Beaver Creek Pottery Company example shown in Exhibit 3.18.

Exhibit 3.18

Adjustable Cells

Cell	Name	Final Value	Reduced Cost	Objective Coefficient	Allowable Increase	Allowable Decrease
$B$10	Bowls =	24	0	40	26.67	15
$B$11	Mugs =	8	0	50	30	20

Constraints

Cell	Name	Final Value	Shadow Price	Constraint R.H. Side	Allowable Increase	Allowable Decrease
$E$6	labor (hr/unit) Usage	40	16	40	40	10
$E$7	clay (lb/unit) Usage	120	6	120	40	60

Shadow prices (dual values)

The shadow price (or marginal value) for labor is $16 per hour, and the shadow price for clay is $6 per pound. This means that for every additional hour of labor that can be obtained, profit will increase by $16. If the manager of the pottery company can secure more labor at $16 per hour, how much more can be obtained before the optimal solution mix will change and the current shadow price is no longer valid? The answer is at the upper limit of the sensitivity range for the labor constraint value. A maximum of 80 hours of labor can be used before the optimal solution mix changes. Thus, the manager can secure 40 more hours, the allowable increase shown in the Excel sensitivity output for the labor constraint. If 40 extra hours of labor can be obtained, what is its total value? The answer is ($16/hr.)(40 hr.) = $640. In other words, profit is increased by $640 if 40 extra hours of labor can be obtained. This is shown in the Excel output in Exhibit 3.19, where increasing the labor constraint from 40 to 80 hours has increased profit from $1,360 to $2,000, or $640.

Looking back to Figure 3.8(a), this is the solution point at C′. Increasing the labor hours to more than 80 hours (the upper limit of the sensitivity range) will not result in an additional increase in profit or a new solution; it will only result in slack hours of labor.

Exhibit 3.19

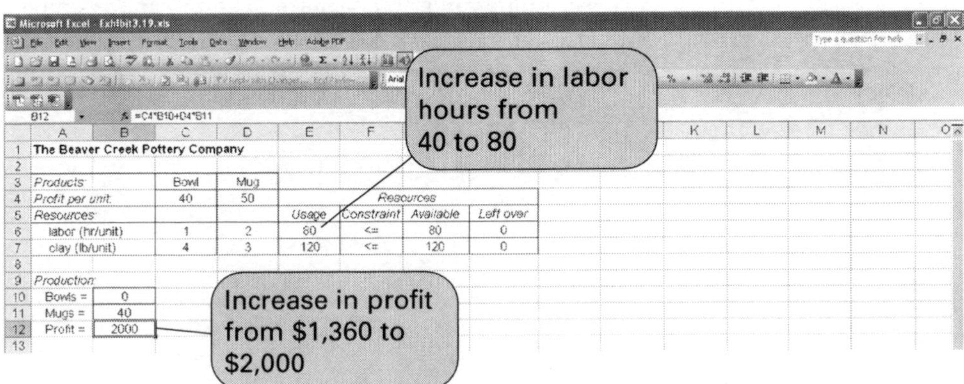

Alternatively, what would be the effect on profit if one of the Native American artisans were sick one day during the week, and the available labor hours decreased from 40 to 32? Profit in this case would decrease by $16 per hour, or a total amount of $128. Thus, total profit would fall from $1,360 to $1,232.

Similarly, if the pottery company could obtain only 100 pounds of clay instead of its normal weekly allotment of 120 pounds, what would be the effect on profit? Profit would decrease by $6 per pound for 20 pounds, or a total of $120. This would result in an overall reduction in profit from $1,360 to $1,240.

The sensitivity range for a constraint quantity value is also the range over which the shadow price is valid.

Thus, another piece of information that is provided by the sensitivity ranges for the constraint quantity values is the range over which the shadow price remains valid. When q_i increases past the upper limit of the sensitivity range or decreases below the lower limit, the shadow price will change, specifically because slack (or surplus) will be created. Therefore, the sensitivity range for the constraint quantity value is the range over which the shadow price is valid.

The shadow price of $16 for 1 hour of labor is not necessarily what the manager would *pay* for an hour of labor. This depends on how the objective function is defined. In the Beaver Creek Pottery Company example, we are assuming that all the resources available, 40 hours of labor and 120 pounds of clay, are already paid for. Even if the company does not use all the resources, it still must pay for them. These are *sunk* costs. Therefore, the individual profit values in the objective function for each product are not affected by how much of a resource is actually used; the total profit is independent of the resources used. In this case, the shadow prices are the maximum amounts the manager would pay for additional units of resource. The manager would pay up to $16 for 1 extra hour of labor and up to $6 for an extra pound of clay.

Alternatively, if each hour of labor and each pound of clay were purchased separately, and thus were not sunk costs, profit would be a function of the cost of the resources. In this case, the shadow price would be the additional amount, over and above the original cost of the resource, that would be paid for one more unit of the resource.

Summary

This chapter has focused primarily on the computer solution of linear programming problems. This required us first to show how a linear programming model is put into standard form, with the addition of slack variables or the subtraction of surplus variables. Computer solution also enabled us to consider the topic of sensitivity analysis, the analysis of the effect of model parameter changes on the solution of a linear programming model. In the next chapter we will provide some examples of more complex linear programming model formulations than the simple ones we have described so far.

References

See the references at the end of Chapter 2.

Example Problem Solution

This example demonstrates the transformation of a linear programming model into standard form, sensitivity analysis, computer solution, and shadow prices.

Problem Statement

The Xecko Tool Company is considering bidding on a job for two airplane wing parts. Each wing part must be processed through three manufacturing stages—stamping, drilling, and finishing—for which the company has limited available hours. The linear programming model to determine how many of part 1 (x_1) and part 2 (x_2) the company should produce in order to maximize its profit is as follows:

$$\text{maximize } Z = \$650x_1 + 910x_2$$

subject to

$$4x_1 + 7.5x_2 \leq 105 \text{ (stamping, hr.)}$$
$$6.2x_1 + 4.9x_2 \leq 90 \text{ (drilling, hr.)}$$
$$9.1x_1 + 4.1x_2 \leq 110 \text{ (finishing, hr.)}$$
$$x_1, x_2 \geq 0$$

A. Solve the model graphically.
B. Indicate how much slack resource is available at the optimal solution point.
C. Determine the sensitivity ranges for the profit for wing part 1 and the stamping hours available.
D. Solve this model by using Excel.

Solution

A.

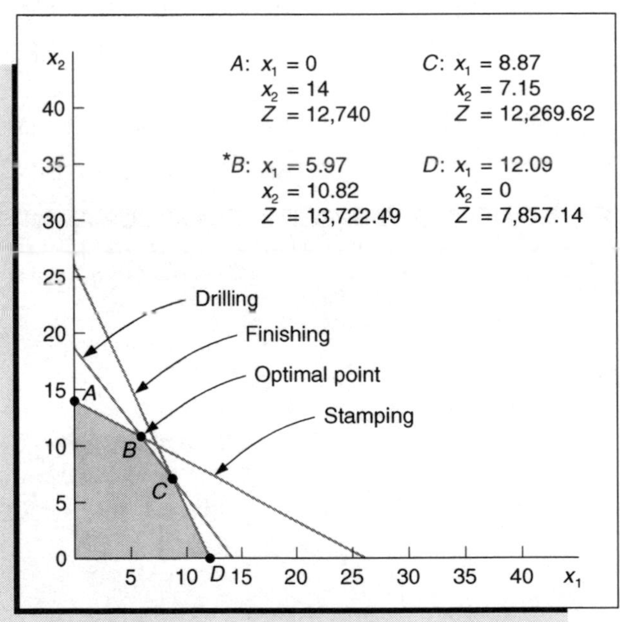

B. The slack at point B, where $x_1 = 5.97$ and $x_2 = 10.82$, is computed as follows:

$$4(5.97) + 7.5(10.82) + s_1 = 105 \text{ (stamping, hr.)}$$
$$s_1 = 0 \text{ hr.}$$
$$6.2(5.97) + 4.9(10.82) + s_2 = 90 \text{ (drilling, hr.)}$$
$$s_2 = 0 \text{ hr.}$$
$$9.1(5.97) + 4.1(10.82) + s_3 = 110 \text{ (finishing, hr.)}$$
$$s_3 = 11.35 \text{ hr.}$$

C. The sensitivity range for the profit for part 1 is determined by observing the graph of the model and computing how much the slope of the objective function must increase to make the optimal point move from B to C. This is the upper limit of the range and is determined by computing the value of c_1 that will make the slope of the objective function equal with the slope of the constraint line for drilling, $6.2x_1 + 4.9x_2 = 90$:

$$\frac{-c_1}{910} = \frac{-6.2}{4.9}$$
$$c_1 = 1,151.43$$

The lower limit is determined by computing the value of c_1 that will equate the slope of the objective function with the slope of the constraint line for stamping, $4x_1 + 7.5x_2 = 105$:

$$\frac{-c_1}{910} = \frac{-4}{7.5}$$
$$c_1 = 485.33$$

Summarizing,

$$485.33 \le c_1 \le 1,151.43$$

The upper limit of the range for stamping hours is determined by first computing the value for q_1 that would move the solution point from B to where the drilling constraint intersects with the x_2 axis, where $x_1 = 0$ and $x_2 = 18.37$:

$$4(0) + 7.5(18.37) = q_1$$
$$q_1 = 137.76$$

The lower limit of the sensitivity range occurs where the optimal point B moves to C, where $x_1 = 8.87$ and $x_2 = 7.15$:

$$4(8.87) + 7.5(7.15) = q_1$$
$$q_1 = 89.10$$

Summarizing, $89.10 \le q_1 \le 137.76$.

D. The Excel spreadsheet solution to this example problem is as follows:

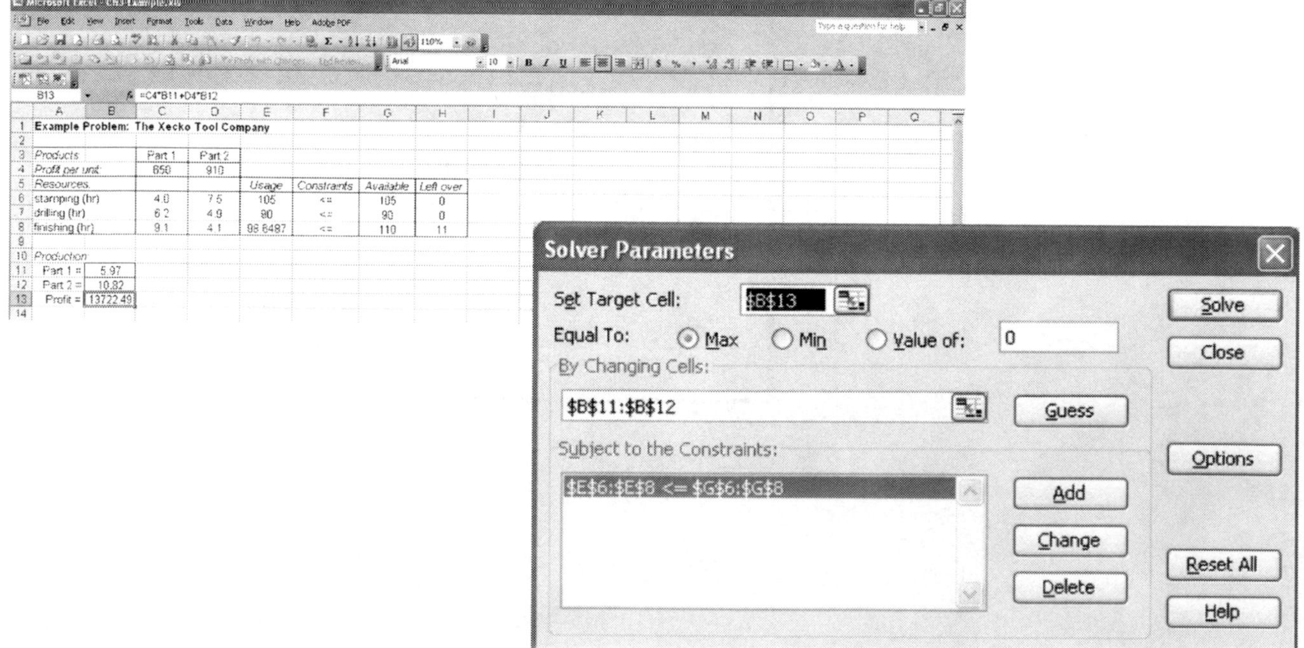

Problems

1. Given the following QM for Windows computer solution of a linear programming model, graph the problem and identify the solution point, including variable values and slack, from the computer output:

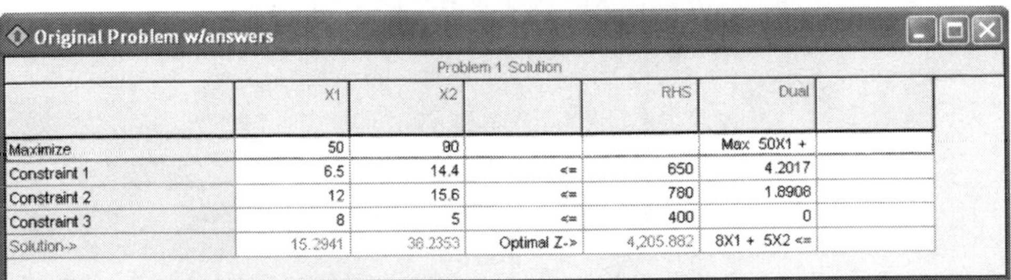

Original Problem w/answers

Problem 1 Solution

	X1	X2		RHS	Dual
Maximize	50	90			Max 50X1 +
Constraint 1	6.5	14.4	<=	650	4.2017
Constraint 2	12	15.6	<=	780	1.8908
Constraint 3	8	5	<=	400	0
Solution->	15.2941	38.2353	Optimal Z->	4,205.882	8X1 + 5X2 <=

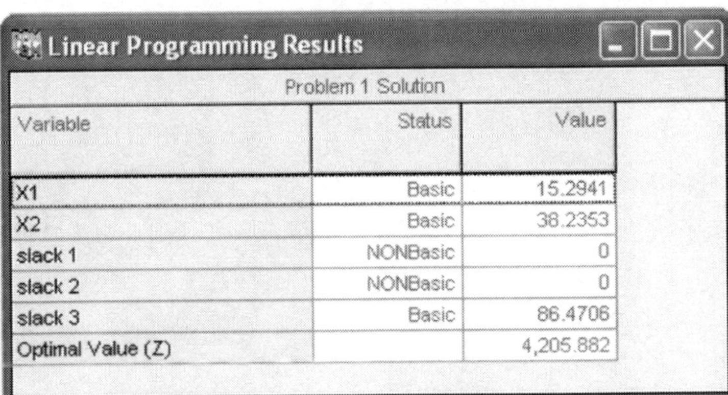

Linear Programming Results

Problem 1 Solution

Variable	Status	Value
X1	Basic	15.2941
X2	Basic	38.2353
slack 1	NONBasic	0
slack 2	NONBasic	0
slack 3	Basic	86.4706
Optimal Value (Z)		4,205.882

2. Explain the primary differences between a software package such as QM for Windows and Excel spreadsheets for solving linear programming problems.

3. Given the following Excel spreadsheet for a linear programming model and Solver window, indicate the formula for cell B13 and fill in the Solver window with the appropriate information to solve the problem:

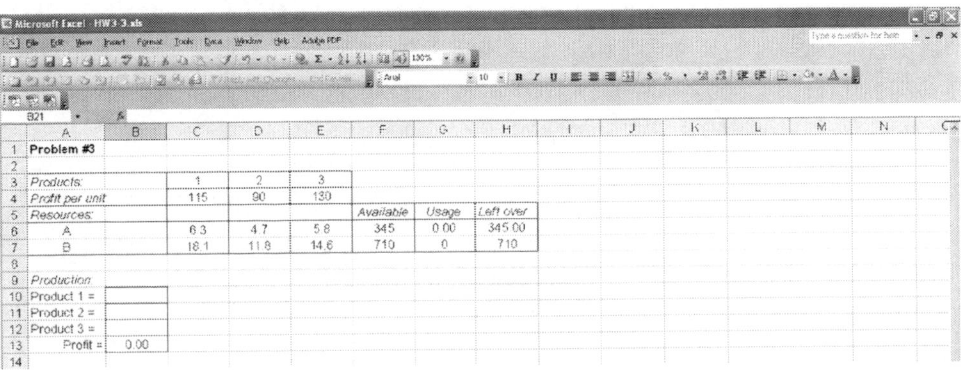

Microsoft Excel HW3-3.xls

	A	B	C	D	E	F	G	H
1	Problem #3							
2								
3	Products:		1	2	3			
4	Profit per unit		115	90	130			
5	Resources:					Available	Usage	Left over
6	A		6.3	4.7	5.8	345	0.00	345.00
7	B		18.1	11.8	14.6	710	0	710
8								
9	Production:							
10	Product 1 =							
11	Product 2 =							
12	Product 3 =							
13	Profit =	0.00						
14								

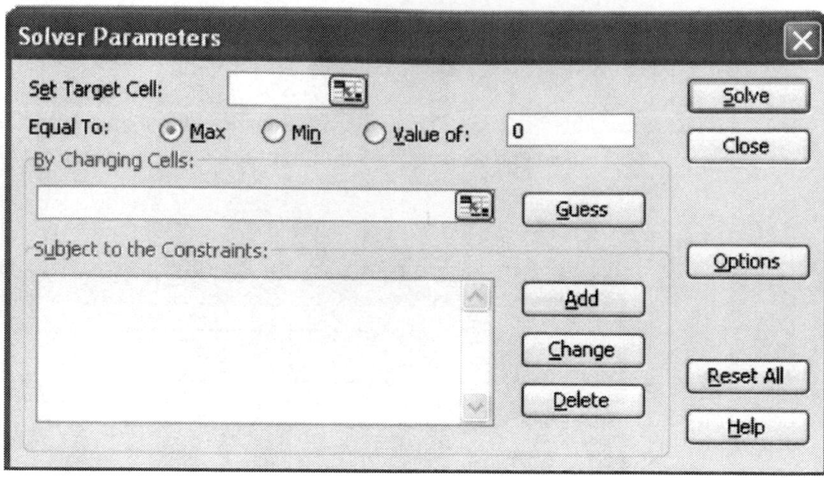

4. Given the following graph of a linear programming model with a single constraint and the objective function maximize $Z = 30x_1 + 50x_2$, determine the optimal solution point:

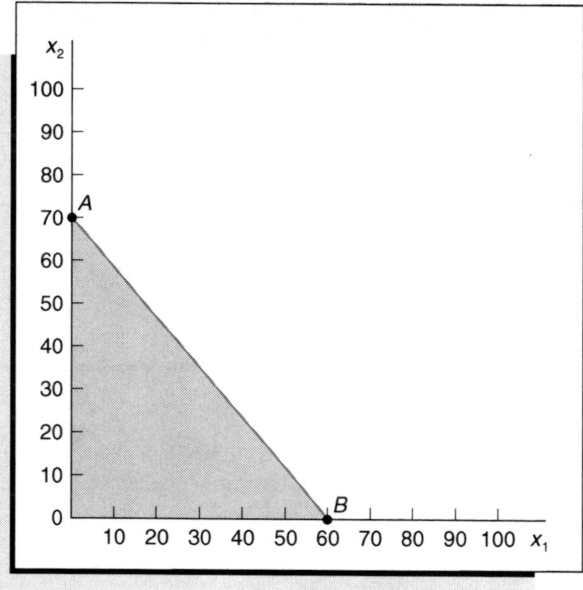

Determine the values by which c_1 and c_2 must decrease or increase in order to change the current solution point to the other extreme point.

5. Southern Sporting Goods Company makes basketballs and footballs. Each product is produced from two resources—rubber and leather. The resource requirements for each product and the total resources available are as follows:

	Resource Requirements per Unit	
Product	Rubber (lb.)	Leather (ft.^{2})
Basketball	3	4
Football	2	5
Total resources available	500 lb.	800 ft.^{2}

Each basketball produced results in a profit of \$12, and each football earns \$16 in profit.

a. Formulate a linear programming model to determine the number of basketballs and footballs to produce in order to maximize profit.
b. Transform this model into standard form.

6. Solve the model formulated in Problem 5 for Southern Sporting Goods Company graphically.
   a. Identify the amount of unused resources (i.e., slack) at each of the graphical extreme points.
   b. What would be the effect on the optimal solution if the profit for a basketball changed from \$12 to \$13? What would be the effect if the profit for a football changed from \$16 to \$15?
   c. What would be the effect on the optimal solution if 500 additional pounds of rubber could be obtained? What would be the effect if 500 additional square feet of leather could be obtained?

7. For the linear programming model for Southern Sporting Goods Company, formulated in Problem 5 and solved graphically in Problem 6:
   a. Determine the sensitivity ranges for the objective function coefficients and constraint quantity values, using graphical analysis.
   b. Verify the sensitivity ranges determined in (a) by using the computer.
   c. Using the computer, determine the shadow prices for the resources and explain their meaning.

8. A company produces two products, A and B, which have profits of \$9 and \$7, respectively. Each unit of product must be processed on two assembly lines, where the required production times are as follows.

	Hours/Unit	
Product	Line 1	Line 2
A	12	4
B	4	8
Total hours	60	40

   a. Formulate a linear programming model to determine the optimal product mix that will maximize profit.
   b. Transform this model into standard form.

9. Solve Problem 8 graphically.
   a. Identify the amount of unused resources (i.e., slack) at each of the graphical extreme points.
   b. What would be the effect on the optimal solution if the production time on line 1 were reduced to 40 hours?
   c. What would be the effect on the optimal solution if the profit for product B were increased from \$7 to \$15? to \$20?

10. For the linear programming model formulated in Problem 8 and solved graphically in Problem 9:
    a. Determine the sensitivity ranges for the objective function coefficients, using graphical analysis.
    b. Verify the sensitivity ranges determined in (a) by using the computer.
    c. Using the computer, determine the shadow prices for additional hours of production time on line 1 and line 2 and indicate whether the company would prefer additional line 1 or line 2 hours.

11. Irwin Textile Mills produces two types of cotton cloth—denim and corduroy. Corduroy is a heavier grade of cotton cloth and, as such, requires 7.5 pounds of raw cotton per yard, whereas denim requires 5 pounds of raw cotton per yard. A yard of corduroy requires 3.2 hours of processing time; a yard of denim requires 3.0 hours. Although the demand for denim is practically unlimited, the maximum demand for corduroy is 510 yards per month. The manufacturer has 6,500 pounds of cotton and 3,000 hours of processing time available each month. The manufacturer makes a profit of $2.25 per yard of denim and $3.10 per yard of corduroy. The manufacturer wants to know how many yards of each type of cloth to produce to maximize profit.
    a. Formulate a linear programming model for this problem.
    b. Transform this model into standard form.

12. Solve the model formulated in Problem 11 for Irwin Textile Mills graphically.
    a. How much extra cotton and processing time are left over at the optimal solution? Is the demand for corduroy met?
    b. What is the effect on the optimal solution if the profit per yard of denim is increased from $2.25 to $3.00? What is the effect if the profit per yard of corduroy is increased from $3.10 to $4.00?
    c. What would be the effect on the optimal solution if Irwin Mills could obtain only 6,000 pounds of cotton per month?

13. Solve the linear programming model formulated in Problem 11 for Irwin Mills by using the computer.
    a. If Irwin Mills can obtain additional cotton or processing time, but not both, which should it select? How much? Explain your answer.
    b. Identify the sensitivity ranges for the objective function coefficients and for the constraint quantity values. Then explain the sensitivity range for the demand for corduroy.

14. United Aluminum Company of Cincinnati produces three grades (high, medium, and low) of aluminum at two mills. Each mill has a different production capacity (in tons per day) for each grade, as follows:

	Mill	
Aluminum Grade	1	2
High	6	2
Medium	2	2
Low	4	10

The company has contracted with a manufacturing firm to supply at least 12 tons of high-grade aluminum, 8 tons of medium-grade aluminum, and 5 tons of low-grade aluminum. It costs United $6,000 per day to operate mill 1 and $7,000 per day to operate mill 2. The company wants to know the number of days to operate each mill in order to meet the contract at the minimum cost.

Formulate a linear programming model for this problem.

15. Solve the linear programming model formulated in Problem 14 for United Aluminum Company graphically.
    a. How much extra (i.e., surplus) high-, medium-, and low-grade aluminum does the company produce at the optimal solution?
    b. What would be the effect on the optimal solution if the cost of operating mill 1 increased from $6,000 to $7,500 per day?

c. What would be the effect on the optimal solution if the company could supply only 10 tons of high-grade aluminum?

16. Solve the linear programming model formulated in Problem 14 for United Aluminum Company by using the computer.
    a. Identify and explain the shadow prices for each of the aluminum grade contract requirements.
    b. Identify the sensitivity ranges for the objective function coefficients and the constraint quantity values.
    c. Would the solution values change if the contract requirements for high-grade aluminum were increased from 12 tons to 20 tons? If yes, what would the new solution values be?

17. The Bradley family owns 410 acres of farmland in North Carolina on which they grow corn and tobacco. Each acre of corn costs $105 to plant, cultivate, and harvest; each acre of tobacco costs $210. The Bradleys have a budget of $52,500 for next year. The government limits the number of acres of tobacco that can be planted to 100. The profit from each acre of corn is $300; the profit from each acre of tobacco is $520. The Bradleys want to know how many acres of each crop to plant in order to maximize their profit.

    Formulate a linear programming model for this problem.

18. Solve the linear programming model formulated in Problem 17 for the Bradley family farm graphically.
    a. How many acres of farmland will not be cultivated at the optimal solution? Do the Bradleys use the entire 100-acre tobacco allotment?
    b. What would the profit for corn have to be for the Bradleys to plant only corn?
    c. If the Bradleys can obtain an additional 100 acres of land, will the number of acres of corn and tobacco they plan to grow change?
    d. If the Bradleys decide not to cultivate a 50-acre section as part of a crop recovery program, how will it affect their crop plans?

19. Solve the linear programming model formulated in Problem 17 for the Bradley farm by using the computer.
    a. The Bradleys have an opportunity to lease some extra land from a neighbor. The neighbor is offering the land to them for $110 per acre. Should the Bradleys lease the land at that price? What is the maximum price the Bradleys should pay their neighbor for the land, and how much land should they lease at that price?
    b. The Bradleys are considering taking out a loan to increase their budget. For each dollar they borrow, how much additional profit would they make? If they borrowed an additional $1,000, would the number of acres of corn and tobacco they plant change?

20. The manager of a Burger Doodle franchise wants to determine how many sausage biscuits and ham biscuits to prepare each morning for breakfast customers. The two types of biscuits require the following resources:

Biscuit	Labor (hr.)	Sausage (lb.)	Ham (lb.)	Flour (lb.)
Sausage	0.010	0.10	—	0.04
Ham	0.024	—	0.15	0.04

The franchise has 6 hours of labor available each morning. The manager has a contract with a local grocer for 30 pounds of sausage and 30 pounds of ham each morning. The manager also purchases 16 pounds of flour. The profit for a sausage biscuit is $0.60; the profit for a ham biscuit is $0.50. The manager wants to know the number of each type of biscuit to prepare each morning in order to maximize profit.

Formulate a linear programming model for this problem.

21. Solve the linear programming model formulated in Problem 20 for the Burger Doodle restaurant graphically.
    a. How much extra sausage and ham is left over at the optimal solution point? Is there any idle labor time?
    b. What would the solution be if the profit for a ham biscuit were increased from $0.50 to $0.60?
    c. What would be the effect on the optimal solution if the manager could obtain 2 more pounds of flour?

22. Solve the linear programming model developed in Problem 20 for the Burger Doodle restaurant by using the computer.
    a. Identify and explain the shadow prices for each of the resource constraints.
    b. Which of the resources constraints profit the most?
    c. Identify the sensitivity ranges for the profit of a sausage biscuit and the amount of sausage available. Explain these sensitivity ranges.

23. Rucklehouse Public Relations has been contracted to do a survey following an election primary in New Hampshire. The firm must assign interviewers to conduct the survey by telephone or in person. One person can conduct 80 telephone interviews or 40 personal interviews in a single day. The following criteria have been established by the firm to ensure a representative survey:
    - At least 3,000 interviews must be conducted.
    - At least 1,000 interviews must be by telephone.
    - At least 800 interviews must be personal.

    An interviewer conducts only one type of interview each day. The cost is $50 per day for a telephone interviewer and $70 per day for a personal interviewer. The firm wants to know the minimum number of interviewers to hire in order to minimize the total cost of the survey.

    Formulate a linear programming model for this problem.

24. Solve the linear programming model formulated in Problem 23 for Rucklehouse Public Relations graphically.
    a. Determine the sensitivity ranges for the daily cost of a telephone interviewer and the number of personal interviews required.
    b. Does the firm conduct any more telephone and personal interviews than are required, and if so, how many more?
    c. What would be the effect on the optimal solution if the firm were required by the client to increase the number of personal interviews conducted from 800 to a total of 1,200?

25. Solve the linear programming model formulated in Problem 23 for Rucklehouse Public Relations by using the computer.
    a. If the firm could reduce the minimum interview requirement for either telephone or personal interviews, which should the firm select? How much would a reduction of one interview in the requirement you selected reduce total cost? Solve the model again, using the computer, with the reduction of this one interview in the constraint requirement to verify your answer.
    b. Identify the sensitivity ranges for the cost of a personal interview and the number of total interviews required.

26. The Bluegrass Distillery produces custom-blended whiskey. A particular blend consists of rye and bourbon whiskey. The company has received an order for a minimum of 400 gallons of the custom

blend. The customer specified that the order must contain at least 40% rye and not more than 250 gallons of bourbon. The customer also specified that the blend should be mixed in the ratio of two parts rye to one part bourbon. The distillery can produce 500 gallons per week, regardless of the blend. The production manager wants to complete the order in 1 week. The blend is sold for $5 per gallon.

The distillery company's cost per gallon is $2 for rye and $1 for bourbon. The company wants to determine the blend mix that will meet customer requirements and maximize profits.

Formulate a linear programming model for this problem.

27. Solve the linear programming model formulated in Problem 26 for the Bluegrass Distillery graphically.
    a. Indicate the slack and surplus available at the optimal solution point and explain their meanings.
    b. What increase in the objective function coefficients in this model would change the optimal solution point? Explain your answer.

28. Solve the linear programming model formulated in Problem 26 for the Bluegrass Distillery by using the computer.
    a. Identify the sensitivity ranges for the objective function coefficients and explain what the upper and lower limits are.
    b. How much would it be worth to the distillery to obtain additional production capacity?
    c. If the customer decided to change the blend requirement for its custom-made whiskey to a mix of three parts rye to one part bourbon, how would this change the optimal solution?

29. Alexis Harrington received an inheritance of $95,000, and she is considering two speculative investments—the purchase of land and the purchase of cattle. Each investment would be for 1 year. Under the present (normal) economic conditions, each dollar invested in land will return the principal plus 20% of the principal; each dollar invested in cattle will return the principal plus 30%. However, both investments are relatively risky. If economic conditions were to deteriorate, there is an 18% chance she would lose everything she invested in land and a 30% chance she would lose everything she invested in cattle. Alexis does not want to lose more than $20,000 (on average). She wants to know how much to invest in each alternative to maximize the cash value of the investments at the end of 1 year.

    Formulate a linear programming model for this problem.

30. Solve the linear programming model formulated in Problem 29 for Alexis Harrington graphically.
    a. How much would the return for cattle have to increase in order for Alexis to invest only in cattle?
    b. Should all of Alexis's inheritance be invested according to the optimal solution?
    c. How much "profit" would the optimal solution earn Alexis over and above her investment?

31. Solve the linear programming model formulated in Problem 29 for Alexis Harrington by using the computer.
    a. If Alexis decided to invest some of her own savings along with the money from her inheritance, what return would she realize for each dollar of her own money that she invested? How much of her own savings could she invest before this return would change?
    b. If the risk of losing the investment in land increased to 30%, how would this change the optimal investment mix?

32. Transform the following linear programming model into standard form and solve by using the computer:

$$\text{maximize } Z = 140x_1 + 205x_2 + 190x_3$$
$$\text{subject to}$$
$$10x_1 + 15x_2 + 8x_3 \leq 610$$
$$\frac{x_1}{x_2} \leq 3$$
$$x_1 \geq 0.4\,(x_1 + x_2 + x_3)$$
$$x_2 \geq x_3$$
$$x_1, x_2, x_3 \geq 0$$

33. Chemco Corporation produces a chemical mixture for a specific customer in 1,000-pound batches. The mixture contains three ingredients—zinc, mercury, and potassium. The mixture must conform to formula specifications that are supplied by the customer. The company wants to know the amount of each ingredient it needs to put in the mixture that will meet all the requirements of the mix and minimize total cost.

The customer has supplied the following formula specifications for each batch of mixture:

- The mixture must contain at least 200 pounds of mercury.
- The mixture must contain at least 300 pounds of zinc.
- The mixture must contain at least 100 pounds of potassium.
- The ratio of potassium to the other two ingredients cannot exceed 1 to 4.

The cost per pound of mercury is \$400; the cost per pound of zinc, \$180; and the cost per pound of potassium, \$90.

a. Formulate a linear programming model for this problem.
b. Solve the model formulated in (a) by using the computer.

34. The following linear programming model formulation is used for the production of four different products, with two different manufacturing processes and two different material requirements:

$$\text{maximize } Z = \$50x_1 + 58x_2 + 46x_3 + 62x_4$$
$$\text{subject to}$$
$$4x_1 + 3.5x_2 + 4.6x_3 + 3.9x_4 \leq 600 \text{ hr. (process 1)}$$
$$2.1x_1 + 2.6x_2 + 3.5x_3 + 1.9x_4 \leq 500 \text{ hr. (process 2)}$$
$$15x_1 + 23x_2 + 18x_3 + 25x_4 \leq 3{,}600 \text{ lb. (material A)}$$
$$8x_1 + 12.6x_2 + 9.7x_3 + 10.5x_4 \leq 1{,}700 \text{ lb. (material B)}$$
$$\frac{x_1 + x_2}{x_1 + x_2 + x_3 + x_4} \geq .60$$
$$x_1, x_2, x_3, x_4 \geq 0$$

a. Solve this problem by using the computer.
b. Identify the sensitivity ranges for the objective function coefficients and the constraint quantity values.
c. Which is the most valuable resource to the firm?
d. One of the four products is not produced in the optimal solution. How much would the profit for this product have to be for it to be produced?

35. Island Publishing Company publishes two types of magazines on a monthly basis: a restaurant and entertainment guide and a real estate guide. The company distributes the magazines free to

businesses, hotels, and stores on Hilton Head Island in South Carolina. The company's profits come exclusively from the paid advertising in the magazines. Each of the restaurant and entertainment guides distributed generates $0.50 per magazine in advertising revenue, whereas the real estate guide generates $0.75 per magazine. The real estate magazine is a more sophisticated publication that includes color photos, and accordingly it costs $0.25 per magazine to print, compared with only $0.17 for the restaurant and entertainment guide. The publishing company has a printing budget of $4,000 per month. There is enough rack space to distribute at most 18,000 magazines each month. In order to entice businesses to place advertisements, Island Publishing promises to distribute at least 8,000 copies of each magazine. The company wants to determine the number of copies of each magazine it should print each month in order to maximize advertising revenue.

Formulate a linear programming model for this problem.

36. Solve the linear programming model formulation in Problem 35 for Island Publishing Company graphically.
    a. Determine the sensitivity range for the advertising revenue generated by the real estate guide.
    b. Does the company spend all of its printing budget? If not, how much slack is left over?
    c. What would be the effect on the optimal solution if the local real estate agents insisted that 12,000 copies of the real estate guide be distributed instead of the current 8,000 copies, or they would withdraw their advertising?

37. Solve the linear programming model formulated in Problem 35 for Island Publishing Company by using the computer.
    a. How much would it be worth to Island Publishing Company to obtain enough additional rack space to distribute 18,500 copies instead of the current 18,000 copies? 20,000 copies?
    b. How much would it be worth to Island Publishing to reduce the requirement to distribute the entertainment guide from 8,000 to 7,000 copies?

38. Mega-Mart, a discount store chain, is to build a new store in Rock Springs. The parcel of land the company has purchased is large enough to accommodate a store with 140,000 square feet of floor space. Based on marketing and demographic surveys of the area and historical data from its other stores, Mega-Mart estimates its annual profit per square foot for each of the store's departments to be as shown in the following table:

Department	Profit per ft.^{2}
Men's clothing	$4.25
Women's clothing	5.10
Children's clothing	4.50
Toys	5.20
Housewares	4.10
Electronics	4.90
Auto supplies	3.80

Each department must have at least 15,000 ft.^{2} of floor space, and no department can have more than 20% of the total retail floor space. Men's, women's, and children's clothing plus housewares keep all their stock on the retail floor; however, toys, electronics, and auto supplies keep some items (such as bicycles, televisions, and tires) in inventory. Thus, 10% of the total retail floor space devoted to these three departments must be set aside outside the retail area for stocking inventory. Mega-Mart wants to know the floor space that should be devoted to each department in order to maximize profit.

a. Formulate a linear programming model for this problem.
b. Solve this model by using the computer.

39. a. In Problem 38 Mega-Mart is considering purchasing a parcel of land adjacent to the current site on which it plans to build its store. The cost of the parcel is \$190,000, and it would enable Mega-Mart to increase the size of its store to 160,000 ft.^{2} Discuss whether Mega-Mart should purchase the land and increase the planned size of the store.
   b. Suppose that the profit per ft.^{2} will decline in all departments by 20% if the store size increases to 160,000 ft.^{2} (If the stock does not turn over as fast, increasing inventory costs will reduce profit.) How might this affect Mega-Mart's decision in (a)?

40. The Food Max grocery store sells three brands of milk in half-gallon cartons—its own brand, a local dairy brand, and a national brand. The profit from its own brand is \$0.97 per carton, the profit from the local dairy brand is \$0.83 per carton, and the profit from the national brand is \$0.69 per carton. The total refrigerated shelf space allotted to half-gallon cartons of milk is 36 square feet per week. A half-gallon carton takes up 16 square inches of shelf space. The store manager knows that each week Food Max always sells more of the national brand than of the local dairy brand and its own brand combined and at least three times as much of the national brand as its own brand. In addition, the local dairy can supply only 10 dozen cartons per week. The store manager wants to know how many half-gallon cartons of each brand to stock each week in order to maximize profit.
   a. Formulate a linear programming model for this problem.
   b. Solve this model by using the computer.

41. a. If Food Max in Problem 40 could increase its shelf space for half-gallon cartons of milk, how much would profit increase per carton?
   b. If Food Max could get the local dairy to increase the amount of milk it could supply each week, would it increase profit?
   c. Food Max is considering discounting its own brand in order to increase sales. If it were to do so, it would decrease the profit margin for its own brand to \$0.86 per carton, but it would cut the demand for the national brand relative to its own brand in half. Discuss whether the store should implement the price discount.

42. John Hoke owns Hoke's Spokes, a bicycle shop. Most of John's bicycle sales are customer orders; however, he also stocks bicycles for walk-in customers. He stocks three types of bicycles—road-racing, cross-country, and mountain. A road-racing bike costs \$1,200, a cross-country bike costs \$1,700, and a mountain bike costs \$900. He sells road-racing bikes for \$1,800, cross-country bikes for \$2,100, and mountain bikes for \$1,200. He has \$12,000 available this month to purchase bikes. Each bike must be assembled; a road-racing bike requires 8 hours to assemble, a cross-country bike requires 12 hours, and a mountain bike requires 16 hours. He estimates that he and his employees have 120 hours available to assemble bikes. He has enough space in his store to order 20 bikes this month. Based on past sales, John wants to stock at least twice as many mountain bikes as the other two combined because mountain bikes sell better.

    Formulate a linear programming model for this problem.

43. Solve the linear programming model formulated in Problem 42 for Hoke's Spokes by using the computer.
   a. Should John Hoke try to increase his budget for purchasing bikes, increase space to stock bikes, or increase labor hours to assemble bikes? Why?
   b. If John were to hire an additional worker for 30 hours at \$10 per hour, how much additional profit would he make, if any?
   c. If John were to purchase a cheaper cross-country bike for \$1,200 and sell it for \$1,900, would this affect the original solution?

44. Metro Food Services Company delivers fresh sandwiches each morning to vending machines throughout the city. The company makes three kinds of sandwiches—ham and cheese, bologna,

and chicken salad. A ham and cheese sandwich requires a worker 0.45 minutes to assemble, a bologna sandwich requires 0.41 minutes, and a chicken salad sandwich requires 0.50 minutes to make. The company has 960 available minutes each night for sandwich assembly. Vending machine capacity is available for 2,000 sandwiches each day. The profit for a ham and cheese sandwich is \$0.35, the profit for a bologna sandwich is \$0.42, and the profit for a chicken salad sandwich is \$0.37. The company knows from past sales records that its customers buy as many or more of the ham and cheese sandwiches than the other two sandwiches combined, but customers need a variety of sandwiches available, so Metro stocks at least 200 of each. Metro management wants to know how many of each sandwich it should stock to maximize profit.

Formulate a linear programming model for this problem.

45. Solve the linear programming problem formulated in Problem 44 for Metro Food Services Company by using the computer.
    a. If Metro Food Services could hire another worker and increase its available assembly time by 480 minutes or increase its vending machine capacity by 100 sandwiches, which should it do? Why? How much additional profit would your decision result in?
    b. What would the effect be on the optimal solution if the requirement that at least 200 sandwiches of each kind be stocked were eliminated? Compare the profit between the optimal solution and this solution. Which solution would you recommend?
    c. What would the effect be on the optimal solution if the profit for a ham and cheese sandwich were increased to \$0.40? to \$0.45?

46. Mountain Laurel Vineyards produces three kinds of wine—Mountain Blanc, Mountain Red, and Mountain Blush. The company has 17 tons of grapes available to produce wine this season. A cask of Blanc requires 0.21 tons of grapes, a cask of Red requires 0.24 tons, and a cask of Blush requires 0.18 tons. The vineyard has enough storage space in its aging room to store 80 casks of wine.

    The vineyard has 2,500 hours of production capacity, and it requires 12 hours to produce a cask of Blanc, 14.5 hours to produce a cask of Red, and 16 hours to produce a cask of Blush. From past sales the vineyard knows that demand for the Blush will be no more than half of the sales of the other two wines combined. The profit for a cask of Blanc is \$7,500, the profit for a cask of Red is \$8,200, and the profit for a cask of Blush is \$10,500.

    Formulate a linear programming model for this problem.

47. Solve the linear programming model formulated in Problem 46 for Mountain Laurel Vineyards by using the computer.
    a. If the vineyard were to determine that the profit from Red was \$7,600 instead of \$8,200, how would that affect the optimal solution?
    b. If the vineyard could secure one additional unit of any of the resources used in the production of wine, which one should it select?
    c. If the vineyard could obtain 0.5 more tons of grapes, 500 more hours of production capacity, or enough storage capacity to store 4 more casks of wine, which should it choose?
    d. All three wines are produced in the optimal solution. How little would the profit for Blanc have to be for it to no longer be produced?

48. Exeter Mines produces iron ore at four different mines; however, the ores extracted at each mine are different in their iron content. Mine 1 produces magnetite ore, which has a 70% iron content; mine 2 produces limonite ore, which has a 60% iron content; mine 3 produces pyrite ore, which has a 50% iron content; and mine 4 produces taconite ore, which has only a 30% iron content. Exeter has three customers that produce steel—Armco, Best, and Corcom. Armco needs 400 tons of pure (100%) iron, Best requires 250 tons of pure iron, and Corcom requires 290 tons. It costs \$37 to extract and process 1 ton of magnetite ore at mine 1, \$46 to produce 1 ton of limonite ore at mine 2,

$50 per ton of pyrite ore at mine 3, and $42 per ton of taconite ore at mine 4. Exeter can extract 350 tons of ore at mine 1; 530 tons at mine 2; 610 tons at mine 3; and 490 tons at mine 4. The company wants to know how much ore to produce at each mine in order to minimize cost and meet its customers' demand for pure (100%) iron.

Formulate a linear programming model for this problem

49. Solve the linear programming problem formulated in Problem 48 for Exeter Mines by using the computer.
    a. Do any of the mines have slack capacity? If yes, which one(s)?
    b. If Exeter Mines could increase production capacity at any one of its mines, which should it be? Why?
    c. If Exeter were to decide to increase capacity at the mine identified in (b), how much could it increase capacity before the optimal solution point (i.e., the optimal set of variables) would change?
    d. If Exeter were to determine that it could increase production capacity at mine 1 from 350 tons to 500 tons, at an increase in production costs to $43 per ton, should it do so?

50. Given the following linear programming model:

$$\text{minimize } Z = 8.2x_1 + 7.0x_2 + 6.5x_3 + 9.0x_4$$

subject to

$$6x_1 + 2x_2 + 5x_3 + 7x_4 \geq 820$$

$$\frac{x_1}{x_1 + x_2 + x_3 + x_4} \geq .3$$

$$\frac{x_2 + x_3}{x_1 + x_4} \leq .2$$

$$x_3 \geq x_1 + x_4$$

$$x_1, x_2, x_3, x_4 \geq 0$$

transform the model into standard form and solve by using the computer.

51. Marie McCoy has committed to the local PTA to make some items for a bake sale on Saturday. She has decided to make some combination of chocolate cakes, loaves of white bread, custard pies, and sugar cookies. Thursday evening she went to the store and purchased 20 pounds of flour, 10 pounds of sugar, and 3 dozen eggs, which are the three main ingredients in all the baked goods she is thinking about making. The following table shows how much of each of the main ingredients is required for each baked good:

	Ingredient			
	Flour (cups)	Sugar (cups)	Eggs	Baking Time (min.)
Cake	2.5	2	2	45
Bread	9	0.25	0	35
Pie	1.3	1	5	50
Cookies	2.5	1	2	16

There are 18.5 cups in a 5 pound bag of flour and 12 cups in a 5 pound bag of sugar. Marie plans to get up and start baking on Friday morning after her kids leave for school and finish before they return after soccer practice (8 hours). She knows that the PTA will sell a chocolate cake for $12, a loaf of bread for $8, a custard pie for $10, and a batch of cookies for $6. Marie wants to decide how many of each type of baked good she should make in order for the PTA to make the most money possible.

Formulate a linear programming model for this problem.

52. Solve the linear programming model formulated in Problem 51 for Marie McCoy.
    a. Are any of the ingredients left over?
    b. If Marie could get more of any ingredient, which should it be? Why?
    c. If Marie could get 6 more eggs, 20 more cups of flour, or 30 more minutes of oven time, which should she choose? Why?
    d. The solution values for this problem should logically be integers. If the solution values are not integers, discuss how Marie should decide how many of each item to bake. How do total sales for this integer solution compare with those in the original, non-integer solution?

CASE PROBLEM

MOSSAIC TILES, LTD.

Gilbert Moss and Angela Pasaic spent several summers during their college years working at archaeological sites in the Southwest. While at those digs, they learned how to make ceramic tiles from local artisans. After college they made use of their college experiences to start a tile manufacturing firm called Mossaic Tiles, Ltd. They opened their plant in New Mexico, where they would have convenient access to a special clay they intend to use to make a clay derivative for their tiles. Their manufacturing operation consists of a few relatively simple but precarious steps, including molding the tiles, baking, and glazing.

Gilbert and Angela plan to produce two basic types of tile for use in home bathrooms, kitchens, sunrooms, and laundry rooms. The two types of tile are a larger, single-colored tile and a smaller, patterned tile. In the manufacturing process, the color or pattern is added before a tile is glazed. Either a single color is sprayed over the top of a baked set of tiles or a stenciled pattern is sprayed on the top of a baked set of tiles.

The tiles are produced in batches of 100. The first step is to pour the clay derivative into specially constructed molds. It takes 18 minutes to mold a batch of 100 larger tiles and 15 minutes to prepare a mold for a batch of 100 smaller tiles. The company has 60 hours available each week for molding. After the tiles are molded, they are baked in a kiln: 0.27 hour for a batch of 100 larger tiles and 0.58 hour for a batch of 100 smaller tiles. The company has 105 hours available each week for baking. After baking, the tiles are either colored or patterned and glazed. This process takes 0.16 hour for a batch of 100 larger tiles and 0.20 hour for a batch of 100 smaller tiles. Forty hours are available each week for the glazing process. Each batch of 100 large tiles requires 32.8 pounds of the clay derivative to produce, whereas each batch of smaller tiles requires 20 pounds. The company has 6,000 pounds of the clay derivative available each week.

Mossaic Tiles earns a profit of $190 for each batch of 100 of the larger tiles and $240 for each batch of 100 smaller patterned tiles. Angela and Gilbert want to know how many batches of each type of tile to produce each week to maximize profit. In addition, they have some questions about resource usage they would like answered.

A. Formulate a linear programming model for Mossaic Tiles, Ltd., and determine the mix of tiles it should manufacture each week.
B. Transform the model into standard form.
C. Solve the linear programming model graphically.
D. Determine the resources left over and not used at the optimal solution point.
E. Determine the sensitivity ranges for the objective function coefficients and constraint quantity values by using the graphical solution of the model.
F. For artistic reasons, Gilbert and Angela like to produce the smaller, patterned tiles better. They also believe that in the long run, the smaller tiles will be a more successful product. What must the profit be for the smaller tiles in order for the company to produce only the smaller tiles?
G. Solve the linear programming model by using the computer and verify the sensitivity ranges computed in (E).
H. Mossaic believes it may be able to reduce the time required for molding to 16 minutes for a batch of larger tiles and 12 minutes for a batch of the smaller tiles. How will this affect the solution?
I. The company that provides Mossaic with clay has indicated that it can deliver an additional 100 pounds each week. Should Mossaic agree to this offer?
J. Mossaic is considering adding capacity to one of its kilns to provide 20 additional glazing hours per week, at a cost of $90,000. Should it make the investment?
K. The kiln for glazing had to be shut down for 3 hours, reducing the available kiln hours from 40 to 37. What effect will this have on the solution?

Case Problem

"The Possibility" Restaurant—Continued

In "The Possibility" Restaurant case problem in Chapter 2, Angela Fox and Zooey Caulfield opened a French restaurant called "The Possibility." Initially, Angela and Zooey could not offer a full, varied menu, so their chef, Pierre, prepared two full-course dinners with beef and fish each evening. In the case problem, Angela and Zooey wanted to develop a linear programming model to help determine the number of beef and fish meals they should prepare each night. Solve Zooey and Angela's linear programming model by using the computer.

A. Angela and Zooey are considering investing in some advertising to increase the maximum number of meals they serve. They estimate that if they spend $30 per day on a newspaper ad, it will increase the maximum number of meals they serve per day from 60 to 70. Should they make the investment?
B. Zooey and Angela are concerned about the reliability of some of their kitchen staff. They estimate that on some evenings they could have a staff reduction of as much as 5 hours. How would this affect their profit level?
C. The final question they would like to explore is raising the price of the fish dinner. Angela believes the price for a fish dinner is a little low and that it could be closer to the price of a beef dinner without affecting customer demand. However, Zooey has noted that Pierre has already made plans based on the number of dinners recommended by the linear programming solution. Angela has suggested a price increase that will increase profit for the fish dinner to $14. Would this be acceptable to Pierre, and how much additional profit would be realized?

Case Problem

Julia's Food Booth

Julia Robertson is a senior at Tech, and she's investigating different ways to finance her final year at school. She is considering leasing a food booth outside the Tech stadium at home football games. Tech sells out every home game, and Julia knows, from attending the games herself, that everyone eats a lot of food. She has to pay $1,000 per game for a booth, and the booths are not very large. Vendors can sell either food or drinks on Tech property, but not both. Only the Tech athletic department concession stands can sell both inside the stadium. She thinks slices of cheese pizza, hot dogs, and barbecue sandwiches are the most popular food items among fans and so these are the items she would sell.

Most food items are sold during the hour before the game starts and during half time; thus it will not be possible for Julia to prepare the food while she is selling it. She must prepare the food ahead of time and then store it in a warming oven. For $600 she can lease a warming oven for the six-game home season. The oven has 16 shelves, and each shelf is 3 feet by 4 feet. She plans to fill the oven with the three food items before the game and then again before half time.

Julia has negotiated with a local pizza delivery company to deliver 14-inch cheese pizzas twice each game—2 hours before the game and right after the opening kickoff. Each pizza will cost her $6 and will include 8 slices. She estimates it will cost her $0.45 for each hot dog and $0.90 for each barbecue sandwich if she makes the barbecue herself the night before. She measured a hot dog and found it takes up about 16 in.^{2} of space, whereas a barbecue sandwich takes up about 25 in.^{2} She plans to sell a slice of pizza and a hot dog for $1.50 apiece and a barbecue sandwich for $2.25. She has $1,500 in cash available to purchase and prepare the food items for the first home game; for the remaining five games she will purchase her ingredients with money she has made from the previous game.

Julia has talked to some students and vendors who have sold food at previous football games at Tech as well as at other universities. From this she has discovered that she can expect to sell at least as many slices of pizza as hot dogs and barbecue sandwiches combined. She also anticipates that she will probably sell at least twice as many hot dogs as barbecue sandwiches. She believes that she will sell everything she can stock and develop a customer base for the season if she follows these general guidelines for demand.

If Julia clears at least $1,000 in profit for each game after paying all her expenses, she believes it will be worth leasing the booth.

A. Formulate and solve a linear programming model for Julia that will help you advise her if she should lease the booth.
B. If Julia were to borrow some more money from a friend before the first game to purchase more ingredients, could she increase her profit? If so, how much should she borrow and how much additional profit would she make? What factor constrains her from borrowing even more money than this amount (indicated in your answer to the previous question)?

C. When Julia looked at the solution in (A), she realized that it would be physically difficult for her to prepare all the hot dogs and barbecue sandwiches indicated in this solution. She believes she can hire a friend of hers to help her for $100 per game. Based on the results in (A) and (B), is this something you think she could reasonably do and should do?

D. Julia seems to be basing her analysis on the assumption that everything will go as she plans. What are some of the uncertain factors in the model that could go wrong and adversely affect Julia's analysis? Given these uncertainties and the results in (A), (B), and (C), what do you recommend that Julia do?

Topic 16

Linear Programming: Modeling Examples

4 Linear Programming: Modeling Examples

In Chapters 2 and 3, two basic linear programming models, one for a maximization problem and one for a minimization problem, were used to demonstrate model formulation, graphical solution, computer solution, and sensitivity analysis. Most of these models were very straightforward, consisting of only two decision variables and two constraints. They were necessarily simple models so that the linear programming topics being introduced could be easily understood.

In this chapter, more complex examples of model formulation are presented. These examples have been selected to illustrate some of the more popular application areas of linear programming. They also provide guidelines for model formulation for a variety of problems and computer solutions with Excel and QM for Windows.

You will notice as you go through each example that the model formulation is presented in a systematic format. First, decision variables are identified, then the objective function is formulated, and finally the model constraints are developed. Model formulation can be difficult and complicated, and it is usually beneficial to follow this set of steps in which you identify a specific model component at each step instead of trying to "see" the whole formulation after the first reading.

A Product Mix Example

Quick-Screen is a clothing manufacturing company that specializes in producing commemorative shirts immediately following major sporting events such as the World Series, Super Bowl, and Final Four. The company has been contracted to produce a standard set of shirts for the winning team, either State University or Tech, following a college football bowl game on New Year's Day. The items produced include two sweatshirts, one with silk-screen printing on the front and one with print on both sides, and two T-shirts of the same configuration. The company has to complete all production within 72 hours after the game, at which time a trailer truck will pick up the shirts. The company will work around the clock. The truck has enough capacity to accommodate 1,200 standard-size boxes. A standard-size box holds 12 T-shirts, and a box of 12 sweatshirts is three times the size of a standard box. The company has budgeted $25,000 for the production run. It has 500 dozen blank sweatshirts and T-shirts each in stock, ready for production. This scenario is illustrated in Figure 4.1.

The resource requirements, unit costs, and profit per dozen for each type of shirt are shown in the following table:

	Processing Time (hr.) per Dozen	Cost per Dozen	Profit per Dozen
Sweatshirt—F	0.10	$36	$ 90
Sweatshirt—B/F	0.25	48	125
T-shirt—F	0.08	25	45
T-shirt—B/F	0.21	35	65

The company wants to know how many dozen (boxes) of each type of shirt to produce in order to maximize profit.

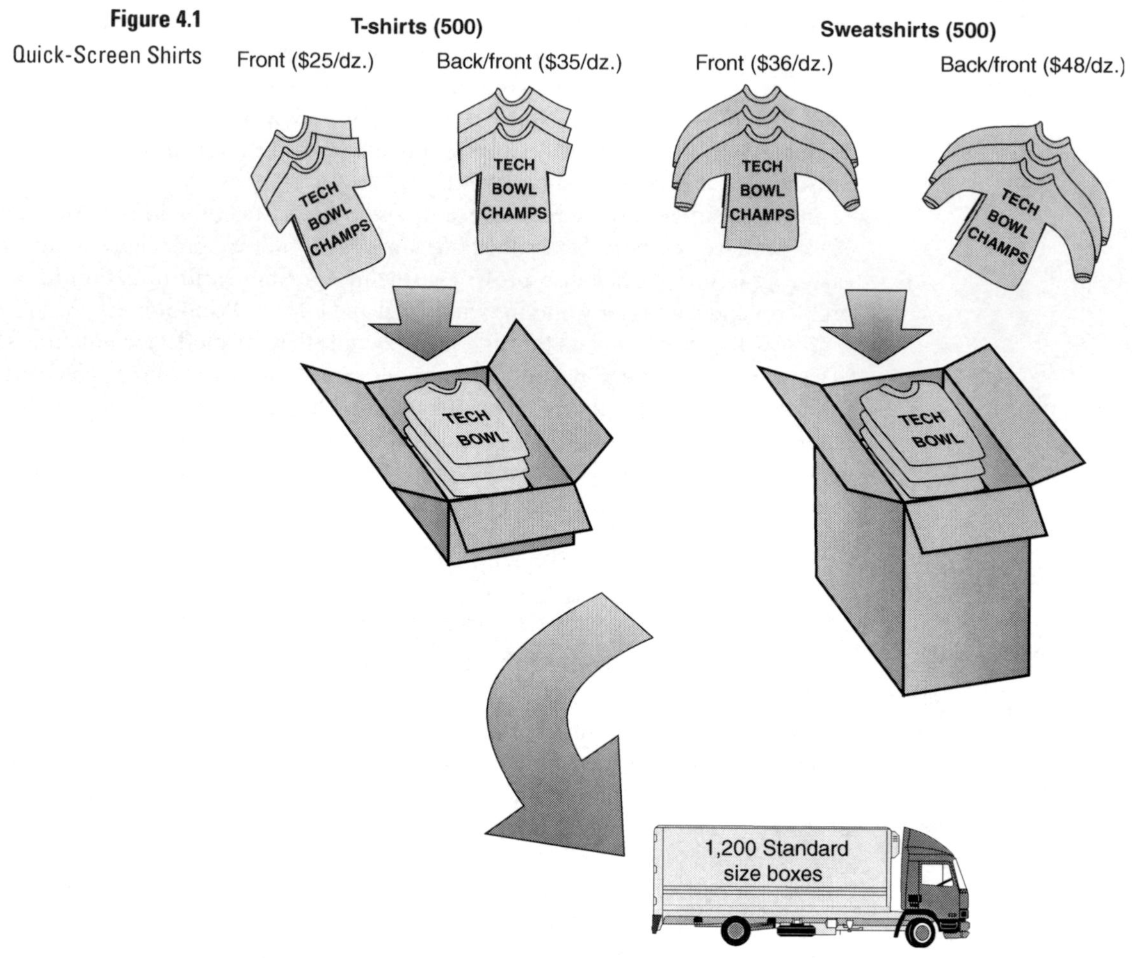

Figure 4.1
Quick-Screen Shirts

Following is a review of the model formulation steps for this problem:

Summary of Linear Programming Model Formulation Steps

Step 1: Define the decision variables

How many (dozens of) T-shirts and sweatshirts of each type to produce

Step 2: Define the objective function

Maximize profit

Step 3: Define the constraints

The resources available, including processing time, blank shirts, budget, and shipping capacity

Decision Variables

This problem contains four decision variables, representing the number of dozens (boxes) of each type of shirt to produce:

x_1 = sweatshirts, front printing
x_2 = sweatshirts, back and front printing

x_3 = T-shirts, front printing
x_4 = T-shirts, back and front printing

The Objective Function

The company's objective is to maximize profit. The total profit is the sum of the individual profits gained from each type of shirt. The objective function is expressed as

$$\text{maximize } Z = \$90x_1 + 125x_2 + 45x_3 + 65x_4$$

Model Constraints

The first constraint is for processing time. The total available processing time is the 72-hour period between the end of the game and the truck pickup:

$$0.10x_1 + 0.25x_2 + 0.08x_3 + 0.21x_4 \leq 72 \text{ hr}$$

The second constraint is for the available shipping capacity, which is 1,200 standard-size boxes. A box of sweatshirts is three times the size of a standard-size box. Thus, each box of sweatshirts is equivalent in size to three boxes of T-shirts. This relative size differential is expressed in the following constraint:

$$3x_1 + 3x_2 + x_3 + x_4 \leq 1{,}200 \text{ boxes}$$

The third constraint is for the cost budget. The total budget available for production is $25,000:

$$\$36x_1 + 48x_2 + 25x_3 + 35x_4 \leq \$25{,}000$$

The last two constraints reflect the available blank sweatshirts and T-shirts the company has in storage:

$$x_1 + x_2 \leq 500 \text{ dozen sweatshirts}$$
$$x_3 + x_4 \leq 500 \text{ dozen T-shirts}$$

Model Summary

This model can be input as shown for computer solution.

The linear programming model for Quick-Screen is summarized as follows:

$$\begin{aligned} \text{maximize } Z &= 90x_1 + 125x_2 + 45x_3 + 65x_4 \\ \text{subject to} & \\ 0.10x_1 + 0.25x_2 + 0.08x_3 + 0.21x_4 &\leq 72 \\ 3x_1 + 3x_2 + x_3 + x_4 &\leq 1{,}200 \\ 36x_1 + 48x_2 + 25x_3 + 35x_4 &\leq 25{,}000 \\ x_1 + x_2 &\leq 500 \\ x_3 + x_4 &\leq 500 \\ x_1, x_2, x_3, x_4 &\geq 0 \end{aligned}$$

Computer Solution with Excel

The Excel spreadsheet solution for this product mix example is shown in Exhibit 4.1. The decision variables are located in cells **B14:B17**. The profit is computed in cell B18, and the formula for profit, **=B14*D5+B15*E5+B16*F5+B17*G5**, is shown on the formula bar at the top of the spreadsheet. The constraint formulas are embedded in cells H7 through H11, under the column titled "Usage." For example, the constraint formula for processing time in cell H7 is **=D7*B14+E7*B15+F7*B16+G7*B17**. Cells H8 through H11 have similar formulas.

Exhibit 4.1

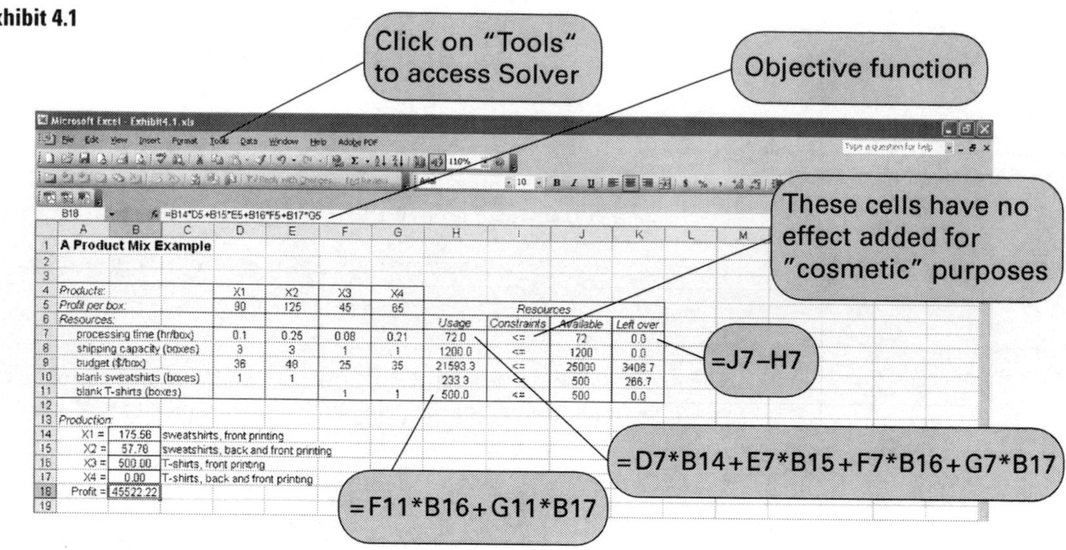

Cells K7 through K11 contain the formulas for the leftover resources, or slack. For example, cell K7 contains the formula **=J7–H7**. These formulas for leftover resources enable us to demonstrate a spreadsheet operation that can save you time in developing the spreadsheet model. First, enter the formula for leftover resources, **=J7–H7**, in cell K7, as we have already shown. Next, using the right mouse button, click on "Copy." Then cover cells K8:K11 with the cursor (by holding the left mouse button down). Click the right mouse button again and then click on "Paste." This will automatically insert the correct formulas for leftover resources in cells K8 through K11 so that you do not have to type them all in individually. This copying operation can be used when the variables in the formula are all in the same row or column. The copying operation simply increases the row number for each cell that the formulas are copied into (i.e., J8 and H8, J9 and H9, J10 and H10, and J11 and H11).

The Solver window for this model is shown in Exhibit 4.2. Notice that we were able to insert all five constraint formulas with one line in the "Subject to the Constraints:" window. We used the constraint **H7:H11** <= **J7:J11**, which means that all the constraint usage values

Exhibit 4.2

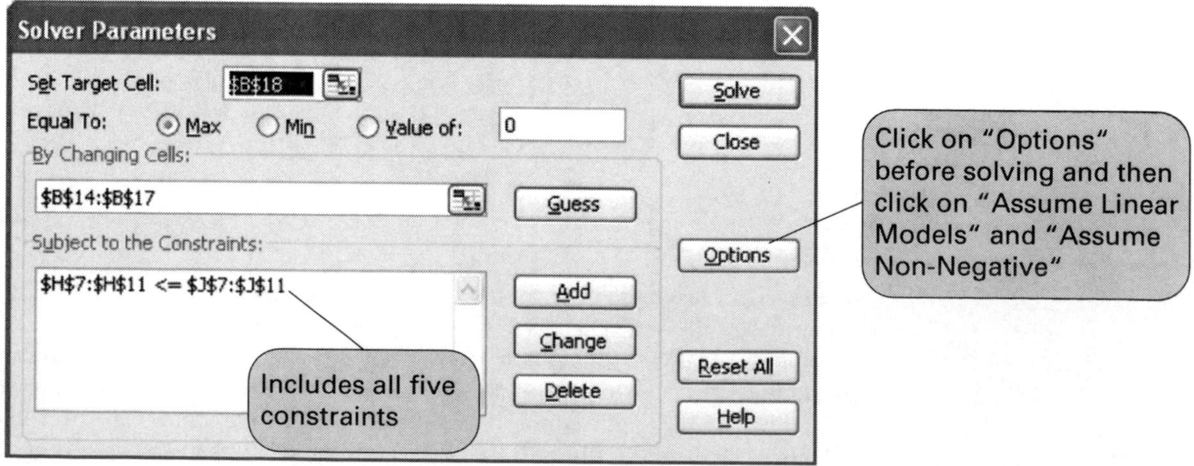

computed in cells H7 through H11 are less than the corresponding available resource values computed in cells J7 through J11.

Computer Solution with QM for Windows

The QM for Windows solution for this problem is shown in Exhibits 4.3 and 4.4.

Exhibit 4.3

Original Problem w/answers

Product Mix Example Solution							
	X1	X2	X3	X4		RHS	Dual
Maximize	90	125	45	65			Max 90X1 + 125X2 + 45X3 + 65X4
Processing time (hrs)	.1	.25	.08	.21	<=	72	233.3333
Shipping capacity (boxes)	3	3	1	1	<=	1,200	22.2222
Budget ($)	36	40	25	35	<=	26,000	0
Blank sweats (dozens)	1	1	0	0	<=	500	0
Blank T's (dozens)	0	0	1	1	<=	500	4.1111
Solution->	175.5556	57.7778	500	0	Optimal Z->	45,522.22	X3 + X4 <= 500

Exhibit 4.4

Ranging

Product Mix Example Solution					
Variable	Value	Reduced Cost	Original Val	Lower Bound	Upper Bound
X1	175.5556	0	90	50	101.9231
X2	57.7778	0	125	113.0769	138.2143
X3	500	0	45	40.8889	Infinity
X4	0	10.3333	65	-Infinity	75.3333
Constraint	Dual Value	Slack/Surplus	Original Val	Lower Bound	Upper Bound
Processing time (hrs)	233.3333	0	72	63.3333	98.3333
Shipping capacity (boxes)	22.2222	0	1,200	884	1,460
Budget ($)	0	3,406.666	25,000	21,593.33	Infinity
Blank sweats (dozens)	0	266.6667	500	233.3333	Infinity
Blank T's (dozens)	4.1111	0	500	0	685.7144

Solution Analysis

The model solution is

$$x_1 = 175.56 \text{ boxes of front-only sweatshirts}$$
$$x_2 = 57.78 \text{ boxes of front and back sweatshirts}$$
$$x_3 = 500 \text{ boxes of front-only T-shirts}$$
$$Z = \$45,522.22 \text{ profit}$$

The manager of Quick-Screen might have to round off the solution to send whole boxes—for example, 175 boxes of front-only sweatshirts, 57 of front and back sweatshirts, and 500 of front-only T-shirts. This would result in a profit of $45,375.00, which is only $147.22 less than the optimal profit value of $45,522.22.

After formulating and solving this model, Quick-Screen might decide that it needs to produce and ship at least some of each type of shirt. Management could evaluate this possibility by adding four constraints that establish minimum levels of production for each type of shirt, including front and back T-shirts, x_4, none of which are produced in the current solution. The manager might also like to experiment with the constraints to see the effect on the solution of adding resources. For example, the dual value for processing time shows profit would increase by $233.33 per hour (up to 98.33 hours, the upper limit of the sensitivity range for this constraint quality value). Although the 72-hour limit seems pretty strict, it might be possible to reduce individual processing times and achieve the same result.

A Diet Example

Breathtakers, a health and fitness center, operates a morning fitness program for senior citizens. The program includes aerobic exercise, either swimming or step exercise, followed by a healthy breakfast in the dining room. Breathtakers' dietitian wants to develop a breakfast that will be high in calories, calcium, protein, and fiber, which are especially important to senior citizens, but low in fat and cholesterol. She also wants to minimize cost. She has selected the following possible food items, whose individual nutrient contributions and cost from which to develop a standard breakfast menu are shown in the following table:

Breakfast Food	Calories	Fat (g)	Cholesterol (mg)	Iron (mg)	Calcium (mg)	Protein (g)	Fiber (g)	Cost
1. Bran cereal (cup)	90	0	0	6	20	3	5	$0.18
2. Dry cereal (cup)	110	2	0	4	48	4	2	0.22
3. Oatmeal (cup)	100	2	0	2	12	5	3	0.10
4. Oat bran (cup)	90	2	0	3	8	6	4	0.12
5. Egg	75	5	270	1	30	7	0	0.10
6. Bacon (slice)	35	3	8	0	0	2	0	0.09
7. Orange	65	0	0	1	52	1	1	0.40
8. Milk—2% (cup)	100	4	12	0	250	9	0	0.16
9. Orange juice (cup)	120	0	0	0	3	1	0	0.50
10. Wheat toast (slice)	65	1	0	1	26	3	3	0.07

The dietitian wants the breakfast to include at least 420 calories, 5 milligrams of iron, 400 milligrams of calcium, 20 grams of protein, and 12 grams of fiber. Furthermore, she wants to limit fat to no more than 20 grams and cholesterol to 30 milligrams.

Decision Variables

This problem includes 10 decision variables, representing the number of standard units of each food item that can be included in each breakfast:

$$
\begin{aligned}
x_1 &= \text{cups of bran cereal} \\
x_2 &= \text{cups of dry cereal} \\
x_3 &= \text{cups of oatmeal} \\
x_4 &= \text{cups of oat bran} \\
x_5 &= \text{eggs} \\
x_6 &= \text{slices of bacon} \\
x_7 &= \text{oranges} \\
x_8 &= \text{cups of milk} \\
x_9 &= \text{cups of orange juice} \\
x_{10} &= \text{slices of wheat toast}
\end{aligned}
$$

The Objective Function

The dietitian's objective is to minimize the cost of a breakfast. The total cost is the sum of the individual costs of each food item:

$$
\begin{aligned}
\text{minimize } Z = \$0.18x_1 + 0.22x_2 + 0.10x_3 + 0.12x_4 + 0.10x_5 + 0.09x_6 + 0.40x_7 \\
+ 0.16x_8 + 0.50x_9 + 0.07x_{10}
\end{aligned}
$$

Model Constraints

The constraints are the requirements for the nutrition items:

$$90x_1 + 110x_2 + 100x_3 + 90x_4 + 75x_5 + 35x_6 + 65x_7 + 100x_8 + 120x_9 + 65x_{10} \geq 420 \text{ calories}$$
$$2x_2 + 2x_3 + 2x_4 + 5x_5 + 3x_6 + 4x_8 + x_{10} \leq 20 \text{ g of fat}$$
$$270x_5 + 8x_6 + 12x_8 \leq 30 \text{ mg of cholesterol}$$
$$6x_1 + 4x_2 + 2x_3 + 3x_4 + x_5 + x_7 + x_{10} \geq 5 \text{ mg of iron}$$
$$20x_1 + 48x_2 + 12x_3 + 8x_4 + 30x_5 + 52x_7 + 250x_8 + 3x_9 + 26x_{10} \geq 400 \text{ mg of calcium}$$
$$3x_1 + 4x_2 + 5x_3 + 6x_4 + 7x_5 + 2x_6 + x_7 + 9x_8 + x_9 + 3x_{10} \geq 20 \text{ g of protein}$$
$$5x_1 + 2x_2 + 3x_3 + 4x_4 + x_7 + 3x_{10} \geq 12 \text{ g of fiber}$$

Model Summary

The linear programming model for this problem can be summarized as follows:

$$\text{minimize } Z = 0.18x_1 + 0.22x_2 + 0.10x_3 + 0.12x_4 + 0.10x_5 + 0.09x_6 + 0.40x_7 + 0.16x_8 + 0.50x_9 + 0.07x_{10}$$

subject to

$$90x_1 + 110x_2 + 100x_3 + 90x_4 + 75x_5 + 35x_6 + 65x_7 + 100x_8 + 120x_9 + 65x_{10} \geq 420$$
$$2x_2 + 2x_3 + 2x_4 + 5x_5 + 3x_6 + 4x_8 + x_{10} \leq 20$$
$$270x_5 + 8x_6 + 12x_8 \leq 30$$
$$6x_1 + 4x_2 + 2x_3 + 3x_4 + x_5 + x_7 + x_{10} \geq 5$$
$$20x_1 + 48x_2 + 12x_3 + 8x_4 + 30x_5 + 52x_7 + 250x_8 + 3x_9 + 26x_{10} \geq 400$$
$$3x_1 + 4x_2 + 5x_3 + 6x_4 + 7x_5 + 2x_6 + x_7 + 9x_8 + x_9 + 3x_{10} \geq 20$$
$$5x_1 + 2x_2 + 3x_3 + 4x_4 + x_7 + 3x_{10} \geq 12$$
$$x_i \geq 0$$

Computer Solution with Excel

The solution to our diet example using an Excel spreadsheet is shown in Exhibit 4.5. The decision variables (i.e., "servings" of each menu item) for our problem are contained in cells **C5:C14** inclusive, and the constraint formulas are in cells F15 through L15. Cells F17 through L17 contain the constraint (right-hand-side) values. For example, cell F15 contains the constraint formula for calories, **=SUMPRODUCT(C5:C14,F5:F14)**. Then when the Solver Parameters screen is accessed, the constraint **F15>=F17** will be added in. This constraint formula in cell F15 could have been constructed by multiplying each of the values in column C by each of the corresponding column F cell values. The equivalent constraint formula in cell F15 to our SUMPRODUCT formula is **=C5*F5+C6*F6+C7*F7+C8*F8+C9*F9+C10*F10+C11*F11+C12*F12+C13*F13+C14*F14.**

The objective function formula is contained in cell C19, **=SUMPRODUCT(C5:C14, E5:E14)**. In this case the objective function value is also computed by using the Excel SUMPRODUCT command rather than by individually multiplying each cell value in column C by each cell value in column E and then summing them. This would be a tedious formula to type into cell C19. Alternatively, the SUMPRODUCT() formula multiplies all the values in cells C5 through C14 by all the corresponding values in cells E5 through E14 and then sums them.

The Solver dialog box for this problem is shown in Exhibit 4.6. Notice that the constraint box on this screen is not large enough to show all the constraints in the problem.

Solution Analysis

The solution is

$$x_3 = 1.025 \text{ cups of oatmeal}$$
$$x_8 = 1.241 \text{ cups of milk}$$
$$x_{10} = 2.975 \text{ slices of wheat toast}$$
$$Z = \$0.509 \text{ cost per meal}$$

Exhibit 4.5

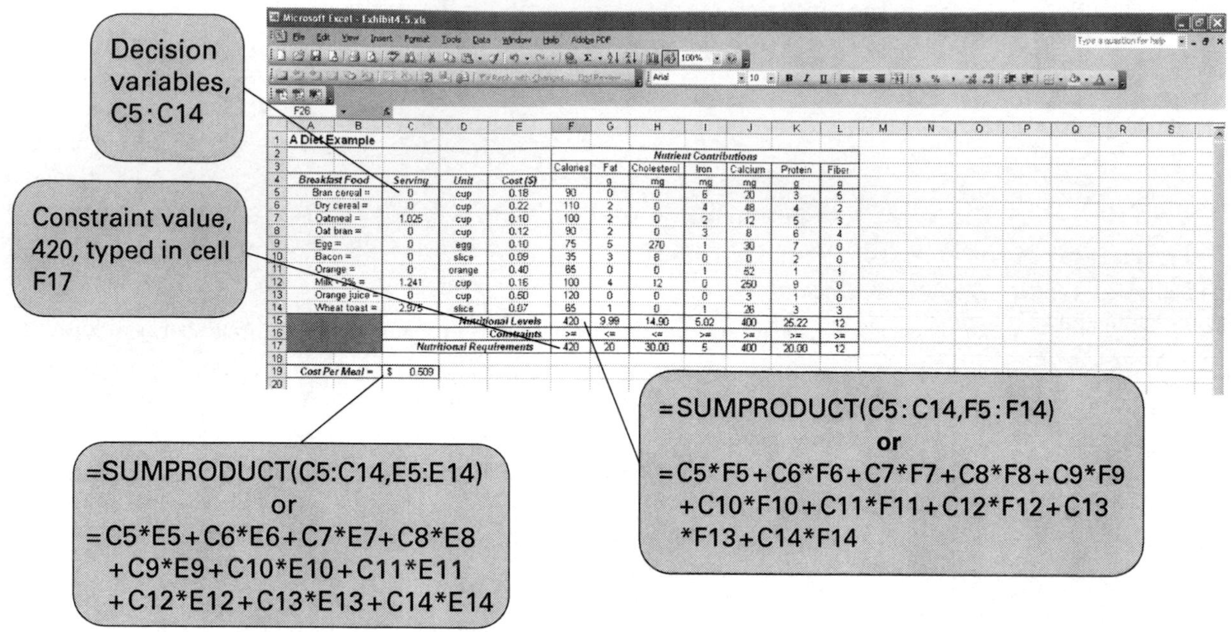

A Diet Example

Breakfast Food	Serving	Unit	Cost ($)	Calories	Fat (g)	Cholesterol (mg)	Iron (mg)	Calcium (mg)	Protein (g)	Fiber (g)
Bran cereal =	0	cup	0.18	90	0	0	6	20	3	5
Dry cereal =	0	cup	0.22	110	2	0	4	48	4	2
Oatmeal =	1.025	cup	0.10	100	2	0	2	12	5	3
Oat bran =	0	cup	0.12	90	2	0	3	8	6	4
Egg =	0	egg	0.10	75	5	270	1	30	7	0
Bacon =	0	slice	0.09	35	3	8	0	0	2	0
Orange =	0	orange	0.40	65	0	0	1	52	1	1
Milk - 2% =	1.241	cup	0.16	100	4	12	0	250	9	0
Orange juice =	0	cup	0.50	120	0	0	0	3	1	0
Wheat toast =	2.975	slice	0.07	65	1	0	1	26	3	3
			Nutritional Levels	420	9.99	14.90	5.02	400	25.22	12
			Constraints	>=	<=	<=	>=	>=	>=	>=
			Nutritional Requirements	420	20	30.00	5	400	20.00	12

Cost Per Meal = $ 0.509

Exhibit 4.6

Decision variables; "servings" in column C

Solver Parameters

Set Target Cell: $C$19

Equal To: ○ Max ⦿ Min ○ Value of: 0

By Changing Cells: $C$5:$C$14

Subject to the Constraints:

$F$15 >= $F$17
$G$15 <= $G$17
$H$15 <= $H$17
$I$15 >= $I$17
$J$15 >= $J$17
$K$15 >= $K$17

Solve | Close | Guess | Options | Add | Change | Delete | Reset All | Help

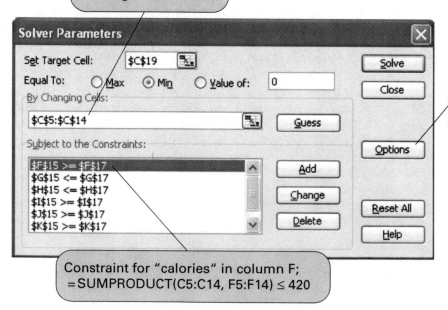

For nonnegativity constraints click on "Options" and then "Assume Non-Negative."

Constraint for "calories" in column F; =SUMPRODUCT(C5:C14, F5:F14) ≤ 420

The result of this simplified version of a real menu planning model (see the application box "The Evolution of the Diet Problem") is interesting in that it suggests a very practical breakfast menu. This would be a healthy breakfast for anyone.

This model includes a daily minimum requirement of only 420 calories. The recommended daily calorie requirement for an adult is approximately 2,000 calories. Thus, the breakfast requirement is only about 21% of normal daily adult needs. In this model the dietitian must have felt a low-calorie breakfast was needed because the senior citizens had high-calorie lunches and dinners. An alternative approach to a healthy diet is a high-calorie breakfast followed by low-calorie, light meals and snacks the rest of the day. However, in this model, as the calorie requirements are increased above 420, the model simply increases the cups of oatmeal. For example, a 700-calorie requirement results in about 5 or 6 cups of oatmeal—not a very appetizing breakfast. This difficulty can be alleviated by establishing upper limits on the servings for each food item and solving the model again with a higher calorie requirement.

An Investment Example

Kathleen Allen, an individual investor, has $70,000 to divide among several investments. The alternative investments are municipal bonds with an 8.5% annual return, certificates of deposit with a 5% return, treasury bills with a 6.5% return, and a growth stock fund with a 13% annual return. The investments are all evaluated after 1 year. However, each investment alternative has a different perceived risk to the investor; thus, it is advisable to diversify. Kathleen wants to know how much to invest in each alternative in order to maximize the return.

The following guidelines have been established for diversifying the investments and lessening the risk perceived by the investor:

1. No more than 20% of the total investment should be in municipal bonds.
2. The amount invested in certificates of deposit should not exceed the amount invested in the other three alternatives.
3. At least 30% of the investment should be in treasury bills and certificates of deposit.
4. To be safe, more should be invested in CDs and treasury bills than in municipal bonds and the growth stock fund, by a ratio of at least 1.2 to 1.

Kathleen wants to invest the entire $70,000.

Decision Variables

Four decision variables represent the monetary amount invested in each investment alternative:

x_1 = amount ($) invested in municipal bonds
x_2 = amount ($) invested in certificates of deposit
x_3 = amount ($) invested in treasury bills
x_4 = amount ($) invested in growth stock fund

The Objective Function

The objective of the investor is to maximize the total return from the investment in the four alternatives. The total return is the sum of the individual returns from each alternative. Thus, the objective function is expressed as

Management Science Application

The Evolution of the Diet Problem

When George Dantzig developed the simplex method for solving linear programming models, he illustrated the new technique by using the "diet problem" developed in 1945 by George Stigler. The problem was to determine a menu of foods that would satisfy nutritional requirements at a minimum cost. The diet problem has evolved over the years and continues to be a popular application of linear programming as institutional feeding programs at hospitals, military installations, nursing homes, schools, prisons, shelters, and restaurants have proliferated. Menu planning represents a formidable problem, with more than 30 nutritional constraints and thousands of variables, as well as consumer food preferences. Recommended daily allowances include minimum levels of 29 nutrients, while various health groups recommend maximum daily levels of fat, cholesterol, and sodium. Today, software packages are available for menu planning, including computer-assisted menu planning (CAMP), part of the IBM contributed programs library.

CAMP has had numerous reported applications around the world, including the development of a 90-day planned menu cycle at a state hospital and planned menus for schools that lower fat content while meeting nutritional requirements at a lower cost. In general, mathematical programming–based meal planning models have been formed to reduce food costs by approximately 10% while meeting government-established nutritional standards. Other traditional menu planning methods have generally not achieved this level of success.

Source: L. M. Lancaster, "The Evolution of the Diet Model in Managing Food Systems," *Interfaces* 22, no. 5 (September–October 1992): 59–68.

$$\text{maximize } Z = \$0.085x_1 + 0.05x_2 + 0.065x_3 + 0.130x_4$$

where

Z = total return from all investments

$0.085x_1$ = return from the investment in municipal bonds

$0.05x_2$ = return from the investment in certificates of deposit

$0.065x_3$ = return from the investment in treasury bills

$0.130x_4$ = return from the investment in growth stock fund

Model Constraints

In this problem the constraints are the guidelines established for diversifying the total investment. Each guideline is transformed into a mathematical constraint separately.

The first guideline states that no more than 20% of the total investment should be in municipal bonds. The total investment is $70,000; 20% of $70,000 is $14,000. Thus, this constraint is

$$x_1 \leq \$14{,}000$$

The second guideline indicates that the amount invested in certificates of deposit should not exceed the amount invested in the other three alternatives. Because the investment in certificates of deposit is x_2 and the amount invested in the other alternatives is $x_1 + x_3 + x_4$, the constraint is

$$x_2 \leq x_1 + x_3 + x_4$$

Standard form requires all variables to be to the left of the inequality and numeric values to the right.

This constraint is not in what we referred to in Chapter 3 as *standard form* for a computer solution. In standard form, all the variables would be on the left-hand side of the inequality (≤), and all the numeric values would be on the right side. This type of constraint can be used in Excel just as it is shown here; however, for solution with QM for Windows, all constraints must be in standard form. We will go ahead and convert this constraint and others in this model to standard form, but when we solve this model with Excel, we will explain how the model constraints could be used in their original (nonstandard) form. To convert this constraint to standard form, $x_1 + x_3 + x_4$ must be subtracted from both sides of the ≤ sign to put this constraint in proper form:

$$x_2 - x_1 - x_3 - x_4 \leq 0$$

The third guideline specifies that at least 30% of the investment should be in treasury bills and certificates of deposit. Because 30% of \$70,000 is \$21,000 and the amount invested in certificates of deposit and treasury bills is represented by $x_2 + x_3$, the constraint is

$$x_2 + x_3 \geq \$21{,}000$$

The fourth guideline states that the ratio of the amount invested in certificates of deposit and treasury bills to the amount invested in municipal bonds and the growth stock fund should be at least 1.2 to 1:

$$[(x_2 + x_3)/(x_1 + x_4)] \geq 1.2$$

Standard form requires that fractional relationships between variables be eliminated.

This constraint is not in standard linear programming form because of the fractional relationship of the decision variables, $(x_2 + x_3)/(x_1 + x_4)$. It is converted as follows:

$$x_2 + x_3 \geq 1.2\,(x_1 + x_4)$$
$$-1.2x_1 + x_2 + x_3 - 1.2x_4 \geq 0$$

Finally, the investor wants to invest the entire \$70,000 in the four alternatives. Thus, the sum of all the investments in the four alternatives must *equal* \$70,000:

$$x_1 + x_2 + x_3 + x_4 = \$70{,}000$$

Model Summary

The complete linear programming model for this problem can be summarized as

$$\text{maximize } Z = \$0.085x_1 + 0.05x_2 + 0.065x_3 + 0.130x_4$$

subject to

$$\begin{aligned}
x_1 &\leq 14{,}000 \\
x_2 - x_1 - x_3 - x_4 &\leq 0 \\
x_2 + x_3 &\geq 21{,}000 \\
-1.2x_1 + x_2 + x_3 - 1.2x_4 &\geq 0 \\
x_1 + x_2 + x_3 + x_4 &= 70{,}000 \\
x_1, x_2, x_3, x_4 &\geq 0
\end{aligned}$$

Computer Solution with Excel

The Excel spreadsheet solution for the investment example is shown in Exhibit 4.7, and its Solver window is shown in Exhibit 4.8. The spreadsheet is set up very similarly to the spreadsheet for our product mix example in Exhibit 4.1. The decision variables are

Exhibit 4.7

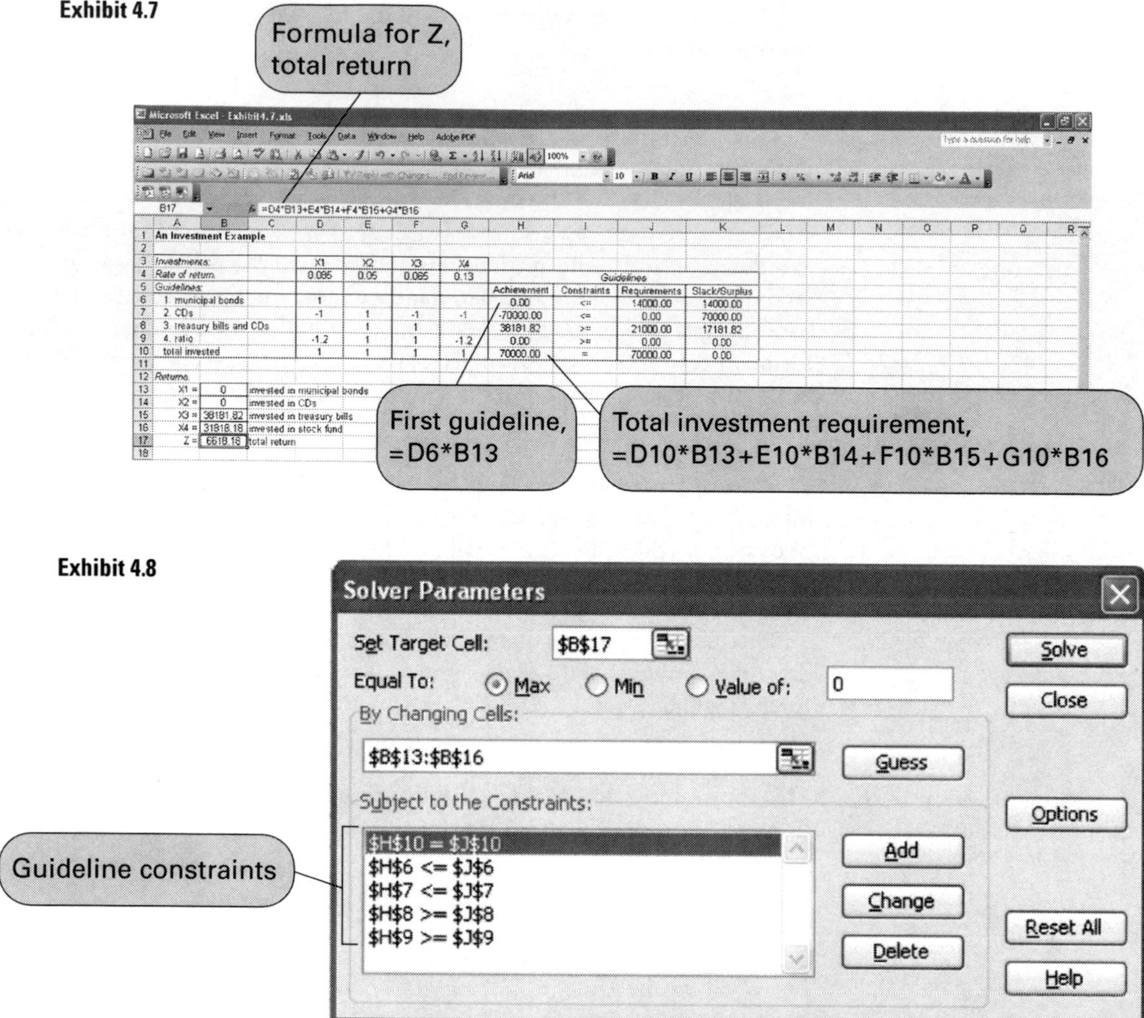

Exhibit 4.8

located in cells **B13:B16**. The total return (Z) is computed in cell B17, and the formula for Z is shown on the formula bar at the top of the spreadsheet. The constraint formulas for the investment guidelines are embedded in cells H6 through H10. For example, the first guideline formula, in cell H6, is **=D6*B13**, and the second guideline formula, in cell H7, is **=D7*B13+E7*B14+F7*B15+G7*B16**. (Note that it would probably have been easier just to type the guideline formulas directly into cells H6 through H10 rather than create the array of constraint coefficients in **D6:G10**; however, for demonstration purposes, we wanted to show all the parameter values.)

As mentioned earlier, it is not necessary to convert the original model constraints into standard form to solve this model using Excel. For example, the constraint for certificates of deposit, $x_2 \leq x_1 + x_3 + x_4$, could be entered in the spreadsheet in row 7 in Exhibit 4.7 as follows. The value, 1, the coefficient for x_2, could be entered in cell E7, **=E7*B14** could be entered in cell J7, and the remainder of the constraint to the right side of the inequality could be entered as **=B13+B15+B16** in cell H7. In the Solver window this constraint is entered as it originally was, **H7<=J7**. The fourth guideline constraint could be entered in its original form similarly.

Solution Analysis

The solution is

$$x_3 = \$38{,}181.82 \text{ invested in treasury bonds}$$
$$x_4 = \$31{,}818.18 \text{ invested in a growth stock fund}$$
$$Z = \$6{,}818.18$$

The sensitivity report for our Excel spreadsheet solution to this problem is shown in Exhibit 4.9.

Exhibit 4.9

Adjustable Cells

Cell	Name	Final Value	Reduced Cost	Objective Coefficient	Allowable Increase	Allowable Decrease
$B$13	X1 =	0	-0.045	0.085	0.045	1E+30
$B$14	X2 =	0	-0.015	0.050	0.015	1E+30
$B$15	X3 =	38181.82	0	0.065	0.065	0.015
$B$16	X4 =	31818.18	0	0.13	45354.805	0.045

Constraints

Cell	Name	Final Value	Shadow Price	Constraint R.H. Side	Allowable Increase	Allowable Decrease
$H$6	1. municipal bonds Achievement	0.00	0.000	14000	1E+30	14000
$H$7	2. CDs Achievement	-70000.00	0.000	0	1E+30	70000
$H$8	3. treasury bills and CDs Achievement	38181.82	0.000	21000	17181.82	1E+30
$H$9	4. ratio Achievement	0.00	-0.030	0	70000	37800
$H$10	total invested Achievement	70000.00	0.095	70000	1E+30	31500

Shadow price for the amount available to invest

Notice that the dual (shadow price) value for constraint 5 (i.e., the sum of the investments must equal $70,000) is 0.095. This indicates that for each additional $1 Kathleen Allen invests (above $70,000), according to the existing investment guidelines she has established, she could expect a return of 9.5%. The sensitivity ranges show that there is no upper bound on the amount she could invest and still receive this return.

An interesting variation of the problem is to not specify that the entire amount available (in this case, $70,000) must be invested. This changes the constraints for the first and third guidelines and the constraint that requires that the entire $70,000 be invested.

Recall that the first guideline is "no more than 20% of the total investment should be in municipal bonds." The total investment is no longer exactly $70,000, but the sum of all four investments, $x_1 + x_2 + x_3 + x_4$. The constraint showing that the amount invested in municipal bonds, x_1, as a percentage (or ratio) of this total cannot exceed 20% is written as

$$\frac{x_1}{x_1 + x_2 + x_3 + x_4} \leq 0.20$$

Rewriting this constraint in a form more consistent with a linear programming solution (to eliminate the fractional relationship between variables) results in

$$x_1 \leq 0.2(x_1 + x_2 + x_3 + x_4)$$

Management Science Application

A Linear Programming Model for Optimal Portfolio Selection at Prudential Securities, Inc.

In the secondary mortgage market, government agencies purchase mortgage loans from the original mortgage lenders and pool them to create mortgage-backed securities (MBSs). These securities are traded in capital markets along with other fixed-income securities, such as treasury and corporate bonds. The total size of this market for MBSs is well over \$1 trillion. There are a number of types of MBSs. The market for MBSs is maintained by a network of dealers, including Prudential Securities, Inc. This firm and others like it underwrite and issue new market-based securities. This market is somewhat more complex than standard bond investments, such as treasury or corporate securities, because the principal on mortgages is returned gradually over the life of the security rather than in a lump sum at the end. In addition, cash flows fluctuate because of the homeowner's right to prepay mortgages. In order to deal with these complexities, Prudential Securities has developed and implemented a number of management science models to reduce investment risk and properly value securities for its investors. One such model employs linear programming to design an optimal securities portfolio to meet various investors' criteria under different interest rate environments. The linear programming model determines the amount to invest in different MBSs to meet a client's objectives for portfolio performance. Constraints might include maximum and minimum percentages (of the total portfolio investment) that could be invested in any one or more securities, the duration of the securities, the amount to be invested, and the amount of the different securities available. This linear programming model and other management science models are used hundreds of times each day at Prudential Securities by traders, salespeople, and clients. The models allow the firm to participate successfully in the mortgage market. Prudential's secondary market trading in MBSs typically exceeds \$5 billion per week.

Source: Y. Ben-Dow, L. Hayre, and V. Pica, "Mortgage Valuation Models at Prudential Securities," *Interfaces* 22, no. 1 (January–February 1992): 55–71.

and

$$0.8x_1 - 0.2x_2 - 0.2x_3 - 0.2x_4 \leq 0$$

The constraint for the third guideline, which stipulates that at least 30% of the total investment $(x_1 + x_2 + x_3 + x_4)$ should be in treasury bills and CDs $(x_2 + x_3)$, is formulated similarly as

$$\frac{x_2 + x_3}{x_1 + x_2 + x_3 + x_4} \geq 0.30$$

and

$$-0.3x_1 + 0.7x_2 + 0.7x_3 - 0.3x_4 \geq 0$$

Because the entire \$70,000 does not have to be invested, the last constraint becomes

$$x_1 + x_2 + x_3 + x_4 \leq 70,000$$

The complete linear programming model is summarized as

$$\text{maximize } Z = \$0.085x_1 + 0.05x_2 + 0.065x_3 + 0.130x_4$$

subject to

$$\begin{aligned}
0.8x_1 - 0.2x_2 - 0.2x_3 - 0.2x_4 &\leq 0 \\
x_2 - x_1 - x_3 - x_4 &\leq 0 \\
-0.3x_1 + 0.7x_2 + 0.7x_3 - 0.3x_4 &\geq 0 \\
-1.2x_1 + x_2 + x_3 - 1.2x_4 &\geq 0 \\
x_1 + x_2 + x_3 + x_4 &\leq 70{,}000 \\
x_1, x_2, x_3, x_4 &\geq 0
\end{aligned}$$

The solution to this altered model is exactly the same as the solution to our original model, wherein the entire \$70,000 must be invested. This is logical because only positive returns are achieved from investing, and thus the investor would leave no money not invested. However, if losses could be realized from some investments, then it might be a good idea to construct the model so that the entire amount would not have to be invested.

A Marketing Example

The Biggs Department Store chain has hired an advertising firm to determine the types and amount of advertising it should invest in for its stores. The three types of advertising available are television and radio commercials and newspaper ads. The retail chain desires to know the number of each type of advertisement it should purchase in order to maximize exposure. It is estimated that each ad or commercial will reach the following potential audience and cost the following amount:

	Exposure (people/ad or commercial)	Cost
Television commercial	20,000	\$15,000
Radio commercial	12,000	6,000
Newspaper ad	9,000	4,000

The company must consider the following resource constraints:

1. The budget limit for advertising is \$100,000.
2. The television station has time available for 4 commercials.
3. The radio station has time available for 10 commercials.
4. The newspaper has space available for 7 ads.
5. The advertising agency has time and staff available for producing no more than a total of 15 commercials and/or ads.

Decision Variables

This model consists of three decision variables that represent the number of each type of advertising produced:

x_1 = number of television commercials
x_2 = number of radio commercials
x_3 = number of newspaper ads

The Objective Function

The objective of this problem is different from the objectives in the previous examples, in which only profit was to be maximized (or cost minimized). In this problem, profit is not to be maximized; instead, audience exposure is to be maximized. Thus, this objective function demonstrates that although a linear programming model must either maximize or minimize some objective, the objective itself can be in terms of any type of activity or valuation.

For this problem the objective audience exposure is determined by summing the audience exposure gained from each type of advertising:

$$\text{maximize } Z = 20{,}000x_1 + 12{,}000x_2 + 9{,}000x_3$$

where

$$\begin{aligned} Z &= \text{total level of audience exposure} \\ 20{,}000x_1 &= \text{estimated number of people reached by television commercials} \\ 12{,}000x_2 &= \text{estimated number of people reached by radio commercials} \\ 9{,}000x_3 &= \text{estimated number of people reached by newspaper ads} \end{aligned}$$

Model Constraints

The first constraint in this model reflects the limited budget of \$100,000 allocated for advertisement:

$$\$15{,}000x_1 + 6{,}000x_2 + 4{,}000x_3 \leq \$100{,}000$$

where

$$\begin{aligned} \$15{,}000x_1 &= \text{amount spent for television advertising} \\ 6{,}000x_2 &= \text{amount spent for radio advertising} \\ 4{,}000x_3 &= \text{amount spent for newspaper advertising} \end{aligned}$$

The next three constraints represent the fact that television and radio commercials are limited to 4 and 10, respectively, and newspaper ads are limited to 7:

$$\begin{aligned} x_1 &\leq 4 \text{ television commercials} \\ x_2 &\leq 10 \text{ radio commercials} \\ x_3 &\leq 7 \text{ newspaper ads} \end{aligned}$$

The final constraint specifies that the total number of commercials and ads cannot exceed 15 because of the limitations of the advertising firm:

$$x_1 + x_2 + x_3 \leq 15 \text{ commercials and ads}$$

Model Summary

The complete linear programming model for this problem is summarized as

$$\begin{aligned} &\text{maximize } Z = 20{,}000x_1 + 12{,}000x_2 + 9{,}000x_3 \\ &\text{subject to} \\ &\$15{,}000x_1 + 6{,}000x_2 + 4{,}000x_3 \leq \$100{,}000 \\ &x_1 \leq 4 \\ &x_2 \leq 10 \\ &x_3 \leq 7 \\ &x_1 + x_2 + x_3 \leq 15 \\ &x_1, x_2, x_3 \geq 0 \end{aligned}$$

Computer Solution with Excel

The solution to our marketing example using Excel is shown in Exhibit 4.10. The model decision variables are contained in cells **D6:D8**. The formula for the objective function in cell E10 is shown on the formula bar at the top of the screen. When Solver is accessed from the "Tools" menu, as shown in Exhibit 4.11, it is necessary to use only one formula to enter the model constraints: **H6:H10 <= J6:J10**.

Exhibit 4.10

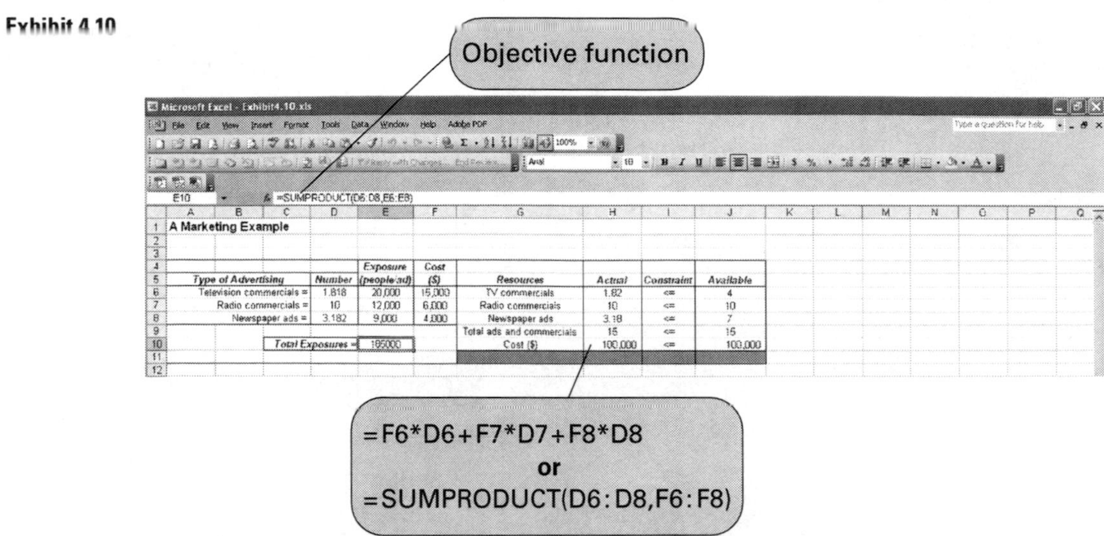

Exhibit 4.11

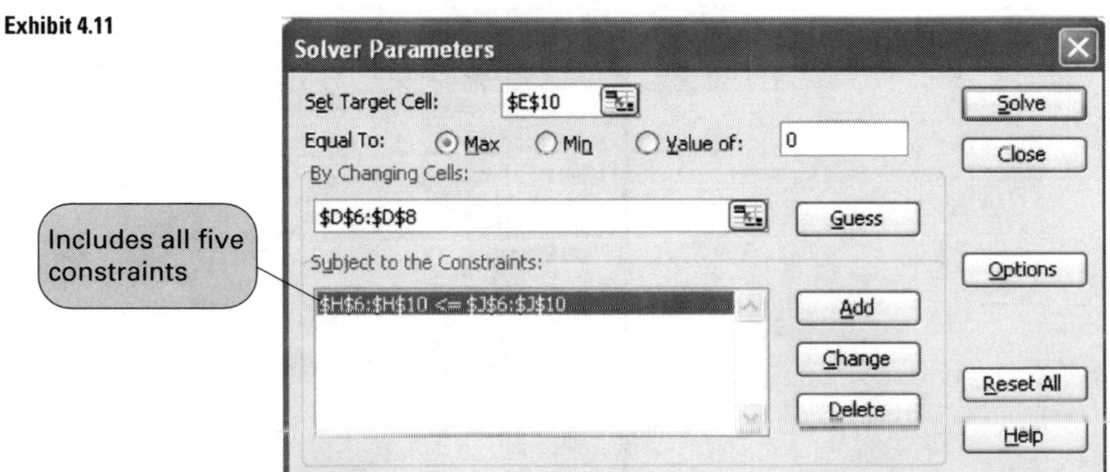

Solution Analysis

The solution shows

$$
\begin{aligned}
x_1 &= 1.818 \text{ television commercials} \\
x_2 &= 10 \text{ radio commercials} \\
x_3 &= 3.182 \text{ newspaper ads} \\
Z &= 185{,}000 \text{ audience exposure}
\end{aligned}
$$

This is a case where a non-integer solution can create difficulties. It is not realistic to round 1.818 television commercials to 2 television commercials, with 10 radio commercials and 3 newspaper ads. Some quick arithmetic with the budget constraint shows that such a solution will exceed the $100,000 budget limitation, although only by $2,000. Thus, the store must either increase its advertising or plan for 1 television commercial, 10 radio commercials, and 3 newspaper ads. The audience exposure for this solution will be 167,000 people, or 18,000 fewer than the optimal number, almost a 10% decrease. There may, in fact, be a better solution than this "rounded-down" solution.

The integer linear programming technique, which restricts solutions to integer values, should be used. Although we will discuss the topic of integer programming in more detail in Chapter 5, for now we can derive an integer solution by using Excel with a simple change when we input our constraints in the Solver window. We specify that our variable cells, **D6:D8**, are integers in the Change Constraint window, as shown in Exhibits 4.12 and 4.13. This will result in the spreadsheet solution in Exhibit 4.14 when the problem is solved, which you will notice is better (i.e., more total exposures) than the rounded-down solution.

Exhibit 4.12

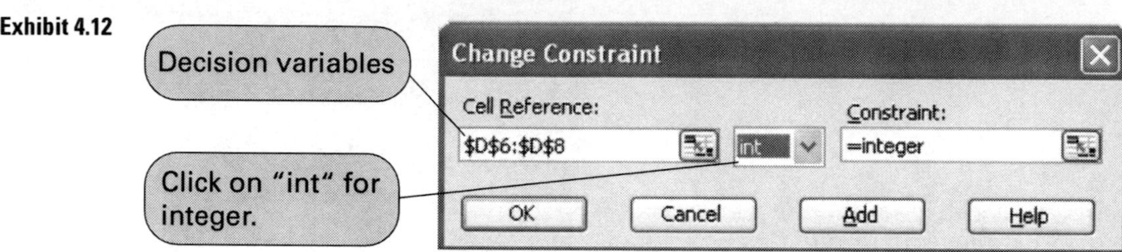

Exhibit 4.13

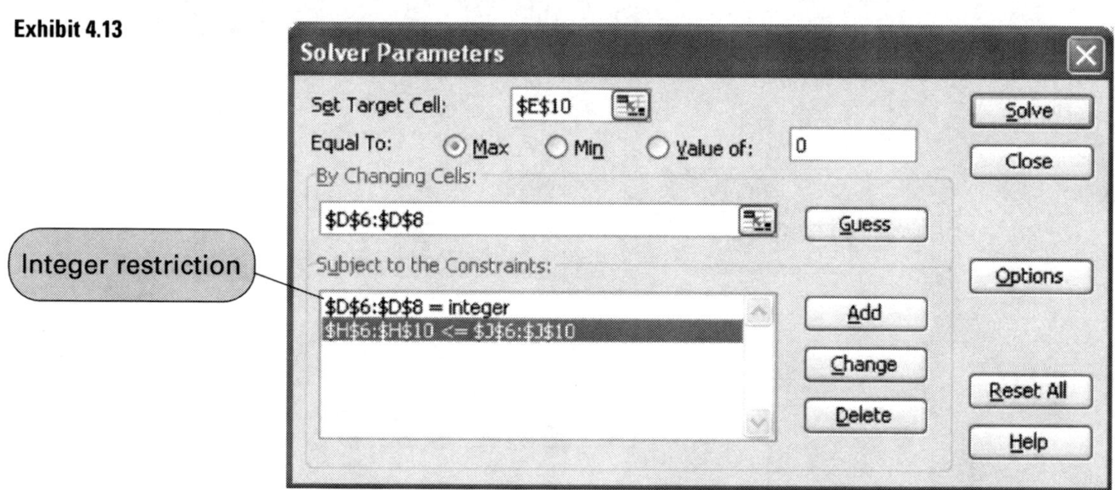

Exhibit 4.14

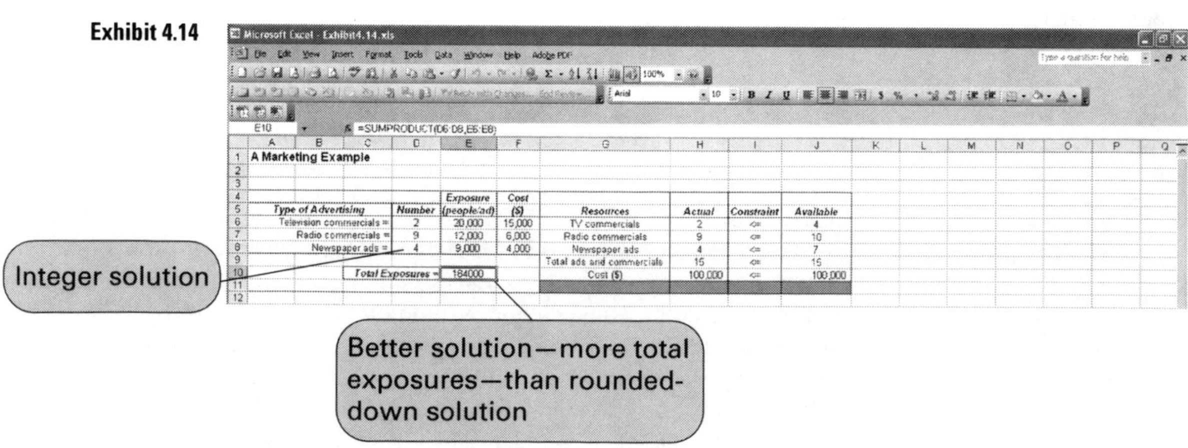

A Transportation Example

The Zephyr Television Company ships televisions from three warehouses to three retail stores on a monthly basis. Each warehouse has a fixed supply per month, and each store has a fixed demand per month. The manufacturer wants to know the number of television sets to ship from each warehouse to each store in order to minimize the total cost of transportation.

Each warehouse has the following supply of televisions available for shipment each month:

Warehouse	*Supply (sets)*
1. Cincinnati	300
2. Atlanta	200
3. Pittsburgh	200
	700

Each retail store has the following monthly demand for television sets:

Store	*Demand (sets)*
A. New York	150
B. Dallas	250
C. Detroit	200
	600

Costs of transporting television sets from the warehouses to the retail stores vary as a result of differences in modes of transportation and distances. The shipping cost per television set for each route is as follows:

From Warehouse	To Store A	B	C
1	\$16	\$18	\$11
2	14	12	13
3	13	15	17

Decision Variables

The model for this problem consists of nine decision variables, representing the number of television sets transported from each of the three warehouses to each of the three stores:

$$x_{ij} = \text{number of television sets shipped from warehouse } i \text{ to store } j$$
$$\text{where } i = 1, 2, 3, \text{ and } j = \text{A, B, C}$$

A double-subscripted variable is simply another form of variable name.

The variable x_{ij} is referred to as a double-subscripted variable. The subscript, whether double or single, simply gives a "name" to the variable (i.e., distinguishes it from other decision variables). For example, the decision variable x_{3A} represents the number of television sets shipped from warehouse 3 in Pittsburgh to store A in New York.

The Objective Function

The objective function of the television manufacturer is to minimize the total transportation costs for all shipments. Thus, the objective function is the sum of the individual shipping costs from each warehouse to each store:

$$\text{minimize } Z = \$16x_{1A} + 18x_{1B} + 11x_{1C} + 14x_{2A} + 12x_{2B} + 13x_{2C} + 13x_{3A} + 15x_{3B} + 17x_{3C}$$

Model Constraints

The constraints in this model are the number of television sets available at each warehouse and the number of sets demanded at each store. There are six constraints—one for each warehouse's supply and one for each store's demand. For example, warehouse 1 in Cincinnati is able to supply 300 television sets to any of the three retail stores. Because the number shipped to the three stores is the sum of x_{1A}, x_{1B}, and x_{1C}, the constraint for warehouse 1 is

$$x_{1A} + x_{1B} + x_{1C} \leq 300$$

In a ***"balanced" transportation model****, supply equals demand such that all constraints are equalities; in an* ***"unbalanced" transportation model****, supply does not equal demand, and one set of constraints is ≤.*

This constraint is a ≤ inequality for two reasons. First, no more than 300 television sets can be shipped because that is the maximum available at the warehouse. Second, fewer than 300 can be shipped because 300 are not needed to meet the total demand of 600. That is, total demand is less than total supply, which equals 700. To meet the total demand at the three stores, all that can be supplied by the three warehouses is not needed. Thus, the other two supply constraints for warehouses 2 and 3 are also inequalities:

$$x_{2A} + x_{2B} + x_{2C} \leq 200$$
$$x_{3A} + x_{3B} + x_{3C} \leq 200$$

The three demand constraints are developed in the same way as the supply constraints, except that the variables summed are the number of television sets supplied from each of the three warehouses. Thus, the number shipped to one store is the sum of the shipments from the three warehouses. They are equalities because all demands can be met:

$$x_{1A} + x_{2A} + x_{3A} = 150$$
$$x_{1B} + x_{2B} + x_{3B} = 250$$
$$x_{1C} + x_{2C} + x_{3C} = 200$$

Model Summary

The complete linear programming model for this problem is summarized as follows:

minimize $Z = \$16x_{1A} + 18x_{1B} + 11x_{1C} + 14x_{2A} + 12x_{2B} + 13x_{2C} + 13x_{3A} + 15x_{3B} + 17x_{3C}$
subject to

$$x_{1A} + x_{1B} + x_{1C} \leq 300$$
$$x_{2A} + x_{2B} + x_{2C} \leq 200$$
$$x_{3A} + x_{3B} + x_{3C} \leq 200$$
$$x_{1A} + x_{2A} + x_{3A} = 150$$
$$x_{1B} + x_{2B} + x_{3B} = 250$$
$$x_{1C} + x_{2C} + x_{3C} = 200$$
$$x_{ij} \geq 0$$

Computer Solution with Excel

The computer solution for this model was achieved using Excel and is shown in Exhibit 4.15. Notice that the objective function contained in cell C11 is shown on the formula bar at the top of the screen. The constraints for supply are included in cells F5, F6, and F7, whereas the demand constraints are in cells C8, D8, and E8. Thus, a typical supply constraint for Cincinnati would be **C5+D5+E5≤H5**. The Solver window is shown in Exhibit 4.16 .

Solution Analysis

The solution is

$x_{1C} = 200$ TVs shipped from Cincinnati to Detroit
$x_{2B} = 200$ TVs shipped from Atlanta to Dallas

Exhibit 4.15

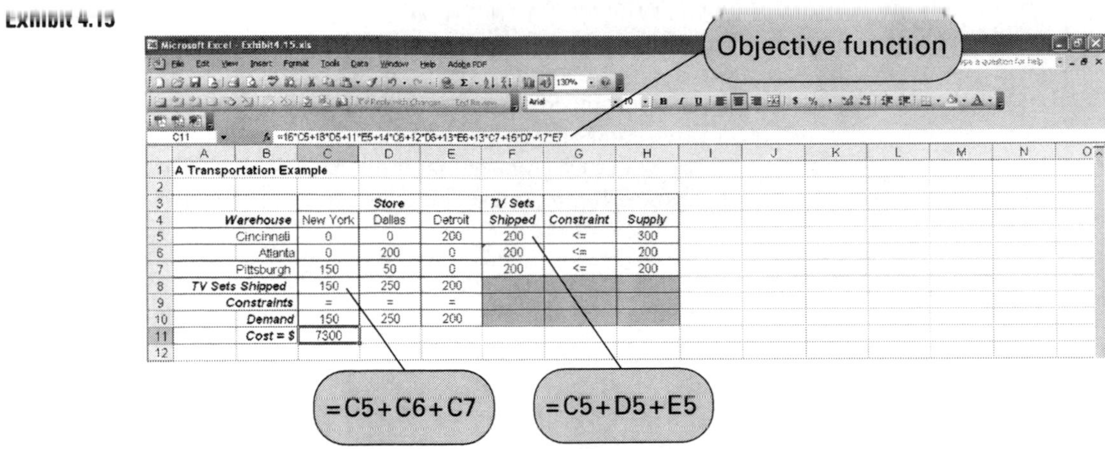

	Store			TV Sets		
Warehouse	New York	Dallas	Detroit	Shipped	Constraint	Supply
Cincinnati	0	0	200	200	<=	300
Atlanta	0	200	0	200	<=	200
Pittsburgh	150	50	0	200	<=	200
TV Sets Shipped	150	250	200			
Constraints	=	=	=			
Demand	150	250	200			
Cost = $	7300					

Exhibit 4.16

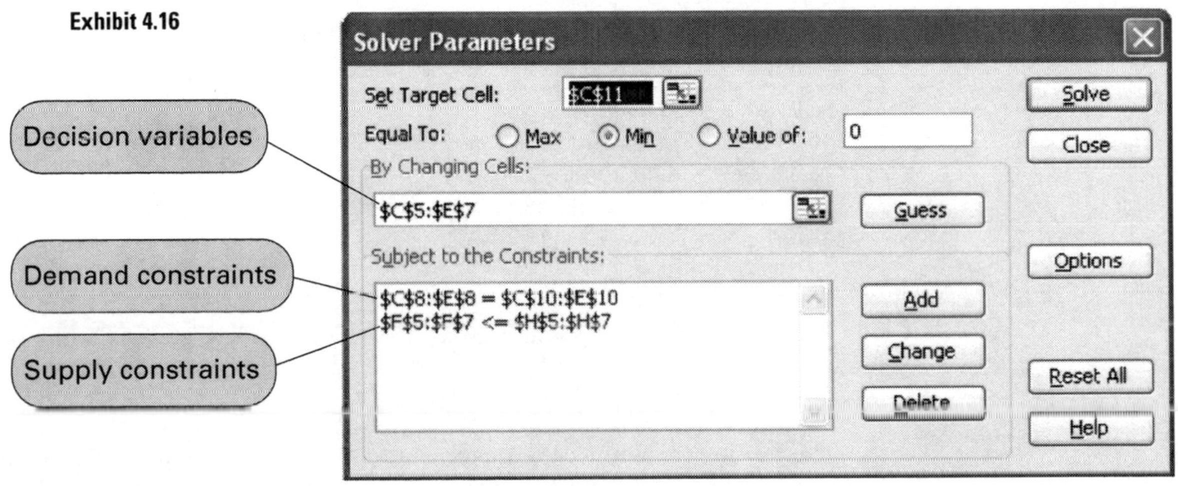

x_{3A} = 150 TVs shipped from Pittsburgh to New York
x_{3B} = 50 TVs shipped from Pittsburgh to Dallas
Z = $7,300 shipping cost

Note that the surplus for the first constraint, which is the supply at the Cincinnati warehouse, equals 100 TVs. This means that 100 TVs are left in the Cincinnati warehouse, which has inventory and storage implications for the manager.

This is an example of a type of linear programming model known as a *transportation problem*, which is the topic of Chapter 6. Notice that all the solution values are integer values. This is always the case with transportation problems because of the unique characteristic that all the coefficient parameter values are ones and zeros.

A Blend Example

A petroleum company produces three grades of motor oil—super, premium, and extra—from three components. The company wants to determine the optimal mix of the three components in each grade of motor oil that will maximize profit. The maximum quantities available of each component and their cost per barrel are as follows:

Component	Maximum Barrels Available/Day	Cost/Barrel
1	4,500	$12
2	2,700	10
3	3,500	14

To ensure the appropriate blend, each grade has certain general specifications. Each grade must have a minimum amount of component 1 plus a combination of other components, as follows:

Grade	Component Specifications	Selling Price/Barrel
Super	At least 50% of 1	$23
	Not more than 30% of 2	
Premium	At least 40% of 1	20
	Not more than 25% of 3	
Extra	At least 60% of 1	18
	At least 10% of 2	

The company wants to produce at least 3,000 barrels of each grade of motor oil.

Decision Variables

The decision variables for this problem must specify the quantity of each of the three components used in each grade of motor oil. This requires nine decision variables, as follows: x_{ij} = barrels of component i used in motor oil grade j per day, where i = 1, 2, 3 and $j = s$ (super), p (premium), e (extra). For example, the amount of component 1 in super motor oil is x_{1s}. The total amount of each grade of motor oil will be

super: $x_{1s} + x_{2s} + x_{3s}$
premium: $x_{1p} + x_{2p} + x_{3p}$
extra: $x_{1e} + x_{2e} + x_{3e}$

The Objective Function

"Profit" is maximized in the objective function by subtracting cost from revenue.

The company's objective is to maximize profit. This requires that the cost of each barrel be subtracted from the revenue obtained from each barrel. Revenue is determined by multiplying the selling price of each grade of motor oil by the total barrels of each grade produced. Cost is achieved by multiplying the cost of each component by the total barrels of each component used:

$$\text{maximize } Z = \$23(x_{1s} + x_{2s} + x_{3s}) + 20(x_{1p} + x_{2p} + x_{3p}) + 18(x_{1e} + x_{2e} + x_{3e}) \\ - 12(x_{1s} + x_{1p} + x_{1e}) - 10(x_{2s} + x_{2p} + x_{2e}) - 14(x_{3s} + x_{3p} + x_{3e})$$

Combining terms results in the following objective function.

$$\text{maximize } Z = 11x_{1s} + 13x_{2s} + 9x_{3s} + 8x_{1p} + 10x_{2p} + 6x_{3p} + 6x_{1e} + 8x_{2e} + 4x_{3e}$$

Model Constraints

This problem has several sets of constraints. The first set reflects the limited amount of each component available on a daily basis:

$$x_{1s} + x_{1p} + x_{1e} \leq 4{,}500 \text{ bbl.}$$
$$x_{2s} + x_{2p} + x_{2e} \leq 2{,}700 \text{ bbl.}$$
$$x_{3s} + x_{3p} + x_{3e} \leq 3{,}500 \text{ bbl.}$$

The next group of constraints is for the blend specifications for each grade of motor oil. The first specification is that super contain at least 50% of component 1, which is expressed as

$$\frac{x_{1s}}{x_{1s} + x_{2s} + x_{3s}} \geq 0.50$$

Standard form requires that fractional relationships between variables be eliminated.

This constraint says that the ratio of component 1 in super to the total amount of super produced, $x_{1s} + x_{2s} + x_{3s}$, must be at least 50%. Rewriting this constraint in a form more consistent with linear programming solution results in

$$x_{1s} \geq 0.50(x_{1s} + x_{2s} + x_{3s})$$

and

$$0.50x_{1s} - 0.50x_{2s} - 0.50x_{3s} \geq 0$$

This is the general form a linear programming constraint must be in before you can enter it for computer solution. All variables are on the left-hand side of the inequality, and only numeric values are on the right-hand side.

The constraint for the other blend specification for super grade, not more than 30% of component 2, is developed in the same way:

$$\frac{x_{2s}}{x_{1s} + x_{2s} + x_{3s}} \leq 0.30$$

and

$$0.70x_{2s} - 0.30x_{1s} - 0.30x_{3s} \leq 0$$

The two blend specifications for premium motor oil are

$$60x_{1p} - 0.40x_{2p} - 0.40x_{3p} \geq 0$$
$$0.75x_{3p} - 0.25x_{1p} - 0.25x_{2p} \leq 0$$

The two blend specifications for extra motor oil are

$$0.40x_{1e} - 0.60x_{2e} - 0.60x_{3e} \geq 0$$
$$0.90x_{2e} - 0.10x_{1e} - 0.10x_{3e} \geq 0$$

The final set of constraints reflects the requirement that at least 3,000 barrels of each grade be produced:

$$x_{1s} + x_{2s} + x_{3s} \geq 3{,}000 \text{ bbl.}$$
$$x_{1p} + x_{2p} + x_{3p} \geq 3{,}000 \text{ bbl.}$$
$$x_{1e} + x_{2e} + x_{3e} \geq 3{,}000 \text{ bbl.}$$

Model Summary

The complete linear programming model for this problem is summarized as follows:

$$\text{maximize } Z = 11x_{1s} + 13x_{2s} + 9x_{3s} + 8x_{1p} + 10x_{2p} + 6x_{3p} + 6x_{1e} + 8x_{2e} + 4x_{3e}$$

subject to

$$\begin{aligned}
x_{1s} + x_{1p} + x_{1e} &\leq 4{,}500 \\
x_{2s} + x_{2p} + x_{2e} &\leq 2{,}700 \\
x_{3s} + x_{3p} + x_{3e} &\leq 3{,}500 \\
0.50x_{1s} - 0.50x_{2s} - 0.50x_{3s} &\geq 0 \\
0.70x_{2s} - 0.30x_{1s} - 0.30x_{3s} &\leq 0 \\
0.60x_{1p} - 0.40x_{2p} - 0.40x_{3p} &\geq 0 \\
0.75x_{3p} - 0.25x_{1p} - 0.25x_{2p} &\leq 0 \\
0.40x_{1e} - 0.60x_{2e} - 0.60x_{3e} &\geq 0 \\
0.90x_{2e} - 0.10x_{1e} - 0.10x_{3e} &\geq 0 \\
x_{1s} + x_{2s} + x_{3s} &\geq 3{,}000 \\
x_{1p} + x_{2p} + x_{3p} &\geq 3{,}000 \\
x_{1e} + x_{2e} + x_{3e} &\geq 3{,}000 \\
x_{ij} &\geq 0
\end{aligned}$$

Computer Solution with Excel

The Excel spreadsheet solution for this blend example is shown in Exhibit 4.17. Solver is shown in Exhibit 4.18. The decision variables are located in cells **B7:B15** in Exhibit 4.17. The total profit is computed in cell C16, using the formula **=SUMPRODUCT(B7:B15,C7:C15)**, which is also shown on the formula bar at the top of the spreadsheet. The constraint formulas are embedded in cells H6 through H17. Notice that we did not develop an array of constraint coefficients on the spreadsheet for this model; instead, we typed the constraint formulas directly into cells H6:H17, which seemed easier. For example, the constraint formula in cell H6 is **=B7+B10+B13**, and the constraint formula in cell H9 is **=.5*B7–.5*B8–.5*B9**. The remaining cells in column H have similar constraint formulas.

Exhibit 4.17

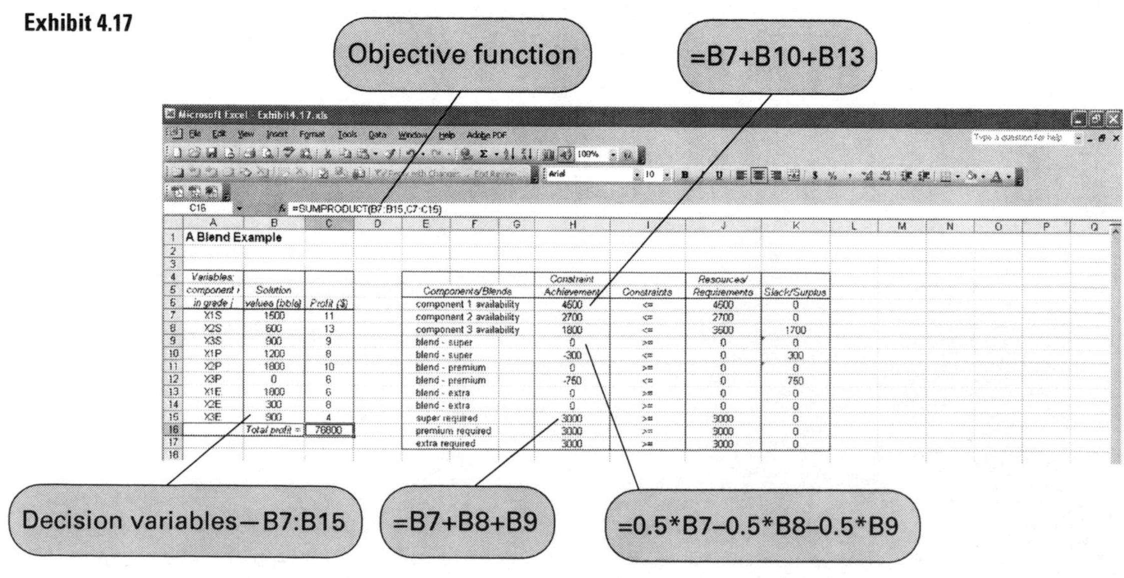

Exhibit 4.10

```
Solver Parameters
Set Target Cell: $C$16
Equal To: (•) Max ( ) Min ( ) Value of: 0
By Changing Cells:
$B$7:$B$15
Subject to the Constraints:
$H$10 <= $J$10
$H$11 >= $J$11
$H$12 <= $J$12
$H$13:$H$17 >= $J$13:$J$17
$H$6:$H$8 <= $J$6:$J$8
$H$9 = $J$9
Solve  Close  Guess  Options  Add  Change  Delete  Reset All  Help
```

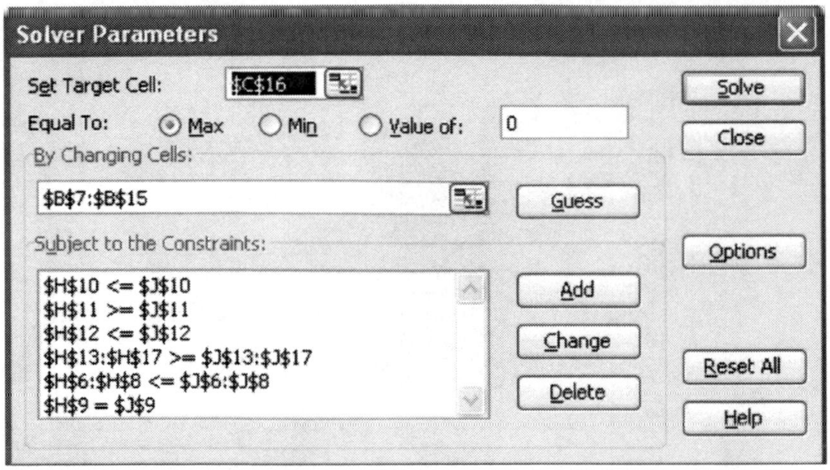

Solution Analysis

The solution is

$$\begin{aligned} x_{1s} &= 1{,}500 \text{ bbl.} \\ x_{2s} &= 600 \text{ bbl.} \\ x_{3s} &= 900 \text{ bbl.} \\ x_{1p} &= 1{,}200 \text{ bbl.} \\ x_{2p} &= 1{,}800 \text{ bbl.} \\ x_{1e} &= 1{,}800 \text{ bbl.} \\ x_{2e} &= 300 \text{ bbl.} \\ x_{3e} &= 900 \text{ bbl.} \\ Z &= \$76{,}800 \end{aligned}$$

Summarizing these results, 3,000 barrels of super grade, premium, and extra are produced. Also, 4,500 barrels of component 1, and 2,700 barrels of component 2, and 1,800 barrels of component 3 are used. (This problem also contains multiple optimal solutions.)

Recall that the ***shadow price*** *is the marginal economic value of one additional unit of a resource.*

Exhibit 4.19 shows the sensitivity report for our Excel solution of the blend problem. Notice that the **shadow price** for component 1 is $20. This indicates that component 1 is by far the most critical resource for increasing profit. For every additional barrel of component 1 that can be acquired, profit will increase by $20. For example, if the current available amount of component 1 were increased from 4,500 barrels to 4,501 barrels, profit would increase from $76,800 to $76,820. (This dual price is valid up to 6,200 barrels of component 1, the upper limit for the sensitivity range for this constraint quantity value.)

In the refinery industry, different grade stocks of oil and gasoline are available based on the makeup and quality of the crude oil that is received. Thus, as crude oil properties change, it is necessary to change blend requirements. Component availability changes as well. The general structure of this model can be used on a daily basis to plan production based on component availability and blend specification changes.

A Multiperiod Scheduling Example

PM Computer Services assembles its own brand of personal computers from component parts it purchases overseas and domestically. PM sells most of its computers locally to different departments at State University as well as to individuals and businesses in the immediate geographic region.

Exhibit 4.19

Adjustable Cells

Cell	Name	Final Value	Reduced Cost	Objective Coefficient	Allowable Increase	Allowable Decrease
$B$7	X1S values (bbls)	1500	0	11	1E+30	3
$B$8	X2S values (bbls)	600	0	13	0	0
$B$9	X3S values (bbls)	900	0	9	0	0
$B$10	X1P values (bbls)	1200	0	8	3	1E+30
$B$11	X2P values (bbls)	1800	0	10	2	0
$B$12	X3P values (bbls)	0	0	6	0	1E+30
$B$13	X1E values (bbls)	1800	0	6	3	1E+30
$B$14	X2E values (bbls)	300	0	8	0	1E+30
$B$15	X3E values (bbls)	900	0	4	22.67	0

Constraints

Cell	Name	Final Value	Shadow Price	Constraint R.H. Side	Allowable Increase	Allowable Decrease
$H$13	blend - extra Achievement	0	-18	0	1.1E-05	8.5E+02
$H$14	blend - extra Achievement	0	0	0	6.0E+02	3.0E+02
$H$15	super required Achievement	3000	0	3000	2.2E-05	1.0E+30
$H$16	premium required Achievement	3000	-1	3000	2.7E-05	8.3E+02
$H$17	extra required Achievement	3000	-7	3000	1.8E-05	3.0E+03
$H$12	blend - premium Achievement	-750	0	0	1.0E+30	7.5E+02
$H$11	blend - premium Achievement	0	-18	0	1.1E-05	6.0E+02
$H$9	blend - super Achievement	0	-18	0	1.1E-05	8.5E+02
$H$10	blend - super Achievement	-300	0	0	1.0E+30	3.0E+02
$H$6	component 1 availability Achievement	4500	20	4500	1.7E+03	1.1E-05
$H$7	component 2 availability Achievement	2700	4	2700	3.0E+02	6.0E+02
$H$8	component 3 availability Achievement	1800	0	3500	1.0E+30	1.7E+03

The shadow price for component 1 is $20.

The upper limit for the sensitivity range for component 1 is 4500 + 1700 = 6200.

PM has enough regular production capacity to produce 160 computers per week. It can produce an additional 50 computers with overtime. The cost of assembling, inspecting, and packaging a computer during regular time is $190. Overtime production of a computer costs $260. Furthermore, it costs $10 per computer per week to hold a computer in inventory for future delivery. PM wants to meet all customer orders, with no shortages, to provide quality service. PM's order schedule for the next 6 weeks is as follows:

Week	*Computer Orders*
1	105
2	170
3	230
4	180
5	150
6	250

PM Computers wants to determine a schedule that will indicate how much regular and overtime production it will need each week to meet its orders at the minimum cost. The company wants no inventory left over at the end of the 6-week period.

Management Science Application

Gasoline Blending at Texaco

The petroleum industry first began using linear programming to solve gasoline blending problems in the 1950s. A single grade of gasoline can be a blend of from 3 to 10 different components. A typical refinery might have as many as 20 different components it blends into 4 or more grades of gasoline. Each grade of gasoline differs according to octane level, volatility, and area marketing requirements.

At Texaco, for example, the typical gasoline blends are Power and unleaded regular, Plus, and Power Premium. These different grades are blended from a variety of available stocks that are intermediate refinery products, such as distilled gasoline, reformate gasoline, and catalytically cracked gasoline. Additives include, among other things, octane enhancers. As many as 15 stocks can be blended to yield up to 8 different blends. The properties or attributes of a blend are determined by a combination of properties that exist in the gasoline stocks and those of any additives. Examples of stock properties (that originally emanated from crude oil) include to some extent vapor pressure, sulfur content, aromatic content, and octane value, among other items. A linear programming model determines the volume of each blend, subject to constraints for stock availability, demand, and the property (or attribute) specifications for each blend. A single blend may have up to 14 different characteristics. In a typical blend analysis involving 7 input stocks and 4 blends, the problem will include 40 variables and 71 constraints.

Sources: C. E. Bodington and T. E. Baker, "A History of Mathematical Programming in the Petroleum Industry," *Interfaces* 20, no. 4 (July–August 1990): 117–127; and C. W. DeWitt et al., "OMEGA: An Improved Gasoline Blending System for Texaco," *Interfaces* 19, no. 1 (January–February 1989): 85–101.

Decision Variables

This model consists of three different sets of decision variables for computers produced during regular time each week, overtime production each week, and extra computers carried over as inventory each week. This results in a total of 17 decision variables. Because this problem contains a large number of decision variables, we will define them with names that will make them a little easier to keep up with:

r_j = regular production of computers per week j ($j = 1, 2, 3, 4, 5, 6$)
o_j = overtime production of computers per week j ($j = 1, 2, 3, 4, 5, 6$)
i_j = extra computers carried over as inventory in week j ($j = 1, 2, 3, 4, 5$)

This will result in 6 decision variables for regular production (r_1, r_2, etc.) and 6 decision variables for overtime production. There are only 5 decision variables for inventory because the problem stipulates that there is to be no inventory left over at the end of the 6-week period.

The Objective Function

The objective is to minimize total production cost, which is the sum of regular and overtime production costs and inventory costs:

$$\text{minimize } Z = \$190(r_1 + r_2 + r_3 + r_4 + r_5 + r_6) + 260(o_1 + o_2 + o_3 + o_4 + o_5 + o_6) + 10(i_1 + i_2 + i_3 + i_4 + i_5)$$

Model Constraints

This model includes three sets of constraints. The first two sets reflect the available capacity for regular and overtime production, while the third set establishes the production schedule per week.

The available regular production capacity of 160 computers for each of the 6 weeks results in six constraints, as follows:

$$r_j \leq 160 \text{ computers in week } j\ (j = 1, 2, 3, 4, 5, 6)$$

The available overtime production capacity of 50 computers per week also results in six constraints:

$$o_j \leq 50 \text{ computers in week } j\ (j = 1, 2, 3, 4, 5, 6)$$

The next set of six constraints shows the regular and overtime production and inventory necessary to meet the order requirement each week:

$$\begin{aligned}
&\text{week 1: } r_1 + o_1 - i_1 = 105\\
&\text{week 2: } r_2 + o_2 + i_1 - i_2 = 170\\
&\text{week 3: } r_3 + o_3 + i_2 - i_3 = 230\\
&\text{week 4: } r_4 + o_4 + i_3 - i_4 = 180\\
&\text{week 5: } r_5 + o_5 + i_4 - i_5 = 150\\
&\text{week 6: } r_6 + o_6 + i_5 = 250
\end{aligned}$$

For example, 105 computers have been ordered in week 1. Regular production, r_1, and overtime production, o_1, will meet this order, whereas any extra production that might be needed in a future week to meet an order, i_1, is subtracted because it does not go to meet the order. Subsequently, in week 2 the order of 110 computers is met by regular and overtime production, $r_2 + o_2$, plus inventory carried over from week 1, i_1.

Model Summary

The complete model for this problem is summarized as follows:

$$\begin{aligned}
\text{minimize } Z = {}&\$190(r_1 + r_2 + r_3 + r_4 + r_5 + r_6) + \$260(o_1 + o_2 + o_3 + o_4 + o_5 + o_6)\\
&+ 10(i_1 + i_2 + i_3 + i_4 + i_5)
\end{aligned}$$

subject to

$$\begin{aligned}
r_j &\leq 160\ (j = 1, 2, 3, 4, 5, 6)\\
o_j &\leq 50\ (j = 1, 2, 3, 4, 5, 6)\\
r_1 + o_1 - i_1 &= 105\\
r_2 + o_2 + i_1 - i_2 &= 170\\
r_3 + o_3 + i_2 - i_3 &= 230\\
r_4 + o_4 + i_3 - i_4 &= 180\\
r_5 + o_5 + i_4 - i_5 &= 150\\
r_6 + o_6 + i_5 &= 250\\
r_j, o_j, i_j &\geq 0
\end{aligned}$$

Computer Solution with Excel

The Excel spreadsheet for this multiperiod scheduling example is shown in Exhibit 4.20, and the accompanying Solver window is shown in Exhibit 4.21. The formula for the objective function is embedded in cell C13 and is shown on the formula bar at the top of the screen. The decision variables for regular production are included in cells **B6:B11**, whereas the variables for overtime production are in cells **D6:D11**. The computers available each week in column G includes the regular production plus overtime production plus the inventory from the previous week. For example, cell G7 (computers available in week 2) has the formula **=B7+D7+I6.** Cell I7 (the inventory left over in week 2) includes the formula **=G7–H7** (i.e., computers available minus computers ordered).

Exhibit 4.20

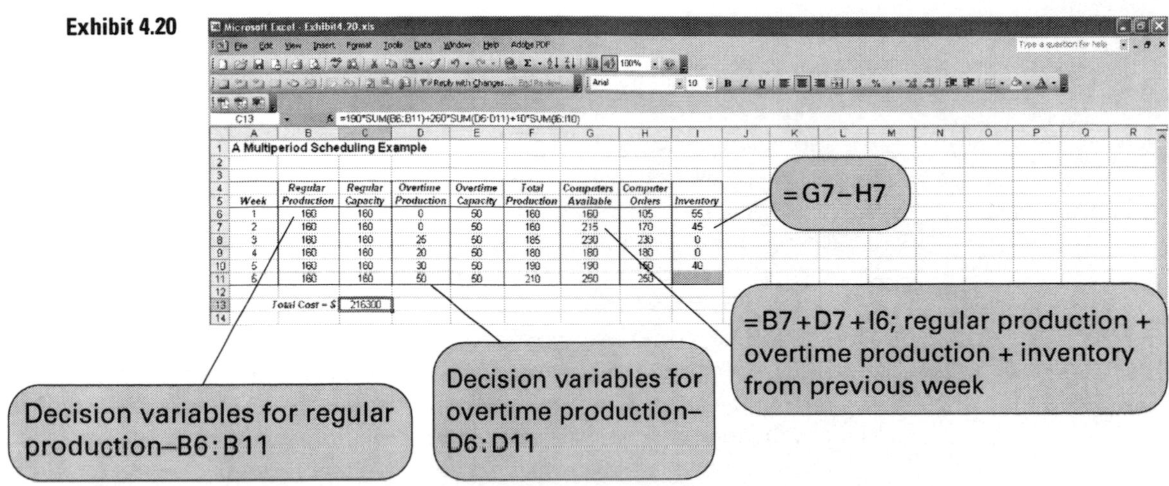

Exhibit 4.21

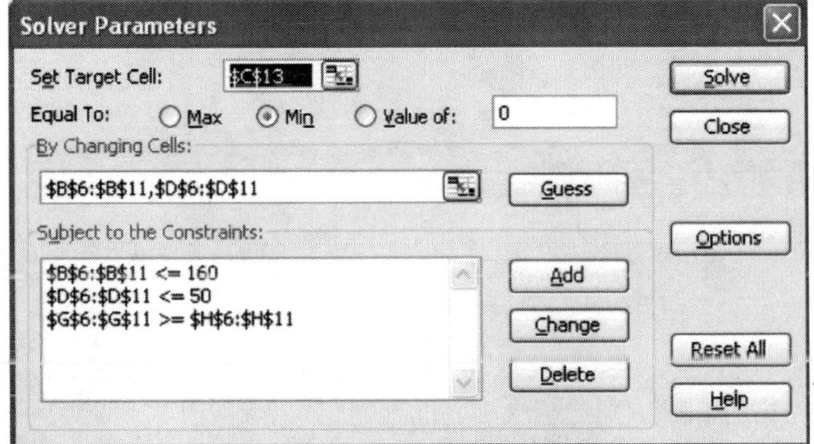

The actual constraint for week 2 would be **G7 = H7**. It is also necessary to enter the constraints for available regular and overtime production capacities into Solver. For example, the constraint for regular capacity would be **B6:B11 ≤ 160.**

Solution Analysis

The solution is

$r_1 = 160$ computers produced in regular time in week 1
$r_2 = 160$ computers produced in regular time in week 2
$r_3 = 160$ computers produced in regular time in week 3
$r_4 = 160$ computers produced in regular time in week 4
$r_5 = 160$ computers produced in regular time in week 5
$r_6 = 160$ computers produced in regular time in week 6
$o_3 = 25$ computers produced with overtime in week 3
$o_4 = 20$ computers produced with overtime in week 4

$o_5 = 30$ computers produced with overtime in week 5
$o_6 = 50$ computers produced with overtime in week 6
$i_1 = 55$ computers carried over in inventory in week 1
$i_2 = 45$ computers carried over in inventory in week 2
$i_5 = 40$ computers carried over in inventory in week 5

PM Computers must operate with regular production at full capacity during the entire 6-week period. It must also resort to overtime production in weeks 3, 4, 5, and 6 in order to meet heavier order volume in weeks 3 through 6.

As each week passes, PM Computers can use this model to update its production schedule should order sizes change. For example, if PM is in week 2, and the orders for week 5 change from 150 computers to 200, the model can be altered and a new schedule computed. The model can also be extended further out into the planning horizon to develop future production schedules.

PM may want to consider expanding its regular production capacity because of the heavy overtime requirements in weeks 3 through 6. The dual values (from the sensitivity analysis report from the computer output) for the constraints representing regular production in weeks 3 through 6 show that for each capacity increase for regular production time that will enable the production of one more computer, cost can be reduced by between \$70 and \$80. (This total reduction would occur if processing time could be reduced without acquiring additional labor, etc. If additional resources were acquired to achieve an increase in capacity, the cost would have to be subtracted from the shadow price.)

A Data Envelopment Analysis Example

Data envelopment analysis (DEA) is a linear programming application that compares a number of service units of the same type—such as banks, hospitals, restaurants, and schools—based on their inputs (resources) and outputs. The model solution result indicates whether a particular unit is less productive, or inefficient, compared to other units. For example, DEA has compared hospitals where inputs include hospital beds and staff size and outputs include patient days for different age groups.

As an example of a DEA linear programming application, consider a town with four elementary schools—Alton, Beeks, Carey, and Delancey. The state has implemented a series of standards of learning (SOL) tests in reading, math, and history that all schools are required to administer to all students in the fifth grade. The average test scores are a measurable output of the school's performance. The school board has identified three key resources, or inputs, that affect a school's SOL scores—the teacher-to-student ratio, supplementary funds per student (i.e., funding generated by the PTA and other private sources over and above the normal budget), and the average educational level of the parents (where 12 = high school graduate, 16 = college graduate, etc.). These inputs and outputs are summarized as follows:

input 1 = teacher-to-student ratio
input 2 = supplementary funds/student
input 3 = average educational level of parents

output 1 = average reading SOL score
output 2 = average math SOL score
output 3 = average history SOL score

The actual input and output values for each school are

	Inputs			Outputs		
School	1	2	3	1	2	3
Alton	.06	$260	11.3	86	75	71
Beeks	.05	320	10.5	82	72	67
Carey	.08	340	12.0	81	79	80
Delancey	.06	460	13.1	81	73	69

For example, at Alton, the teacher-to-student ratio is 0.06 (or approximately 16.67 students per teacher), there is $260 per student supplemental funds, and the average parent educational grade level is 11.3. The average scores on Alton's reading, math, and history tests are 86, 75, and 71, respectively.

The school board wants to identify the school or schools that are less efficient in converting their inputs to outputs relative to the other elementary schools in the town. The

Management Science Application

Analyzing Bank Branch Efficiency by Using DEA

Data envelopment analysis (DEA) is an application of linear programming that is used to determine the less productive (i.e., inefficient) service units among a group of similar service units. DEA bases this determination on the inputs (resources) and outputs of the service units.

A major northeastern bank, with 33 branches, used DEA to identify ways to improve its productivity. Bank management did not know how to identify the more efficient branches. The bank identified five resource inputs available to all branches—customer service (tellers), sales service, management, expenses, and office space. Five groups of branch outputs were also identified—deposits, withdrawals, and checking; bank and traveler's checks and bonds; night deposits; loans; and new accounts. The DEA model found that only 10 branches were operating efficiently, whereas 23 branches were using excess resources to provide their volume and mix of services and were, thus, inefficient. The DEA model results provided the basis for reviewing and evaluating branch operations, which revealed operating differences between inefficient branches and best-practice branches. The bank was able to improve its branch productivity and profits substantially, reducing its total branch staff by approximately 20% within 1 year of the completion of the DEA analysis and implementing changes in branch operations that resulted in annual savings of over $6 million.

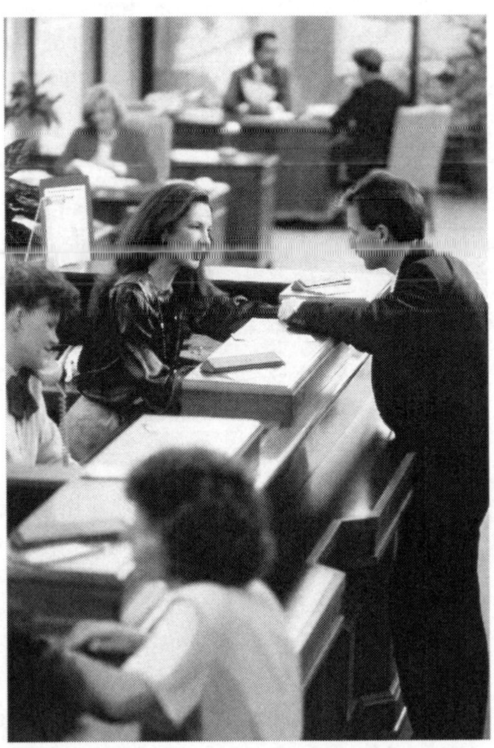

Source: H. D. Sherman and G. Ladino, "Managing Bank Productivity Using Data Envelopment Analysis (DEA)," *Interfaces* 25, no. 2 (March–April 1995): 60–73.

DEA linear programming model will compare one particular school with all the others. For a complete analysis, a separate model is necessary for each school. For this example, we will evaluate the Delancey school as compared to the other schools.

Decision Variables

The formulation of a DEA linear programming model is not as readily apparent as the previous example models in this chapter. It is particularly difficult to define the decision variables in a meaningful way.

In a DEA model, the decision variables are defined as a price per unit of each output and each input. These are not the actual prices that inputs or outputs would be valued at. In economic terms, these prices are referred to as *implicit prices*, or *opportunity costs*. These prices are a relative valuation of inputs and outputs among the schools. They do not have much meaning for us, as will become apparent as the model is developed. For now, the decision variables will simply be defined as

$$x_i = \text{a price per unit of each output where } i = 1, 2, 3$$
$$y_i = \text{a price per unit of each input where } i = 1, 2, 3$$

The Objective Function

The objective of our model is to determine whether Delancey is efficient. In a DEA model, when we are attempting to determine whether a unit (i.e., a school) is efficient, it simplifies things to scale the input prices so that the total value of a unit's inputs equals 1. The efficiency of the unit will then equal the value of the unit's outputs. For this example, this means that once we scale Delancey's input prices so that they equal 1 (which we will do by formulating a constraint), the efficiency of Delancey will equal the value of its outputs. The objective, then, is to maximize the value of Delancey's outputs, which also equals efficiency:

$$\text{maximize } Z = 81x_1 + 73x_2 + 69x_3$$

Because the school's inputs will be scaled to 1, the maximum value that Delancey's outputs, as formulated in the objective function, can take on is 1. If the objective function equals 1, the school is efficient; if the objective function is less than 1, the school is inefficient.

Model Constraints

The constraint that will scale the Delancey school's inputs to 1 is formulated as

$$.06y_1 + 460y_2 + 13.1y_3 = 1$$

This sets the value of the inputs to 1 and ultimately forces the value of the outputs to 1 or less. This also has the effect of making the values of the decision variables even less meaningful.

The values of the outputs are forced to be 1 or less by the next set of constraints. In general terms, the efficiency of a school (or any productive unit) can be defined as

$$\text{efficiency} = \frac{\text{value of outputs}}{\text{value of inputs}}$$

It is not possible for a school or any service unit to be more than 100% efficient; thus, the efficiency of the school must be less than or equal to 1 and

$$\frac{\text{value of school's outputs}}{\text{value of school's inputs}} \leq 1$$

Converting this to standard linear form,

$$\text{value of school's outputs} \leq \text{value of school's inputs}$$

Substituting the model's decision variables and parameters for inputs and outputs into this general constraint form results in four constraints, one for each school:

$$86x_1 + 75x_2 + 71x_3 \leq .06y_1 + 260y_2 + 11.3y_3$$
$$82x_1 + 72x_2 + 67x_3 \leq .05y_1 + 320y_2 + 10.5y_3$$
$$81x_1 + 79x_2 + 80x_3 \leq .08y_1 + 340y_2 + 12.0y_3$$
$$81x_1 + 73x_2 + 69x_3 \leq .06y_1 + 460y_2 + 13.1y_3$$

Model Summary

The complete linear programming model for determining the efficiency of the Delancey school is

$$\text{maximize } Z = 81x_1 + 73x_2 + 69x_3$$
$$\text{subject to}$$
$$.06y_1 + 460y_2 + 13.1y_3 = 1$$
$$86x_1 + 75x_2 + 71x_3 \leq .06y_1 + 260y_2 + 11.3y_3$$
$$82x_1 + 72x_2 + 67x_3 \leq .05y_1 + 320y_2 + 10.5y_3$$
$$81x_1 + 79x_2 + 80x_3 \leq .08y_1 + 340y_2 + 12.0y_3$$
$$81x_1 + 73x_2 + 69x_3 \leq .06y_1 + 460y_2 + 13.1y_3$$
$$x_i, y_i \geq 0$$

The objective of this model is to determine whether Delancey is inefficient: If the value of the objective function equals 1, the school is efficient; if it is less than 1, it is inefficient. As mentioned previously, the values of the decision variables, x_i and y_i, have little meaning for us. They are the implicit prices of converting an input into an output, but they have been scaled to 1 to simplify the model. The model solution selects values of x_i and y_i that will maximize the school's efficiency, the maximum of which is 1, but these values have no easily interpretable meaning beyond that.

Computer Solution with Excel

The Excel spreadsheet for this DEA example is shown in Exhibit 4.22. The Solver window is shown in Exhibit 4.23. The decision variables are located in cells B12:B14 and D12:D14. The objective function value, Z, which is also the indicator of whether Delancey is inefficient, is

Exhibit 4.22

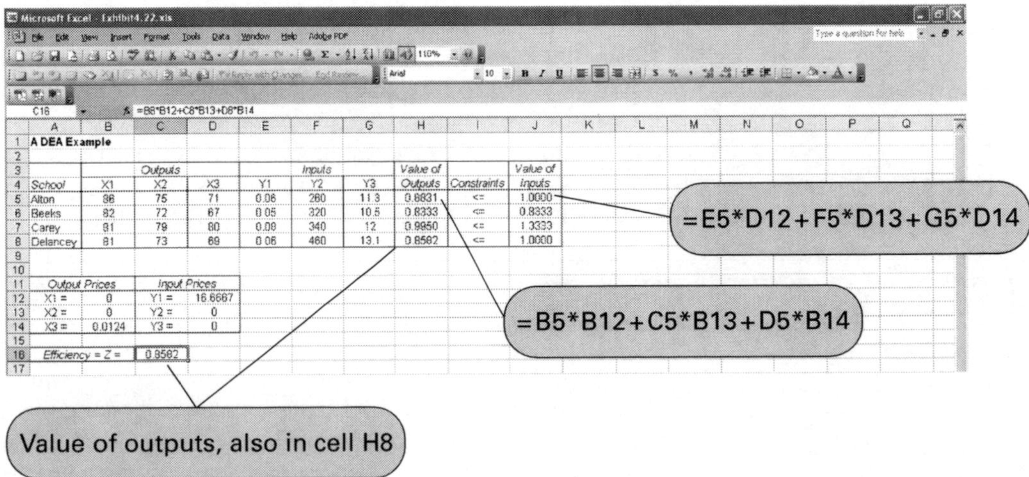

Exhibit 4.23

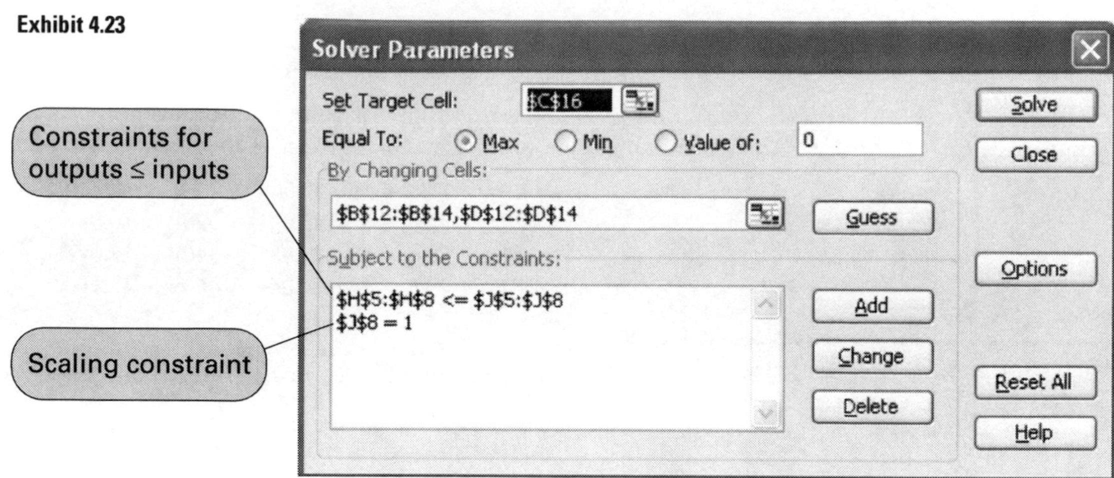

shown in cell C16. This value is computed using the formula for the value of the Delancey school's output, **=B8*B12+C8*B13+D8*D14**, which is also shown in cell H8 and is a measure of the school's efficiency.

The output and input values for each school are embedded in cells **H5:H8** and **J5:J8**, respectively. These values are used to develop the model constraints shown in Solver as **H5:H8 ≤ J5:J8**. The scaling constraint is shown as **J8=1**, where the formula for the value of the inputs for the Delancey school, **=E8*D12+F8*D13+G8*D14**, is embedded in cell J8.

Solution Analysis

The only relevant solution value is the value of the objective function:

$$Z = 0.8582$$

Because this value is less than 1, the Delancey school is inefficient relative to the other schools. It is less efficient at converting its resources into outputs than the other schools. This means that a combination of efficient schools can achieve at least the same level of output as the Delancey school achieved with fewer input resources than required by the Delancey school. In retrospect, we can see that this is a logical result by looking back at the school's inputs and outputs. While Delancey's input values are among the highest, its output test scores are among the lowest.

It is a simple process to access the efficiency of the other three schools in the town. For example, to ascertain the efficiency of the Alton school, make the value of its output in cell H5 the objective function in Solver, and make the formula for the value of the Alton school's inputs in cell I5 the scaling constraint, **I5=1**, in Solver. The efficiency of the other two schools can be assessed similarly. Doing so indicates an objective function value of 1 for each of the three other schools, indicating that all three are efficient.

Summary

Generally, it is not feasible to attempt to "see" the whole formulation of the constraints and objective function at once, following the definition of the decision variables. A more prudent approach is to construct the objective function first (without direct concern for the constraints) and then to direct attention to each problem

A systematic approach to model formulation is first to define decision variables, construct the objective function, and finally develop each constraint separately; don't try to "see" it all at once.

restriction and its corresponding model constraint. This is a systematic approach to model formulation, in which steps are taken one at a time. In other words, it is important not to attempt to swallow the whole problem during the first reading.

Formulating a linear programming model from a written problem statement is often difficult, but formulating a model of a "real" problem that has no written statement is even more difficult. The steps for model formulation described in this section are generally followed; however, the problem must first be defined (i.e., a problem statement or some similar descriptive apparatus must be developed). Developing such a statement can be a formidable task, requiring the assistance of many individuals and units within an organization.

Developing the parameter values that are presented as givens in the written problem statements of this chapter frequently requires extensive data collection efforts. The objective function and model constraints can be very complex, requiring much time and effort to develop. Simply making sure that all the model constraints have been identified and no important problem restrictions have been omitted is difficult. Finally, the problems that one confronts in actual practice are typically much larger than those presented in this chapter. It is not uncommon for linear programming models of real problems to encompass hundreds of functional relationships and decision variables. Unfortunately, it is not possible in a textbook to re-create a realistic problem environment with no written problem statement and a model of large dimensions. What is possible is to provide the fundamentals of linear programming model formulation and solution—prerequisite to solving linear programming problems in actual practice.

References

See the references at the end of Chapter 2.

Example Problem Solution

As a prelude to the problems, this section presents an example solution of the formulation and computer solution of a linear programming problem.

Problem Statement

Bark's Pet Food Company produces canned cat food called Meow Chow and canned dog food called Bow Chow. The company produces the pet food from horse meat, ground fish, and a cereal additive. Each week the company has 600 pounds of horse meat, 800 pounds of ground fish, and 1,000 pounds of cereal additive available to produce both kinds of pet food. Meow Chow must be at least half fish, and Bow Chow must be at least half horse meat. The company has 2,250 16-ounce cans available each week. A can of Meow Chow earns $0.80 in profit, and a can of Bow Chow earns $0.96 in profit. The company wants to know how many cans of Meow Chow and Bow Chow to produce each week in order to maximize profit.

A. Formulate a linear programming model for this problem.
B. Solve the model by using the computer

Solution

A. Model Formulation

Step 1: Define the Decision Variables

This problem encompasses six decision variables, representing the amount of each ingredient i in pet food j:

x_{ij} = ounces of ingredient i in pet food j per week, where $i = h$ (horse meat), f (fish), and c (cereal), and $j = m$ (Meow Chow) and b (Bow Chow)

To determine the number of cans of each pet food produced per week, the total ounces of Meow Chow produced, $x_{hm} + x_{fm} + x_{cm}$, and the total amount of Bow Chow produced, $x_{hb} + x_{fb} + x_{cb}$, would each be divided by 16 ounces.

Step 2: Formulate the Objective Function

The objective function is to maximize the total profit earned each week, which is determined by multiplying the number of cans of each pet food produced by the profit per can. However, because the decision variables are defined in terms of ounces, they must be converted to equivalent cans by dividing by 16 ounces, as follows:

$$\text{maximize } Z = \frac{0.80}{16}(x_{hm} + x_{fm} + x_{cm}) + \frac{0.96}{16}(x_{hb} + x_{fb} + x_{cb})$$

or

$$\text{maximize } Z = \$0.05(x_{hm} + x_{fm} + x_{cm}) + 0.06(x_{hb} + x_{fb} + x_{cb})$$

Step 3: Formulate the Model Constraints

The first set of constraints represents the amount of each ingredient available each week. The problem provides these in terms of pounds of horse meat, fish, and cereal additives. Thus, because the decision variables are expressed as ounces, the ingredient amounts must be converted to ounces by multiplying each pound by 16 ounces. This results in these three constraints:

$$\begin{aligned} x_{hm} + x_{hb} &\leq 9{,}600 \text{ oz. of horse meat} \\ x_{fm} + x_{fb} &\leq 12{,}800 \text{ oz. of fish} \\ x_{cm} + x_{cb} &\leq 16{,}000 \text{ oz. of cereal additive} \end{aligned}$$

Next, there are two recipe requirements specifying that at least half of Meow Chow be fish and at least half of Bow Chow be horse meat. The requirement for Meow Chow is formulated as

$$\frac{x_{fm}}{x_{hm} + x_{fm} + x_{cm}} \geq \frac{1}{2}$$

or

$$-x_{hm} + x_{fm} - x_{cm} \geq 0$$

The constraint for Bow Chow is developed similarly:

$$\frac{x_{hb}}{x_{hb} + x_{fb} + x_{cb}} \geq \frac{1}{2}$$

or

$$x_{hb} - x_{fb} - x_{cb} \geq 0$$

Finally, the problem indicates that the company has 2,250 16-ounce cans available each week. These cans must also be converted to ounces to conform to our decision variables, which results in the following constraint:

$$x_{hm} + x_{fm} + x_{cm} + x_{hb} + x_{fb} + x_{cb} \leq 36{,}000 \text{ oz.}$$

Step 4: The Model Summary

The complete model is summarized as

$$\text{maximize } Z = \$0.05x_{hm} + 0.05x_{fm} + 0.05x_{cm} + 0.06x_{hb} + 0.06x_{fb} + 0.06x_{cb}$$

subject to

$$\begin{aligned} x_{hm} + x_{hb} &\leq 9{,}600 \\ x_{fm} + x_{fb} &\leq 12{,}800 \\ x_{cm} + x_{cb} &\leq 16{,}000 \\ -x_{hm} + x_{fm} - x_{cm} &\geq 0 \end{aligned}$$

$$x_{hb} - x_{fb} - x_{cb} \geq 0$$
$$x_{hm} + x_{fm} + x_{cm} + x_{hb} + x_{fb} + x_{cb} \leq 36{,}000$$
$$x_{ij} \geq 0$$

B. Computer Solution

Original Problem w/answers

Example Problem Solution

	Xhm	Xfm	Xcm	Xhb	Xfb	Xcb		RHS	Dual
Maximize	.05	.05	.05	.06	.06	.06			Max .05Xhm +
Horse meat (oz)	1	0	0	1	0	0	<=	9,600	.02
Fish (oz)	0	1	0	0	1	0	<=	12,800	0
Cereal additive (oz)	0	0	1	0	0	1	<=	16,000	0
Meow Chow recipe	-1	1	-1	0	0	0	>=	0	0
Bow Chow recipe	0	0	0	1	-1	-1	>=	0	-.01
Cans (oz)	1	1	1	1	1	1	<=	36,000	.05
Solution->	0	8,400	8,400	9,600	4,400	5,200	Optimal Z->	1,992	Xhm + Xfm +

The computer solution for this model was generated by using the QM for Windows computer software package.

The solution is

$$x_{hm} = 0$$
$$x_{fm} = 8{,}400$$
$$x_{cm} = 8{,}400$$
$$x_{hb} = 9{,}600$$
$$x_{fb} = 4{,}400$$
$$x_{cb} = 5{,}200$$
$$Z = \$1{,}992$$

To determine the number of cans of each pet food, we must sum the ingredient amounts for each pet food and divide by 16 ounces (the size of a can):

$$x_{hm} + x_{fm} + x_{cm} = 0 + 8{,}400 + 8{,}400 = 16{,}800 \text{ oz. of Meow Chow}$$

or

$$16{,}800 \div 16 = 1{,}050 \text{ cans of Meow Chow}$$
$$x_{hb} + x_{fb} + x_{cb} = 9{,}600 + 4{,}400 + 5{,}200 = 19{,}200 \text{ oz. of Bow Chow}$$

or

$$19{,}200 \div 16 = 1{,}200 \text{ cans of Bow Chow}$$

Note that this model has multiple optimal solutions. An alternate optimal solution is $x_{fm} = 10{,}400$, $x_{cm} = 6{,}400$, $x_{hb} = 9{,}600$, and $x_{cb} = 9{,}600$. This converts to the same number of cans of each pet food; however, the ingredient mix per can is different.

Problems

1. In the product mix example in this chapter, Quick-Screen is considering adding some extra operators who would reduce processing times for each of the four clothing items by 10%. This would also increase the cost of each item by 10% and thus reduce unit profits by this same amount (because an increase in selling price would not be possible). Can this type of sensitivity analysis be evaluated using only original solution output, or will the model need to be solved again? Should Quick-Screen undertake this alternative?

   In this problem, the profit per shirt is computed from the selling price less fixed and variable costs. The computer solution output shows the shadow price for T-shirts to be \$4.11. If Quick-Screen decided to acquire extra T-shirts, could the company expect to earn an additional \$4.11 for each extra T-shirt it acquires above 500, up to the sensitivity range limit of T-shirts?

If Quick-Screen were to produce equal numbers of each of the four shirts, how would the company reformulate the linear programming model to reflect this condition? What is the new solution to this reformulated model?

2. In the diet example in this chapter, what would be the effect on the optimal solution of increasing the minimum calorie requirement for the breakfast to 500 calories? to 600 calories?

   Increase the breakfast calorie requirement to 700 calories and reformulate the model to establish upper limits on the servings of each food item to what you think would be realistic and appetizing. Determine the solution for this reformulated model.

3. In the investment example in this chapter, how would the solution be affected if the requirement that the entire $70,000 be invested were relaxed such that it is the maximum amount available for investment?

   If the entire amount available for investment does not have to be invested and the amount available is increased by $10,000 (to $80,000), how much will the total optimal return increase? Will the entire $10,000 increase be invested in one alternative?

4. For the marketing example in this chapter, if the budget is increased by $20,000, how much will audience exposures be increased?

   If Biggs Department Store were to want the same total number of people exposed to each of the three types of advertisements, how should the linear programming model be reformulated? What would be the new solution for this reformulated model?

5. For the transportation example in this chapter, suppose that television sets not shipped were to incur storage costs of $9 at Cincinnati, $6 at Atlanta, and $7 at Pittsburgh. How would these storage costs be reflected in the linear programming model for this example problem, and what would the new solution be, if any?

   The Zephyr Television Company is considering leasing a new warehouse in Memphis. The new warehouse would have a supply of 200 television sets, with shipping costs of $18 to New York, $9 to Dallas, and $12 to Detroit. If the total transportation cost for the company (ignoring the cost of leasing the warehouse) is less than with the current warehouses, the company will lease the new warehouse. Should the warehouse be leased?

   If supply could be increased at any one warehouse, which should it be? What restrictions would there be on the amount of the increase?

6. For the blend example in this chapter, if the requirement that "at least 3,000 barrels of each grade of motor oil" were changed to *exactly* 3,000 barrels of each grade, how would this affect the optimal solution?

   If the company could acquire more of one of the three components, which should it be? What would be the effect on the total profit of acquiring more of this component?

7. On their farm, the Friendly family grows apples that they harvest each fall and make into three products—apple butter, applesauce, and apple jelly. They sell these three items at several local grocery stores, at craft fairs in the region, and at their own Friendly Farm Pumpkin Festival for 2 weeks in October. Their three primary resources are cooking time in their kitchen, their own labor time, and the apples. They have a total of 500 cooking hours available, and it requires 3.5 hours to cook a 10-gallon batch of apple butter, 5.2 hours to cook 10 gallons of applesauce, and 2.8 hours to cook 10 gallons of jelly. A 10-gallon batch of apple butter requires 1.2 hours of labor, a batch of sauce takes 0.8 hour, and a batch of jelly requires 1.5 hours. The Friendly family has 240 hours of labor available during the fall. They produce about 6,500 apples each fall. A batch of apple butter requires 40 apples, a 10-gallon batch of applesauce requires 55 apples, and a batch of jelly requires 20 apples. After the products are canned, a batch of apple butter will generate $190 in sales revenue, a batch of applesauce will generate a sales revenue of $170, and a batch of jelly will generate sales revenue

of $155. The Friendlys want to know how many batches of apple butter, applesauce, and apple jelly to produce in order to maximize their revenues.

a. Formulate a linear programming model for this problem.
b. Solve the model by using the computer.

8. a. If the Friendlys in Problem 7 were to use leftover apples to feed livestock, which they estimate is a cost savings that is worth $0.08 per apple in revenue, how would this affect the model and solution?
b. Instead of feeding the leftover apples to the livestock, the Friendlys are thinking about producing apple cider. Cider will require 1.5 hours of cooking, 0.5 hour of labor, and 60 apples per batch, and it will sell for $45 per batch. Should the Friendlys use all their apples and produce cider along with their other three products?

9. A hospital dietitian prepares breakfast menus every morning for the hospital patients. Part of the dietitian's responsibility is to make sure that minimum daily requirements for vitamins A and B are met. At the same time, the cost of the menus must be kept as low as possible. The main breakfast staples providing vitamins A and B are eggs, bacon, and cereal. The vitamin requirements and vitamin contributions for each staple follow:

	Vitamin Contributions			
Vitamin	mg/Egg	mg/Bacon Strip	mg/Cereal Cup	**Minimum Daily Requirements**
A	2	4	1	16
B	3	2	1	12

An egg costs $0.04, a bacon strip costs $0.03, and a cup of cereal costs $0.02. The dietitian wants to know how much of each staple to serve per order to meet the minimum daily vitamin requirements while minimizing total cost.

a. Formulate a linear programming model for this problem.
b. Solve the model by using the computer.

10. Lakeside Boatworks is planning to manufacture three types of molded fiberglass recreational boats—a fishing (bass) boat, a ski boat, and a small speedboat. The estimated selling price and variable cost for each type of boat are summarized in the following table:

Boat	Variable Cost	Selling Price
Bass	$12,500	$23,000
Ski	8,500	18,000
Speed	13,700	26,000

The company has incurred fixed costs of $2,800,000 to set up its manufacturing operation and begin production. Lakeside has also entered into agreements with several boat dealers in the region to provide a minimum of 70 bass boats, 50 ski boats, and 50 speedboats. Alternatively, the company is unsure of what actual demand will be, so it has decided to limit production to no more than 120 of any one boat. The company wants to determine the number of boats that it must sell to break even while minimizing its total variable cost.

a. Formulate a linear programming model for this problem.
b. Solve the model by using the computer.

11. The Pyrotec Company produces three electrical products—clocks, radios, and toasters. These products have the following resource requirements:

	Resource Requirements	
	Cost/Unit	Labor Hours/Unit
Clock	$ 7	2
Radio	10	3
Toaster	5	2

The manufacturer has a daily production budget of $2,000 and a maximum of 660 hours of labor. Maximum daily customer demand is for 200 clocks, 300 radios, and 150 toasters. Clocks sell for $15, radios for $20, and toasters for $12. The company wants to know the optimal product mix that will maximize profit.

a. Formulate a linear programming model for this problem.
b. Solve the model by using the computer.

12. Betty Malloy, owner of the Eagle Tavern in Pittsburgh, is preparing for Super Bowl Sunday, and she must determine how much beer to stock. Betty stocks three brands of beer—Yodel, Shotz, and Rainwater. The cost per gallon (to the tavern owner) of each brand is as follows:

Brand	Cost/Gallon
Yodel	$1.50
Shotz	0.90
Rainwater	0.50

The tavern has a budget of $2,000 for beer for Super Bowl Sunday. Betty sells Yodel at a rate of $3.00 per gallon, Shotz at $2.50 per gallon, and Rainwater at $1.75 per gallon. Based on past football games, Betty has determined the maximum customer demand to be 400 gallons of Yodel, 500 gallons of Shotz, and 300 gallons of Rainwater. The tavern has the capacity to stock 1,000 gallons of beer; Betty wants to stock up completely. Betty wants to determine the number of gallons of each brand of beer to order so as to maximize profit.

a. Formulate a linear programming model for this problem.
b. Solve the model by using the computer.

13. The Kalo Fertilizer Company produces two brands of lawn fertilizer—Super Two and Green Grow—at plants in Fresno, California, and Dearborn, Michigan. The plant at Fresno has resources available to produce 5,000 pounds of fertilizer daily; the plant at Dearborn has enough resources to produce 6,000 pounds daily. The cost per pound of producing each brand at each plant is as follows:

	Plant	
Product	Fresno	Dearborn
Super Two	$2	$4
Green Grow	2	3

The company has a daily budget of $45,000 for both plants combined. Based on past sales, the company knows the maximum demand (converted to a daily basis) is 6,000 pounds for Super Two and 7,000 pounds for Green Grow. The selling price is $9 per pound for Super Two and $7 per pound for Green Grow. The company wants to know the number of pounds of each brand of fertilizer to produce at each plant in order to maximize profit.

a. Formulate a linear programming model for this problem.
b. Solve the model by using the computer.

14. Grafton Metalworks Company produces metal alloys from six different ores it mines. The company has an order from a customer to produce an alloy that contains four metals according to the following specifications: at least 21% of metal A, no more than 12% of metal B, no more than 7% of metal C, and between 30% and 65% of metal D. The proportion of the four metals in each of the six ores and the level of impurities in each ore are provided in the following table:

	Metal (%)					
Ore	A	B	C	D	**Impurities (%)**	**Cost/Ton**
1	19	15	12	14	40	$27
2	43	10	25	7	15	25
3	17	0	0	53	30	32
4	20	12	0	18	50	22
5	0	24	10	31	35	20
6	12	18	16	25	29	24

When the metals are processed and refined, the impurities are removed.

The company wants to know the amount of each ore to use per ton of the alloy that will minimize the cost per ton of the alloy.

a. Formulate a linear programming model for this problem.
b. Solve the model by using the computer.

15. The Roadnet Transport Company has expanded its shipping capacity by purchasing 90 trailer trucks from a bankrupt competitor. The company subsequently located 30 of the purchased trucks at each of its shipping warehouses in Charlotte, Memphis, and Louisville. The company makes shipments from each of these warehouses to terminals in St. Louis, Atlanta, and New York. Each truck is capable of making one shipment per week. The terminal managers have each indicated their capacity for extra shipments. The manager at St. Louis can accommodate 40 additional trucks per week, the manager at Atlanta can accommodate 60 additional trucks, and the manager at New York can accommodate 50 additional trucks. The company makes the following profit per truckload shipment from each warehouse to each terminal. The profits differ as a result of differences in products shipped, shipping costs, and transport rates:

	Terminal		
Warehouse	St. Louis	Atlanta	New York
Charlotte	$1,800	$2,100	$1,600
Memphis	1,000	700	900
Louisville	1,400	800	2,200

The company wants to know how many trucks to assign to each route (i.e., warehouse to terminal) to maximize profit.

a. Formulate a linear programming model for this problem.
b. Solve the model by using the computer.

16. The Hickory Cabinet and Furniture Company produces sofas, tables, and chairs at its plant in Greensboro, North Carolina. The plant uses three main resources to make furniture—wood, upholstery, and labor. The resource requirements for each piece of furniture and the total resources available weekly are as follows:

	Resource Requirements		
	Wood (lb.)	Upholstery (yd.)	Labor (hr.)
Sofa	7	12	6
Table	5	—	9
Chair	4	7	5
Total available resources	2,250	1,000	240

The furniture is produced on a weekly basis and stored in a warehouse until the end of the week, when it is shipped out. The warehouse has a total capacity of 650 pieces of furniture. Each sofa earns \$400 in profit, each table, \$275, and each chair, \$190. The company wants to know how many pieces of each type of furniture to make per week to maximize profit.

a. Formulate a linear programming model for this problem.
b. Solve the model by using the computer.

17. Lawns Unlimited is a lawn care and maintenance company. One of its services is to seed new lawns as well as bare or damaged areas in established lawns. The company uses three basic grass seed mixes it calls Home 1, Home 2, and Commercial 3. It uses three kinds of grass seed—tall fescue, mustang fescue, and bluegrass. The requirements for each grass mix are as follows:

Mix	Mix Requirements
Home 1	No more than 50% tall fescue
	At least 20% mustang fescue
Home 2	At least 30% bluegrass
	At least 30% mustang fescue
	No more than 20% tall fescue
Commercial 3	At least 50% but no more than 70% tall fescue
	At least 10% bluegrass

The company believes it needs to have at least 1,200 pounds of Home 1 mix, 900 pounds of Home 2 mix, and 2,400 pounds of Commercial 3 seed mix on hand. A pound of tall fescue costs the company \$1.70, a pound of mustang fescue costs \$2.80, and a pound of bluegrass costs \$3.25. The company wants to know how many pounds of each type of grass seed to purchase to minimize cost.

a. Formulate a linear programming model for this problem.
b. Solve this model by using the computer.

18. Alexandra Bergson has subdivided her 2,000-acre farm into three plots and has contracted with three local farm families to operate the plots. She has instructed each sharecropper to plant three crops: corn, peas, and soybeans. The size of each plot has been determined by the capabilities of each local farmer. Plot sizes, crop restrictions, and profit per acre are given in the following tables:

Plot	Acreage
1	500
2	800
3	700

	Maximum Acreage	Profit/Acre
Corn	900	$600
Peas	700	450
Soybeans	1,000	300

Any of the three crops may be planted on any of the plots; however, Alexandra has placed several restrictions on the farming operation. At least 60% of each plot must be under cultivation. Further, to ensure that each sharecropper works according to his or her potential and resources (which determined the acreage allocation), she wants the same proportion of each plot to be under cultivation. Her objective is to determine how much of each crop to plant on each plot to maximize profit.

a. Formulate a linear programming model for this problem.
b. Solve the model by using the computer.

19. As a result of a recently passed bill, a congressman's district has been allocated $4 million for programs and projects. It is up to the congressman to decide how to distribute the money. The congressman has decided to allocate the money to four ongoing programs because of their importance to his district—a job training program, a parks project, a sanitation project, and a mobile library. However, the congressman wants to distribute the money in a manner that will please the most voters, or, in other words, gain him the most votes in the upcoming election. His staff's estimates of the number of votes gained per dollar spent for the various programs are as follows:

Program	Votes/Dollar
Job training	0.02
Parks	0.09
Sanitation	0.06
Mobile library	0.04

In order also to satisfy several local influential citizens who financed his election, he is obligated to observe the following guidelines:

- None of the programs can receive more than 40% of the total allocation.
- The amount allocated to parks cannot exceed the total allocated to both the sanitation project and the mobile library.
- The amount allocated to job training must at least equal the amount spent on the sanitation project.

Any money not spent in the district will be returned to the government; therefore, the congressman wants to spend it all. The congressman wants to know the amount to allocate to each program to maximize his votes.

a. Formulate a linear programming model for this problem.
b. Solve the model by using the computer.

20. Anna Broderick is the dietitian for the State University football team, and she is attempting to determine a nutritious lunch menu for the team. She has set the following nutritional guidelines for each lunch serving:

- Between 1,500 and 2,000 calories
- At least 5 mg of iron
- At least 20 but no more than 60 g of fat
- At least 30 g of protein
- At least 40 g of carbohydrates
- No more than 30 mg of cholesterol

She selects the menu from seven basic food items, as follows, with the nutritional contribution per pound and the cost as given:

	Calories (per lb.)	Iron (mg/lb.)	Protein (g/lb.)	Carbohydrates (g/lb.)	Fat (g/lb.)	Cholesterol (mg/lb.)	$/lb.
Chicken	520	4.4	17	0	30	180	0.80
Fish	500	3.3	85	0	5	90	3.70
Ground beef	860	0.3	82	0	75	350	2.30
Dried beans	600	3.4	10	30	3	0	0.90
Lettuce	50	0.5	6	0	0	0	0.75
Potatoes	460	2.2	10	70	0	0	0.40
Milk (2%)	240	0.2	16	22	10	20	0.83

The dietitian wants to select a menu to meet the nutritional guidelines while minimizing the total cost per serving.

a. Formulate a linear programming model for this problem.
b. Solve the model by using the computer.
c. If a serving of each of the food items (other than milk) were limited to no more than a half pound, what effect would this have on the solution?

21. The Midland Tool Shop has four heavy presses it uses to stamp out prefabricated metal covers and housings for electronic consumer products. All four presses operate differently and are of different sizes. Currently the firm has a contract to produce three products. The contract calls for 400 units of product 1; 570 units of product 2; and 320 units of product 3. The time (in minutes) required for each product to be produced on each machine is as follows:

	Machine			
Product	1	2	3	4
1	35	41	34	39
2	40	36	32	43
3	38	37	33	40

Machine 1 is available for 150 hours, machine 2 for 240 hours, machine 3 for 200 hours, and machine 4 for 250 hours. The products also result in different profits, according to the machine they are produced on, because of time, waste, and operating cost. The profit per unit per machine for each product is summarized as follows:

	Machine			
Product	1	2	3	4
1	$7.8	$7.8	$8.2	$7.9
2	6.7	8.9	9.2	6.3
3	8.4	8.1	9.0	5.8

The company wants to know how many units of each product to produce on each machine in order to maximize profit.

a. Formulate this problem as a linear programming model.
b. Solve the model by using the computer.

22. The Cabin Creek Coal (CCC) Company operates three mines in Kentucky and West Virginia, and it supplies coal to four utility power plants along the East Coast. The cost of shipping coal from each mine to each plant, the capacity at each of the three mines, and the demand at each plant are shown in the following table:

	Plant				
Mine	1	2	3	4	Mine Capacity (tons)
1	$7	$9	$10	$12	220
2	9	7	8	12	170
3	11	14	5	7	280
Demand (tons)	110	160	90	180	

The cost of mining and processing coal is $62 per ton at mine 1, $67 per ton at mine 2, and $75 per ton at mine 3. The percentage of ash and sulfur content per ton of coal at each mine is as follows:

Mine	% Ash	% Sulfur
1	9	6
2	5	4
3	4	3

Each plant has different cleaning equipment. Plant 1 requires that the coal it receives have no more than 6% ash and 5% sulfur; plant 2 coal can have no more than 5% ash and sulfur combined; plant 3 can have no more than 5% ash and 7% sulfur; and plant 4 can have no more than 6% ash and sulfur combined. CCC wants to determine the amount of coal to produce at each mine and ship to its customers that will minimize its total cost.

a. Formulate a linear programming model for this problem.
b. Solve this model by using the computer.

23. Ampco is a manufacturing company that has a contract to supply a customer with parts from April through September. However, Ampco does not have enough storage space to store the parts during this period, so it needs to lease extra warehouse space during the 6-month period. Following are Ampco's space requirements:

Month	Required Space (ft.^{2})
April	47,000
May	35,000
June	52,000
July	27,000
August	19,000
September	15,000

The rental agent Ampco is dealing with has provided it with the following cost schedule for warehouse space. This schedule shows that the longer the space is rented, the cheaper it is. For example, if Ampco rents space for all 6 months, it costs $1.00/ft.^{2} per month, whereas if it rents the same space for only 1 month, it costs $1.70/ft.^{2} per month:

Rental Period (months)	$/ft.^{2}/Month
6	$1.00
5	1.05
4	1.10
3	1.20
2	1.40
1	1.70

Ampco can rent any amount of warehouse space on a monthly basis at any time for any number of (whole) months. Ampco wants to determine the least costly rental agreement that will exactly meet its space needs each month and avoid having any unused space.

a. Formulate a linear programming model for this problem.
b. Solve the model by using the computer.
c. Suppose that Ampco were to relax its restriction that it rent exactly the space it needs every month such that it would rent excess space if it were cheaper. How would this affect the optimal solution?

24. Brooks City has three consolidated high schools, each with a capacity of 1,200 students. The school board has partitioned the city into five busing districts—north, south, east, west, and central—each with different high school student populations. The three schools are located in the central, west, and south districts. Some students must be bused outside their districts, and the school board wants to minimize the total bus distance traveled by these students. The average distances from each district to the three schools and the total student population in each district are as follows:

	Distance (miles)			
District	Central School	West School	South School	Student Population
North	8	11	14	700
South	12	9	—	300
East	9	16	10	900
West	8	—	9	600
Central	—	8	12	500

The school board wants to determine the number of students to bus from each district to each school to minimize the total busing miles traveled.

a. Formulate a linear programming model for this problem.
b. Solve the model by using the computer.

25. a. In Problem 24 the school board has decided that because all students in the north and east districts must be bused, then at least 50% of the students who live in the south, west, and central districts must also be bused to another district. Reformulate the linear programming model to reflect this new set of constraints and solve by using the computer.
b. The school board has further decided that the enrollment at all three high schools should be equal. Formulate this additional restriction in the linear programming model and solve by using the computer.

26. The Southfork Feed Company makes a feed mix from four ingredients—oats, corn, soybeans, and a vitamin supplement. The company has 300 pounds of oats, 400 pounds of corn, 200 pounds of soybeans, and 100 pounds of vitamin supplement available for the mix. The company has the following requirements for the mix:
    - At least 30% of the mix must be soybeans.
    - At least 20% of the mix must be the vitamin supplement.
    - The ratio of corn to oats cannot exceed 2 to 1.
    - The amount of oats cannot exceed the amount of soybeans.
    - The mix must be at least 500 pounds.

    A pound of oats costs $0.50; a pound of corn, $1.20; a pound of soybeans, $0.60; and a pound of vitamin supplement, $2.00. The feed company wants to know the number of pounds of each ingredient to put in the mix in order to minimize cost.
    a. Formulate a linear programming model for this problem.
    b. Solve the model by using the computer.

27. The United Charities annual fund-raising drive is scheduled to take place next week. Donations are collected during the day and night, by telephone, and through personal contact. The average donation resulting from each type of contact is as follows:

	Phone	Personal
Day	$2	$4
Night	3	7

The charity group has enough donated gasoline and cars to make at most 300 personal contacts during one day and night combined. The volunteer minutes required to conduct each type of interview are as follows:

	Phone (min.)	Personal (min.)
Day	6	15
Night	5	12

The charity has 20 volunteer hours available each day and 40 volunteer hours available each night. The chairperson of the fund-raising drive wants to know how many different types of contacts to schedule in a 24-hour period (i.e., 1 day and 1 night) to maximize total donations.
    a. Formulate a linear programming model for this problem.
    b. Solve the model by using the computer.

28. Ronald Thump is interested in expanding his firm. After careful consideration, he has determined three areas in which he might invest additional funds: (1) product research and development, (2) manufacturing operations improvements, and (3) advertising and sales promotion. He has $500,000 available for investment in the firm. He can invest in its advertising and sales promotion program every year, and each dollar invested in this manner is expected to yield a return of the amount invested plus 20% yearly. He can invest in manufacturing operations improvements every 2 years, with an expected return of the investment plus 30% (at the end of each 2-year period). An investment in product research and development would be for a 3-year period, with an expected return of the investment plus 50% (at the end of the 3-year period). To diversify the total initial

investment, he wishes to include the requirement that at least $30,000 must be invested on the advertising and sales promotion program, at least $40,000 on manufacturing operations improvements, and at least $50,000 on product research and development initially (at the beginning of the first year). Ronald wants to know how much should be invested in each of the three alternatives, during each year of a 4-year period, to maximize the total ending cash value of the initial $500,000 investment.

a. Formulate a linear programming model for this problem.
b. Solve the model by using the computer.

29. Iggy Olweski, a professional football player, is retiring, and he is thinking about going into the insurance business. He plans to sell three types of policies—homeowner's insurance, auto insurance, and life insurance. The average amount of profit returned per year by each type of insurance policy is as follows:

Policy	Yearly Profit/Policy
Homeowner's	$35
Auto	20
Life	58

Each homeowner's policy will cost $14 to sell and maintain; each auto policy, $12; and each life insurance policy, $35. Iggy has projected a budget of $35,000 per year. In addition, the sale of a homeowner's policy will require 6 hours of effort; the sale of an auto policy, 3 hours; and the sale of a life insurance policy, 12 hours. Based on the number of working hours he and several employees could contribute, Iggy has estimated that he would have available 20,000 hours per year. Iggy wants to know how many of each type of insurance policy he would have to sell each year in order to maximize profit.

a. Formulate a linear programming model for this problem.
b. Solve the model by using the computer.

30. A publishing house publishes three weekly magazines—*Daily Life*, *Agriculture Today*, and *Surf's Up*. Publication of one issue of each of the magazines requires the following amounts of production time and paper:

	Production (hr.)	Paper (lb.)
Daily Life	0.01	0.2
Agriculture Today	0.03	0.5
Surf's Up	0.02	0.3

Each week the publisher has available 120 hours of production time and 3,000 pounds of paper. Total circulation for all three magazines must exceed 5,000 issues per week if the company is to keep its advertisers. The selling price per issue is $2.25 for *Daily Life*, $4.00 for *Agriculture Today*, and $1.50 for *Surf's Up*. Based on past sales, the publisher knows that the maximum weekly demand for *Daily Life* is 3,000 issues; for *Agriculture Today*, 2,000 issues; and for *Surf's Up*, 6,000 issues. The production manager wants to know the number of issues of each magazine to produce weekly in order to maximize total sales revenue.

a. Formulate a linear programming model for this problem.
b. Solve the model by using the computer.

31. The manager of a department store in Seattle is attempting to decide on the types and amounts of advertising the store should use. He has invited representatives from the local radio station, television station, and newspaper to make presentations in which they describe their audiences. The television station representative indicates that a TV commercial, which costs $15,000, would reach 25,000 potential customers. The breakdown of the audience is as follows:

	Male	Female
Senior	5,000	5,000
Young	5,000	10,000

The newspaper representative claims to be able to provide an audience of 10,000 potential customers at a cost of $4,000 per ad. The breakdown of the audience is as follows:

	Male	Female
Senior	4,000	3,000
Young	2,000	1,000

The radio station representative says that the audience for one of the station's commercials, which costs $6,000, is 15,000 customers. The breakdown of the audience is as follows:

	Male	Female
Senior	1,500	1,500
Young	4,500	7,500

The store has the following advertising policy:

- Use at least twice as many radio commercials as newspaper ads.
- Reach at least 100,000 customers.
- Reach at least twice as many young people as senior citizens.
- Make sure that at least 30% of the audience is female.

Available space limits the number of newspaper ads to seven. The store wants to know the optimal number of each type of advertising to purchase to minimize total cost.

a. Formulate a linear programming model for this problem.
b. Solve the model by using the computer.
c. Suppose a second radio station approaches the department store and indicates that its commercials, which cost $7,500, reach 18,000 customers with the following demographic breakdown:

	Male	Female
Senior	2,400	3,600
Young	4,000	8,000

If the store were to consider this station along with the other media alternatives, how would this affect the solution?

32. The Mill Mountain Coffee Shop blends coffee on the premises for its customers. It sells three basic blends in 1-pound bags, Special, Mountain Dark, and Mill Regular. It uses four different types of coffee to produce the blends—Brazilian, mocha, Columbian, and mild. The shop has the following blend recipe requirements:

Blend	Mix Requirements	Selling Price/Pound
Special	At least 40% Columbian, at least 30% mocha	$6.50
Dark	At least 60% Brazilian, no more than 10% mild	5.25
Regular	No more than 60% mild, at least 30% Brazilian	3.75

The cost of Brazilian coffee is $2.00 per pound, the cost of mocha is $2.75 per pound, the cost of Columbian is $2.90 per pound, and the cost of mild is $1.70 per pound. The shop has 110 pounds of Brazilian coffee, 70 pounds of mocha, 80 pounds of Columbian, and 150 pounds of mild coffee available per week. The shop wants to know the amount of each blend it should prepare each week to maximize profit.

a. Formulate a linear programming model for this problem.
b. Solve this model by using the computer.

33. Toyz is a large discount toy store in Valley Wood Mall. The store typically has slow sales in the summer months that increase dramatically and rise to a peak at Christmas. During the summer and fall, the store must build up its inventory to have enough stock for the Christmas season. To purchase and build up its stock during the months when its revenues are low, the store borrows money.

Following is the store's projected revenue and liabilities schedule for July through December (where revenues are received and bills are paid at the first of each month):

Month	Revenues	Liabilities
July	$ 20,000	$60,000
August	30,000	60,000
September	40,000	80,000
October	50,000	30,000
November	80,000	30,000
December	100,000	20,000

At the beginning of July, the store can take out a 6-month loan that carries an 11% interest rate and must be paid back at the end of December. The store cannot reduce its interest payment by paying back the loan early. The store can also borrow money monthly at a rate of 5% interest per month.

Money borrowed on a monthly basis must be paid back at the beginning of the next month. The store wants to borrow enough money to meet its cash flow needs while minimizing its cost of borrowing.

a. Formulate a linear programming model for this problem.
b. Solve this model by using the computer.
c. What would the effect be on the optimal solution if Toyz could secure a 9% interest rate for a 6-month loan from another bank?

34. The Skimmer Boat Company manufactures the Water Skimmer bass fishing boat. The company purchases the engines it installs in its boats from the Mar-gine Company, which specializes

in marine engines. Skimmer has the following production schedule for April, May, June, and July:

Month	Production
April	60
May	85
June	100
July	120

Mar-gine usually manufactures and ships engines to Skimmer during the month the engines are due. However, from April through July, Mar-gine has a large order with another boat customer, and it can manufacture only 40 engines in April, 60 in May, 90 in June, and 50 in July. Mar-gine has several alternative ways to meet Skimmer's production schedule. It can produce up to 30 engines in January, February, and March and carry them in inventory at a cost of $50 per engine per month until it ships them to Skimmer. For example, Mar-gine could build an engine in January and ship it to Skimmer in April, incurring $150 in inventory charges. Mar-gine can also manufacture up to 20 engines in the month they are due on an overtime basis, with an additional cost of $400 per engine. Mar-gine wants to determine the least costly production schedule that will meet Skimmer's schedule.

a. Formulate a linear programming model for this problem.
b. Solve this model by using the computer.
c. If Mar-gine were able to increase its production capacity in January, February, and March from 30 to 40 engines, what would the effect be on the optimal solution?

35. The Donnor meat processing firm produces wieners from four ingredients: chicken, beef, pork, and a cereal additive. The firm produces three types of wieners: regular, beef, and all-meat. The company has the following amounts of each ingredient available on a daily basis:

	Pounds/Day	Cost/Pound
Chicken	200	$.20
Beef	300	.30
Pork	150	.50
Cereal additive	400	.05

Each type of wiener has certain ingredient specifications, as follows.

	Specifications	Selling Price/Pound
Regular	Not more than 10% beef and pork combined	
	Not less than 20% chicken	$0.90
Beef	Not less than 75% beef	1.25
All-meat	No cereal additive	
	Not more than 50% beef and pork combined	1.75

The firm wants to know how many pounds of wieners of each type to produce to maximize profits.

a. Formulate a linear programming model for this problem.
b. Solve the model by using the computer.

36. Joe Henderson runs a small metal parts shop. The shop contains three machines—a drill press, a lathe, and a grinder. Joe has three operators, each certified to work on all three machines. However, each operator performs better on some machines than on others. The shop has contracted to do a big job that requires all three machines. The times required by the various operators to perform the required operations on each machine are summarized as follows:

Operator	Drill Press (min.)	Lathe (min.)	Grinder (min.)
1	22	18	35
2	41	30	28
3	25	36	18

Joe Henderson wants to assign one operator to each machine so that the total operating time for all three operators is minimized.

a. Formulate a linear programming model for this problem.
b. Solve the model by using the computer.
c. Joe's brother, Fred, has asked him to hire his wife, Kelly, who is a machine operator. Kelly can perform each of the three required machine operations in 20 minutes. Should Joe hire his sister-in-law?

37. Green Valley Mills produces carpet at plants in St. Louis and Richmond. The plants ship the carpet to two outlets in Chicago and Atlanta. The cost per ton of shipping carpet from each of the two plants to the two warehouses is as follows:

	To	
From	Chicago	Atlanta
St. Louis	$40	$65
Richmond	70	30

The plant at St. Louis can supply 250 tons of carpet per week, and the plant at Richmond can supply 400 tons per week. The Chicago outlet has a demand of 300 tons per week; the outlet at Atlanta demands 350 tons per week. Company managers want to determine the number of tons of carpet to ship from each plant to each outlet in order to minimize the total shipping cost.

a. Formulate a linear programming model for this problem.
b. Solve the model by using the computer.

38. Dr. Maureen Becker, the head administrator at Jefferson County Regional Hospital, must determine a schedule for nurses to make sure there are enough of them on duty throughout the day. During the day, the demand for nurses varies. Maureen has broken the day into twelve 2-hour periods. The slowest time of the day encompasses the three periods from 12:00 A.M. to 6:00 A.M., which, beginning at midnight, require a minimum of 30, 20, and 40 nurses, respectively. The demand for nurses steadily increases during the next four daytime periods. Beginning with the 6:00 A.M.–8:00 A.M. period, a minimum of 50, 60, 80, and 80 nurses are required for these four periods, respectively. After 2:00 P.M. the demand for nurses decreases during the afternoon and evening hours. For the five 2-hour periods beginning at 2:00 P.M. and ending at midnight, 70, 70, 60, 50, and 50 nurses are required, respectively. A nurse reports for duty at the beginning of one of the 2-hour periods and works 8 consecutive hours (which is required in the nurses' contract). Dr. Becker wants to

determine a nursing schedule that will meet the hospital's minimum requirements throughout the day while using the minimum number of nurses.

a. Formulate a linear programming model for this problem.
b. Solve this model by using the computer.

39. A manufacturer of bathroom fixtures produces fiberglass bathtubs in an assembly operation that consists of three processes—molding, smoothing, and painting. The number of units that can undergo each process in an hour is as follows:

Process	Output (units/hr.)
Molding	7
Smoothing	12
Painting	10

(*Note:* The three processes are continuous and sequential; thus, no more units can be smoothed or painted than have been molded.) The labor costs per hour are \$8 for molding, \$5 for smoothing, and \$6.50 for painting. The company's labor budget is \$3,000 per week. A total of 120 hours of labor is available for all three processes per week. Each completed bathtub requires 90 pounds of fiberglass, and the company has a total of 10,000 pounds of fiberglass available each week. Each bathtub earns a profit of \$175. The manager of the company wants to know how many hours per week to run each process to maximize profit.

a. Formulate a linear programming model for this problem.
b. Solve the model by using the computer.

40. The admissions office at State University wants to develop a planning model for next year's entering freshman class. The university has 4,500 available openings for freshmen. Tuition is \$8,600 for an in-state student and \$19,200 for an out-of-state student. The university wants to maximize the money it receives from tuition, but by state mandate it can admit no more than 17% out of state students. Also, each college in the university must have at least 30% in-state students in its freshman class. In order to be ranked in several national magazines, it wants the freshman class to have an average SAT score of 1130. Following are the average SAT scores for last year's freshman class for in-state and out-of-state students in each college in the university plus the maximum size of the freshman class for each college:

	Average SAT Scores		
College	In-State	Out-of-State	Total Capacity
1. Architecture	1350	1460	470
2. Arts and Sciences	1010	1050	1,300
3. Agriculture	1020	1110	240
4. Business	1090	1180	820
5. Engineering	1360	1420	1,060
6. Human Resources	1000	1400	610

a. Formulate and solve a linear programming model to determine the number of in-state and out-of-state students that should enter each college.
b. If the solution in (a) does not achieve the maximum freshman class size, discuss how you might adjust the model to reach this class size.

41. A manufacturing firm located in Chicago ships its product by railroad to Detroit. Several different routes are available, as shown in the following diagram, referred to as a network:

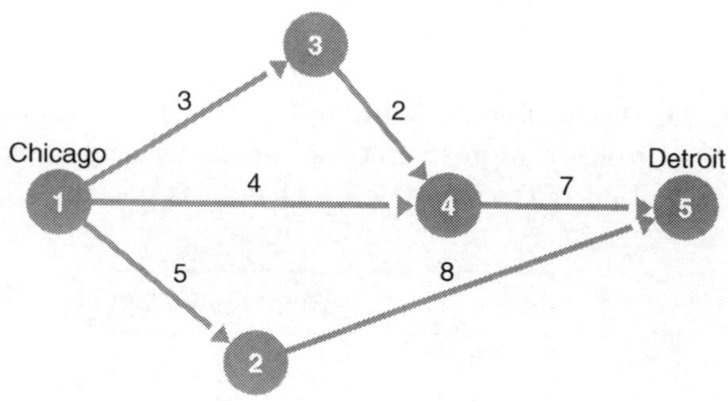

Each circle in the network represents a railroad junction. Each arrow is a railroad branch between two junctions. The number above each arrow is the cost ($1,000s) necessary to ship 1 ton of product from junction to junction. The firm wants to ship 5 tons of its product from Chicago to Detroit at the minimum cost.

a. Formulate a linear programming model for this problem.
b. Solve the model by using the computer.

42. A refinery blends four petroleum components into three grades of gasoline—regular, premium, and diesel. The maximum quantities available of each component and the cost per barrel are as follows:

Component	Maximum Barrels Available/Day	Cost/Barrel
1	5,000	$ 9
2	2,400	7
3	4,000	12
4	1,500	6

To ensure that each gasoline grade retains certain essential characteristics, the refinery has put limits on the percentages of the components in each blend. The limits as well as the selling prices for the various grades are as follows:

Grade	Component Specifications	Selling Price/Barrel
Regular	Not less than 40% of 1	$12
	Not more than 20% of 2	
	Not less than 30% of 3	
Premium	Not less than 40% of 3	18
Diesel	Not more than 50% of 2	10
	Not less than 10% of 1	

The refinery wants to produce at least 3,000 barrels of each grade of gasoline. Management wishes to determine the optimal mix of the four components that will maximize profit.

a. Formulate a linear programming model for this problem.
b. Solve the model by using the computer.

43. The Cash and Carry Building Supply Company has received the following order for boards in three lengths:

Length	Order (quantity)
7 ft.	700
9 ft.	1,200
10 ft.	300

The company has 25-foot standard-length boards in stock. Therefore, the standard-length boards must be cut into the lengths necessary to meet order requirements. Naturally, the company wishes to minimize the number of standard-length boards used. The company must therefore determine how to cut up the 25-foot boards to meet the order requirements and minimize the number of standard-length boards used.

a. Formulate a linear programming model for this problem.
b. Solve the model by using the computer.
c. When a board is cut in a specific pattern, the amount of board left over is referred to as "trim loss." Reformulate the linear programming model for this problem, assuming that the objective is to minimize trim loss rather than to minimize the total number of boards used, and solve this model. How does this affect the solution?

44. An investment firm has $1 million to invest in stocks, bonds, certificates of deposit, and real estate. The firm wishes to determine the mix of investments that will maximize the cash value at the end of 6 years.

Opportunities to invest in stocks and bonds will be available at the beginning of each of the next 6 years. Each dollar invested in stocks will return $1.20 (a profit of $0.20) 2 years later; the return can be immediately reinvested in any alternative. Each dollar invested in bonds will return $1.40 3 years later; the return can be reinvested immediately.

Opportunities to invest in certificates of deposit will be available only once, at the beginning of the second year. Each dollar invested in certificates will return $1.80 four years later. Opportunities to invest in real estate will be available at the beginning of the fifth and sixth years. Each dollar invested will return $1.10 one year later.

To minimize risk, the firm has decided to diversify its investments. The total amount invested in stocks cannot exceed 30% of total investments, and at least 25% of total investments must be in certificates of deposit.

The firm's management wishes to determine the optimal mix of investments in the various alternatives that will maximize the amount of cash at the end of the sixth year.

a. Formulate a linear programming model for this problem.
b. Solve the model by using the computer.

45. The Jones, Jones, Smith, and Rodman commodities trading firm knows the prices at which it will be able to buy and sell a certain commodity during the next 4 months. The buying price (c_i) and selling price (p_i) for each of the given months (i) are as follows:

	Month i			
	1	2	3	4
c_i	$5	$6	$7	$8
p_i	4	8	6	7

The firm's warehouse has a maximum capacity of 10,000 bushels. At the beginning of the first month, 2,000 bushels are in the warehouse. The trading firm wants to know the amounts that should be bought and sold each month in order to maximize profit. Assume that no storage costs are incurred and that sales are made at the beginning of the month, followed by purchases.

a. Formulate a linear programming model for this problem.
b. Solve the model by using the computer.

46. The production manager of Videotechnics Company is attempting to determine the upcoming 5-month production schedule for video recorders. Past production records indicate that 2,000 recorders can be produced per month. An additional 600 recorders can be produced monthly on an overtime basis. Unit cost is $10 for recorders produced during regular working hours and $15 for those produced on an overtime basis. Contracted sales per month are as follows:

Month	Contracted Sales (units)
1	1,200
2	2,100
3	2,400
4	3,000
5	4,000

Inventory carrying costs are $2 per recorder per month. The manager does not want any inventory carried over past the fifth month. The manager wants to know the monthly production that will minimize total production and inventory costs.

a. Formulate a linear programming model for this problem.
b. Solve the model by using the computer.

47. The manager of the Ewing and Barnes Department Store has four employees available to assign to three departments in the store—lamps, sporting goods, and linens. The manager wants each of these departments to have at least one employee, but not more than two. Therefore, two departments will be assigned one employee, and one department will be assigned two. Each employee has different areas of expertise, which are reflected in the daily sales each employee is expected to generate in each department, as follows:

	Department Sales		
Employee	Lamps	Sporting Goods	Linens
1	$130	$150	$ 90
2	275	300	100
3	180	225	140
4	200	120	160

The manager wishes to know which employee(s) to assign to each department in order to maximize expected sales.

a. Formulate a linear programming model for this problem.
b. Solve the model by using the computer.
c. Suppose that the department manager plans to assign only one employee to each department and to lay off the least productive employee. Formulate a new linear programming model that reflects this new condition and solve by using the computer.

48. Tidewater City Bank has four branches with the following inputs and outputs:

input 1 = teller hours (100)
input 2 = space (100s ft.^{2})
input 3 = expenses ($1,000s)

output 1 = deposits, withdrawals, and checks processed (1,000s)
output 2 = loan applications
output 3 = new accounts (100s)

The monthly output and input values for each bank are as follows:

	Outputs			Inputs		
Bank	1	2	3	1	2	3
A	76	125	12	16	22	12
B	82	105	8	12	19	10
C	69	98	9	17	26	16
D	72	117	14	14	18	14

Using data envelopment analysis (DEA), determine which banks, if any, are inefficient.

49. Carillon Health Systems owns three hospitals, and it wants to determine which, if any, of the hospitals are inefficient. The hospital inputs each month are (1) hospital beds (100s), (2) nonphysician labor (1,000 hrs.), and (3) dollar value of supplies ($1000s). The hospital outputs are patient days (100s) for three age groups—(1) under 15, (2) 15 to 65, and (3) over 65. The output and input values for each hospital are as follows:

	Outputs			Inputs		
Hospital	1	2	3	1	2	3
A	9	5	18	7	12	40
B	6	8	9	5	14	32
C	5	10	12	8	16	47

Using DEA, determine which hospitals are inefficient.

50. Managers at the Transcontinent Shipping and Supply Company want to know the maximum tonnage of goods they can transport from city A to city F. The firm can contract for railroad cars on different rail routes linking these cities via several intermediate stations, shown in the following diagram; all railroad cars are of equal capacity:

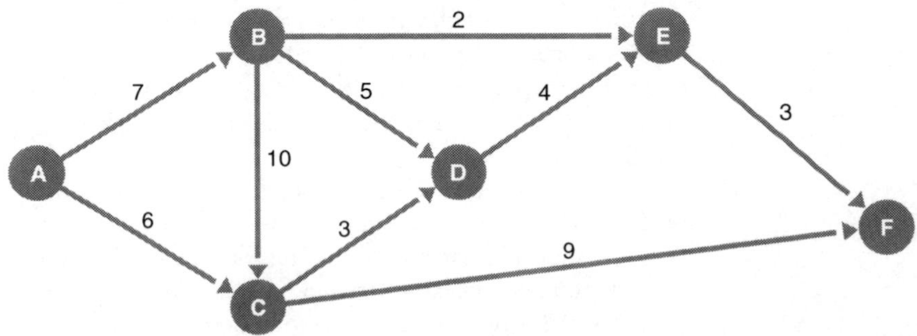

The firm can transport a maximum amount of goods from point to point, based on the maximum number of railroad cars shown on each route segment. Managers want to determine the maximum tonnage that can be shipped from city A to city F.

a. Formulate a linear programming model for this problem.
b. Solve the model by using the computer.

51. The law firm of Smith, Smith, Smith, and Jones is recruiting at law schools for new lawyers for the coming year. The firm has developed the following estimate of the number of hours of casework it will need its new lawyers to handle each month for the following year:

Month	Casework (hr.)	Month	Casework (hr.)
January	650	July	750
February	450	August	900
March	600	September	800
April	500	October	650
May	700	November	700
June	650	December	500

Each new lawyer the firm hires is expected to handle 150 hours per month of casework and to work all year. All casework must be completed by the end of the year. The firm wants to know how many new lawyers it should hire for the year.

a. Formulate a linear programming model for this problem.
b. Solve this model by using the computer.

52. In Problem 51 the optimal solution results in a fractional (i.e., non-integer) number of lawyers being hired. Explain how you would go about logically determining a new solution with a whole (integer) number of lawyers being hired and discuss the difference in results between this new solution and the optimal non-integer solution obtained in Problem 51.

53. The Goliath Tool and Machine Shop produces a single product that consists of three subcomponents that are assembled to form the product. The three components are manufactured in an operation that involves two lathes and three presses. The production time (in minutes per unit) for each machine for the three components is as follows:

	Production Time (min.)		
	Component 1	Component 2	Component 3
Lathe	10	8	6
Press	9	21	15

The shop splits the lathe workload evenly between the two lathes, and it splits the press workload evenly among the three presses. In addition, the firm wishes to produce quantities of components that will balance the daily loading among lathes and presses so that, on the average, no machine is operated more than 1 hour per day longer than any other machine. Each machine operates 8 hours per day.

The firm also wishes to produce a quantity of components that will result in completely assembled products, without any partial assemblies (i.e., in-process inventories). The objective of the firm is to maximize the number of units of assembled product per day.

a. Formulate a linear programming model for this problem.
b. Solve the model by using the computer.

c. The production policies established by the Goliath Tool and Machine Shop are relatively restrictive. If the company were to relax either its machine balancing requirement (that no machine be operated more than an hour longer than any other machine) or its restriction on in-process inventory, which would have the greatest impact on production output? What would be the impact if both requirements were relaxed?

54. A ship has two cargo holds, one fore and one aft. The fore cargo hold has a weight capacity of 70,000 pounds and a volume capacity of 30,000 cubic feet. The aft hold has a weight capacity of 90,000 pounds and a volume capacity of 40,000 cubic feet. The shipowner has contracted to carry loads of packaged beef and grain. The total weight of the available beef is 85,000 pounds; the total weight of the available grain is 100,000 pounds. The volume per mass of the beef is 0.2 cubic foot per pound, and the volume per mass of the grain is 0.4 cubic foot per pound. The profit for shipping beef is $0.35 per pound, and the profit for shipping grain is $0.12 per pound. The shipowner is free to accept all or part of the available cargo; he wants to know how much meat and grain to accept to maximize profit.
    a. Formulate a linear programming model for this problem.
    b. Solve the model by using the computer.

55. Eyewitness News is shown on channel 5 Monday through Friday evenings from 5:00 P.M. to 6:00 P.M. During the hour-long broadcast, 18 minutes are allocated to commercials. The remaining 42 minutes of airtime are allocated to single or multiple time segments for local news and features, national news, sports, and weather. The station has learned through several viewer surveys that viewers do not consistently watch the entire news program; they focus on some segments more closely than others. For example, they tend to pay more attention to the local weather than the national news (because they know they will watch the network news following the local broadcast). As such, the advertising revenues generated for commercials shown during the different broadcast segments are $850 per minute for local news and feature segments, $600 per minute for national news, $750 per minute for sports, and $1,000 per minute for the weather. The production cost for local news is $400 per minute, the cost for national news is $100 per minute, the cost for sports is $175 per minute, and for weather it's $90 per minute. The station budgets $9,000 per show for production costs. The station's policy is that the broadcast time devoted to local news and features must be at least 10 minutes but not more than 25 minutes, whereas national news, sports, and weather must each have segments of at least 5 minutes but not more than 10 minutes. Commercial time must be limited to no more than 6 minutes for each of the four broadcast segment types. The station manager wants to know how many minutes of commercial time and broadcast time to allocate to local news, national news, sports, and weather to maximize advertising revenues.
    a. Formulate a linear programming model for this problem.
    b. Solve by using the computer.

56. The Douglas family raises cattle on their farm in Virginia. They also have a large garden in which they grow ingredients for making two types of relish—chow-chow and tomato. These they sell in 16-ounce jars at local stores and craft fairs in the fall. The profit for a jar of chow-chow is $2.25, and the profit for a jar of tomato relish is $1.95. The main ingredients in each relish are cabbage, tomatoes, and onions. A jar of chow-chow must contain at least 60% cabbage, 5% onions, and 10% tomatoes, and a jar of tomato relish must contain at least 50% tomatoes, 5% onions, and 10% cabbage. Both relishes contain no more than 10% onions. The family has enough time to make no more than 700 jars of relish. In checking sales records for the past 5 years, they know that they will sell at least 30% more chow-chow than tomato relish. They will have 300 pounds of cabbage, 350 pounds of tomatoes, and 30 pounds of onions available. The Douglas family wants to know how many jars of relish to produce to maximize profit.
    a. Formulate a linear programming model for this problem.
    b. Solve by using the computer.

57. The White Horse Apple Products Company purchases apples from local growers and makes applesauce and apple juice. It costs $0.60 to produce a jar of applesauce and $0.85 to produce a bottle of apple juice. The company has a policy that at least 30% but not more than 60% of its output must be applesauce.

The company wants to meet but not exceed the demand for each product. The marketing manager estimates that the demand for applesauce is a maximum of 5,000 jars, plus an additional 3 jars for each $1 spent on advertising. The maximum demand for apple juice is estimated to be 4,000 bottles, plus an additional 5 bottles for every $1 spent to promote apple juice. The company has $16,000 to spend on producing and advertising applesauce and apple juice. Applesauce sells for $1.45 per jar; apple juice sells for $1.75 per bottle. The company wants to know how many units of each to produce and how much advertising to spend on each to maximize profit.

a. Formulate a linear programming model for this problem.
b. Solve the model by using the computer.

58. Mazy's Department Store has decided to stay open on a 24-hour basis. The store manager has divided the 24-hour day into six 4-hour periods and determined the following minimum personnel requirements for each period:

Time	Personnel Needed
Midnight–4:00 A.M.	90
4:00–8:00 A.M.	215
8:00–Noon	250
Noon–4:00 P.M.	65
4:00–8:00 P.M.	300
8:00–Midnight	125

Personnel must report for work at the beginning of one of these times and work 8 consecutive hours. The store manager wants to know the minimum number of employees to assign for each 4-hour segment to minimize the total number of employees.

a. Formulate a linear programming model for this problem.
b. Solve the model by using the computer.

59. Venture Systems is a consulting firm that develops e-commerce systems and Web sites for its clients. It has six available consultants and eight client projects under contract. The consultants have different technical abilities and experience, and as a result, the company charges different hourly rates for its services. Also, the consultants' skills are more suited for some projects than others, and clients sometimes prefer some consultants over others. The suitability of a consultant for a project is rated according to a 5-point scale, in which 1 is the worst and 5 is the best. The following table shows the rating for each consultant for each project, as well as the hours available for each consultant and the contracted hours and maximum budget for each project:

		Project								
Consultant	Hourly Rate	1	2	3	4	5	6	7	8	Available Hours
A	$155	3	3	5	5	3	3	3	3	450
B	140	3	3	2	5	5	5	3	3	600
C	165	2	1	3	3	2	1	5	3	500
D	300	1	3	1	1	2	2	5	1	300
E	270	3	1	1	2	2	1	3	3	710
F	150	4	5	3	2	3	5	4	3	860
Project Hours		500	240	400	475	350	460	290	200	
Contract Budget ($1,000s)		100	80	120	90	65	85	50	55	

The company wants to know how many hours to assign each consultant to each project in order to best utilize the consultants' skills while meeting the clients' needs.

a. Formulate a linear programming model for this problem.
b. Solve the model by using the computer.
c. If the company's objective is to maximize revenue while ignoring client preferences and consultant compatibility, will this change the solution in (b)?

60. Great Northwoods Outfitters is a retail phone-catalog company that specializes in outdoor clothing and equipment. A phone station at the company will be staffed with either full-time operators or temporary operators 8 hours per day. Full-time operators, because of their experience and training, process more orders and make fewer mistakes than temporary operators. However, temporary operators are cheaper because they receive a lower wage rate and they are not paid benefits. A full-time operator can process about 360 orders per week, whereas a temporary operator can process about 270 orders per week. A full-time operator averages 1.1 defective orders per week, and a part-time operator incurs about 2.7 defective orders per week. The company wants to limit defective orders to 200 per week. The cost of staffing a station with full-time operators is $610 per week, and the cost of a station with part-time operators is $450 per week. Using historical data and forecasting techniques, the company has developed estimates of phone orders for an 8-week period, as follows:

Week	Orders	Week	Orders
1	19,500	5	33,400
2	21,000	6	29,800
3	25,600	7	27,000
4	27,200	8	31,000

The company does not want to hire or dismiss full-time employees after the first week (i.e., the company wants a constant group of full-time operators over the 8-week period). The company wants to determine how many full-time operators it needs and how many temporary operators to hire each week to meet weekly demand while minimizing labor costs.

a. Formulate a linear programming model for this problem.
b. Solve this model by using the computer.

61. In Problem 60 Great Northwoods Outfitters is going to alter its staffing policy. Instead of hiring a constant group of full-time operators for the entire 8-week planning period, it has decided to hire and add full-time operators as the 8-week period progresses, although once it hires full-time operators, it will not dismiss them. Reformulate the linear programming model to reflect this altered policy and solve to determine the cost savings (if any).

62. Blue Ridge Power and Light Company generates electrical power at four coal-fired power plants along the eastern seaboard in Virginia, North Carolina, Maryland, and Delaware. The company purchases coal from six producers in southwestern Virginia, West Virginia, and Kentucky. Blue Ridge has fixed contracts for coal delivery from the following three coal producers:

Coal Producer	Tons	Cost/Ton	Million BTUs/Ton
ANCO	190,000	$23	26.2
Boone Creek	305,000	28	27.1
Century	310,000	24	25.6

The power-producing capabilities of the coal produced by these suppliers differs according to the quality of the coal. For example, coal produced by ANCO provides 26.2 million BTUs per ton, while coal produced at Boone Creek provides 27.1 million BTUs per ton. Blue Ridge also purchases coal from three backup auxiliary suppliers, as needed (i.e., it does not have fixed contracts with these producers). In general, the coal from these backup suppliers is more costly and lower grade:

Coal Producer	Available Tons	Cost/Ton	Million BTUs/Ton
DACO	125,000	$31	21.4
Eaton	95,000	29	19.2
Franklin	190,000	34	23.6

The demand for electricity at Blue Ridge's four power plants is as follows (note that it requires approximately 10 million BTUs to generate 1 megawatt hour):

Power Plant	Electricity Demand (million BTUs)
1. Afton	4,600,000
2. Surrey	6,100,000
3. Piedmont	5,700,000
4. Chesapeake	7,300,000

For example, the Afton plant must produce at least 4,600,000 million BTUs next year, which translates to approximately 460,000 megawatt hours.

Coal is primarily transported from the producers to the power plants by rail, and the cost of processing coal at each plant is different. Following are the combined transportation and processing costs for coal from each supplier to each plant:

	Power Plant			
Coal Producer	1. Afton	2. Surrey	3. Piedmont	4. Chesapeake
ANCO	$12.20	$14.25	$11.15	$15.00
Boone Creek	10.75	13.70	11.75	14.45
Century	15.10	16.65	12.90	12.00
DACO	14.30	11.90	16.35	11.65
Eaton	12.65	9.35	10.20	9.55
Franklin	16.45	14.75	13.80	14.90

Formulate and solve a linear programming model to determine how much coal should be purchased and shipped from each supplier to each power plant in order to minimize cost.

63. Valley United Soccer Club has 16 boys' and girls' travel soccer teams. The club has access to three town fields, which its teams practice on in the fall during the season. Field 1 is large enough to accommodate two teams at one time, and field 3 can accommodate three teams, while field 2 only

has enough room for one team. The teams practice twice per week, either on Monday and Wednesday from 3 P.M. to 5 P.M. or 5 P.M. to 7 P.M., or on Tuesday and Thursday from 3 P.M. to 5 P.M. or 5 P.M. to 7 P.M. Field 3 is in the worst condition of all the fields, so teams generally prefer the other fields; teams also do not like to practice at field 3 because it can get crowded with three teams. In general, the younger teams like to practice right after school, while the older teams like to practice later in the day. In addition, some teams must practice later because their coaches are available only after work. Some teams also prefer specific fields because they're closer to their players' homes. Each team has been asked by the club field coordinator to select three practice locations and times, in priority order, and they have responded as follows:

	Priority		
Team	1	2	3
U11B	2, 3–5M	1, 3–5M	3, 3–5M
U11G	1, 3–5T	2, 3–5T	3, 3–5T
U12B	2, 3–5T	1, 3–5T	3, 3–5T
U12G	1, 3–5M	1, 3–5T	2, 3–5M
U13B	2, 3–5T	2, 3–5M	1, 3–5M
U13G	1, 3–5M	2, 3–5M	1, 3–5T
U14B	1, 5–7M	1, 5–7T	2, 5–7T
U14G	2, 3–5M	1, 3–5M	2, 3–5T
U15B	1, 5–7T	2, 5–7T	1, 5–7M
U15G	2, 5–7M	1, 5–7M	1, 5–7T
U16B	1, 5–7T	2, 5–7T	3, 5–7T
U16G	2, 5–7T	1, 5–7T	3, 5–7T
U17B	2, 5–7M	1, 5–7T	1, 5–7M
U17G	1, 5–7T	2, 5–7T	1, 5–7M
U18B	2, 5–7M	2, 5–7T	1, 5–7M
U18G	1, 5–7M	1, 5–7T	2, 5–7T

For example, the under-11 boys' age group team has selected field 2 from 3 P.M. to 5 P.M. on Monday and Wednesday as its top priority, field 1 from 3 P.M. to 5 P.M. on Monday and Wednesday as its second priority, and so on.

Formulate and solve a linear programming model to optimally assign the teams to fields and times, according to their priorities. Are any of the teams not assigned to one of their top three selections? If not, how might you modify or use the model to assign these teams to the best possible time and location? How could you make sure that the model does not assign teams to unacceptable locations and times—for example, a team whose coach can only be at practice at 5 P.M.?

64. The city of Salem has four police stations, with the following inputs and outputs:

input 1 = number of police officers
input 2 = number of patrol vehicles
input 3 = space (100s ft.^{2})

output 1 = calls responded to (100s)
output 2 = traffic citations (100s)
output 3 = convictions

The monthly output and input data for each station are

	Outputs			Inputs		
Police Station	1	2	3	1	2	3
A	12.7	3.6	35	34	18	54
B	14.2	4.9	42	29	22	62
C	13.8	5.2	56	38	16	50
D	15.1	4.2	39	35	24	57

Help the city council determine which of the police stations are relatively inefficient.

65. USAir South Airlines operates a hub at the Pittsburgh International Airport. During the summer, the airline schedules 7 flights daily from Pittsburgh to Orlando and 10 flights daily from Orlando to Pittsburgh, according to the following schedule:

Flight	Leave Pittsburgh	Arrive Orlando	Flight	Leave Orlando	Arrive Pittsburgh
1	6 A.M.	9 A.M.	A	6 A.M.	9 A.M.
2	8 A.M.	11 A.M.	B	7 A.M.	10 A.M.
3	9 A.M.	Noon	C	8 A.M.	11 A.M.
4	3 P.M.	6 P.M.	D	10 A.M.	1 P.M.
5	5 P.M.	8 P.M.	E	Noon	3 P.M.
6	7 P.M.	10 P.M.	F	2 P.M.	5 P.M.
7	8 P.M.	11 P.M.	G	3 P.M.	6 P.M.
			H	6 P.M.	9 P.M.
			I	7 P.M.	10 P.M.
			J	9 P.M.	Midnight

The flight crews live in Pittsburgh or Orlando, and each day a new crew must fly one flight from Pittsburgh to Orlando and one flight from Orlando to Pittsburgh. A crew must return to its home city at the end of each day. For example, if a crew originates in Orlando and flies a flight to Pittsburgh, it must then be scheduled for a return flight from Pittsburgh back to Orlando. A crew must have at least 1 hour between flights at the city where it arrives. Some scheduling combinations are not possible; for example, a crew on flight 1 from Pittsburgh cannot return on flights A, B, or C from Orlando. It is also possible for a flight to ferry one additional crew to a city in order to fly a return flight, if there are not enough crews in that city.

The airline wants to schedule its crews in order to minimize the total amount of crew ground time (i.e., the time the crew is on the ground between flights). Excessive ground time for a crew lengthens its workday, is bad for crew morale, and is expensive for the airline. Formulate a linear programming model to determine a flight schedule for the airline and solve by using the computer. How many crews need to be based in each city? How much ground time will each crew experience?

66. The National Cereal Company produces a Light-Snak cereal package with a selection of small pouches of four different cereals—Crunchies, Toasties, Snakmix, and Granolies. Each cereal is produced at a different production facility and then shipped to three packaging facilities, where the four different cereal pouches are combined into a single box. The boxes are then sent to one of three distribution centers, where they are combined to fill customer orders and shipped. The following diagram shows the weekly flow of the product through the production, packaging, and distribution facilities (referred to as a "supply chain"):

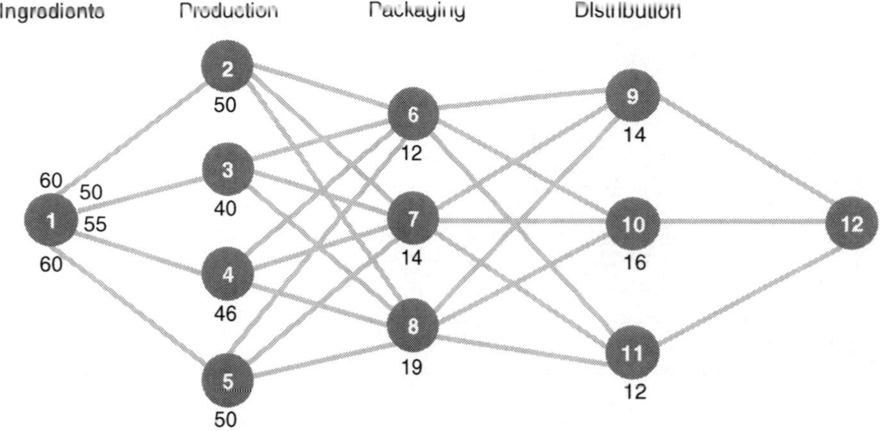

Ingredients capacities (per 1,000 pouches) per week are shown along branches 1–2, 1–3, 1–4, and 1–5. For example, ingredients for 60,000 pouches are available at the production facility, as shown on branch 1–2. The weekly production capacity at each plant (in 1,000s of pouches) is shown at nodes 2, 3, 4, and 5. The packaging facilities at nodes 6, 7, and 8 and the distribution centers at nodes 9, 10, and 11 have capacities for boxes (1,000s) as shown.

The various production, packaging, and distribution costs per unit at each facility are shown in the following table:

Facility	2	3	4	5	6	7	8	9	10	11
Unit cost	$.17	.20	.18	.16	.26	.29	.27	.12	.11	.14

Weekly demand for the Light-Snak product is 37,000 boxes.

Formulate and solve a linear programming model that indicates how much product must be produced at each facility to meet weekly demand at the minimum cost.

67. Valley Fruit Products Company has contracted with apple growers in Ohio, Pennsylvania, and New York to purchase apples that the company then ships to its plants in Indiana and Georgia, where they are processed into apple juice. Each bushel of apples produces 2 gallons of apple juice. The juice is canned and bottled at the plants and shipped by rail and truck to warehouses/distribution centers in Virginia, Kentucky, and Louisiana. The shipping costs per bushel from the farms to the plants and the shipping costs per gallon from the plants to the distribution centers are summarized in the following tables:

	Plant		
Farm	4. Indiana	5. Georgia	Supply (bushels)
1. Ohio	.41	.57	24,000
2. Pennsylvania	.37	.48	18,000
3. New York	.51	.60	32,000
Plant Capacity	48,000	35,000	

Plant	Distribution Centers		
	6. Virginia	7. Kentucky	8. Louisiana
4. Indiana	.22	.10	.20
5. Georgia	.15	.16	.18
Demand (gal.)	9,000	12,000	15,000

Formulate and solve a linear programming model to determine the optimal shipments from the farms to the plants and from the plants to the distribution centers in order to minimize total shipping costs.

Case Problem

Summer Sports Camp at State University

Mary Kelly is a scholarship soccer player at State University. During the summer, she works at a youth all-sports camp that several of the university's coaches operate. The sports camp runs for 8 weeks during July and August. Campers come for a 1-week period, during which time they live in the State dormitories and use the State athletic fields and facilities. At the end of a week, a new group of kids comes in. Mary primarily serves as one of the camp soccer instructors. However, she has also been placed in charge of arranging for sheets for the beds the campers will sleep on in the dormitories. Mary has been instructed to develop a plan for purchasing and cleaning sheets each week of camp at the lowest possible cost.

Clean sheets are needed at the beginning of each week, and the campers use the sheets all week. At the end of the week, the campers strip their beds and place the sheets in large bins. Mary must arrange either to purchase new sheets or to clean old sheets. A set of new sheets costs $10. A local laundry has indicated that it will clean a set of sheets for $4. Also, a couple of Mary's friends have asked her to let them clean some of the sheets. They have told her they will charge only $2 for each set of sheets they clean. However, while the laundry will provide cleaned sheets in a week, Mary's friends can only deliver cleaned sheets in 2 weeks. They are going to summer school and plan to launder the sheets at night at a neighborhood Laundromat.

The accompanying table lists the number of campers who have registered during each of the 8 weeks the camp will operate. Based on discussions with camp administrators from previous summers and on some old camp records and receipts, Mary estimates that each week about 20% of the cleaned sheets that are returned will have to be discarded and replaced. The campers spill food and drinks on the sheets, and sometimes the stains do not come out during cleaning. Also, the campers occasionally tear the sheets, or the sheets get torn at the cleaners. In either case, when the sheets come back from the cleaners and are put on the beds, 20% are taken off and thrown away.

At the beginning of the summer, the camp has no sheets available, so initially sheets must be purchased. Sheets are thrown away at the end of the summer.

Week	Registered Campers
1	115
2	210
3	250
4	230
5	260
6	300
7	250
8	190

Mary's major at State is management science, and she wants to develop a plan for purchasing and cleaning sheets by using linear programming. Help Mary formulate a linear programming model for this problem and solve it by using the computer.

Case Problem

Spring Garden Tools

The Spring family has owned and operated a garden tool and implements manufacturing company since 1952. The company sells garden tools to distributors and also directly to hardware stores and home improvement discount chains. The Spring Company's four most popular small garden tools are a trowel, a hoe, a rake, and a shovel. Each of these tools is made from durable steel and has a wooden handle. The Spring family prides itself on its high-quality tools.

The manufacturing process encompasses two stages. The first stage includes two operations—stamping out the metal tool heads and drilling screw holes in them. The completed tool heads then flow to the second stage, which includes an assembly operation where the handles are attached to the tool heads, a finishing step and packaging. The processing times per tool for each operation are provided in the following table:

Operation	Tool (hr./unit) Trowel	Hoe	Rake	Shovel	Total Hours Available per Month
Stamping	0.04	0.17	0.06	0.12	500
Drilling	0.05	0.14	—	0.14	400
Assembly	0.06	0.13	0.05	0.10	600
Finishing	0.05	0.21	0.02	0.10	550
Packaging	0.03	0.15	0.04	0.15	500

The steel the company uses is ordered from an iron and steel works in Japan. The company has 10,000 square feet of sheet steel available each month. The metal required for each tool and the monthly contracted production volume per tool are provided in the following table:

	Sheet Metal (ft.^{2})	Monthly Contracted Sales
Trowel	1.2	1,800
Hoe	1.6	1,400
Rake	2.1	1,600
Shovel	2.4	1,800

The primary reasons the company has survived and prospered are its ability always to meet customer demand on time and its high quality. As a result, the Spring Company will produce on an overtime basis in order to meet its sales requirements, and it also has a long-standing arrangement with a local tool and die company to manufacture its tool heads. The Spring Company feels comfortable subcontracting the first-stage operations because it is easier to detect defects prior to assembly and finishing. For the same reason, the company will not subcontract for the entire tool because defects would be particularly hard to detect after the tool is finished and packaged. However, the company does have 100 hours of overtime available each month for each operation in both stages. The regular production and overtime costs per tool for both stages are provided in the following table:

	Stage 1 Regular Cost	Stage 1 Overtime Cost	Stage 2 Regular Cost	Stage 2 Overtime Cost
Trowel	$ 6.00	$ 6.20	$3.00	$3.10
Hoe	10.00	10.70	5.00	5.40
Rake	8.00	8.50	4.00	4.30
Shovel	10.00	10.70	5.00	5.40

The cost of subcontracting in stage 1 adds 20% to the regular production cost.

The Spring Company wants to establish a production schedule for regular and overtime production in each stage and for the number of tool heads subcontracted, at the minimum cost. Formulate a linear programming model for this problem and solve the model using the computer. Which resources appear to be most critical in the production process?

CASE PROBLEM

SUSAN WONG'S PERSONAL BUDGETING MODEL[1]

After Susan Wong graduated from State University with a degree in management science, she went to work for a computer systems development firm in the Washington, D.C., area. As a student at State, Susan paid her normal monthly living expenses for apartment rent, food, and entertainment out of a bank account set up by her parents. Each month they would deposit a specific amount of cash into Susan's account. Her parents also paid her gas, telephone, and bank credit card bills, which were sent directly to them. Susan never had to worry about things like health, car, homeowners', and life insurance; utilities; driver's and car licenses; magazine subscriptions; and so on. Thus, while she was used to spending within a specific monthly budget in college, she was unprepared for the irregular monthly liabilities she encountered once she got a job and was on her own.

In some months Susan's bills would be modest and she would spend accordingly, only to be confronted the next month with a large insurance premium, or a bill for property taxes on her condominium, or a large credit card bill, or a bill for a magazine subscription, and so on the next month. Such unexpected expenditures would result in months when she could not balance her checking account; she would have to pay her bills with her bank credit card and then pay off her accumulated debt in installments while incurring high interest charges. By the end of her first year out of school, she had hoped to have some money saved to begin an investment program, but instead she found herself in debt.

Frustrated by her predicament, Susan decided to get her financial situation in order. First, she sold the condominium that her

[1]This case was adapted from T. Lewis, "Personal Operations Research: Practicing OR on Ourselves," *Interfaces* 26, no. 5 (September–October 1996): 34–41.

parents had helped her purchase and moved into a cheaper apartment. This gave her enough cash to clear her outstanding debts, with $3,800 left over to start the new year with. Susan then decided to use some of the management science she had learned in college to help develop a budget. Specifically, she decided to develop a linear programming model to help her decide how much she should put aside each month in short-term investments to meet the demands of irregular monthly liabilities and save some money.

First, Susan went through all her financial records for the year and computed her expected monthly liabilities for the coming year, as shown in the following table:

Month	Bills	Month	Bills
January	$2,750	July	$3,050
February	2,860	August	2,300
March	2,335	September	1,975
April	2,120	October	1,670
May	1,205	November	2,710
June	1,600	December	2,980

Susan's after-taxes-and-benefits salary is $29,400 per year, which she receives in 12 equal monthly paychecks that are deposited directly into her bank account.

Susan has decided that she will invest any money she doesn't use to meet her liabilities each month in either 1-month, 3-month, or 7-month short-term investment vehicles rather than just leaving the money in an interest-bearing checking account. The yield on 1-month investments is 6% per year nominal; on 3-month investments, the yield is 8% per year nominal; and on a 7-month investment, the yield is 12% per year nominal. As part of her investment strategy, any time one of the short-term investments comes due, she uses the principal as part of her budget, but she transfers any interest earned to another long-term investment (which she doesn't consider in her budgeting process). For example, if she has $100 left over in January that she invests for 3 months, in April, when the investment matures, she uses the $100 she originally invested in her budget, but any interest on the $100 is invested elsewhere. (Thus, the interest is not compounded over the course of the year.)

Susan wants to develop a linear programming model to maximize her investment return during the year so she can take that money and reinvest it at the end of the year in a longer-term investment program. However, she doesn't have to confine herself to short-term investments that will all mature by the end of the year; she can continue to put money toward the end of the year in investments that won't mature until the following year. Her budgeting process will continue to the next year, so she can take out any surplus left over after December and reinvest it in a long-term program if she wants to.

A. Help Susan develop a model for the year that will meet her irregular monthly financial obligations while achieving her investment objectives and solve the model.
B. If Susan decides she doesn't want to include all her original $3,800 in her budget at the beginning of the year, but instead she wants to invest some of it directly in alternative longer-term investments, how much does she need to develop a feasible budget?

CASE PROBLEM

WALSH'S JUICE COMPANY

Walsh's Juice Company produces three products from unprocessed grape juice—bottled juice, frozen juice concentrate, and jelly. It purchases grape juice from three vineyards near the Great Lakes. The grapes are harvested at the vineyards and immediately converted into juice at plants at the vineyard sites and stored there in refrigerated tanks. The juice is then transported to four different plants in Virginia, Michigan, Tennessee, and Indiana, where it is processed into bottled grape juice, frozen juice concentrate, and jelly. Vineyard output typically differs each month in the harvesting season, and the plants have different processing capacities.

In a particular month the vineyard in New York has 1,400 tons of unprocessed grape juice available, whereas the vineyard in Ohio has 1,700 tons and the vineyard in Pennsylvania has 1,100 tons. The processing capacity per month is 1,200 tons of unprocessed juice at the plant in Virginia, 1,100 tons of juice at the plant in Michigan, 1,400 tons at the plant in Tennessee, and 1,400 tons at the plant in Indiana. The cost per ton of transporting unprocessed juice from the vineyards to the plant is as follows:

	Plant			
Vineyard	*Virginia*	*Michigan*	*Tennessee*	*Indiana*
New York	$850	$720	$910	$750
Pennsylvania	970	790	1,050	880
Ohio	900	830	780	820

The plants are different ages, have different equipment, and have different wage rates; thus, the cost of processing each product at each plant ($/ton) differs, as follows:

Product	Plant			
	Virginia	*Michigan*	*Tennessee*	*Indiana*
Juice	$2,100	$2,350	$2,200	$1,900
Concentrate	4,100	4,300	3,950	3,900
Jelly	2,600	2,300	2,500	2,800

This month the company needs to process a total of 1,200 tons of bottled juice, 900 tons of frozen concentrate, and 700 tons of jelly at the four plants combined. However, the production process for frozen concentrate results in some juice dehydration, and the process for jelly includes a cooking stage that evaporates water content. To process 1 ton of frozen concentrate requires 2 tons of unprocessed juice; 1 ton of jelly requires 1.5 tons of unprocessed juice; and 1 ton of bottled juice requires 1 ton of unprocessed juice.

Walsh's management wants to determine how many tons of grape juice to ship from each of the vineyards to each of the plants and the number of tons of each product to process at each plant. Thus, management needs a model that includes both the logistical aspects of this problem and the production processing aspects. It wants a solution that will minimize total costs, including the cost of transporting grape juice from the vineyards to the plants and the product processing costs. Help Walsh's solve this problem by formulating a linear programming model and solve it by using the computer.

Case Problem

The King's Landing Amusement Park

King's Landing is a large amusement theme park located in Virginia. The park hires high school and college students to work during the summer months of May, June, July, August, and September. The student employees operate virtually all the highly mechanized, computerized rides; perform as entertainers; perform most of the custodial work during park hours; make up the workforce for restaurants, food services, retail shops, and stores; drive trams; and park cars. Park management has assessed the park's monthly needs based on previous summers' attendance at the park and the expected available workforce. Park attendance is relatively low in May, until public schools are out, and then it increases through June, July, and August, and decreases dramatically in September, when schools reopen after Labor Day. The park is open 7 days a week through the summer, until September, when it cuts back to weekends only. Management estimates that it will require 22,000 hours of labor in each of the first 2 weeks of May, 25,000 hours during the third week of May, and 30,000 hours during the last week in May. During the first 2 weeks of June, it will require at least 35,000 hours of labor and 40,000 hours during the last 2 weeks in June. In July 45,000 hours will be required each week, and in August 45,000 hours will be needed each week. In September the park will need only 12,000 hours in the first week, 10,000 hours in each of the second and third weeks, and 8,000 hours the last week of the month.

The park hires new employees each week from the first week in May through August. A new employee mostly trains the first week by observing and helping more experienced employees; however, he or she works approximately 10 hours under the supervision of an experienced employee. An employee is considered experienced after completing 1 week on the job. Experienced employees are considered part-time and are scheduled to work 30 hours per week in order to eliminate overtime and reduce the cost of benefits, and to give more students the opportunity to work. However, no one is ever laid off or will be scheduled for fewer (or more) than 30 hours, even if more employees are available than needed. Management believes this is a necessary condition of employment because many of the student employees move to the area during the summer just to work in the park and live near the beach nearby. If these employees were sporadically laid off and were stuck with lease payments and other expenses, it would be bad public relations and hurt employment efforts in future summers. Although no one is laid off, 15% of all experienced employees quit each week for a variety of reasons, including homesickness, illness, and other personal reasons, plus some are asked to leave because of very poor job performance.

Park management is able to start the first week in May with 700 experienced employees who worked in the park in previous summers and live in the area. These employees are generally able to work a lot of hours on the weekends and then some during the week; however, in May attendance is much heavier on the weekends, so most of the labor hours are needed then. The park expects to have a pool of 1,500 available applicants to hire for the first week in May. After the first week, the pool is diminished by the number of new employees hired the previous week, but each week through June the park gets 200 new job applicants, which decreases to 100 new applicants each week for the rest of the summer. For example, the available applicant pool in the second week in May would be the previous week's pool, which in week 1 is 1,500, minus the number of new employees hired in week 1 plus 200 new applicants. At the end of the last week in August, 75% of all the experienced employees will quit to go back to school, and the park will not hire any new employees in September. The park must operate in September, using experienced employees who live in the area, but the weekly attrition rate for these employees in September drops to 10%.

Formulate and solve a linear programming model to assist the park's management to plan and schedule the number of new employees it hires each week in order to minimize the total number of new employees it must hire during the summer.

Topic 17

Planning Large Projects: Network Analysis

Chapter

15

Planning large projects: network analysis

Objectives

- To know how to construct an activity-on-node network to represent a project
- To be able to calculate the earliest and latest start and finish times for each activity
- To be able to calculate the float for each activity, and to identify the critical path
- To be able to draw a Gantt chart and a resource histogram to smooth the use of resources required by a project
- To know how to apply the technique of cost scheduling

Quantitative methods in action: How did they build that? The Second Severn Crossing

• Overall length of crossing structure	5128 m
• Length of Shoots Bridge	948 m
• Length of main span	456 m
• Navigation clearance	37 m
• Length of Welsh approach viaduct	2077 m
• Length of English approach viaduct	2103 m
• Height of main span pylon towers	137 m
• Number of approach spans: Welsh side	24
• Number of approach spans: English side	25
• Maximum height of approach piers	48 m
• Number of foundations in caissons	37
• Total volume of concrete required	320 000 m cubic
• Weight of reinforcing steel	30 000 tons
• Total length of pre-stressing steel	150 000 m
• Number of stay cables in Shoots Bridge	240
• Total number of concrete deck units	2434
• Approximate number of people employed	1000
• Construction period	1992–1996

The construction of the Second Severn Crossing took four years, but there were probably several years before that when its construction was being designed down to the last detail. Any large project requires careful planning to avoid delays, and when problems do occur there should be contingency plans to deal with them effectively.

Because there were many thousands and thousands of activities and items used to build the bridge, for this project – as for any other a large structure – each part of the construction would have been broken down into even smaller parts, and the time to complete each part would have been estimated carefully. Not only would the *time* to complete each activity have been important, but the *sequence* of events would have been crucial. The ultimate aim would have been to create a project plan that specified which part would be completed in what order and by what time.

Another useful piece of information would have been an analysis of those activities that were 'critical' to the project – any activities that if delayed by a day would delay the whole project by a day. These critical activities would have been monitored with particular care.

Source: www.severnbridge.co.uk/content/ssc.html

Introduction

Whenever a large or complex project is undertaken, a great deal of planning is necessary. Building a bridge is a good example as in projects such as this there are many tasks or activities that have to be completed, some of which can proceed at the same time while others have to wait until preceding tasks have been completed. To illustrate the techniques involved in the planning and control of large projects, the example chosen in this chapter is the building of a garage: though clearly much simpler than building a bridge, this will still illustrate the techniques employed in network analysis.

The activity-on-node method

This technique allows the time of the project and the slack (or *float*) of individual activities to be determined. If an activity has zero float you would say that it was *critical* because any delay in that activity would delay the entire project.

Before *critical path analysis* (or *CPA*) is used it is first necessary to make a list of all the activities, their durations and which activities must immediately precede them.

Once this list has been completed, you should represent the project by the means of a diagram. The diagram used in this book uses the *activity-on-node* method. The basic diagram for this method is shown in Figure 15.1. The nodes represent the activity, and the lines the dependencies between activities.

EXAMPLE 15.1

You have just obtained planning permission to build a garage and you are now in the process of planning the project. With a little help from a friendly builder you have made a list of activities that need to be completed, the durations of these activities and the order in which they can be tackled. This list is shown in Table 15.1.

Activity 15.1

Draw the network for the garage problem using the activity-on-node method.

The basic diagram for the garage problem is shown in Figure 15.2. You will see that the name of each activity is displayed in the box together with the duration. You will also see that there are start and end nodes. This is to ensure that every activity has at least one line entering and one line leaving its node.

Table 15.1 Details of the garage building project

Activity	Description	Immediate preceding activities	Duration (days)
A	Obtain bricklayer	–	10
B	Dig the foundations	–	8
C	Lay the base	B	1
D	Build the walls	A and C	8
E	Build the roof	D	3
F	Tile the roof	E	2
G	Make window frames	–	3
H	Fit the window frames	D and G	1
I	Fit glass to frames	H	1
J	Fit the door	E	1
K	Paint the door and window frames	I and J	2
L	Point the brickwork	D	2

Figure 15.1 Activity-on-node

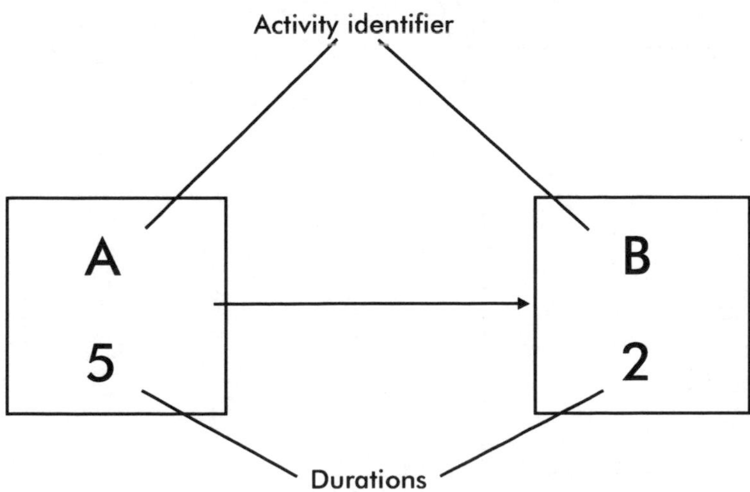

Figure 15.2 The network for the garage problem

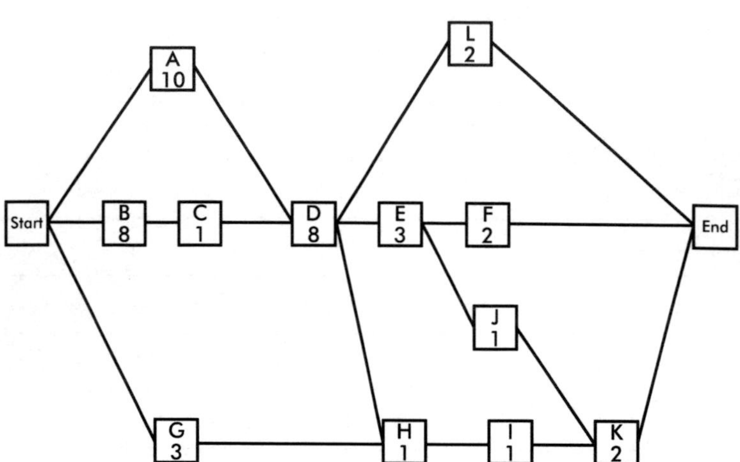

For this method you need to display 4 additional pieces of information on each node: the earliest start time of the activity (EST), the latest start time (LST), the earliest finish time (EFT), and the latest finish time (LFT). This information should be displayed as in Figure 15.3.

In order to calculate the EST and EFT a *forward pass* is made through the network. If the start is at time zero, then the EST of activities A, B and G is zero and their EFT is 10, 8 and 3 respectively. The EST of activity C must be 8, since it can start as soon as B is completed. However, what about activity D? This activity cannot start until both A and C are completed, and as A is completed later than C, then activity A determines the EST of D, which must be 10. This is

Figure 15.3 Information displayed on each node

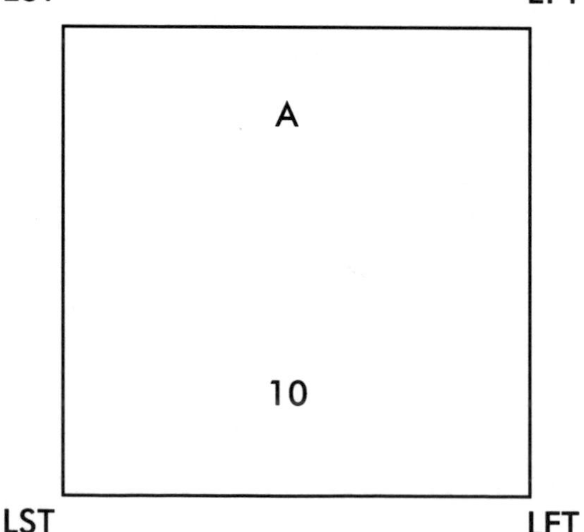

the general rule when calculating the EST – if there are two or more choices the EST is the *larger* of the EFTs of the preceding activities. From this you will see that the EST of K must be 22 and not 20.

Activity 15.2

Continue the forward pass through the network and add this information to your network. How long will it take you to complete the project?

You can now check your answers with Figure 15.4. From this diagram you will see that the project will take 24 days in total.

To enable the LFT and LST to be calculated a *backward pass* is made through the network, starting at the END node. The LFT of activities F, K and L must be 24 since the project is only complete when all these activities have been completed. The LST of F, K and L must all be 22 days since the duration of all three activities is 2 days. To calculate the LFT of all other activities involves a process similar to that for the forward pass, with one difference, which is that when there is a choice, the *smallest* value is chosen.

Activity 15.3

Continue the backward pass through the network.

Figure 15.4 A forward pass through the network

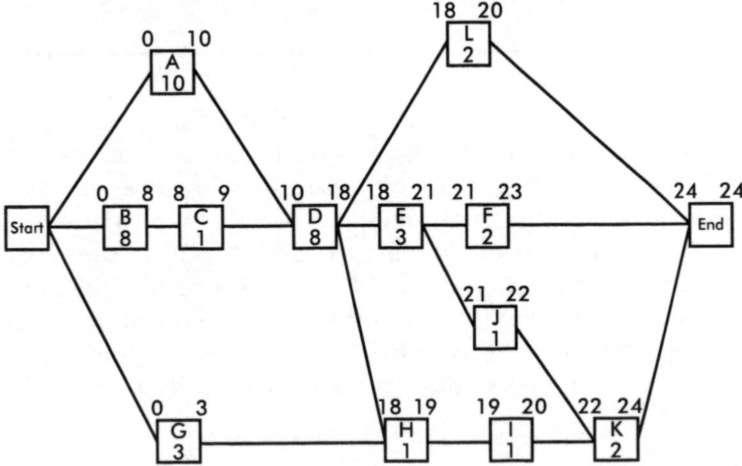

Figure 15.5 The completed network

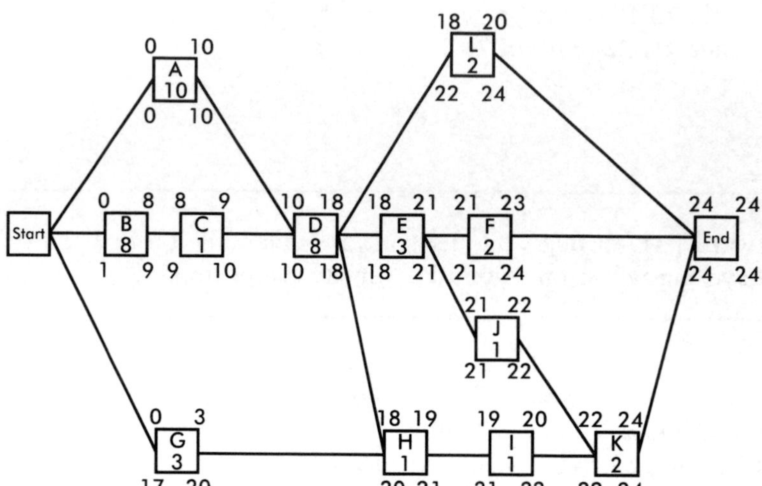

The float of an activity

The float or slack of an activity is the difference between the EST and LST (or between the EFT and LFT) for each activity. For example, activity D has a zero float since the EST and LST are the same (10), while activity F has a float of 1 day (22 – 21).

Activity 15.4

Obtain the floats for the remainder of the activities. Which activities are 'critical'; that is, have no float?

You should have obtained the information shown in Table 15.2.

From this you can see that activities A, D, E, J and K have zero floats and are therefore *critical*. Any delay in the start or finish times of these activities would delay the entire project by the same amount. The other activities could be delayed by up to their float without affecting the overall project time. For example, activity B (dig foundations) could be delayed by one day, but this activity would then become critical. You will notice that the critical activities form a path through the network – this is called the *critical path*. However, it is possible to have more than one critical path, as you will see in *Cost scheduling*, below.

Table 15.2 Calculation of the floats

Activity	EST	LST	Float
A	0	0	0
B	0	1	1
C	8	9	1
D	10	10	0
E	18	18	0
F	21	22	1
G	0	17	17
H	18	20	2
I	19	21	2
J	21	21	0
K	22	22	0
L	18	22	4

Resource scheduling

Activities of a project often involve resources of one kind or another. In the garage building example, labour is the obvious resource since each activity requires people to do the work. Perhaps you have asked a friend or neighbour to help and the two of you intend to help the bricklayer and do the less skilled jobs.

Since some activities, such as digging the foundations and making the window frames, can take place at the same time, the number of people required at a particular time may be greater than the availability. However, it may be possible to delay non-critical activities, such as making the window frames, sufficiently to avoid this problem. The critical path network cannot easily solve this problem because this network is designed to show the *order* in which activities take place rather than *when* they take place. A better chart to use is the *Gantt* chart. A Gantt chart is like a bar chart that has been turned on its side. The horizontal axis is time and each activity is represented by a bar; the start of the bar is initially the EST and the end of the bar is the EFT. The float of an activity is represented by a dotted line.

EXAMPLE 15.2

For each activity in the garage building project you decide how many people are required to do these jobs, and you get the list shown in Table 15.3.

Table 15.3 Resource requirements for the garage project

Activity	No. of people required
A	0
B	2
C	2
D	1
E	1
F	2
G	1
H	1
I	1
J	2
K	1
L	1

Activity 15.5

Draw the Gantt chart for the garage project.

This chart is shown in Figure 15.6.

You will see that the bars representing the critical activities have all been placed on one line – this is because each activity follows one another on the critical path. The non-critical activities should, however, be placed on separate lines so that their floats can be clearly shown. The number of people required has

Figure 15.6 The Gantt chart

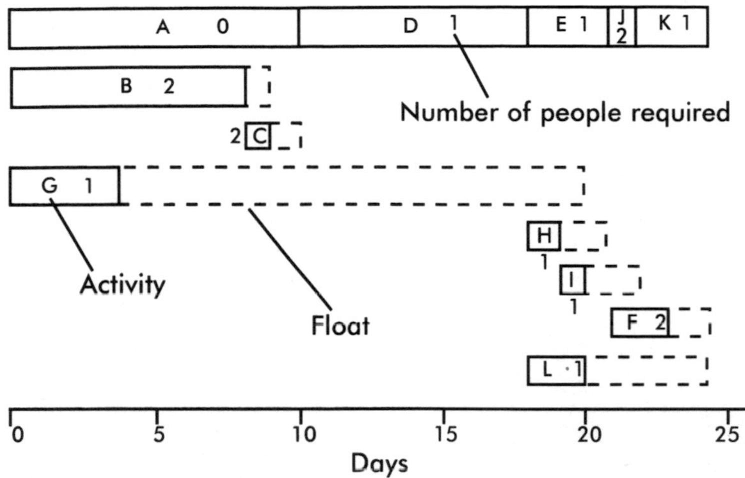

been added to each bar. From this you can see that 3 people are required during the first 3 days (0 + 2 + 1).

Activity 15.6

Repeat this procedure for the entire project. When are more than 2 people required?

The figures are shown in Table 15.4.

You can see that more than 2 people are required on several occasions. You might find this easier to see on the *resource histogram* in Figure 15.7.

From this histogram you will see clearly the peaks and troughs in the resource requirements. If a peak could be moved into a trough, the net result would be a smoother histogram. A perfectly smooth histogram would mean that the resource is being fully utilised and no further savings would be possible. In the case of the garage it would be possible to delay the start of activity G (make window frames) until day 9, since G has a float of 17 days. This would mean that from the start of the project until day 12, 2 people would be required all the time. The peaks at the end of the project are not so easy to solve. If the start of activity F (tile the roof) was delayed by its float of one day, the peak of 4 people during day 21 could be reduced by 1, so 3 people are required for much of the latter part of the project. The alternative to increasing the number of people is to extend the project. For example, if the critical activities J (fitting the door) and K (painting) were delayed until activity F had been completed, the completion of the project would be delayed by 2 days but only 2 people would be required for the entire time.

Table 15.4 Daily resource requirement

Day	Number of people required
First 3 days	3
Next 6 days	2
Next day	0
Next 8 days	1
Next 2 days	3
Next day	1
Next day	4
Next day	3
Next day	1

Figure 15.7 The resource histogram

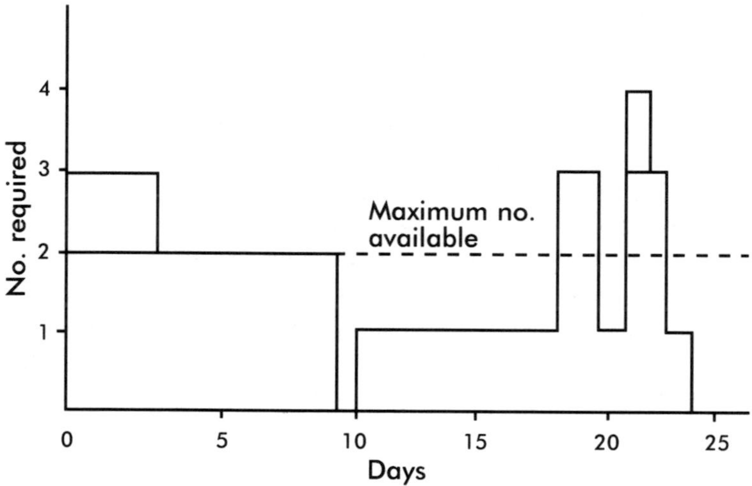

Cost scheduling

A very important resource in network analysis is money. This resource is usually so important that a separate technique has been devised to solve problems posed by financial considerations. This technique is called *crashing*.

It is usually desirable to reduce the time a project takes because there are often financial advantages in doing so. For example, the Department of Transport pays a bonus to contractors who complete a road building or repair project early (and a penalty is charged if the project time is overrun). It is often possible to speed up the completion of an activity at an extra cost. This cost may be because a machine is hired or because more people are employed. The reduced duration is called the *crashed* duration, and the increased cost is called the *crashed* cost.

EXAMPLE 15.3

It is possible to reduce the time for completing activities B, D, E, F, G, K and L of the garage building project by employing additional labour. If this is done costs will increase for these activities. Table 15.5 gives you the durations and costs for all activities.

Table 15.5 Cost details for the garage project

Activity	Normal duration (days)	Crash duration (days)	Normal cost	Crash cost
A	10	10	£5	£5
B	8	2	£100	£700
C	1	1	£200	£200
D	8	5	£800	£1700
E	3	2	£500	£900
F	2	1	£200	£400
G	3	1	£150	£550
H	1	1	£50	£50
I	1	1	£20	£20
J	1	1	£20	£20
K	2	1	£30	£130
L	2	1	£100	£200

Activity 15.7

What is the normal total cost of the project?

The total cost is simply the sum of *all* the activities, since all must be completed. This is £2175. If some of the activities are crashed this cost will increase. The question is which activities should be crashed in order to reduce the project time to a minimum but without incurring unnecessary costs.

Activity 15.8

Would it be worth crashing all the activities identified above?

The answer to this question is no because not all the activities are on the critical path. Even if they were, some of the activities are more economic to crash than others. For instance, activity D costs £300 per day to crash (an extra cost of £900 and a time reduction of 3 days) while activity E costs £400 per day. The objective of crashing should be to find the minimum project duration at the minimum extra cost. In order to satisfy this objective it is first necessary to find the crash cost per day for each activity. This is necessary as the crashing can make non-critical activities become critical.

Activity 15.9

Calculate the cost per day for activities B, D, E, F, G, K and L using the information given in Table 15.5.

This calculation is summarised in Table 15.6.

Table 15.6 Daily cost of crashing

Activity	Max. reduction by crashing (days)	Extra cost	Crash cost/day
B	6	£600	£100
D	3	£900	£300
E	1	£400	£400
F	1	£200	£200
G	2	£400	£200
K	1	£100	£100
L	1	£100	£100

The next step is to write down all the paths through the network together with their durations. (Path GHIK can be ignored because it has a relatively short duration.)

Activity 15.10

Make a list of all major paths through the network.

You should have found 8 major paths, which are shown in Table 15.7.

Path ADEJK must be reduced first because it is the longest path through the network and therefore the critical path. Activities D, E and K can be crashed, but, of the 3, K is the cheapest. If K is crashed by 1 day then not only will the duration of path ADEJK be reduced by 1, but so will paths BCDEJK, ADHIK and BCDHIK. The project duration has now been reduced by 1 day at a cost of £100, but path ADEF is now critical, in addition to ADEJK. These 2 paths must now be crashed together. Both D and E are common to these 2 paths and, since D is the cheapest, this will be crashed by 3 days at a cost of £900. Finally, E is crashed by 1 day to reduce the project duration to 19 days at a cumulative extra cost of £1400. No further crashing is worthwhile because it is not possible to crash both critical paths (only F has any crashing capability left). You might find it easier to write the necessary steps in a table similar to the one shown in Table 15.8.

Is it worthwhile reducing the project time by 5 days at an extra cost of £1400? It may be that you are paying someone by the day to help you and any reduction

Table 15.7 Paths through the network

Path	Duration
ADEJK	24
BCDEJK	23
ADEF	23
ADHIK	22
BCDEF	22
BCDHIK	21
ADL	20
BCDL	19

Table 15.8 Steps involved in crashing the network

Path	Duration	Step 1	Step 2	Step 3
ADEJK	24	23	20	19
BCDEJK	23	22	19	18
ADEF	23	23	20	19
ADHIK	22	21	18	18
BCDEF	22	22	19	18
BCDHIK	21	20	17	17
ADL	20	20	17	17
BCDL	19	19	16	16
Activities crashed		K – 1	D – 3	E – 1
Extra cost		£100	£900	£400
Cumulative extra cost		£100	£1000	£1400

in time would save you this 'overhead' charge. For example, suppose you were paying this person £150 per day. It would be worthwhile crashing K because for an expenditure of £100 you would save £150; a net gain of £50. However, it wouldn't be worthwhile crashing D because for each day saved it has cost you £150 (£300 – £150).

Key points

- There are two main methods for planning and monitoring a project: the *activity-on-node* and the *activity-on-arrow* methods. In this chapter we have used the former procedure.
- *Network analysis* identifies the minimum time in which the project can be completed, together with the *critical activities* and the *float of the non-critical activities.*
- A *Gantt chart* is effective in showing when activities occur. By using such a chart it is often possible to reduce the *resources* required for a project.
- In some cases the total *duration* of a project can be reduced by reducing the duration of individual activities. The technique of *crashing* allows this reduction to be carried out at minimum additional cost.

Reflection

Network analysis is one of the most useful and easily understood techniques in the analyst's 'toolbox'. Software such as Microsoft Project^{TM} is available which can help in applying this technique.

Many large government contracts now have a bonus/penalty clause with legally binding project durations and costs. If the project overruns, the company will pay a penalty for every day it is unfinished; on the other hand if it is completed before the target date, the company will receive a bonus. The Wembley National Stadium Ltd obviously had a contract on-cost, as the construction company Multiplex announced on 17 November 2005 that it was going to make a loss of at least £75 million on the project (*source*: *The Times*) and that the contract finish date would be put back until March 2006. Clearly this company did not do its planning very well, although it blamed poor productivity levels as one of its problems.

Further reading

Anderson, Sweeney and Williams (1994) *An Introduction to Management Science*, seventh edition, West Publishing Company (Chapter 10).

Exercises

Answers to some of these practice questions, together with additional progress questions, can be found on the companion website for this book.

PRACTICE QUESTIONS

1 Please refer to Figure 15.8 for this question.
   (a) How long will the project take?
   (b) How much float has activity D?
   (c) How much float has activity F?

Figure 15.8 Diagram for Question 16

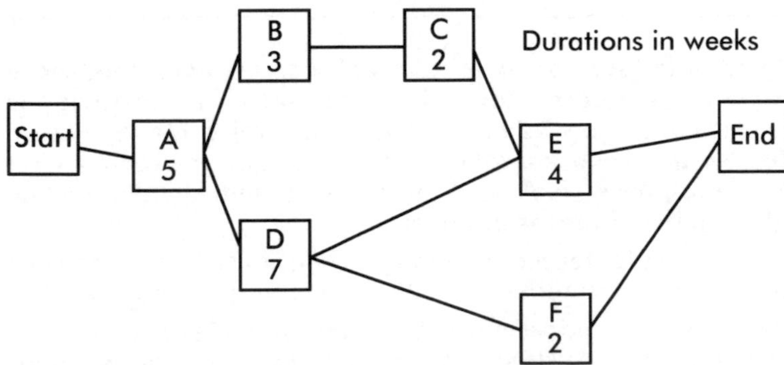

(d) If activity B takes 3 weeks longer than expected, will the project be delayed?

(e) If activity B requires 3 people continuously, D requires 2 people and C requires 1 person, how many people are required during week 6?

2 Yachtsteer manufacture a self-steering device for pleasure yachts and, as a result of increased competition from foreign manufacturers, it has decided to design and manufacture a new model in time for the next Boat Show. As a first step in planning the project, the major tasks and durations have been identified (Table 15.9). Draw a network to represent the logical sequence of tasks and determine how long it will be before the new product can be marketed.

Table 15.9 Details for Question 2

	Task	Time (weeks)	Preceding tasks
A	Design new product	8	–
B	Design electronics	4	–
C	Organise production facilities	4	A
D	Obtain production materials	2	A
E	Manufacture trial gear	3	C, D
F	Obtain electronic circuit boards	2	B
G	Decide on yacht for trials	1	–
H	Assemble trial gear and electronics	2	E, F
I	Test product in workshops	3	H, G
J	Test product at sea	4	I
K	Assess product's performance	3	J
L	Plan national marketing	4	K

3 Shipways boatyard undertakes spring refits on cabin cruisers and yachts, and in the past the company has received complaints from customers regarding the time taken to complete the job. As a consequence the Project Manager, Alan Waters, has decided to carry out a critical path analysis on the cabin cruiser refit. Table 15.10 gives, for each activity, the duration, immediate preceding activities and the number of yard assistants required.

(a) Draw the network and determine how long the refit will take. What are the critical activities and how much float do the non-critical activities have?

(b) (i) Draw a Gantt chart and resource histogram for the refit. What is the maximum number of yard workers required and when is this required?

Table 15.10 Details for Question 3

Activity	Description	Duration (days)	Immediate preceding activities	Yard assistants required
A	Bring craft up slipway	1	–	2
B	Check and overhaul seacocks, etc.	3	A	1
C	Scrape and prepare hull for painting	7	A	2
D	Paint hull	4	C	1
E	Remove engine	2	A	3
F	Overhaul engine	16	E	1
G	Clean and paint engine bilges	3	E	1
H	Refit engine	3	F and G	3
I	Apply antifoul paint to hull	2	D and H	2
J	Refloat	1	B and I	2

NOTE: The reason that I follows from both D and H is that a boat must be refloated no more than 48 hours after the antifouling paint has been applied. Antifouling should not therefore be started until the boat is ready for the water.

(ii) Unfortunately there are only 4 yard workers available during the period of the refit. Using your Gantt chart and/or histogram, reschedule the activities so that no more than 4 yard workers will be required.

4 Revor plc are urgently planning the production of their new lightweight car battery, the 'Epsilon'. They would like to exhibit their battery at a trade fair, which is to take place in 48 weeks' time. Various activities have to take place before production can start, and these are shown in Table 15.11.

(a) Draw the network and show that it is not possible to start production within 48 weeks. What are the critical activities and how much total float do the non-critical activities have?

(b) It is possible to 'crash' (i.e., reduce the duration of) certain activities at increased cost. These activities are shown in Table 15.12.

(i) Ron Smith, the Production Manager, suggests that only activity I need be crashed because this is the cheapest option and allows the greatest reduction in time to be made. Explain why this would not help the situation.

(ii) It has been estimated that for every week over 48 weeks that this project takes, a loss of £8000 is made as a result of lost profits. Decide on the strategy that will minimise the sum of crashed costs and loss of profits.

Table 15.11 Activities for Question 4

	Task	Preceding tasks	Duration (weeks)
A	Clear area	–	20
B	Commission consulting engineers to design equipment	–	2
C	Receive consultant's report	B	10
D	Place equipment out to tender	C	1
E	Obtain equipment	D	6
F	Install equipment	A, E	30
G	Recruit additional staff	C	6
H	Train new staff	G	4
I	Order and obtain materials	–	16
J	Pilot production run	F, H, I	3
K	Advertise new product	–	2

Table 15.12 Crash and cost details for Question 4

Activity	Crashed duration (weeks)	Normal cost (£000's)	Crashed cost (£000's)
A	18	4	10
E	5	1	3
F	28	15	27
I	8	0.5	8.5
J	2	16	26

5 A painting and decorating firm has decided to use critical path analysis in order to plan its next job. The activities of this job are as shown in Table 15.13.

(a) Draw a network representing the sequence of activities and the interdependencies between them.

(b) Determine how long it will take to complete the job and identify the critical activities.

Table 15.13 Activities for Question 5

Activity	Description	Duration (days)	Preceding activities	Number of operatives
A	Order materials	3	None	0
B	Remove curtains and cover furniture	0.5	None	1
C	Wash interior woodwork	2	B	1
D	Sand exterior woodwork	1	None	2
E	Paint ceilings	2	A & C	2
F	Paint interior woodwork	4	E	3
G	Paint exterior woodwork	5	A & D	2
H	Hang wallpaper	2	F	4
I	Remove covers and replace curtains	0.5	H	1
J	Clean up and depart	0.5	G & I	4

(c) If it were to rain for 4 out of the 5 days allocated for painting the exterior woodwork, what effect would this have on the duration of the job? (Assume that it is dry for the remaining time.)

(d) It has now been decided to analyse the labour requirements for this job. Using graph paper, draw a Gantt chart for the job (assuming earliest start times apply). What is the maximum number of operatives required and when does this occur? Unfortunately, only 4 operatives are available. Explain how this will affect the time taken to complete the job.

ASSIGNMENT

There have been recurring problems with the food canning process at Riglen plc and a decision has been taken at Board level to replace the machinery with more modern computer-controlled equipment. Holder and Holder Consulting Engineers have been commissioned to advise on the system to purchase and their report is expected in 5 weeks' time. Although the fine details of the recommended system will not be known until this report has been received, the essential characteristics of all the alternatives are the same. Planning for the installation can therefore start immediately, and this is important because during the installation all food canning has to be contracted out and this will be expensive.

In order to ensure that the project is completed as quickly as possible and at minimum cost, you have been asked to use the relevant network analysis techniques on the data given in Table 15.14. You should also note that fitters are to be employed on a fixed-term contract, and it is important that only the minimum number necessary are recruited.

(a) Draw the network and calculate the start and finish times for each activity. How long will the project take, and what are the critical activities?

(b) Draw a Gantt chart for this project. What is the maximum number of fitters required, and during what weeks does this occur? What is the minimum number of fitters required that will still allow the project to be completed in the time found in (a) above?

Table 15.14 Details for the assignment

Activity	Description	Duration	Immediate predecessors	Fitters required	Cost (£000's)
A	Obtain report	5	–	0	5
B	Remove existing machinery	4	–	8	3
C	Purchase new machinery	5	A	0	50
D	Purchase electrics	7	A	0	15
E	Purchase computers	6	A	0	25
F	Install machinery	4	B and C	5	5
G	Install computers	3	E	6	5
H	Connect electrics	3	F and D	2	4
I	Recruit and train staff	6	–	0	3
J	Pilot production run	1	G and H	6	6
K	Prepare for full production	4	I and J	5	2

(c) An attempt is to be made to reduce the total project time since for every week's reduction a saving of £10 000 can be achieved through not having to contract out the week's canning. This will be possible because some activities such as B can be completed in less time than scheduled. Of course, this reduction in time will be at an increased cost. The activities that can be reduced (crashed) in time are given in Table 15.15.

(i) What is the total normal cost of the project, including the £10 000 per week canning charge?
(ii) Using the figures above, calculate for each activity the cost of reducing the time by one week.
(iii) Starting with the critical path, make a list of all paths through the network. Alongside each path write down the duration in weeks of the path.
(iv) Try and reduce the critical path to the same duration as the next largest in the cheapest way possible. Now reduce both paths until the duration is

Table 15.15 Cost of crashing activities

Activity	Normal time (weeks)	Crashed time (weeks)	Normal cost (£000's)	Crashed cost (£000's)
B	4	2	10	16
D	7	6	15	21
F	6	3	5	20
G	3	2	5	12
K	4	3	2	10

equal to the next highest path and so on. Repeat this until no further reduction is possible. What is the new total cost of the project?

(v) What is the project duration that will minimise the total cost of the project?

Topic 18

Inventory Management

16
Inventory Management

Inventory analysis is one of the most popular topics in management science. One reason is that almost all types of business organizations have inventory. Although we tend to think of inventory only in terms of stock on a store shelf, it can take on a variety of forms, such as partially finished products at different stages of a manufacturing process, raw materials, resources, labor, or cash. In addition, the purpose of inventory is not always simply to meet customer demand. For example, companies frequently stock large inventories of raw materials as a hedge against strikes. Whatever form inventory takes or whatever its purpose, it often represents a significant cost to a business firm. It is estimated that the average annual cost of manufactured goods inventory in the United States is approximately 30% of the total value of the inventory. Thus, if a company has $10.0 million worth of products in inventory, the cost of holding the inventory (including insurance, obsolescence, depreciation, interest, opportunity costs, storage costs, etc.) would be approximately $3.0 million. If the amount of inventory could be reduced by half to $5.0 million, then $1.5 million would be saved in inventory costs, a significant cost reduction.

In this chapter we describe the classic economic order quantity models, which represent the most basic and fundamental form of inventory analysis. These models provide a means for determining how much to order (the order quantity) and when to place an order so that inventory-related costs are minimized. The underlying assumption of these models is that demand is known with certainty and is constant. In addition, we will describe models for determining the order size and reorder points (when to place an order) when demand is uncertain.

Elements of Inventory Management

Inventory *is a stock of items kept on hand to meet demand.*

Inventory is defined as a stock of items kept on hand by an organization to use to meet customer demand. Virtually every type of organization maintains some form of inventory. A department store carries inventories of all the retail items it sells; a nursery has inventories of different plants, trees, and flowers; a rental car agency has inventories of cars; and a major league baseball team maintains an inventory of players on its minor league teams. Even a family household will maintain inventories of food, clothing, medical supplies, personal hygiene products, and so on.

The Role of Inventory

A company or an organization keeps stocks of inventory for a variety of important reasons. The most prominent is holding finished goods inventories to meet customer demand for a product, especially in a retail operation. However, customer demand can also be in the form of a secretary going to a storage closet to get a printer cartridge or paper, or a carpenter getting a board or nail from a storage shed. A level of inventory is normally maintained that will meet anticipated or expected customer demand. However, because demand is usually not known with certainty, additional amounts of inventory, called **safety**, or *buffer*, **stocks**, are often kept on hand to meet unexpected variations in excess of expected demand.

Additional stocks of inventories are sometimes built up to meet seasonal or cyclical demand. Companies will produce items when demand is low to meet high seasonal demand for which their production capacity is insufficient. For example, toy manufacturers produce large inventories during the summer and fall to meet anticipated demand during the Christmas season. Doing so enables them to maintain a relatively smooth production flow throughout the year. They would not normally have the production capacity or logistical support to produce enough to meet all of the Christmas demand during that season. Correspondingly, retailers might find it necessary to keep large stocks of inventory on their shelves to meet peak seasonal demand, such as at Christmas, or for display purposes to attract buyers.

A company will often purchase large amounts of inventory to take advantage of price discounts, as a hedge against anticipated future price increases, or because it can get a lower price by purchasing in volume. For example, Wal-Mart has long been known to purchase an entire manufacturer's stock of soap powder or other retail items because it can get a very low price, which it subsequently passes on to its customers. Companies will often purchase large stocks of items when a supplier liquidates to get a low price. In some cases, large orders will be made simply because the cost of an order may be very high, and it is more cost-effective to have higher inventories than to make a lot of orders.

Many companies find it necessary to maintain in-process inventories at different stages in a manufacturing process to provide independence between operations and to avoid work stoppages or delays. Inventories of raw materials and purchased parts are kept on hand so that the production process will not be delayed as a result of missed or late deliveries or shortages from a supplier. Work-in-process inventories are kept between stages in the manufacturing process so that production can continue smoothly if there are temporary machine breakdowns or other work stoppages. Similarly, a stock of finished parts or products allows customer demand to be met in the event of a work stoppage or problem with the production process.

Demand

A crucial component and the basic starting point for the management of inventory is customer demand. Inventory exists for the purpose of meeting the demand of customers. Customers can be inside the organization, such as a machine operator waiting for a part or a partially completed product to work on, or outside the organization, such as an individual purchasing groceries or a new stereo. As such, an essential determinant of effective inventory management is an accurate forecast of demand. For this reason the topics of forecasting (Chapter 15) and inventory management are directly interrelated.

__Dependent demand__ items are used internally to produce a final product.

In general, the demand for items in inventory is classified as dependent or independent. **Dependent demand** items are typically component parts, or materials, used in the process of producing a final product. For example, if an automobile company plans to produce 1,000 new cars, it will need 5,000 wheels and tires (including spares). In this case the demand for wheels is dependent on the production of cars; that is, the demand for one item is a function of demand for another item.

__Independent demand__ items are final products demanded by an external customer.

Alternatively, cars are an example of an **independent demand** item. In general, independent demand items are final or finished products that are not a function of, or dependent upon, internal production activity. Independent demand is usually external, and, thus, beyond the direct control of the organization. In this chapter we will focus on the management of inventory for independent demand items.

Inventory Costs

Inventory costs include __carrying__, __ordering__, and __shortage costs__.

There are three basic costs associated with inventory: carrying (or holding) costs, ordering costs, and shortage costs. **Carrying costs** are the costs of holding items in storage. These vary with the level of inventory and occasionally with the length of time an item is held; that is, the greater the level of inventory over time, the higher the carrying cost(s). Carrying costs can include the cost of losing the use of funds tied up in inventory; direct storage costs, such as rent, heating, cooling, lighting, security, refrigeration, record keeping, and logistics; interest on loans used to purchase inventory; depreciation; obsolescence as markets for products in inventory diminish; product deterioration and spoilage; breakage; taxes; and pilferage.

Carrying costs are normally specified in one of two ways. The most general form is to assign total carrying costs, determined by summing all the individual costs mentioned previously, on a per-unit basis per time period, such as a month or a year. In this form, carrying costs would commonly be expressed as a per-unit dollar amount on an annual basis (for example, $10 per year). Alternatively, carrying costs are sometimes expressed as a percentage of the value of an item or as a percentage of average inventory value. It is generally estimated that carrying costs range from 10% to 40% of the value of a manufactured item.

Ordering costs are the costs associated with replenishing the stock of inventory being held. These are normally expressed as a dollar amount per order and are independent of the order size. Thus, ordering costs vary with the number of orders made (i.e., as the number of orders increases, the ordering cost increases). Costs incurred each time an order is made can include requisition costs, purchase orders, transportation and shipping, receiving, inspection, handling and placing in storage, and accounting and auditing.

Ordering costs generally react inversely to carrying costs. As the size of orders increases, fewer orders are required, thus reducing annual ordering costs. However, ordering larger amounts results in higher inventory levels and higher carrying costs. In general, as the order size increases, annual ordering costs decrease and annual carrying costs increase.

Shortage costs, also referred to as *stockout costs*, occur when customer demand cannot be met because of insufficient inventory on hand. If these shortages result in a permanent loss of sales for items demanded but not provided, shortage costs include the loss of profits. Shortages can also cause customer dissatisfaction and a loss of goodwill that can result in a permanent loss of customers and future sales. In some instances the inability to meet customer demand or lateness in meeting demand results in specified penalties in the form of price discounts or rebates. When demand is internal, a shortage can cause work stoppages in the production process and create delays, resulting in downtime costs and the cost of lost production (including indirect and direct production costs).

Costs resulting from immediate or future lost sales because demand could not be met are more difficult to determine than carrying or ordering costs. As a result, shortage costs are frequently subjective estimates and many times no more than educated guesses.

Shortages occur because it is costly to carry inventory in stock. As a result, shortage costs have an inverse relationship to carrying costs; as the amount of inventory on hand increases, the carrying cost increases, while shortage costs decrease.

*The purpose of **inventory management** is to determine how much and when to order.*

The objective of **inventory management** is to employ an inventory control system that will indicate how much should be ordered and when orders should take place to minimize the sum of the three inventory costs described here.

Inventory Control Systems

An inventory system is a structure for controlling the level of inventory by determining how much to order (the level of replenishment) and when to order. There are two basic types of inventory systems: a *continuous* (or *fixed–order quantity*) *system* and a *periodic* (or *fixed–time period*) *system*. The primary difference between the two systems is that in a continuous system, an order is placed for the same constant amount whenever the inventory on hand decreases to a certain level, whereas in a periodic system, an order is placed for a variable amount after an established passage of time.

Continuous Inventory Systems

In a *continuous inventory system*, alternatively referred to as a *perpetual system* or a *fixed–order quantity system*, a continual record of the inventory level for every item is maintained. Whenever the inventory on hand decreases to a predetermined level, referred to as

In a continuous inventory system, a constant amount is ordered when inventory declines to a predetermined level.

the *reorder point*, a new order is placed to replenish the stock of inventory. The order that is placed is for a "fixed" amount that minimizes the total inventory carrying, ordering, and shortage costs. This fixed order quantity is called the *economic order quantity*; its determination will be discussed in greater detail in a later section.

A positive feature of a continuous system is that the inventory level is closely and continuously monitored so that management always knows the inventory status. This is especially advantageous for critical inventory items such as replacement parts or raw materials and supplies. However, the cost of maintaining a continual record of the amount of inventory on hand can also be a disadvantage of this type of system.

A simple example of a continuous inventory system is a ledger-style checkbook that many of us use on a daily basis. Our checkbook comes with 300 checks; after the 200th check has been used (and there are 100 left), there is an order form for a new batch of checks that has been inserted by the printer. This form, when turned in at the bank, initiates an order for a new batch of 300 checks from the printer. Many office inventory systems use "reorder" cards that are placed within stacks of stationery or at the bottom of a case of pens or paper clips to signal when a new order should be placed. If you look behind the items on a hanging rack in a Kmart store, you will see a card indicating that it is time to place an order for this item, for an amount indicated on the card.

A more sophisticated example of a continuous inventory system is a computerized checkout system with a laser scanner, used by many supermarkets and retail stores. In this system a laser scanner reads the Universal Product Code (UPC), or bar code, off the product package, and the transaction is instantly recorded and the inventory level updated. Such a system is not only quick and accurate, but it also provides management with continuously updated information on the status of inventory levels. Although not as publicly visible as supermarket systems, many manufacturing companies, suppliers, and distributors also use bar code systems and handheld laser scanners to inventory materials, supplies, equipment, in-process parts, and finished goods.

Because continuous inventory systems are much more common than periodic systems, models that determine fixed order quantities and the time to order will receive most of our attention in this chapter.

Periodic Inventory Systems

In a ***periodic inventory system****, an order is placed for a variable amount after a fixed passage of time.*

In a **periodic inventory system**, also referred to as a *fixed–time period system* or *periodic review system*, the inventory on hand is counted at specific time intervals—for example, every week or at the end of each month. After the amount of inventory in stock is determined, an order is placed for an amount that will bring inventory back up to a desired level. In this system the inventory level is not monitored at all during the time interval between orders, so it has the advantage of requiring little or no record keeping. However, it has the disadvantage of less direct control. This typically results in larger inventory levels for a periodic inventory system than in a continuous system, to guard against unexpected stockouts early in the fixed period. Such a system also requires that a new order quantity be determined each time a periodic order is made.

Periodic inventory systems are often found at a college or university bookstore. Textbooks are normally ordered according to a periodic system, wherein a count of textbooks in stock (for every course) is made after the first few weeks or month during the semester or quarter. An order for new textbooks for the next semester is then made according to estimated course enrollments for the next term (i.e., demand) and the number remaining in stock. Smaller retail stores, drugstores, grocery stores, and offices often use periodic systems; the stock level is checked every week or month, often by a vendor, to see how much (if anything) should be ordered.

for Ford Harris

The earliest published derivation of the classic economic lot size model is credited to Ford Harris of Westinghouse Corporation in 1915. His equation determined a minimum sum of inventory costs and setup costs, given demand that was known and constant and a rate of production that was assumed to be higher than demand.

Economic Order Quantity Models

***EOQ** is a continuous inventory system.*

You will recall that in a continuous or fixed–order quantity system, when inventory reaches a specific level, referred to as the *reorder point*, a fixed amount is ordered. The most widely used and traditional means for determining how much to order in a continuous system is the **economic order quantity (EOQ)** model, also referred to as the economic lot size model.

The function of the EOQ model is to determine the optimal order size that minimizes total inventory costs. There are several variations of the EOQ model, depending on the assumptions made about the inventory system. In this and following sections we will describe three model versions: the basic EOQ model, the EOQ model with noninstantaneous receipt, and the EOQ model with shortages.

The Basic EOQ Model

EOQ is the optimal order quantity that will minimize total inventory costs.

The simplest form of the economic order quantity model on which all other model versions are based is called the basic EOQ model. It is essentially a single formula for determining the optimal order size that minimizes the sum of carrying costs and ordering costs. The model formula is derived under a set of simplifying and restrictive assumptions, as follows:

Assumptions of the EOQ model include constant demand, no shortages, constant lead time, and instantaneous order receipt.

- Demand is known with certainty and is relatively constant over time.
- No shortages are allowed.
- Lead time for the receipt of orders is constant.
- The order quantity is received all at once.

The graph in Figure 16.1 reflects these basic model assumptions.

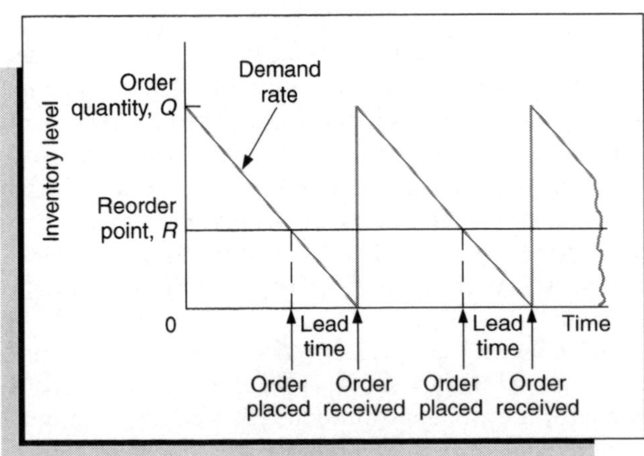

Figure 16.1
The inventory order cycle

Figure 16.1 describes the continuous inventory order cycle system inherent in the EOQ model. An order quantity, Q, is received and is used up over time at a constant rate. When the inventory level decreases to the reorder point, R, a new order is placed, and a period of time, referred to as the *lead time*, is required for delivery. The order is received all at once, just at the moment when demand depletes the entire stock of inventory (and the inventory level reaches zero), thus allowing no shortages. This cycle is continuously repeated for the same order quantity, reorder point, and lead time.

As we mentioned earlier, Q is the order size that minimizes the sum of carrying costs and holding costs. These two costs react inversely to each other in response to an increase in the order size. As the order size increases, fewer orders are required, causing the ordering cost to decline, whereas the average amount of inventory on hand increases, resulting in an increase in carrying costs. Thus, in effect, the optimal order quantity represents a compromise between these two conflicting costs.

Carrying Cost

Carrying cost is usually expressed on a per-unit basis for some period of time (although it is sometimes given as a percentage of average inventory). Traditionally, the carrying cost is referred to on an annual basis (i.e., per year).

The total carrying cost is determined by the amount of inventory on hand during the year. The amount of inventory available during the year is illustrated in Figure 16.2.

Figure 16.2
Inventory usage

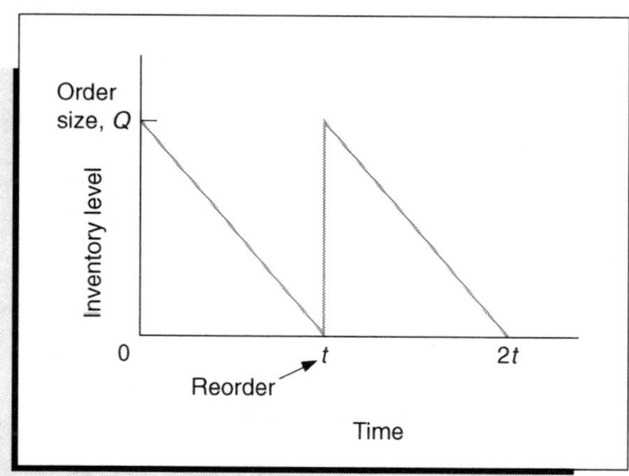

In Figure 16.2, Q represents the size of the order needed to replenish inventory, which is what a manager wants to determine. The line connecting Q to time, t, in our graph represents the rate at which inventory is depleted, or *demand*, during the time period, t. Demand is assumed to be *known with certainty* and is thus constant, which explains why the line representing demand is straight. Also, notice that inventory never goes below zero; shortages do not exist. In addition, when the inventory level does reach zero, it is assumed that an order arrives immediately after an infinitely small passage of time, a condition referred to as **instantaneous receipt**. This is a simplifying assumption that we will maintain for the moment.

Referring to Figure 16.2, we can see that the amount of inventory is Q, the size of the order, for an infinitely small period of time because Q is always being depleted by demand. Similarly, the amount of inventory is zero for an infinitely small period of time because the only time there is no inventory is at the specific time t. Thus, the amount of inventory available is somewhere between these two extremes. A logical deduction is that the amount of inventory available is the *average inventory* level, defined as

$$\text{average inventory} = \frac{Q}{2}$$

To verify this relationship, we can specify any number of points—values of Q—over the entire time period, t, and divide by the number of points. For example, if $Q = 5{,}000$, the six points designated from 5,000 to 0, as shown in Figure 16.3, are summed and divided by 6:

$$\text{average inventory} = \frac{5{,}000 + 4{,}000 + 3{,}000 + 2{,}000 + 1{,}000 + 0}{6}$$
$$= 2{,}500$$

Figure 16.3
Levels of Q

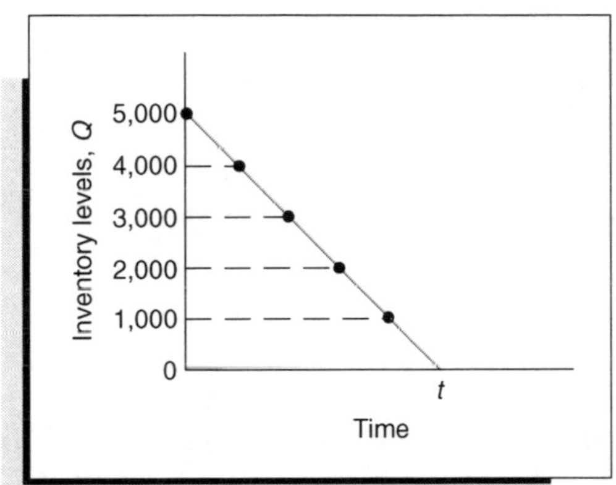

Alternatively, we can sum just the two extreme points (which also encompass the range of time, t) and divide by 2. This also equals 2,500. This computation is the same, in principle, as adding Q and 0 and dividing by 2, which equals $Q/2$. This relationship for average inventory is maintained, regardless of the size of the order, Q, or the frequency of orders (i.e., the time period, t). Thus, the average inventory on an *annual basis* is also $Q/2$, as shown in Figure 16.4.

Figure 16.4
Annual average inventory

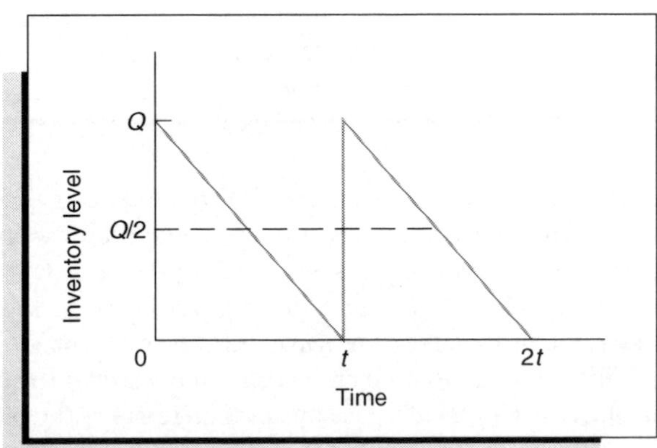

Now that we know that the amount of inventory available *on an annual basis* is the average inventory, $Q/2$, we can determine the total annual carrying cost by multiplying the average number of units in inventory by the carrying cost per unit per year, C_c:

$$\text{annual carrying cost} = C_c \frac{Q}{2}$$

Ordering Cost

The total annual ordering cost is computed by multiplying the cost per order, designated as C_o, by the number of orders per year. Because annual demand is assumed to be known and constant, the number of orders will be D/Q, where Q is the order size:

$$\text{annual ordering cost} = C_o \frac{D}{Q}$$

The only variable in this equation is Q; both C_o and D are constant parameters. In other words, demand is known with certainty. Thus, the relative magnitude of the ordering cost is dependent upon the order size.

Total Inventory Cost

The total annual inventory cost is simply the sum of the ordering and carrying costs:

$$TC = C_o \frac{D}{Q} + C_c \frac{Q}{2}$$

These cost functions are shown in Figure 16.5. Notice the inverse relationship between ordering cost and carrying cost, resulting in a convex total cost curve.

Figure 16.5

The EOQ cost model

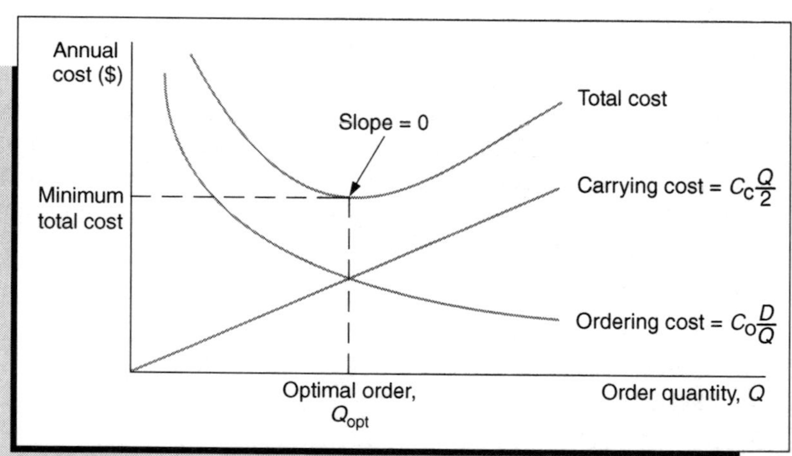

Observe the general upward trend of the total carrying cost curve. As the order size Q (shown on the horizontal axis) increases, the total carrying cost (shown on the vertical axis) increases. This is logical because larger orders will result in more units carried in inventory. Next, observe the ordering cost curve in Figure 16.5. As the order size, Q, increases, the ordering cost *decreases* (just the opposite of what occurred with the carrying cost). This is logical because an increase in the size of the orders will result in fewer orders being placed each year. Because one cost increases as the other decreases, the result of summing the two costs is a convex total cost curve.

The optimal value of Q corresponds to the lowest point on the total cost curve.

The optimal order quantity occurs at the point in Figure 16.5 where the total cost curve is at a minimum, which also coincides exactly with the point where the ordering cost curve intersects with the carrying cost curve. This enables us to determine the optimal value of Q by equating the two cost functions and solving for Q, as follows:

$$C_o \frac{D}{Q} = C_c \frac{Q}{2}$$

$$Q^2 = \frac{2C_o D}{C_c}$$

$$Q_{opt} = \sqrt{\frac{2C_o D}{C_c}}$$

Alternatively, the optimal value of Q can be determined by differentiating the total cost curve with respect to Q, setting the resulting function equal to zero (the slope at the minimum point on the total cost curve), and solving for Q, as follows:

$$TC = C_o \frac{D}{Q} + C_c \frac{Q}{2}$$

$$\frac{\delta TC}{\delta Q} = -\frac{C_o D}{Q^2} + \frac{C_c}{2}$$

$$0 = -\frac{C_o D}{Q^2} + \frac{C_c}{2}$$

$$Q_{opt} = \sqrt{\frac{2C_o D}{C_c}}$$

The total minimum cost is determined by substituting the value for the optimal order size, Q_{opt}, into the total cost equation:

$$TC_{min} = \frac{C_o D}{Q_{opt}} + C_o \frac{Q_{opt}}{2}$$

We will use the following example to demonstrate how the optimal value of Q is computed. The I-75 Carpet Discount Store in north Georgia stocks carpet in its warehouse and sells it through an adjoining showroom. The store keeps several brands and styles of carpet in stock; however, its biggest seller is Super Shag carpet. The store wants to determine the optimal order size and total inventory cost for this brand of carpet, given an estimated annual demand of 10,000 yards of carpet, an annual carrying cost of \$0.75 per yard, and an ordering cost of \$150. The store would also like to know the number of orders that will be made annually and the time between orders (i.e., the order cycle), given that the store is open every day except Sunday, Thanksgiving Day, and Christmas Day (which is not on a Sunday).

We can summarize the model parameters as follows:

$$C_c = \$0.75$$
$$C_o = \$150$$
$$D = 10{,}000 \text{ yd.}$$

The optimal order size is computed as follows:

$$Q_{opt} = \sqrt{\frac{2C_oD}{C_c}}$$
$$= \sqrt{\frac{2(150)(10,000)}{(0.75)}}$$
$$Q_{opt} = 2,000 \text{ yd.}$$

The total annual inventory cost is determined by substituting Q_{opt} into the total cost formula, as follows:

$$TC_{min} = C_o \frac{D}{Q_{opt}} + C_c \frac{Q_{opt}}{2}$$
$$= (150)\frac{10,000}{2,000} + (0.75)\frac{(2,000)}{2}$$
$$= \$750 + 750$$
$$TC_{min} = \$1,500$$

The number of orders per year is computed as follows:

$$\text{number of orders per year} = \frac{D}{Q_{opt}} = \frac{10,000}{2,000} = 5$$

Given that the store is open 311 days annually (365 days minus 52 Sundays, plus Thanksgiving and Christmas), the order cycle is determined as follows:

$$\text{order cycle time} = \frac{311 \text{ days}}{D/Q_{opt}} = \frac{311}{5} = 62.2 \text{ store days}$$

The EOQ model is robust; because Q is a square root, errors in the estimation of D, C_c, and C_o are dampened.

It should be noted that the optimal order quantity determined in this example, and in general, is an approximate value because it is based on estimates of carrying and ordering costs as well as uncertain demand (although all these parameters are treated as known, certain values in the EOQ model). Thus, in practice it is acceptable to round off the Q values to the nearest whole number. The precision of a decimal place generally is neither necessary nor appropriate. In addition, because the optimal order quantity is computed from a square root, errors or variations in the cost parameters and demand tend to be dampened. For instance, if the order cost had actually been a third higher, or \$200, the resulting optimal order size would have varied by about 15% (i.e., 2,390 yards instead of 2,000 yards). In addition, variations in both inventory costs will tend to offset each other because they have an inverse relationship. As a result, the EOQ model is relatively robust, or resilient to errors in the cost estimates and demand, which has tended to enhance its popularity.

EOQ Analysis Over Time

One aspect of inventory analysis that can be confusing is the time frame encompassed by the analysis. Therefore, we will digress for just a moment to discuss this aspect of EOQ analysis.

Recall that previously we developed the EOQ model "regardless of order size, Q, and time, *t*." Now we will verify this condition. We will do so by developing our EOQ model on a *monthly basis*. First, demand is equal to 833.3 yards per month (which we determined by dividing the annual demand of 10,000 yards by 12 months). Next, by dividing the annual carrying cost, C_c, of \$0.75 by 12, we get the monthly (per-unit) carrying cost: C_c = \$0.0625. (The ordering cost of \$150 is not related to time.) We thus have the values

$$D = 833.3 \text{ yd. per month}$$
$$C_c = \$0.0625 \text{ per yd. per month}$$
$$C_o = \$150 \text{ per order}$$

which we can substitute into our EOQ formula:

$$Q_{opt} = \sqrt{\frac{2C_oD}{C_c}}$$
$$= \sqrt{\frac{2(150)(833.3)}{(0.0625)}} = 2{,}000 \text{ yd.}$$

This is the same optimal order size that we determined on an annual basis. Now we will compute total monthly inventory cost:

$$\text{total monthly inventory cost} = C_c\frac{Q_{opt}}{2} + C_o\frac{D}{Q_{opt}}$$
$$= (\$0.0625)\frac{(2{,}000)}{2} + (\$150)\frac{(833.3)}{(2{,}000)}$$
$$= \$125 \text{ per month}$$

To convert this monthly total cost to an annual cost, we multiply it by 12 (months):

$$\text{total annual inventory cost} = (\$125)(12) = \$1{,}500$$

This brief example demonstrates that regardless of the time period encompassed by EOQ analysis, the economic order quantity (Q_{opt}) is the same.

The EOQ Model with Noninstantaneous Receipt

The ***noninstantaneous receipt model*** *relaxes the assumption that Q is received all at once.*

A variation of the basic EOQ model is achieved when the assumption that orders are received all at once is relaxed. This version of the EOQ model is known as the **noninstan-taneous receipt model**, also referred to as the *gradual usage*, or **production lot size, model**. In this EOQ variation, the order quantity is received gradually over time and the inventory level is depleted at the same time it is being replenished. This is a situation most commonly found when the inventory user is also the producer, as, for example, in a manufacturing operation where a part is produced to use in a larger assembly. This situation can also occur when orders are delivered gradually over time or the retailer and producer of a product are one and the same. The noninstantaneous receipt model is illustrated graphically in Figure 16.6, which highlights the difference between this variation and the basic EOQ model.

The ordering cost component of the basic EOQ model does not change as a result of the gradual replenishment of the inventory level because it is dependent only on the number of annual orders. However, the carrying cost component is not the same for this model variation because average inventory is different. In the basic EOQ model, average inventory was half the maximum inventory level, or $Q/2$, but in this variation, the maximum inventory level is not simply Q; it is an amount somewhat lower than Q, adjusted for the fact that the order quantity is depleted during the order receipt period.

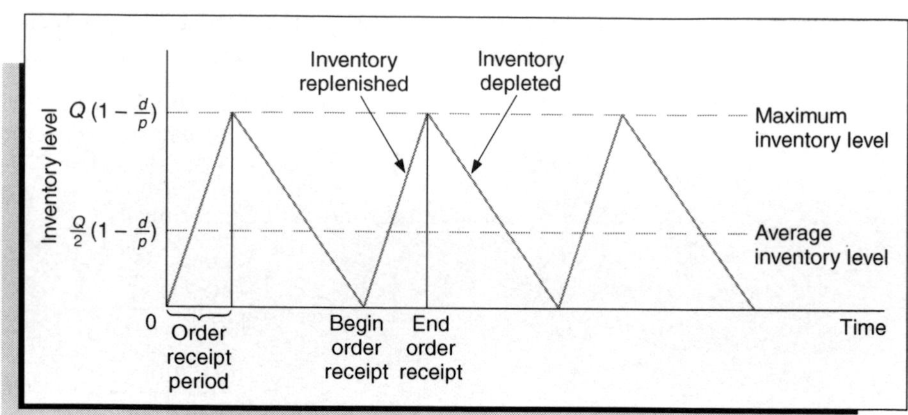

Figure 16.6
The EOQ model with noninstantaneous order receipt

To determine the average inventory level, we define the following parameters that are unique to this model:

p = daily rate at which the order is received over time, also known as the *production rate*
d = the daily rate at which inventory is demanded

The demand rate cannot exceed the production rate because we are still assuming that no shortages are possible, and if $d = p$, then there is no order size because items are used as fast as they are produced. Thus, for this model, the production rate must exceed the demand rate, or $p > d$.

Observing Figure 16.6, the time required to receive an order is the order quantity divided by the rate at which the order is received, or Q/p. For example, if the order size is 100 units and the production rate, p, is 20 units per day, the order will be received in 5 days. The amount of inventory that will be depleted or used up during this time period is determined by multiplying by the demand rate, or $(Q/p)d$. For example, if it takes 5 days to receive the order and during this time inventory is depleted at the rate of 2 units per day, then a total of 10 units is used. As a result, the maximum amount of inventory that is on hand is the order size minus the amount depleted during the receipt period, computed as follows and shown earlier in Figure 16.6:

$$\begin{aligned}\text{maximum inventory level} &= Q - \frac{Q}{p}d \\ &= Q\left(1 - \frac{d}{p}\right)\end{aligned}$$

Because this is the maximum inventory level, the average inventory level is determined by dividing this amount by 2, as follows:

$$\begin{aligned}\text{average inventory level} &= \frac{1}{2}\left[Q\left(1 - \frac{d}{p}\right)\right] \\ &= \frac{Q}{2}\left(1 - \frac{d}{p}\right)\end{aligned}$$

The total carrying cost, using this function for average inventory, is

$$\text{total carrying cost} = C_c \frac{Q}{2}\left(1 - \frac{d}{p}\right)$$

Thus, the total annual inventory cost is determined according to the following formula:

$$TC = C_o \frac{D}{Q} + C_c \frac{Q}{2}\left(1 - \frac{d}{p}\right)$$

The total inventory cost is a function of two other costs, just as in our previous EOQ model. Thus, the minimum inventory cost occurs when the total cost curve is lowest and where the carrying cost curve and ordering cost curve intersect (see Figure 16.5). Therefore, to find optimal Q_{opt}, we equate total carrying cost with total ordering cost:

$$C_c \frac{Q}{2}\left(1 - \frac{d}{p}\right) = C_o \frac{D}{Q}$$

$$C_c \frac{Q^2}{2}\left(1 - \frac{d}{p}\right) = C_o D$$

$$Q_{opt} = \sqrt{\frac{2C_o D}{C_c(1 - d/p)}}$$

For our previous example we will now assume that the I-75 Carpet Discount Store has its own manufacturing facility, in which it produces Super Shag carpet. We will further assume that the ordering cost, C_o, is the cost of setting up the production process to make Super Shag carpet. Recall that $C_c = \$0.75$ per yard and $D = 10{,}000$ yards per year. The manufacturing facility operates the same days the store is open (i.e., 311 days) and produces 150 yards of the carpet per day. The optimal order size, the total inventory cost, the length of time to receive an order, the number of orders per year, and the maximum inventory level are computed as follows:

$$C_o - \$150$$
$$C_c = \$0.75 \text{ per unit}$$
$$D = 10{,}000 \text{ yd.}$$
$$d = \frac{10{,}000}{311} = 32.2 \text{ yd. per day}$$
$$p = 150 \text{ yd. per day}$$

The optimal order size is determined as follows:

$$Q_{opt} = \sqrt{\frac{2C_o D}{C_c\left(1 - \frac{d}{p}\right)}}$$

$$= \sqrt{\frac{2(150)(10{,}000)}{0.75\left(1 - \frac{32.2}{150}\right)}}$$

$$Q_{opt} = 2{,}256.8 \text{ yd.}$$

This value is substituted into the following formula to determine total minimum annual inventory cost:

$$\begin{aligned} TC_{\min} &= C_o\frac{D}{Q} + C_c\frac{Q}{2}\left(1-\frac{d}{p}\right) \\ &= (150)\frac{(10{,}000)}{(2{,}256.8)} + (0.75)\frac{(2{,}256.8)}{2}\left(1-\frac{32.2}{150}\right) \\ &= \$1{,}329 \end{aligned}$$

The length of time to receive an order for this type of manufacturing operation is commonly called the length of the *production run*. It is computed as follows:

$$\text{production run length} = \frac{Q}{p} = \frac{2{,}256.8}{150} = 15.05 \text{ days}$$

The number of orders per year is actually the number of production runs that will be made, computed as follows:

$$\begin{aligned} \text{number of production runs} &= \frac{D}{Q} \\ &= \frac{10{,}000}{2{,}256.8} \\ &= 4.43 \text{ runs} \end{aligned}$$

Finally, the maximum inventory level is computed as follows:

$$\begin{aligned} \text{maximum inventory level} &= Q\left(1-\frac{d}{p}\right) \\ &= 2{,}256.8\left(1-\frac{32.2}{150}\right) \\ &= 1{,}722 \text{ yd.} \end{aligned}$$

The EOQ Model with Shortages

The EOQ model with shortages relaxes the assumption that shortages cannot exist.

One of the assumptions of our basic EOQ model is that shortages and back ordering are not allowed. The third model variation that we will describe, the EOQ model with shortages, relaxes this assumption. However, it will be assumed that all demand not met because of inventory shortage can be back ordered and delivered to the customer later. Thus, all demand is eventually met. The EOQ model with shortages is illustrated in Figure 16.7.

Because back-ordered demand, or shortages, S, are filled when inventory is replenished, the maximum inventory level does not reach Q, but instead a level equal to $Q - S$. It can be seen from Figure 16.7 that the amount of inventory on hand $(Q - S)$ decreases as the amount of the shortage increases, and vice versa. Therefore, the cost associated with shortages, which we described earlier in this chapter as primarily the cost of lost sales and lost customer goodwill, has an inverse relationship to carrying costs. As the order size, Q, increases, the carrying cost increases and the shortage cost declines. This relationship between carrying and shortage cost as well as ordering cost is shown in Figure 16.8.

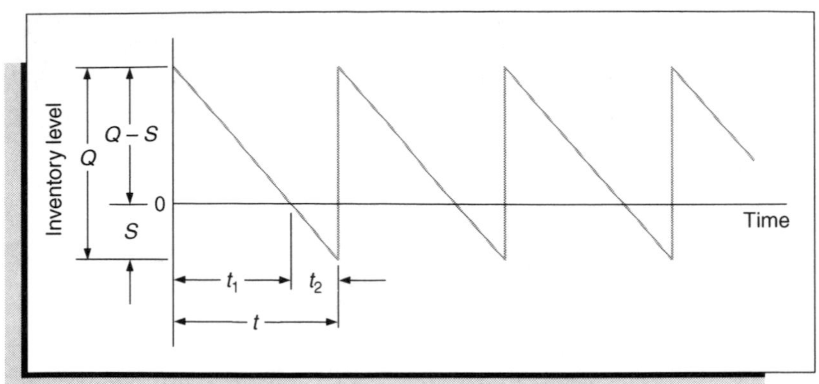

Figure 16.7
The EOQ model with shortages

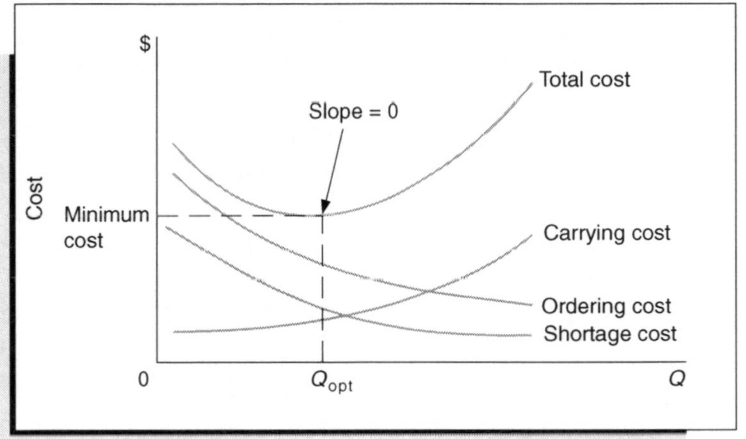

Figure 16.8
Cost model with shortages

We will forgo the lengthy derivation of the individual cost components of the EOQ model with shortages, which requires the application of plane geometry to the graph in Figure 16.8. The individual cost functions are provided as follows, where S equals the shortage level and C_s equals the annual per-unit cost of shortages:

$$\text{total shortage costs} = C_s \frac{S^2}{2Q}$$

$$\text{total carrying cost} = C_c \frac{(Q-S)^2}{2Q}$$

$$\text{total ordering cost} = C_o \frac{D}{Q}$$

Combining these individual cost components results in the total inventory cost formula:

$$TC = C_s \frac{S^2}{2Q} + C_c \frac{(Q-S)^2}{2Q} + C_o \frac{D}{Q}$$

You will notice in Figure 16.8 that the three cost component curves do not intersect at a common point, as was the case in the basic EOQ model. As a result, the only way to determine the optimal order size *and the optimal shortage level, S,* is to differentiate the total cost function with respect to Q and S, set the two resulting equations equal to zero, and solve them simultaneously. Doing so results in the following formulas for the optimal order quantity and shortage level:

$$Q_{\text{opt}} = \sqrt{\frac{2C_oD}{C_c}\left(\frac{C_s + C_c}{C_s}\right)}$$

$$S_{\text{opt}} = Q_{\text{opt}}\left(\frac{C_c}{C_c + C_s}\right)$$

For example, we will now assume that the I-75 Carpet Discount Store allows shortages and the shortage cost, C_s, is \$2 per yard per year. All other costs and demand remain the same ($C_c = \$0.75$, $C_o = \$150$, and $D = 10{,}000$ yd.). The optimal order size and shortage level and total minimum annual inventory cost are computed as follows:

$$\begin{aligned}
C_o &= \$150 \\
C_c &= \$0.75 \text{ per yd.} \\
C_s &= \$2 \text{ per yd.} \\
D &= 10{,}000 \text{ yd.} \\
Q_{\text{opt}} &= \sqrt{\frac{2C_oD}{C_c}\left(\frac{C_s + C_c}{C_s}\right)} \\
&= \sqrt{\frac{2(150)(10{,}000)}{0.75}\left(\frac{2 + 0.75}{2}\right)} \\
&= 2{,}345.2 \text{ yd} \\
S_{\text{opt}} &= Q_{\text{opt}}\left(\frac{C_c}{C_c + C_s}\right) \\
&= 2{,}345.2\left(\frac{0.75}{2 + 0.75}\right) \\
&= 639.6 \text{ yd} \\
TC_{\min} &= \frac{C_sS^2}{2Q} + \frac{C_c(Q - S)^2}{2Q} + C_o\frac{D}{Q} \\
&= \frac{(2)(639.6)^2}{2(2{,}345.2)} + \frac{(0.75)(1{,}705.6)^2}{2(2{,}345.2)} + \frac{(150)(10{,}000)}{2{,}345.2} \\
&= \$174.44 + 465.16 + 639.60 \\
&= \$1{,}279.20
\end{aligned}$$

Several additional parameters of the EOQ model with shortages can be computed for this example, as follows:

$$\begin{aligned}
\text{number of orders} &= \frac{D}{Q} = \frac{10{,}000}{2{,}345.2} = 4.26 \text{ orders per year} \\
\text{maximum inventory level} &= Q - S = 2{,}345.2 - 639.6 = 1{,}705.6 \text{ yd.}
\end{aligned}$$

The time between orders, identified as t in Figure 16.7, is computed as follows:

$$t = \frac{\text{days per year}}{\text{number of orders}} = \frac{311}{4.26} = 73.0 \text{ days between orders}$$

The time during which inventory is on hand, t_1 in Figure 16.7, and the time during which there is a shortage, t_2 in Figure 16.7, during each order cycle can be computed using the following formulas:

$$\begin{aligned} t_1 &= \frac{Q-S}{D} \\ &= \frac{2{,}345.2 - 639.6}{10{,}000} \\ &= 0.171 \text{ year, or } 53.2 \text{ days} \\ t_2 &= \frac{S}{D} \\ &= \frac{639.6}{10{,}000} \\ &= 0.064 \text{ year, or } 19.9 \text{ days} \end{aligned}$$

Management Science Application

Determining Inventory Ordering Policy at Dell

Dell Inc., the world's largest computer-systems company, bypasses retailers and sells directly to customers via phone or the Internet. After an order is processed, it is sent to one of its assembly plants in Austin, Texas, where the product is built, tested, and packaged within 8 hours.

Dell carries very little components inventory itself. Technology changes occur so fast that holding inventory can be a huge liability; some components lose 0.5% to 2.0% of their value per week. In addition, many of Dell's suppliers are located in Southeast Asia, and their shipping times to Austin range from 7 days for air transport to 30 days for water and ground transport. To compensate for these factors, Dell's suppliers keep inventory in small warehouses called "revolvers" (for revolving inventory), which are a few miles from Dell's assembly plants. Dell keeps very little inventory at its own plants, so it withdraws inventory from the revolvers every few hours, while most Dell's suppliers deliver to their revolvers three times per week.

The cost of carrying inventory by Dell's suppliers is ultimately reflected in the final price of a computer. Thus, in order to maintain a competitive price advantage in the market, Dell strives to help its suppliers reduce inventory costs. Dell has a vendor-managed inventory (VMI) arrangement with its suppliers, which decide how much to order and when to send their orders to the revolvers. Dell's suppliers order in batches (to offset ordering costs), using a continuous ordering system with a batch order size, Q, and a reorder point, R, where R is the sum of the inventory on order and a safety stock. The order size estimate, based on long-term data and forecasts, is held constant. Dell sets target inventory levels for its suppliers—typically 10 days of inventory—and keeps track of how much suppliers deviate from these targets and reports this information back to suppliers so that they can make adjustments accordingly.

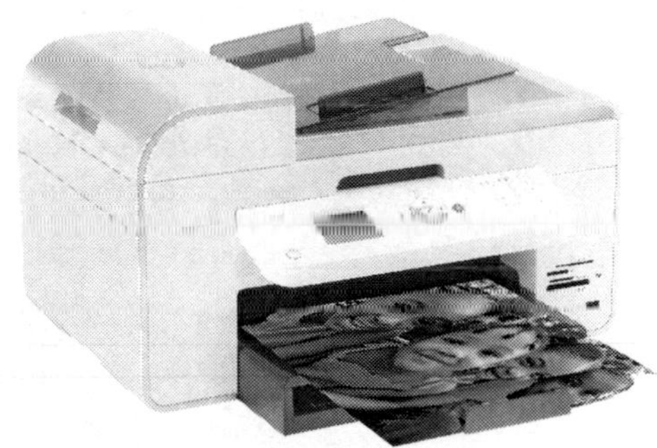

Source: R. Kapuscinski, R. Zhang, P. Carbonneau, R. Moore, and B. Reeves, "Inventory Decisions in Dell's Supply Chain," *Interfaces* 34, no. 3 (May–June 2004): 191–205.

EOQ Analysis with QM for Windows

QM for Windows has modules for all the EOQ models we have presented, including the basic model, the noninstantaneous receipt model, and the model with shortages. To demonstrate the capabilities of this program, we will use our basic EOQ example, for which the solution output summary is shown in Exhibit 16.1.

Exhibit 16.1

Inventory Results

I-75 Carpet Discount Store Solution

Parameter	Value		Parameter	Value
Demand rate(D)	10,000		Optimal order quantity (Q*)	2,000
Setup/Ordering cost(S)	150		Maximum Inventory Level (Imax)	2,000
Holding cost(H)	.75		Average inventory	1,000
Unit cost	0		Orders per period(year)	5
			Annual Setup cost	750
			Annual Holding cost	750
			Unit costs (PD)	0
			Total Cost	1,500

EOQ Analysis with Excel and Excel QM

Exhibit 16.2 shows an Excel spreadsheet set up to perform EOQ analysis for our noninstantaneous receipt model example. The parameters of the model have been input in cells **D3:D8**, and all the formulas for optimal Q, total cost, and so on have been embedded in cells **D10:D14**. Notice that the formula for computing optimal Q in cell D10 is shown on the formula bar at the top of the screen.

Exhibit 16.2

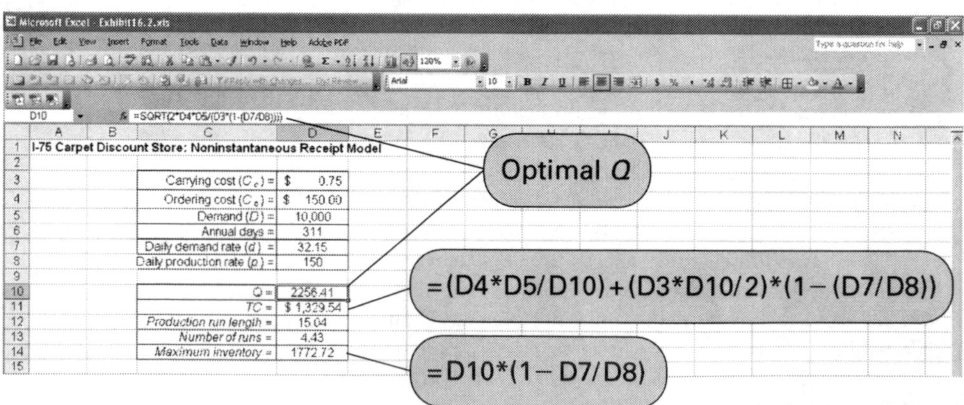

In Chapter 1 we introduced Excel QM, a set of spreadsheet macros that we have also used in several other chapters. Excel QM includes a set of spreadsheet macros for "Inventory" that includes EOQ analysis. After Excel QM is activated, the "Excel QM" menu is accessed by clicking on "QM" on the menu bar at the top of the spreadsheet. Clicking on "Inventory" from this menu results in a Spreadsheet Initialization window, in which you enter the problem title and the form of holding (or carrying) cost. Clicking on "OK" will result in the spreadsheet shown in Exhibit 16.3. Initially, this spreadsheet will have example values in the data cells **B8:B13**. Thus, the first step in using this macro is to type in cells **B8:B13** the data for the noninstantaneous receipt model for our I-75 Carpet Discount Store problem. The model results are computed automatically in cells **B16:B26** from formulas already embedded in the spreadsheet.

Exhibit 16.3

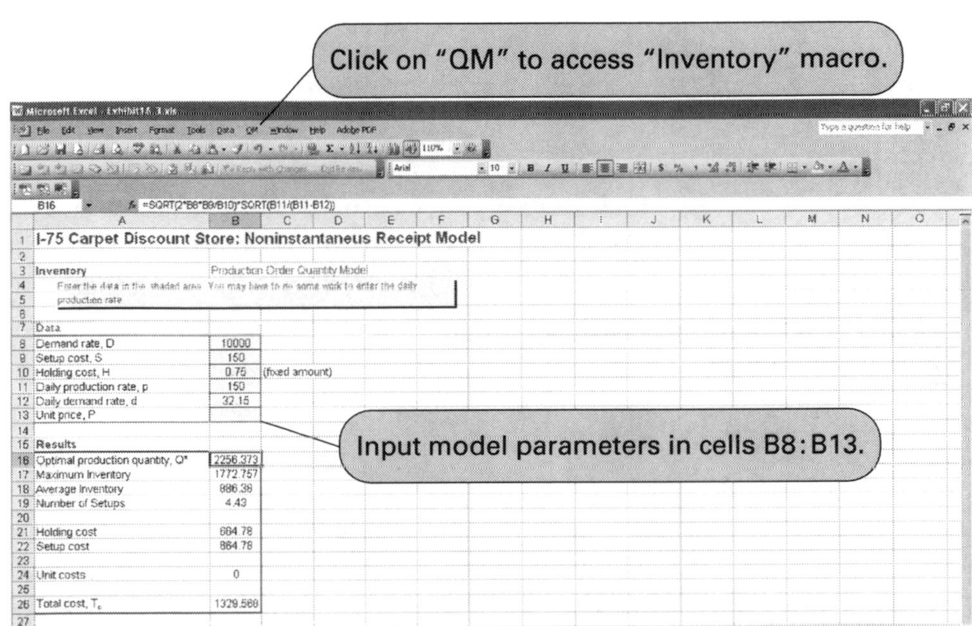

Quantity Discounts

It is often possible for a customer to receive a price discount on an item if a predetermined number of units is ordered. For example, occasionally in the back of a magazine you might see an advertisement for a firm that will produce a coffee mug (or hat) with a company or organizational logo on it, and the price will be $5 per mug if you purchase 100, $4 per mug if you purchase 200, or $3 per mug if you purchase 500 or more. Many manufacturing companies receive price discounts for ordering materials and supplies in high volume, and retail stores receive price discounts for ordering merchandise in large quantities.

Determining whether an order size with a discount is more cost-effective than optimal Q.

The basic EOQ model can be used to determine the optimal order size with quantity discounts; however, the application of the model is slightly altered. The total inventory cost function must now include the purchase price for the order, as follows:

$$TC = C_o \frac{D}{Q} + C_c \frac{Q}{2} + PD$$

where

P = per unit price of the item
D = annual demand

Purchase price was not considered as part of our basic EOQ formulation earlier because it had no real impact on the optimal order size. *PD* in the foregoing formula is a constant value that would not alter the basic shape of the total cost curve (i.e., the minimum point on the cost curve would still be at the same location, corresponding to the same value of Q). Thus, the optimal order size will be the same, no matter what the purchase price. However, when a discount price is available, it is associated with a specific order size that may be different from the optimal order size, and the customer must evaluate the trade-off between possibly higher carrying costs with the discount quantity versus EOQ cost. As a result, the purchase price does influence the order size decision when a discount is available.

Quantity discounts are evaluated with constant C_c and as a percentage of price.

Quantity discounts can be evaluated using the basic EOQ model under two different scenarios—with constant carrying costs and with carrying costs as a percentage of the purchase price. It is not uncommon for carrying costs to be determined as a percentage of purchase price, although it was not considered as such in our previous basic EOQ model. Carrying cost very well could have been a percentage of purchase price, but it was reflected as a constant value, C_c, in the basic EOQ model because the purchase price was not part of the EOQ formula. However, in the case of a quantity discount, carrying cost will vary with the change in price if it is computed as a percentage of purchase price.

Quantity Discounts with Constant Carrying Costs

In the EOQ cost model with constant carrying costs, the optimal order size, Q_{opt}, is the same, regardless of the discount price. Although total cost decreases with each discount in price because ordering and carrying cost are constant, the optimal order size, Q_{opt}, does not change. The total cost with Q_{opt} must be compared with any lower total cost with a discount price to see which is the minimum.

The following example will illustrate the evaluation of an EOQ model with a quantity discount when the carrying cost is a constant value. Comptek Computers wants to reduce a large stock of personal computers it is discontinuing. It has offered the University Bookstore at Tech a quantity discount pricing schedule if the store will purchase the personal computers in volume, as follows:

Quantity	*Price*
1–49	$1,400
50–89	1,100
90+	900

The annual carrying cost for the bookstore for a computer is $190, the ordering cost is $2,500, and annual demand for this particular model is estimated to be 200 units. The bookstore wants to determine whether it should take advantage of this discount or order the basic EOQ order size.

First, determine both the optimal order size and the total cost by using the basic EOQ model:

$$C_o = \$2{,}500$$
$$C_c = \$190 \text{ per unit}$$
$$D = 200$$
$$Q_{opt} = \sqrt{\frac{2C_oD}{C_c}}$$
$$= \sqrt{\frac{2(2{,}500)(200)}{190}}$$
$$Q_{opt} = 72.5$$

This order size is eligible for the first discount of $1,100; therefore, this price is used to compute total cost, as follows:

$$TC = \frac{C_oD}{Q_{opt}} + C_c\frac{Q_{opt}}{2} + PD$$
$$= \frac{(2,500)(200)}{(72.5)} + (190)\frac{(72.5)}{2} + (1,100)(200)$$
$$TC_{min} = \$233,784$$

Because there is a discount for an order size larger than 72.5, this total cost of $233,784 must be compared with total cost with an order size of 90 and a price of $900, as follows:

$$TC = \frac{C_oD}{Q} + C_c\frac{Q}{2} + PD$$
$$= \frac{(2,500)(200)}{(90)} + \frac{(190)(90)}{2} + (900)(200)$$
$$= \$194,105$$

Because this total cost is lower ($194,105 < $233,784), the maximum discount price should be taken and 90 units ordered.

Quantity Discounts with Constant Carrying Costs as a Percentage of Price

The difference between the model in the previous section and the quantity discount model with carrying cost as a percentage of price is that there is a different optimal order size, Q_{opt}, for each price discount. This requires that the optimal order size with a discount be determined a little differently from the case for a constant carrying cost.

The optimal order size and total cost are determined by using the basic EOQ model for the case with no quantity discount. This total cost value is then compared with the various discount quantity order sizes to determine the minimum cost order size. However, once this minimum cost order size is determined, it must be compared with the EOQ-determined order size for the specific discount price because the EOQ order size, Q_{opt}, will change for every discount level.

Reconsider our previous example, except now assume that the annual carrying cost for a computer at the University Bookstore is 15% of the purchase price. Using the same discount pricing schedule, determine the optimal order size.

The annual carrying cost is determined as follows:

Quantity	*Price*	*Carrying Cost*
0–49	$1,400	1,400(.15) = $210
50–89	1,100	1,100(.15) = 165
90+	900	900(.15) = 135

$$C_o = \$2,500$$
$$D = 200 \text{ computers per year}$$

First, compute the optimal order size for the purchase price without a discount and with $C_c = \$210$, as follows:

$$Q_{opt} = \sqrt{\frac{2C_oD}{C_c}}$$
$$= \sqrt{\frac{2(2,500)(200)}{210}}$$
$$Q_{opt} = 69$$

Because this order size exceeds 49 units, it is not feasible for this price, and a lower total cost will automatically be achieved with the first price discount of $1,100. However, the optimal order size will be different for this price discount because carrying cost is no longer constant. Thus, the new order size is computed as follows:

$$Q_{\text{opt}}\sqrt{\frac{2(2{,}500)(200)}{165}} = 77.8$$

This order size is the true optimum for this price discount instead of the 50 units required to receive the discount price; thus, it will result in the minimum total cost, computed as follows:

$$\begin{aligned} TC &= \frac{C_o D}{Q} + C_c\frac{Q}{2} + PD \\ &= \frac{(2{,}500)(200)}{77.8} + 165\frac{(77.8)}{2} + (1{,}100)(200) \\ &= \$232{,}845 \end{aligned}$$

Management Science Application

Quantity Discount Orders at Mars

Mars is one of the world's largest privately owned companies, with over $14 billion in annual sales. It has grown from making and selling buttercream candies door-to-door to a global business spanning 100 countries that includes food, pet care, beverage vending, and electronic payment systems. It produces such well-known products as Mars candies, M&M's, Snickers, and Uncle Ben's rice.

Mars relies on a small number of suppliers for each of the huge number of materials it uses in its products. One way that Mars purchases materials from its suppliers is through online electronic auctions, in which Mars buyers negotiate bids for orders from suppliers. The most important purchases are those of high value and large volume, for which the suppliers provide quantity discounts. The suppliers provide a pricing schedule that includes quantity ranges associated with each price level. Such quantity-discount auctions are tailored (by online brokers) for industries in which volume discounts are common, such as bulk chemicals and agricultural commodities.

A Mars buyer selects the bids that minimize total purchasing costs, subject to several rules: There must be a minimum and maximum number of suppliers so that Mars is not dependent on too few suppliers nor loses quality control by having too many; there must be a maximum amount purchased from each supplier to limit the influence of any one supplier; and a minimum amount must be ordered to avoid economically inefficient orders (i.e., less than a full tuckload).

Source: G. Hohner, J. Rich, E. Ng, A. Davenport, J. Kalagnanam, H. Lee, and C. An, "Combinatorial and Quantity-Discount Procurement Auctions Benefit Mars, Incroporated and Its Suppliers," *Interfaces* 33, no. 1 (January–February 2003): 23–35.

This cost must still be compared with the total cost for lowest discount price ($900) and order quantity (90 units), computed as follows:

$$TC = \frac{(2{,}500)(200)}{90} + \frac{(135)(90)}{2} + (900)(200)$$
$$= \$191{,}630$$

Because this total cost is lower ($191,630 < $232,845), the maximum discount price should be taken and 90 units ordered. However, as before, we still must check to see whether there is a new optimal order size for this discount that will result in an even lower cost. The optimal order size with $C_c = \$135$ is computed as follows:

$$Q_{opt} = \sqrt{\frac{2(2{,}500)(200)}{135}} = 86.1$$

Because this order size is less than the 90 units required to receive the discount, it is not feasible; thus, the optimal order size is 90 units.

Quantity Discount Model Solution with QM for Windows

QM for Windows has the capability to perform EOQ analysis with quantity discounts when carrying costs are constant. Exhibit 16.4 shows the solution summary for our University Bookstore example.

Exhibit 16.4

Inventory Results

University Bookstore Example Solution

Parameter	Value				Parameter	Value
Demand rate(D)	200	xxxxxxx	xxxxxxx		Optimal order quantity (Q*)	90
Setup/Ordering cost(S)	2,500	xxxxxxx	xxxxxxx		Maximum Inventory Level	90
Holding cost(H)	190	xxxxxxx	xxxxxxx		Average inventory	45
					Orders per period(year)	2.2222
	From	To	Price		Annual Setup cost	5,555.556
1	1	49	1,400		Annual Holding cost	8,550
2	50	89	1,100			
3	90	999,999	900		Unit costs (PD)	180,000
					Total Cost	194,105.6

Quantity Discount Model Solution with Excel

It is also possible to use Excel to solve the quantity discount model with constant carrying costs. Exhibit 16.5 shows the Excel solution screen for the University Bookstore example. Notice that the selection of the appropriate order size, Q, that results in the minimum total cost for each discount range is determined by the formulas embedded in cells E8, E9, and E10. For example, the formula for the first quantity discount range, 1–49, is embedded in cell E8 and shown on the formula bar at the top of the screen, **=IF(D8>=B8,D8,B8)**. This means that if the discount order size in cell D8 (i.e., $Q = 72.55$) is greater than or equal to the quantity in cell B8 (i.e., 1), the quantity in cell D8 (72.55) is selected; otherwise, the amount in cell B8 is selected. The formulas in cells E9 and E10 are constructed similarly. The result is that the order quantity for the final discount range, $Q = 90$, is selected.

Exhibit 16.5

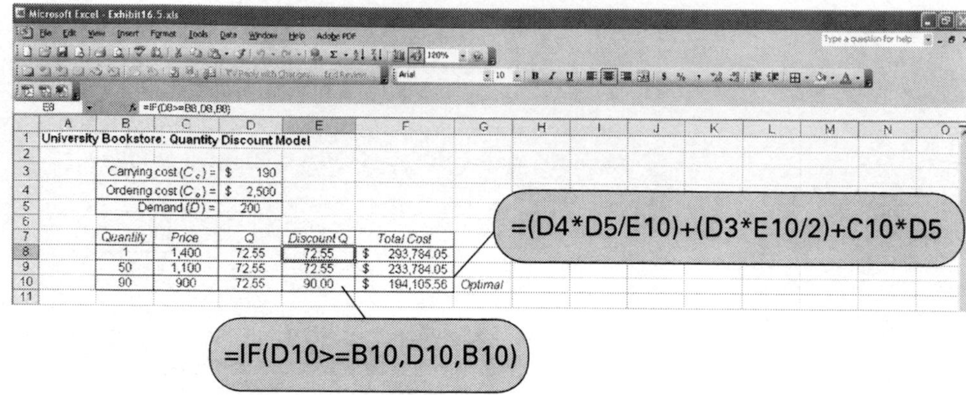

Quantity	Price	Q	Discount Q	Total Cost	
1	1,400	72.55	72.55	$ 293,784.05	
50	1,100	72.55	72.55	$ 233,784.05	
90	900	72.55	90.00	$ 194,105.56	Optimal

Reorder Point

In our presentation of the basic EOQ model in the previous section, we addressed one of the two primary questions related to inventory management: *How much should be ordered?* In this section we will discuss the other aspect of inventory management: *When to order?* The determinant of when to order in a continuous inventory system is the **reorder point**, the inventory level at which a new order is placed.

The concept of lead time is illustrated graphically in Figure 16.9. Notice that the order must be made prior to the time when the level of inventory falls to zero. Because demand is consuming the inventory while the order is being shipped, the order must be made while there is enough inventory in stock to meet demand during the lead-time period. This level of inventory is referred to as the *reorder point* and is so designated in Figure 16.9.

Figure 16.9
Reorder point and lead time

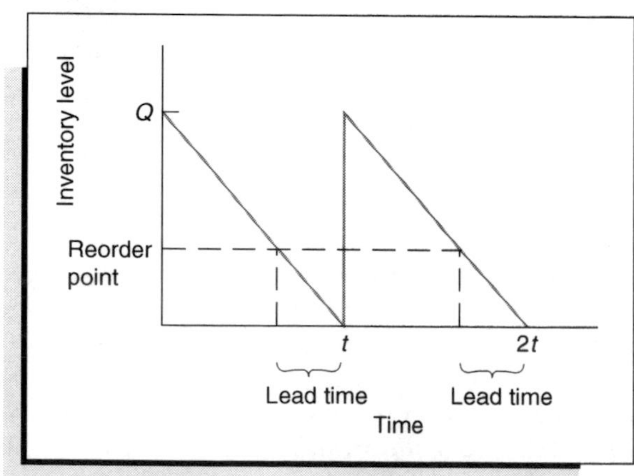

The reorder point for our basic EOQ model with constant demand and a constant lead time to receive an order is relatively straightforward. It is simply equal to the amount demanded during the lead-time period, computed using the following formula:

$$R = dL$$

where
d = demand rate per time period (i.e., daily)
L = lead time

Consider the I-75 Carpet Discount Store example described previously. The store is open 311 days per year. If annual demand is 10,000 yards of Super Shag carpet and the lead time to receive an order is 10 days, the reorder point for carpet is determined as follows:

$$\begin{aligned} R &= dL \\ &= \left(\frac{10{,}000}{311}\right)(10) \\ &= 321.54 \text{ yd.} \end{aligned}$$

Thus, when the inventory level falls to approximately 321 yards of carpet, a new order is placed. Notice that the reorder point is not related to the optimal order quantity or any of the inventory costs.

Safety Stocks

In our previous example for determining the reorder point, an order is made when the inventory level reaches the reorder point. During the lead time, the remaining inventory in stock is depleted as a constant demand rate, such that the new order quantity arrives at exactly the same moment as the inventory level reaches zero in Figure 16.9. Realistically, however, demand—and to a lesser extent lead time—is uncertain. The inventory level might be depleted at a slower or faster rate during lead time. This is depicted in Figure 16.10 for uncertain demand and a constant lead time.

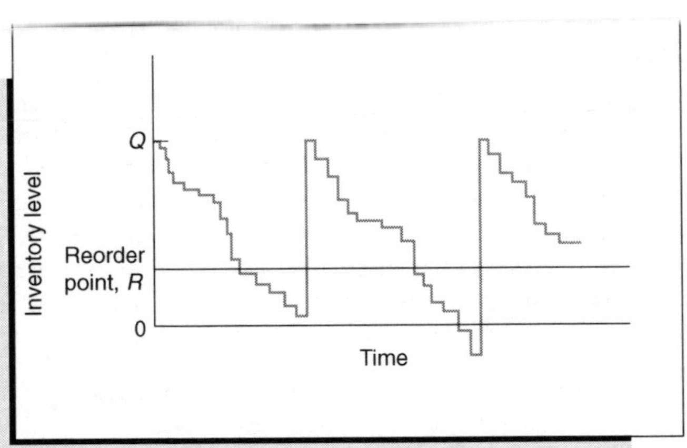

Figure 16.10
Inventory model with uncertain demand

Notice in the second order cycle that a stockout occurs when demand exceeds the available inventory in stock. As a hedge against stockouts when demand is uncertain, a safety (or buffer) stock of inventory is frequently added to the demand during lead time. The addition of a safety stock is shown in Figure 16.11.

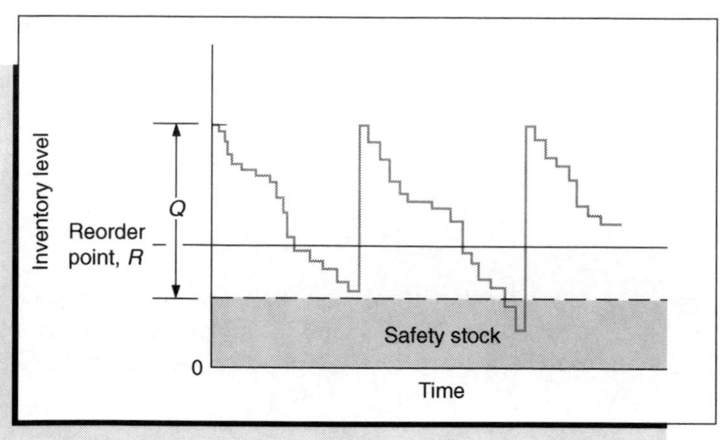

Figure 16.11
Inventory model with safety stock

Determining Safety Stock By Using Service Levels

*The **service level** is the probability that the inventory available during the lead time will meet demand.*

There are several approaches to determining the amount of the safety stock needed. One of the most popular methods is to establish a safety stock that will meet a specified **service level**. The service level is the probability that the amount of inventory on hand during the lead time is sufficient to meet expected demand (i.e., the probability that a stockout will not occur). The word *service* is used because the higher the probability that inventory will be on hand, the more likely that customer demand will be met (i.e., the customer can be served). For example, a service level of 90% means that there is a .90 probability that demand will be met during the lead time period and a .10 probability that a stockout will occur. The specification of the service level is typically a policy decision based on a number of factors, including costs for the "extra" safety stock and present and future lost sales if customer demand cannot be met.

Reorder Point with Variable Demand

To compute the reorder point with a safety stock that will meet a specific service level, we will assume that the individual demands during each day of lead time are uncertain and independent and can be described by a normal probability distribution. The average demand for the lead-time period is the sum of the average daily demands for the days of the lead time, which is also the product of the average daily demand multiplied by the lead time. Likewise, the variance of the distribution is the sum of the daily variances for the number of days in the lead-time period. Using these parameters, the reorder point to meet a specific service level can be computed as follows:

$$R = \bar{d}L + Z\sigma_d\sqrt{L}$$

where

$\bar{d}$ = average daily demand
L = lead time
σ_d = the standard deviation of daily demand
Z = number of standard deviations corresponding to the service level probability
$Z\sigma_d\sqrt{L}$ = safety stock

The term $\sigma_d\sqrt{L}$ in this formula for reorder point is the square root of the sum of the daily variances during lead time:

$$\text{variance} = (\text{daily variances}) \times (\text{number of days of lead time}) = \sigma_d^2 L$$

$$\text{standard deviation} = \sqrt{\sigma_d^2 L} = \sigma_d\sqrt{L}$$

The reorder point relative to the service level is shown in Figure 16.12. The service level is the shaded area, or probability, to the left of the reorder point, *R*.

Figure 16.12

Reorder point for a service level

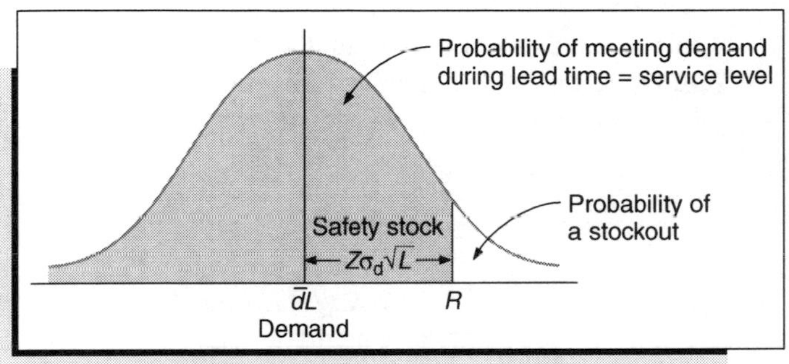

The I-75 Carpet Discount Store sells Super Shag carpet. The average daily customer demand for the carpet stocked by the store is normally distributed, with a mean daily demand of 30 yards and a standard deviation of 5 yards of carpet per day. The lead time for receiving a new order of carpet is 10 days. The store wants a reorder point and safety stock for a service level of 95%, with the probability of a stockout equal to 5%:

$$\bar{d} = 30 \text{ yd. per day}, \; L = 10 \text{ days}, \; \sigma_d = 5 \text{ yd. per day}$$

For a 95% service level, the value of *Z* (from Table A.1 in Appendix A) is 1.65. The reorder point is computed as follows:

$$R = \bar{d}L + Z\sigma_d\sqrt{L} = 30(10) + (1.65)(5)(\sqrt{10}) = 300 + 26.1 = 326.1 \text{ yd.}$$

The safety stock is the second term in the reorder point formula:

$$\text{safety stock} = Z\sigma_d\sqrt{L} = (1.65)(5)(\sqrt{10}) = 26.1 \text{ yd.}$$

Determining the Reorder Point Using Excel

Excel can be used to determine the reorder point with variable demand. Exhibit 16.6 shows an Excel spreadsheet set up to compute the reorder point for our I-75 Carpet Discount Store example. Notice that the formula for computing the reorder point in cell E7 is shown on the formula bar at the top of the spreadsheet.

Exhibit 16.6

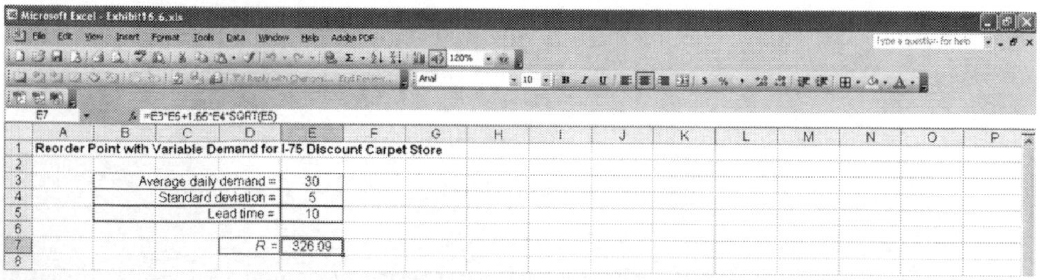

Microsoft Excel - Exhibit16.6.xls

E7 f_x =E3*E5+1.65*E4*SQRT(E5)

	A	B	C	D	E
1	Reorder Point with Variable Demand for I-75 Discount Carpet Store				
2					
3				Average daily demand =	30
4				Standard deviation =	5
5				Lead time =	10
6					
7				R =	326.09
8					

Reorder Point with Variable Lead Time

In the model in the previous section for determining the reorder point, we assumed a variable demand rate and a constant lead time. In the case where demand is constant and the lead time varies, we can use a similar formula, as follows:

$$R = d\bar{L} + Zd\sigma_L$$

where

d = constant daily demand
$\bar{L}$ = average lead time
σ_L = standard deviation of lead time
$d\sigma_L$ = standard deviation of demand during lead time
$Zd\sigma_L$ = safety stock

For our previous example of the I-75 Carpet Discount Store, we will now assume that daily demand for Super Shag carpet is a constant 30 yards. Lead time is normally distributed, with a mean of 10 days and a standard deviation of 3 days. The reorder point and safety stock corresponding to a 95% service level are computed as follows:

d = 30 yd. per day
$\bar{L}$ = 10 days
σ_L = 3 days
Z = 1.65 for a 95% service level
$R = d\bar{L} + Zd\sigma_L = (30)(10) + (1.65)(30)(3) = 300 + 148.5 = 448.5$ yd.

Reorder Point with Variable Demand and Lead Time

The final reorder point case we will consider is the case in which both demand and lead time are variables. The reorder point formula for this model is as follows.

$$R = \bar{d}\,\bar{L} + Z\sqrt{\sigma_d^2\bar{L} + \sigma_L^2\bar{d}^2}$$

where

$\bar{d}$ = average daily demand
$\bar{L}$ = average lead time
$\sqrt{\sigma_d^2\bar{L} + \sigma_L^2\bar{d}^2}$ = standard deviation of demand during lead time
$Z\sqrt{\sigma_d^2\bar{L} + \sigma_L^2\bar{d}^2}$ = safety stock

Management Science Application

Establishing Inventory Safety Stocks at Kellogg's

Kellogg's is the world's largest cereal producer and a leading maker of convenience foods, with worldwide sales in 1999 of almost $7 billion. The company started with a single product, Kellogg's Corn Flakes, in 1906, and over the years has developed a product line of other cereals, including Rice Krispies and Corn Pops, as well as convenience foods, such as Pop-Tarts and Nutri-Grain cereal bars. Kellogg's operates 5 plants in the United States and Canada and 7 distribution centers, and it contracts with 15 co-packers to produce or pack some Kellogg's products. Kellogg's must coordinate the production, packaging, inventory, and distribution of roughly 80 cereal products alone at these various facilities.

For more than a decade, Kellogg's has been using a model called the Kellogg Planning System (KPS) to plan its weekly production, inventory, and distribution decisions. The data used in the model are subject to much uncertainty, and the greatest uncertainty is in product demand. Demand in the first few weeks of a planning horizon is based on customer orders and is fairly accurate; however, demand in the third and fourth weeks may be significantly different from marketing forecasts. However, Kellogg's primary goal is to meet customer demand, and in order to achieve this goal, Kellogg's employs safety stocks as a buffer against uncertain demand. The safety stock for a product at a specific production facility in week t is the sum of demands for weeks t and $t + 1$. However, for a product that is being promoted in an advertising campaign, the safety stock is the sum of forecasted demand for a 4-week horizon or longer. KPS has saved Kellogg's many millions of dollars since the mid-1990s. The tactical version of KPS recently helped the company consolidate production capacity, with estimated projected savings of almost $40 million.

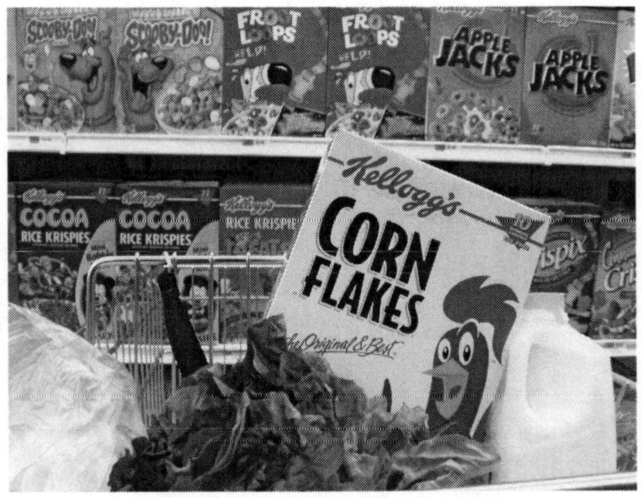

Source: G. Brown, J. Keegan, B. Vigus, and K. Wood, "The Kellogg Company Optimizes Production, Inventory, and Distribution," *Interfaces* 31, no. 6 (November–December 2001): 1–15.

Again we will consider the I-75 Carpet Discount Store example, used previously. In this case, daily demand is normally distributed, with a mean of 30 yards and a standard deviation of 5 yards. Lead time is also assumed to be normally distributed, with a mean of 10 days and a standard deviation of 3 days. The reorder point and safety stock for a 95% service level are computed as follows:

$$\bar{d} = 30 \text{ yd./day}$$
$$\sigma_d = 5 \text{ yd./day}$$
$$\bar{L} = 10 \text{ days}$$
$$\sigma_L = 3 \text{ days}$$
$$Z = 1.65 \text{ for a 95\% service level}$$
$$R = \bar{d}\,\bar{L} + Z\sqrt{\sigma_d^2\bar{L} + \sigma_L^2\bar{d}^2}$$
$$= (30)(10) + (1.65)\sqrt{(5)^2(10) + (3)^2(30)^2}$$
$$= 300 + 150.8$$
$$R = 450.8 \text{ yd.}$$

Thus, the reorder point is 450.8 yards, with a safety stock of 150.8 yards. Notice that this reorder point encompasses the largest safety stock of our three reorder point examples, which would be anticipated, given the increased variability resulting from variable demand and lead time.

Order Quantity for a Periodic Inventory System

*A **periodic inventory** system uses variable order sizes at fixed time intervals.*

Previously we defined a continuous, or fixed–order quantity, inventory system as one in which the order quantity was constant and the time between orders varied. So far, this type of inventory system has been the primary focus of our discussion. The less common **periodic**, or *fixed–time period*, **inventory system** is one in which the time between orders is constant and the order size varies. A drugstore is one example of a business that sometimes uses a fixed-period inventory system. Drugstores stock a number of personal hygiene and health-related products, such as shampoo, toothpaste, soap, bandages, cough medicine, and aspirin. Normally, the vendors that provide these items to the store will make periodic visits—for example, every few weeks or every month—and count the stock of inventory on hand for their products. If the inventory is exhausted or at some predetermined reorder point, a new order will be placed for an amount that will bring the inventory level back up to the desired level. The drugstore managers will generally not monitor the inventory level between vendor visits but instead rely on the vendor to take inventory at the time of the scheduled visit.

A periodic inventory system normally requires a larger safety stock.

A limitation of this type of inventory system is that inventory can be exhausted early in the time period between visits, resulting in a stockout that will not be remedied until the next scheduled order. Alternatively, in a fixed–order quantity system, when inventory reaches a reorder point, an order is made that minimizes the time during which a stockout might exist. As a result of this drawback, a larger safety stock is normally required for the fixed-interval system.

Order Quantity with Variable Demand

If the demand rate and lead time are constant, then the fixed-period model will have a fixed order quantity that will be made at specified time intervals, which is the same as the fixed quantity (EOQ) model under similar conditions. However, as we have already explained, the fixed-period model reacts significantly differently from the fixed–order quantity model when demand is a variable.

The order size for a fixed-period model, given variable daily demand that is normally distributed, is determined by the following formula:

$$Q = \bar{d}(t_b + L) + Z\sigma_d\sqrt{t_b + L} - I$$

where

$\bar{d}$ = average demand rate

t_b = the fixed time between orders

L = lead time

σ_d = standard deviation of demand

$Z\sigma_d\sqrt{t_b + L}$ = safety stock

I = inventory in stock

The first term in the preceding formula, $d(t_b + L)$, is the average demand during the order cycle time plus the lead time. It reflects the amount of inventory that will be needed to protect against shortages during the entire time from this order to the next and the lead time, until the order is received. The second term, $Z\sigma_d\sqrt{t_b + L}$, is the safety stock for a specific service level, determined in much the same way as previously described for a reorder point. The final term, *I*, is the amount of inventory on hand when the inventory level is checked and an order is made. We will demonstrate the computation of *Q* with an example.

The Corner Drug Store stocks a popular brand of sunscreen. The average demand for the sunscreen is 6 bottles per day, with a standard deviation of 1.2 bottles. A vendor for the sunscreen producer checks the drugstore stock every 60 days, and during a particular visit the drugstore had 8 bottles in stock. The lead time to receive an order is 5 days. The order size for this order period that will enable the drugstore to maintain a 95% service level is computed as follows:

$$\begin{aligned}
\bar{d} &= 6 \text{ bottles per day} \\
\sigma_d &= 1.2 \text{ bottles} \\
t_b &= 60 \text{ days} \\
L &= 5 \text{ days} \\
I &= 8 \text{ bottles} \\
Z &= 1.65 \text{ for } 95\% \text{ service level} \\
Q &= \bar{d}(t_b + L) + Z\sigma_d\sqrt{t_b + L} - I \\
&= (6)(60 + 5) + (1.65)(1.2)\sqrt{60 + 5} - 8 \\
&= 398 \text{ bottles}
\end{aligned}$$

Determining the Order Quantity for the Fixed-Period Model with Excel

Exhibit 16.7 shows an Excel spreadsheet set up to compute the order quantity for the fixed-period model with variable demand for our Corner Drug Store example. Notice that the formula for the order quantity in cell D10 is shown on the formula bar at the top of the spreadsheet.

Exhibit 16.7

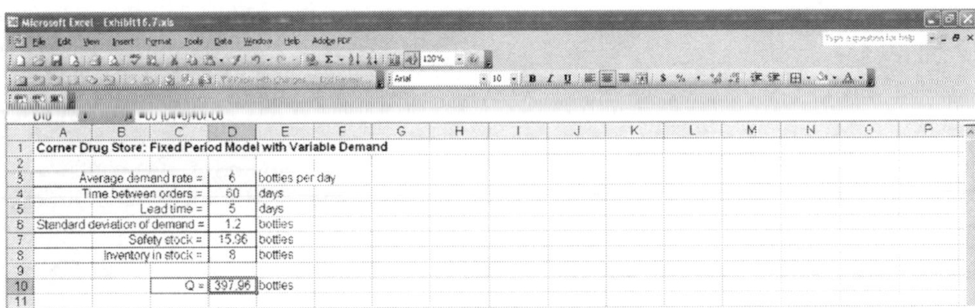

	A	B	C	D	E
1	Corner Drug Store: Fixed Period Model with Variable Demand				
2					
3			Average demand rate =	6	bottles per day
4			Time between orders =	60	days
5			Lead time =	5	days
6	Standard deviation of demand =			1.2	bottles
7			Safety stock =	15.96	bottles
8			Inventory in stock =	8	bottles
9					
10			Q =	397.96	bottles
11					

Summary

In this chapter the classical economic order quantity model has been presented. The basic form of the EOQ model we discussed included simplifying assumptions regarding order receipt, no shortages, and constant demand known with certainty. By relaxing some of these assumptions, we were able to create increasingly complex but realistic models. These EOQ variations included the reorder point model, the noninstantaneous receipt model, the model with shortages, and models with safety stocks. The techniques for inventory analysis presented in this chapter are not widely used to analyze other types of problems. Conversely, however, many of the techniques presented in this text are used for inventory analysis (in addition to the methods presented in these chapters). The wide use of management science techniques for inventory analysis attests to the importance of inventory to all types of organizations.

References

Buchan, J., and Koenigsberg, E. *Scientific Inventory Management.* Upper Saddle River, NJ: Prentice Hall, 1963.

Buffa, E. S., and Miller, J. G. *Production-Inventory Systems: Planning and Control*, 3rd ed. Homewood, IL: Irwin, 1979.

Churchman, C. W., Ackoff, R. L., and Arnoff, E. L. *Introduction to Operations Research.* New York: John Wiley & Sons, 1957.

Hadley, G., and Whitin, T. M. *Analysis of Inventory Systems.* Upper Saddle River, NJ: Prentice Hall, 1963.

Johnson, L. A., and Montgomery, D. C. *Operations Research in Production Planning, Scheduling and Inventory Control.* New York: John Wiley & Sons, 1974.

Magee, J. F., and Boodman, D. M. *Production Planning and Inventory Control*, 2nd ed. New York: McGraw-Hill, 1967.

Starr, M. K., and Miller, D. W. *Inventory Control: Theory and Practice.* Upper Saddle River, NJ: Prentice Hall, 1962.

Wagner, H. M. *Statistical Management of Inventory Systems.* New York: John Wiley & Sons, 1962.

Whitin, T. M. *The Theory of Inventory Management.* Princeton, NJ: Princeton University Press, 1957.

Example Problem Solutions

The following example will demonstrate EOQ analysis for the classical model and the model with shortages and back ordering.

Problem Statement

Electronic Village stocks and sells a particular brand of personal computer. It costs the store $450 each time it places an order with the manufacturer for the personal computers. The annual cost of carrying the PCs in inventory is $170. The store manager estimates the annual demand for the PCs will be 1,200 units.

a. Determine the optimal order quantity and the total minimum inventory cost.
b. Assume that shortages are allowed and that the shortage cost is $600 per unit per year. Compute the optimal order quantity and the total minimum inventory cost.

Solution

Step 1: (part a): Determine the Optimal Order Quantity

$$D = 1{,}200 \text{ personal computers}$$
$$C_c = \$170$$
$$C_o = \$450$$
$$Q = \sqrt{\frac{2C_oD}{C_c}}$$
$$= \sqrt{\frac{2(450)(1{,}200)}{170}}$$
$$= 79.7 \text{ personal computers}$$
$$\text{total cost} = C_c\frac{Q}{2} + C_o\frac{D}{Q}$$
$$= 170\left(\frac{79.7}{2}\right) + 450\left(\frac{1{,}200}{79.7}\right)$$
$$= \$13{,}549.91$$

Step 2: (part b): Compute the EOQ with Shortages

$$C_s = \$600$$

$$Q = \sqrt{\frac{2C_oD}{C_c}\left(\frac{C_s + C_c}{C_s}\right)}$$

$$= \sqrt{\frac{2(450)(1,200)}{170}\left(\frac{600+170}{600}\right)}$$

$$= 90.3 \text{ personal computers}$$

$$S = Q\left(\frac{C_c}{C_c + C_s}\right)$$

$$= 90.3\left(\frac{170}{170+600}\right)$$

$$= 19.9 \text{ personal computers}$$

$$\text{total cost} = \frac{C_sS^2}{2Q} + C_c\frac{(Q-S)^2}{2Q} + \frac{C_oD}{Q}$$

$$= \frac{(600)(19.9)^2}{2(90.3)} + 170\frac{(90.3-19.9)^2}{2(90.3)} + 450\left(\frac{1,200}{90.3}\right)$$

$$= \$1,315.65 + 4,665.27 + 5,980.07$$

$$= \$11,960.98$$

Problem Statement

A computer products store stocks color graphics monitors, and the daily demand is normally distributed, with a mean of 1.6 monitors and a standard deviation of 0.4 monitor. The lead time to receive an order from the manufacturer is 15 days. Determine the reorder point that will achieve a 98% service level.

Solution

Step 1: Identify Parameters

$$\bar{d} = 1.6 \text{ monitors per day}$$
$$L = 15 \text{ days}$$
$$\sigma_d = 0.4 \text{ monitors per day}$$
$$Z = 2.05 \text{ (for a 98\% service level)}$$

Step 2: Solve for *R*

$$R = \bar{d}L + Z\sigma_d\sqrt{L} = (1.6)(15) + (2.05)(0.4)\sqrt{15} = 24 + 3.18 = 27.18 \text{ monitors}$$

Problems

1. Hayes Electronics stocks and sells a particular brand of personal computer. It costs the firm $450 each time it places an order with the manufacturer for the personal computers. The cost of carrying one PC in inventory for a year is $170. The store manager estimates that total annual demand for the computers will be 1,200 units, with a constant demand rate throughout the year. Orders are

received within minutes after placement from a local warehouse maintained by the manufacturer. The store policy is never to have stockouts of the PCs. The store is open for business every day of the year except Christmas Day. Determine the following.

a. The optimal order quantity per order
b. The minimum total annual inventory costs
c. The optimal number of orders per year
d. The optimal time between orders (in working days)

2. Hayes Electronics in Problem 1 assumed with certainty that the ordering cost is $450 per order and the inventory carrying cost is $170 per unit per year. However, the inventory model parameters are frequently only estimates that are subject to some degree of uncertainty. Consider four cases of variation in the model parameters: (a) Both ordering cost and carrying cost are 10% less than originally estimated, (b) both ordering cost and carrying cost are 10% higher than originally estimated, (c) ordering cost is 10% higher and carrying cost is 10% lower than originally estimated, and (d) ordering cost is 10% lower and carrying cost is 10% higher than originally estimated. Determine the optimal order quantity and total inventory cost for each of the four cases. Prepare a table with values from all four cases and compare the sensitivity of the model solution to changes in parameter values.

3. A firm is faced with the attractive situation in which it can obtain immediate delivery of an item it stocks for retail sale. The firm has therefore not bothered to order the item in any systematic way. Recently, however, profits have been squeezed due to increasing competitive pressures, and the firm has retained a management consultant to study its inventory management. The consultant has determined that the various costs associated with making an order for the item stocked are approximately $30 per order. She has also determined that the costs of carrying the item in inventory amount to approximately $20 per unit per year (primarily direct storage costs and forgone profit on investment in inventory). Demand for the item is reasonably constant over time, and the forecast is for 19,200 units per year. When an order is placed for the item, the entire order is immediately delivered to the firm by the supplier. The firm operates 6 days a week plus a few Sundays, or approximately 320 days per year. Determine the following.

a. The optimal order quantity per order
b. The total annual inventory costs
c. The optimal number of orders to place per year
d. The number of operating days between orders, based on the optimal number of orders.

4. The Western Jeans Company purchases denim from Cumberland Textile Mills. The Western Jeans Company uses 35,000 yards of denim per year to make jeans. The cost of ordering denim from the textile company is $500 per order. It costs Western $0.35 per yard annually to hold a yard of denim in inventory. Determine the optimal number of yards of denim the Western Jeans Company should order, the minimum total annual inventory cost, the optimal number of orders per year, and the optimal time between orders.

5. The Metropolitan Book Company purchases paper from the Atlantic Paper Company. Metropolitan produces magazines and paperbacks that require 1,215,000 pounds of paper per year. The cost per order for the company is $1,200; the cost of holding 1 pound of paper in inventory is $0.08 per year. Determine the following.

a. The economic order quantity
b. The minimum total annual cost
c. The optimal number of orders per year
d. The optimal time between orders

6. The Simple Simon Bakery produces fruit pies for freezing and subsequent sale. The bakery, which operates 5 days per week, 52 weeks per year, can produce pies at the rate of 64 pies per day.

The bakery sets up the pie production operation and produces until a predetermined number (Q) of pies has been produced. When not producing pies, the bakery uses its personnel and facilities for producing other bakery items. The setup cost for a production run of fruit pies is \$500. The cost of holding frozen pies in storage is \$5 per pie per year. The annual demand for frozen fruit pies, which is constant over time, is 5,000 pies. Determine the following.

a. The optimal production run quantity (Q)
b. The total annual inventory costs
c. The optimal number of production runs per year
d. The optimal cycle time (time between run starts)
e. The run length, in working days

7. The Pedal Pusher Bicycle Shop operates 7 days per week, closing only on Christmas Day. The shop pays \$300 for a particular bicycle purchased from the manufacturer. The annual holding cost per bicycle is estimated to be 25% of the dollar value of inventory. The shop sells an average of 25 bikes per week. Frequently, the dealer does not have a bike in stock when a customer purchases it, and the bike is back ordered. The dealer estimates his shortage cost per unit back ordered, on an annual basis, to be \$250 due to lost future sales (and profits). The ordering cost for each order is \$100. Determine the optimal order quantity and shortage level and the total minimum cost.

8. The Petroco Company uses a highly toxic chemical in one of its manufacturing processes. It must have the product delivered by special cargo trucks designed for safe shipment of chemicals. As such, ordering (and delivery) costs are relatively high, at \$2,600 per order. The chemical product is packaged in 1-gallon plastic containers. The cost of holding the chemical in storage is \$50 per gallon per year. The annual demand for the chemical, which is constant over time, is 2,000 gallons per year. The lead time from time of order placement until receipt is 10 days. The company operates 310 working days per year. Compute the optimal order quantity, the total minimum inventory cost, and the reorder point.

9. The Big Buy Supermarket stocks Munchies Cereal. Demand for Munchies is 4,000 boxes per year (365 days). It costs the store \$60 per order of Munchies, and it costs \$0.80 per box per year to keep the cereal in stock. Once an order for Munchies is placed, it takes 4 days to receive the order from a food distributor. Determine the following.
   a. The optimal order size
   b. The minimum total annual inventory cost
   c. The reorder point

10. The Wood Valley Dairy makes cheese to supply to stores in its area. The dairy can make 250 pounds of cheese per day, and the demand at area stores is 180 pounds per day. Each time the dairy makes cheese, it costs \$125 to set up the production process. The annual cost of carrying a pound of cheese in a refrigerated storage area is \$12. Determine the optimal order size and the minimum total annual inventory cost.

11. The Rainwater Brewery produces Rainwater Light Beer, which it stores in barrels in its warehouse and supplies to its distributors on demand. The demand for Rainwater is 1,500 barrels of beer per day. The brewery can produce 2,000 barrels of Rainwater per day. It costs \$6,500 to set up a production run for Rainwater. Once it is brewed, the beer is stored in a refrigerated warehouse at an annual cost of \$50 per barrel. Determine the economic order quantity and the minimum total annual inventory cost.

12. The purchasing manager for the Atlantic Steel Company must determine a policy for ordering coal to operate 12 converters. Each converter requires exactly 5 tons of coal per day to operate, and the firm operates 360 days per year. The purchasing manager has determined that the ordering cost is \$80 per order and the cost of holding coal is 20% of the average dollar value of inventory held. The purchasing manager has negotiated a contract to obtain the coal for \$12 per ton for the coming year.

a. Determine the optimal quantity of coal to receive in each order.
b. Determine the total inventory-related costs associated with the optimal ordering policy (do not include the cost of the coal).
c. If 5 days of lead time are required to receive an order of coal, how much coal should be on hand when an order is placed?

13. The Pacific Lumber Company and Mill processes 10,000 logs annually, operating 250 days per year. Immediately upon receiving an order, the logging company's supplier begins delivery to the lumber mill, at a rate of 60 logs per day. The lumber mill has determined that the ordering cost is $1,600 per order and the cost of carrying logs in inventory before they are processed is $15 per log on an annual basis. Determine the following.
    a. The optimal order size
    b. The total inventory cost associated with the optimal order quantity
    c. The number of operating days between orders
    d. The number of operating days required to receive an order

14. The Roadking Tire Store sells a brand of tires called the Roadrunner. The annual demand from the store's customers for Roadrunner tires is 3,700. The cost to order tires from the tire manufacturer is $420 per order. The annual carrying cost is $1.75 per tire. The store allows shortages, and the annual shortage cost per tire is $4. Determine the optimal order size, maximum shortage level, and minimum total annual inventory cost.

15. The Laurel Creek Lawn Shop sells Fastgro Fertilizer. The annual demand for the fertilizer is 270,000 pounds. The cost to order the fertilizer from the Fastgro Company is $105 per order. The annual carrying cost is $0.25 per pound. The store operates with shortages, and the annual shortage cost is $0.70 per pound. Compute the optimal order size, minimum total annual inventory cost, and maximum shortage level.

16. Videoworld is a discount store that sells color televisions. The annual demand for color television sets is 400. The cost per order from the manufacturer is $650. The carrying cost is $45 per set each year. The store has an inventory policy that allows shortages. The shortage cost per set is estimated at $60. Determine the following.
    a. The optimal order size
    b. The maximum shortage level
    c. The minimum total annual inventory cost

17. The University Bookstore at Tech stocks the required textbook for Management Science 2405. The demand for this text is 1,200 copies per year. The cost of placing an order is $350, and the annual carrying cost is $2.75 per book. If a student requests the book and it is not in stock, the student will likely go to the privately owned Tech Bookstore. It is likely that the student will not buy books at the University Bookstore in the future; thus the shortage cost to the University Bookstore is estimated to be $45 per book. Determine the optimal order size, the maximum shortage level, and the total inventory cost.

18. The A-to-Z Office Supply Company is open from 8:00 A.M. to 6:00 P.M., and it receives 200 calls per day for delivery orders. It costs A-to-Z $20 to send out its trucks to make deliveries. The company estimates that each minute a customer spends waiting for an order costs A-to-Z $0.20 in lost sales.
    a. How frequently should A-to-Z send out its delivery trucks each day? Indicate the total daily cost of deliveries.
    b. If a truck could carry only six orders, how often would deliveries be made, and what would be the cost?

19. The Union Street Microbrewery makes 1220 Union beer, which it bottles and sells in its adjoining restaurant and by the case. It costs $1,700 to set up, brew, and bottle a batch of the beer. The annual

cost to store the beer in inventory is $1.25 per bottle. The annual demand for the beer is 18,000 bottles, and the brewery has the capacity to produce 30,000 bottles annually.

a. Determine the optimal order quantity, the total annual inventory cost, the number of production runs per year, and the maximum inventory level.
b. If the microbrewery has only enough storage space to hold a maximum of 2,500 bottles of beer in inventory, how will that affect total inventory costs?

20. Eurotronics is a European manufacturer of electronic components. During the course of a year, it requires container cargo space on ships leaving Hamburg bound for the United States, Mexico, South America, and Canada. Annually, the company needs 160,000 cubic feet of cargo space. The cost of reserving cargo space is $7,000, and the cost of holding cargo space is $0.80/ft^3. Determine how much storage space Eurotronics should optimally order, the total cost, and how many times per year it should place orders to reserve space.

21. The Summer Outdoor Furniture Company produces wooden lawn chairs. The annual demand from its store customers is 17,400 chairs per year. The transport and handling costs are $2,600 each time a shipment of chairs is delivered to stores from its warehouse. The annual carrying cost is $3.75 per chair.
    a. Determine the optimal order quantity and minimum total annual cost.
    b. The company is thinking about relocating its warehouse closer to its customers, which would reduce transport and handling costs to $1,900 per order but increase carrying costs to $4.50 per chair per year. Should the company relocate based on inventory costs?

22. The Spruce Creek Vegetable Farm produces organically grown greenhouse tomatoes that are sold to area grocery stores. The annual demand for Spruce Creek's tomatoes is 270,000 pounds. The farm is able to produce 305,000 pounds annually. The cost to transport the tomatoes from the farm to the stores is $620 per load. The annual carrying cost is $0.12 per pound.
    a. Compute the optimal order size, the maximum inventory level, and the total minimum cost.
    b. If Spruce Creek can increase production capacity to 360,000 tomatoes per year, will it reduce total inventory cost?

23. The Uptown Kiln is an importer of ceramics from overseas. It has arranged to purchase a particular type of ceramic pottery from a Korean artisan. The artisan makes the pottery in 120-unit batches and will ship only that exact number of units. The transportation and handling cost of a shipment is $7,600 (not including the unit cost). The Uptown Kiln estimates its annual demand to be 900 units. What storage and handling cost per unit does it need to achieve in order to minimize its inventory cost?

24. The I-75 Carpet Discount Store has an annual demand of 10,000 yards of Super Shag carpet. The annual carrying cost for a yard of this carpet is $0.75, and the ordering cost is $150. The carpet manufacturer normally charges the store $8 per yard for the carpet; however, the manufacturer has offered a discount price of $6.50 per yard if the store will order 5,000 yards. How much should the store order, and what will be the total annual inventory cost for that order quantity?

25. The Fifth Quarter Bar buys Old World draft beer by the barrel from a local distributor. The bar has an annual demand of 900 barrels, which it purchases at a price of $205 per barrel. The annual carrying cost is 12% of the price, and the cost per order is $160. The distributor has offered the bar a reduced price of $190 per barrel if it will order a minimum of 300 barrels. Should the bar take the discount?

26. The bookstore at State University purchases from a vendor sweatshirts emblazoned with the school name and logo. The vendor sells the sweatshirts to the store for $38 apiece. The cost to the bookstore for placing an order is $120, and the carrying cost is 25% of the average annual inventory value. The bookstore manager estimates that 1,700 sweatshirts will be sold during the year. The vendor has offered the bookstore the following volume discount schedule:

Order Size	Discount %
1–299	0
300–499	2
500–799	4
800+	5

The bookstore manager wants to determine the bookstore's optimal order quantity, given the foregoing quantity discount information.

27. Determine the optimal order quantity of sweatshirts and total annual cost in Problem 26 if the carrying cost is a constant $8 per sweatshirt per year.

28. The office manager for the Gotham Life Insurance Company orders letterhead stationery from an office products firm in boxes of 500 sheets. The company uses 6,500 boxes per year. Annual carrying costs are $3 per box, and ordering costs are $28. The following discount price schedule is provided by the office supply company:

Order Quantity (boxes)	Price per Box
200–999	$16
1,000–2,999	14
3,000–5,999	13
6,000+	12

Determine the optimal order quantity and the total annual inventory cost.

29. Determine the optimal order quantity and total annual inventory cost for boxes of stationery in Problem 28 if the carrying cost is 20% of the price of a box of stationery.

30. The 23,000-seat City Coliseum houses the local professional ice hockey, basketball, indoor soccer, and arena football teams, as well as various trade shows, wrestling and boxing matches, tractor pulls, and circuses. Coliseum vending annually sells large quantities of soft drinks and beer in plastic cups, with the name of the coliseum and the various team logos on them. The local container cup manufacturer that supplies the cups in boxes of 100 has offered coliseum management the following discount price schedule for cups:

Order Quantity (boxes)	Price per Box
2,000–6,999	$47
7,000–11,999	43
12,000–19,999	41
20,000+	38

The annual demand for cups is 2.3 million, the annual carrying cost per box of cups is $1.90, and the ordering cost is $320. Determine the optimal order quantity and total annual inventory cost.

31. Community Hospital orders latex sanitary gloves from a hospital supply firm. The hospital expects to use 40,000 pairs of gloves per year. The cost to order and to have the gloves delivered is $180. The annual carrying cost is $0.18 per pair of gloves. The hospital supply firm offers the following quantity discount pricing schedule:

Quantity	Price
0–9,999	$0.34
10,000–19,999	0.32
20,000–29,999	0.30
30,000–39,999	0.28
40,000–49,000	0.26
50,000+	0.24

Determine the order size for the hospital.

32. Tracy McCoy is the office administrator for the department of management science at Tech. The faculty uses a lot of printer paper, and although Tracy is constantly reordering, paper frequently runs out. She orders the paper from the university central stores. Several faculty members have determined that the lead time to receive an order is normally distributed, with a mean of 2 days and a standard deviation of 0.5 day. The faculty has also determined that daily demand for the paper is normally distributed, with a mean of 2 packages and a standard deviation of 0.8 package. What reorder point should Tracy use in order not to run out 99% of the time?

33. Determine the optimal order quantity and total annual inventory cost for cups in Problem 30 if the carrying cost is 5% of the price of a box of cups.

34. The amount of denim used daily by the Western Jeans Company in its manufacturing process to make jeans is normally distributed, with an average of 3,000 yards of denim and a standard deviation of 600 yards. The lead time required to receive an order of denim from the textile mill is a constant 6 days. Determine the safety stock and reorder point if the Western Jeans Company wants to limit the probability of a stockout and work stoppage to 5%.

35. In Problem 34, what level of service would a safety stock of 2,000 yards provide?

36. The Atlantic Paper Company produces paper from wood pulp ordered from a lumber products firm. The paper company's daily demand for wood pulp is a constant 8,000 pounds. Lead time is normally distributed, with an average of 7 days and a standard deviation of 1.6 days. Determine the reorder point if the paper company wants to limit the probability of a stockout and work stoppage to 2%.

37. The Uptown Bar and Grill serves Rainwater draft beer to its customers. The daily demand for beer is normally distributed, with an average of 18 gallons and a standard deviation of 4 gallons. The lead time required to receive an order of beer from the local distributor is normally distributed, with a mean of 3 days and a standard deviation of 0.8 day. Determine the safety stock and reorder point if the restaurant wants to maintain a 90% service level. What would be the increase in the safety stock if a 95% service level were desired?

38. In Problem 37, the manager of the Uptown Bar and Grill has negotiated with the beer distributor for the lead time to receive orders to be a constant 3 days. What effect does this have on the reorder point developed in Problem 37 for a 90% service level?

39. The daily demand for Sunlight paint at the Rainbow Paint Store in East Ridge is normally distributed, with a mean of 26 gallons and a standard deviation of 10 gallons. The lead time for receiving an order of paint from the Sunlight distributor is 9 days. Because this is the only paint store in East Ridge, the manager is interested in maintaining only a 75% service level. What reorder point should be used to meet this service level? The manager subsequently has learned that a new paint store will open soon in East Ridge, which has prompted her to increase the service level to 95%. What reorder point will maintain this service level?

40. PM Computers assembles personal computers from generic components. It purchases its color monitors from a manufacturer in Taiwan; thus, there is a long and uncertain lead time for receiving orders. Lead time is normally distributed, with a mean of 25 days and a standard deviation of 10 days. Daily demand is also normally distributed, with a mean of 2.5 monitors and a standard deviation of 1.2 monitors. Determine the safety stock and reorder point corresponding to a 90% service level.

41. PM Computers in Problem 40 is considering purchasing monitors from an American manufacturer that would guarantee a lead time of 8 days, instead of the Taiwanese company. Determine the new reorder point, given this lead time, and identify the factors that would enter into the decision to change manufacturers.

42. The Corner Drug Store fills prescriptions for a popular children's antibiotic, amoxicillin. The daily demand for amoxicillin is normally distributed, with a mean of 200 ounces and a standard deviation of 80 ounces. The vendor for the pharmaceutical firm that supplies the drug calls the drugstore pharmacist every 30 days to check the inventory of amoxicillin. During a call, the druggist indicated that the store had 60 ounces of the antibiotic in stock. The lead time to receive an order is 4 days. Determine the order size that will enable the drugstore to maintain a 95% service level.

43. The Fast Service Food Mart stocks frozen pizzas in a refrigerated display case. The average daily demand for the pizzas is normally distributed, with a mean of 8 pizzas and a standard deviation of 2.5 pizzas. A vendor for a packaged food distributor checks the market's inventory of frozen foods every 10 days, and during a particular visit, there were no pizzas in stock. The lead time to receive an order is 3 days. Determine the order size for this order period that will result in a 99% service level. During the vendor's following visit, there were 5 frozen pizzas in stock. What is the order size for the next order period?

44. The Impanema Restaurant stocks a red Brazilian table wine it purchases from a wine merchant in a nearby city. The daily demand for the wine at the restaurant is normally distributed, with a mean of 18 bottles and a standard deviation of 4 bottles. The wine merchant sends a representative to check the restaurant's wine cellar every 30 days, and during a recent visit, there were 25 bottles in stock. The lead time to receive an order is 2 days. The restaurant manager has requested an order size that will enable him to limit the probability of a stockout to 2%. Determine the order size.

45. The concession stand at the Blacksburg High School stadium sells slices of pizza during soccer games. Concession stand sales are a primary source of revenue for high school athletic programs, so the athletic director wants to sell as much food as possible. However, any pizza not sold is given away to the players, coaches, and referees, or it is thrown away. The athletic director wants to determine a reorder point that will meet, not exceed, the demand for pizza. Pizza sales are normally distributed, with a mean of 6 pizzas per hour and a standard deviation of 2.5 pizzas. The pizzas are

ordered from Pizza Town restaurant, and the mean delivery time is 30 minutes, with a standard deviation of 8 minutes.

a. Currently, the concession stand places an order when it has 1 pizza left. What level of service does this result in?
b. What should the reorder point be to have a 98% service level?

CASE PROBLEM

THE NORTHWOODS GENERAL STORE

The Northwoods General Store in Vermont sells a variety of outdoor clothing items and equipment and several food products at its modern but rustic-looking retail store. Its food products include salmon and maple syrup. The store also runs a lucrative catalog operation. One of its most popular products is maple syrup, which is sold in metal half-gallon cans with a picture of the store on the front.

Maple syrup was one of the first products the store produced and sold, and it continues to do so. Setting up the syrup-making equipment to produce a batch of syrup costs $450. Storing the syrup for sales throughout the year is a tricky process because the syrup must be kept in a temperature-controlled facility. The annual cost of carrying a gallon of the syrup is $15. Based on past sales data, the store has forecasted a demand of 7,500 gallons of maple syrup for the coming year. The store can produce approximately 100 gallons of syrup per day during the maple syrup season, which runs from November through February.

Because of the short season when the store can actually get sap out of trees, it obviously must produce enough during this 4-month season to meet demand for the whole year. Specifically, store management would like a production and inventory schedule that minimizes costs and indicates when during the year they need to start operating the syrup-making facility full time on a daily basis to meet demand for the remaining 8 months.

Develop a syrup production and inventory schedule for the Northwoods General Store.

CASE PROBLEM

THE TEXANS STADIUM STORE

The Fort Worth Texans have won three Super Bowls in the past 5 years, including two in a row the past 2 years. As a result, sportswear such as hats, sweatshirts, sweatpants, and jackets with the Texans logo are particularly popular in Texas. The Texans operate a stadium store outside the football stadium where they play. It is near a busy highway, so the store has heavy customer traffic throughout the year, not just on game days. In addition, the stadium holds high school or college football and soccer games almost every week in the fall, and it holds baseball games in the spring and summer. The most popular single item the stadium store sells is a blue and silver baseball cap with the Texans logo embroidered on it in a special and very attractive manner. The cap has an elastic headband inside it, which automatically conforms to different head sizes. However, the store has had a difficult time keeping the cap in stock, especially during the time between the placement and receipt of an order. Often customers come to the store just for the hat; when it is not in stock, customers are visibly upset, and the store management believes they tend to go to competing stores to purchase their Texans clothing. To rectify this problem, the store manager, Jenny Jones, would like to develop an inventory control policy that would ensure that customers would be able to purchase the cap 99% of the time they asked for it. Jenny has accumulated the following demand data for the cap for a 30-week period:

Week	*Demand*	*Week*	*Demand*	*Week*	*Demand*
1	38	11	28	21	52
2	51	12	41	22	38
3	25	13	37	23	49
4	60	14	44	24	46
5	35	15	45	25	47
6	42	16	56	26	41
7	29	17	62	27	39
8	46	18	53	28	50
9	55	19	46	29	28
10	19	20	41	30	34

(Demand includes actual sales plus a record of the times a cap has been requested but not available and an estimate of the number of times a customer wanted a cap when it was not available but did not ask for it.)

The store purchases the hats from a small manufacturing company in Jamaica. The shipments from Jamaica are somewhat erratic, with a lead time anywhere between 10 days and 1 month. The following lead time data (in days) were accumulated during approximately a 1-year period:

Order	*Lead Time*	*Order*	*Lead Time*
1	12	11	14
2	16	12	16
3	25	13	23
4	18	14	18
5	10	15	21
6	30	16	19
7	24	17	17
8	19	18	16
9	17	19	22
10	15	20	18

In the past, Jenny has placed an order whenever the stock got down to 150 caps. To what level of service does this reorder point correspond? What would the reorder point and safety stock need to be to attain the desired service level? Discuss how Jenny might determine the order size for caps and what additional, if any, information would be needed to determine the order size.

Case Problem

THE A-TO-Z OFFICE SUPPLY COMPANY

Christine Yamaguchi is the manager of the A-to-Z Office Supply Company in Charlotte. The company attempts to gain an advantage over its competitors by providing quality customer service, which includes prompt delivery of orders by truck or van and always being able to meet customer demand from its stock. In order to achieve this degree of customer service, A-to-Z must stock a large volume of items on a daily basis at a central warehouse and at three retail stores in the city and suburbs. Christine maintains these inventory levels by borrowing cash on a daily basis from the First Piedmont Bank. She estimates that for the coming fiscal year, the company's demand for cash to pay for inventory will be $17,000 per day for 305 working days. Any money she borrows during the year must be repaid with interest by the end of the year. The annual interest rate currently charged by the bank is 9%. Any time Christine takes out a loan to purchase inventory, the bank charges the company a loan origination fee of $1,200 plus 2¼ points (2.25% of the amount borrowed).

Christine often uses EOQ analysis to determine optimal amounts of inventory to order for different office supplies. Now she is wondering if she can use the same type of analysis to determine an optimal borrowing policy. Determine the amount of the loan Christine should secure from the bank, the total annual cost of the company's borrowing policy, and the number of loans the company should obtain during the year. Also determine the level of cash on hand at which the company should apply for a new loan, given that it takes 15 days for a loan to be processed by the bank.

Suppose the bank offers Christine a discount, as follows: On any loan amount equal to or greater than $500,000, the bank will lower the number of points charged on the loan origination fee from 2.25% to 2.00%. What would the company's optimal loan amount be?

Case Problem

DIAMANT FOODS COMPANY

Diamant Foods Company produces a variety of food products, including a line of candies. One of its most popular candy items is Divine Diamonds, a bag of a dozen individually wrapped, diamond-shaped candies made primarily from a blend of dark and milk chocolates, macadamia nuts, and a blend of heavy cream fillings. The item is relatively expensive, so Diamant Foods produces it only for its eastern market, encompassing urban areas such as New York, Atlanta, Philadelphia, and Boston. The item is not sold in grocery or discount stores but mainly in specialty shops and specialty groceries, candy stores, and department stores. Diamant Foods supplies the candy to a single food distributor, which has several warehouses on the East Coast. The candy is shipped in cases of 60 bags of the candy per case. Diamonds sell well, despite the fact that they are expensive, at $9.85 per bag (wholesale). Diamant uses high-quality, fresh ingredients and does not store large stocks of the candy in inventory for very long periods of time.

Diamant's distributor believes that demand for the candy follows a seasonal pattern. It has collected demand data (i.e., cases sold) for Diamonds from its warehouses and the stores it supplies for the past 3 years, as follows:

	Demand (cases)		
Month	*Year 1*	*Year 2*	*Year 3*
January	192	212	228
February	210	223	231
March	205	216	226
April	260	252	293
May	228	235	246
June	172	220	229
July	160	209	217
August	147	231	226
September	256	263	302
October	342	370	410
November	261	260	279
December	273	277	293

The distributor must hold the candy inventory in climate-controlled warehouses and be careful in handling it. The annual carrying cost is $116 per case. Diamonds must be shipped a long distance from the manufacturer to the distributor, and in order to keep the candy as fresh as possible, trucks must be air-conditioned, shipments must be direct, and shipments are often less than truckload. As a result, the ordering cost is $4,700.

Diamant Foods makes Diamonds from three primary ingredients it orders from different suppliers: dark and milk chocolate, macadamia nuts, and a special heavy cream filling. Except for its unique shape, a Diamond is almost like a chocolate truffle. Each Diamond weighs 1.2 ounces and requires 0.70 ounce of blended chocolates, 0.50 ounce of macadamia nuts, and 0.40 ounce of filling to produce (including spillage and waste). Diamant Foods orders chocolate, nuts, and filling from its suppliers by the pound. The annual ordering cost is $5,700 for chocolate, and the annual carrying cost is $0.45 per pound. The ordering cost for macadamia nuts is $6,300, and the annual carrying cost is $0.63 per pound. The ordering cost for filling is $4,500, and the annual carrying cost is $0.55 per pound.

Each of the suppliers offers the candy manufacturer a quantity discount price schedule for the ingredients, as follows:

Chocolate		Macadamia Nuts		Filling	
Price	*Quantity (lb.)*	*Price*	*Quantity (lb.)*	*Price*	*Quantity (lb.)*
$3.05	0–50,000	$6.50	0–30,000	$1.50	0–40,000
2.90	50,001–100,000	6.25	30,001–70,000	1.35	40,001–80,000
2.75	100,001–150,000	5.95	70,000+	1.25	80,000+
2.60	150,000+				

Determine the inventory order quantity for Diamant's distributor. Compare the optimal order quantity with a seasonally adjusted forecast for demand. Does the order quantity seem adequate to meet the seasonal demand pattern for Diamonds (i.e., is it likely that shortages or excessive inventories will occur)? Can you identify the causes of the seasonal demand pattern for Diamonds? Determine the inventory order quantity for each of the three primary ingredients that Diamant Foods orders from its suppliers.

Topic 19

Simulation

14 Simulation

Simulation represents a major divergence from the topics presented in the previous chapters of this text. Previous topics usually dealt with mathematical models and formulas that could be applied to certain types of problems. The solution approaches to these problems were, for the most part, analytical. However, not all real-world problems can be solved by applying a specific type of technique and then performing the calculations. Some problem situations are too complex to be represented by the concise techniques presented so far in this text. In such cases, **simulation** is an alternative form of analysis.

__Analogue simulation__ replaces a physical system with an analogous physical system that is easier to manipulate.

Analogue simulation is a form of simulation that is familiar to most people. In analogue simulation, an original physical system is replaced by an analogous physical system that is easier to manipulate. Much of the experimentation in staffed spaceflight was conducted using physical simulation that re-created the conditions of space. For example, conditions of weightlessness were simulated using rooms filled with water. Other examples include wind tunnels that simulate the conditions of flight and treadmills that simulate automobile tire wear in a laboratory instead of on the road.

In computer mathematical simulation, a system is replicated with a mathematical model that is analyzed by using the computer.

This chapter is concerned with an alternative type of simulation, *computer mathematical simulation.* In this form of simulation, systems are replicated with mathematical models, which are analyzed using a computer. This form of simulation has become very popular and has been applied to a wide variety of business problems. One reason for its popularity is that it offers a means of analyzing very complex systems that cannot be analyzed by using the other management science techniques in this text. However, because such complex systems are beyond the scope of this text, we will not present actual simulation models; instead, we will present simplified simulation models of systems that can also be analyzed analytically. We will begin with one of the simplest forms of simulation models, which encompasses the Monte Carlo process for simulating random variables.

The Monte Carlo Process

One characteristic of some systems that makes them difficult to solve analytically is that they consist of random variables represented by probability distributions. Thus, a large proportion of the applications of simulations are for probabilistic models.

__Monte Carlo__ is a technique for selecting numbers randomly from a probability distribution.

The term **Monte Carlo** has become synonymous with probabilistic simulation in recent years. However, the Monte Carlo technique can be more narrowly defined as a technique for selecting numbers *randomly* from a probability distribution (i.e., "sampling") for use in a *trial* (computer) run of a simulation. The Monte Carlo technique is not a type of simulation model but rather a mathematical process used within a simulation.

The Monte Carlo process is analogous to gambling devices.

The name *Monte Carlo* is appropriate because the basic principle behind the process is the same as in the operation of a gambling casino in Monaco. In Monaco such devices as roulette wheels, dice, and playing cards are used. These devices produce numbered results at random from well-defined populations. For example, a 7 resulting from thrown dice is a random value from a population of 11 possible numbers (i.e., 2 through 12). This same process is employed, in principle, in the Monte Carlo process used in simulation models.

The Use of Random Numbers

The Monte Carlo process of selecting random numbers according to a probability distribution will be demonstrated using the following example. The manager of Computer-World, a store that sells computers and related equipment, is attempting to determine how many laptop PCs the store should order each week. A primary consideration in this decision is the average number of laptop computers that the store will sell each week and the average weekly revenue generated from the sale of laptop PCs. A laptop sells for $4,300. The number of laptops demanded each week is a random variable (which we will define as x) that ranges from 0 to 4. From past sales records, the manager has determined the frequency of demand for laptop PCs for the past 100 weeks. From this frequency distribution, a probability distribution of demand can be developed, as shown in Table 14.1.

Table 14.1
Probability distribution of demand for laptop PCs

PCs Demanded per Week	Frequency of Demand	Probability of Demand, $P(x)$
0	20	.20
1	40	.40
2	20	.20
3	10	.10
4	10	.10
	100	1.00

In the Monte Carlo process, values for a random variable are generated by sampling from a probability distribution.

The purpose of the Monte Carlo process is to generate the random variable, demand, by sampling from the probability distribution, $P(x)$. The demand per week can be randomly generated according to the probability distribution by spinning a wheel that is partitioned into segments corresponding to the probabilities, as shown in Figure 14.1.

Figure 14.1
A roulette wheel for demand

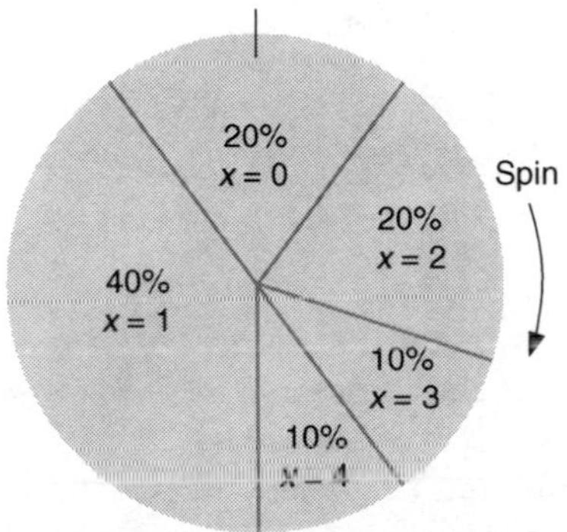

Because the surface area on the roulette wheel is partitioned according to the probability of each weekly demand value, the wheel replicates the probability distribution for demand if the values of demand occur in a random manner. To simulate demand for 1 week, the manager spins the wheel; the segment at which the wheel stops indicates demand for 1 week. Over a period of weeks (i.e., many spins of the wheel), the frequency with which demand values occur will approximate the probability distribution, $P(x)$. This method of generating values of a variable, x, by randomly selecting from the probability distribution—the wheel—is the Monte Carlo process.

A long period of real time is represented by a short period of simulated time.

By spinning the wheel, the manager artificially reconstructs the purchase of PCs during a week. In this reconstruction, a long period of *real time* (i.e., a number of weeks) is represented by a short period of **simulated time** (i.e., several spins of the wheel).

Now let us slightly reconstruct the roulette wheel. In addition to partitioning the wheel into segments corresponding to the probability of demand, we will put numbers along the outer rim, as on a real roulette wheel. This reconstructed roulette wheel is shown in Figure 14.2.

There are 100 numbers from 0 to 99 on the outer rim of the wheel, and they have been partitioned according to the probability of each demand value. For example, 20 numbers

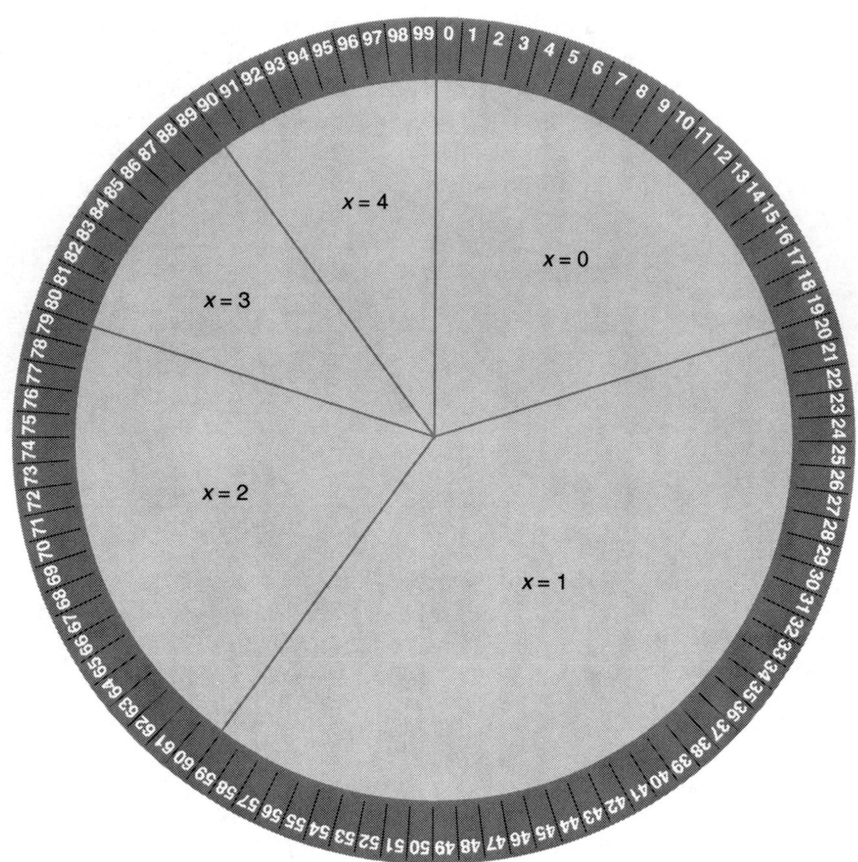

Figure 14.2
Numbered roulette wheel

from 0 to 19 (i.e., 20% of the total 100 numbers) correspond to a demand of no (0) PCs. Now we can determine the value of demand by seeing which number the wheel stops at as well as by looking at the segment of the wheel.

When the manager spins this new wheel, the actual demand for PCs will be determined by a number. For example, if the number 71 comes up on a spin, the demand is 2 PCs per week; the number 30 indicates a demand of 1. Because the manager does not know which number will come up prior to the spin and there is an equal chance of any of the 100 numbers occurring, the numbers occur at random; that is, they are **random numbers**.

Obviously, it is not generally practical to generate weekly demand for PCs by spinning a wheel. Alternatively, the process of spinning a wheel can be replicated by using random numbers alone.

First, we will transfer the ranges of random numbers for each demand value from the roulette wheel to a table, as in Table 14.2. Next, instead of spinning the wheel to get a random

Table 14.2
Generating demand from random numbers

Demand, x		Ranges of Random Numbers, r		
0		0–19		
1	⟵	20–59	⟵	$r = 39$
2		60–79		
3		80–89		
4		90–99		

Random numbers are equally likely to occur.

number, we will select a random number from Table 14.3, which is referred to as a **random number table**. (These random numbers have been generated by computer so that they are all *equally likely to occur*, just as if we had spun a wheel. The development of random numbers is discussed in more detail later in this chapter.) As an example, let us select the number 39, the first entry in Table 14.3. Looking again at Table 14.2, we can see that the random number 39 falls in the range 20–59, which corresponds to a weekly demand of 1 laptop PC.

Table 14.3
Random number table

39 65 76 45 45	19 90 69 64 61	20 26 36 31 62	58 24 97 14 97	95 06 70 99 00
73 71 23 70 90	65 97 60 12 11	31 56 34 19 19	47 83 75 51 33	30 62 38 20 46
72 18 47 33 84	51 67 47 97 19	98 40 07 17 66	23 05 09 51 80	59 78 11 52 49
75 12 25 69 17	17 95 21 78 58	24 33 45 77 48	69 81 84 09 29	93 22 70 45 80
37 17 79 88 74	63 52 06 34 30	01 31 60 10 27	35 07 79 71 53	28 99 52 01 41
02 48 08 16 94	85 53 83 29 95	56 27 09 24 43	21 78 55 09 82	72 61 88 73 61
87 89 15 70 07	37 79 49 12 38	48 13 93 55 96	41 92 45 71 51	09 18 25 58 94
98 18 71 70 15	89 09 39 59 24	00 06 41 41 20	14 36 59 25 47	54 45 17 24 89
10 83 58 07 04	76 62 16 48 68	58 76 17 14 86	59 53 11 52 21	66 04 18 72 87
47 08 56 37 31	71 82 13 50 41	27 55 10 24 92	28 04 67 53 44	95 23 00 84 47
93 90 31 03 07	34 18 04 52 35	74 13 39 35 22	68 95 23 92 35	36 63 70 35 33
21 05 11 47 99	11 20 99 45 18	76 51 94 84 86	13 79 93 37 55	98 16 04 41 67
95 89 94 06 97	27 37 83 28 71	79 57 95 13 91	09 61 87 25 21	56 20 11 32 44
97 18 31 55 73	10 65 81 92 59	77 31 61 95 46	20 44 90 32 64	26 99 76 75 63
69 08 88 86 13	59 71 74 17 32	48 38 75 93 29	73 37 32 04 05	60 82 29 20 25
41 26 10 25 03	87 63 93 95 17	81 83 83 04 49	77 45 85 50 51	79 88 01 97 30
91 47 14 63 62	08 61 74 51 69	92 79 43 89 79	29 18 94 51 23	14 85 11 47 23
80 94 54 18 47	08 52 85 08 40	48 40 35 94 22	72 65 71 08 86	50 03 42 99 36
67 06 77 63 99	89 85 84 46 06	64 71 06 21 66	89 37 20 70 01	61 65 70 22 12
59 72 24 13 75	42 29 72 23 19	06 94 76 10 08	81 30 15 39 14	81 33 17 16 33
63 62 06 34 41	79 53 36 02 95	94 61 09 43 62	20 21 14 68 86	84 95 48 46 45
78 47 23 53 90	79 93 96 38 63	34 85 52 05 09	85 43 01 72 73	14 93 87 81 40
87 68 62 15 43	97 48 72 66 48	53 16 71 13 81	59 97 50 99 52	24 62 20 42 31
47 60 92 10 77	26 97 05 73 51	88 46 38 03 58	72 68 49 29 31	75 70 16 08 24
56 88 87 59 41	06 87 37 78 48	65 88 69 58 39	88 02 84 27 83	85 81 56 39 38
22 17 68 65 84	87 02 22 57 51	68 69 80 95 44	11 29 01 95 80	49 34 35 36 47
19 36 27 59 46	39 77 32 77 09	79 57 92 36 59	89 74 39 82 15	08 58 94 34 74
16 77 23 02 77	28 06 24 25 93	22 45 44 84 11	87 80 61 65 31	09 71 91 74 25
78 43 76 71 61	97 67 63 99 61	30 45 67 93 82	59 73 19 85 23	53 33 65 97 21
03 28 28 26 08	69 30 16 09 05	53 58 47 70 93	66 56 45 65 79	45 56 20 19 47
04 31 17 21 56	33 73 99 19 87	26 72 39 27 67	53 77 57 68 93	60 61 97 22 61
61 06 98 03 91	87 14 77 43 96	43 00 65 98 50	45 60 33 01 07	98 99 46 50 47
23 68 35 26 00	99 53 93 61 28	52 70 05 48 34	56 65 05 61 86	90 92 10 70 80
15 39 25 70 99	93 86 52 77 65	15 33 59 05 28	22 87 26 07 47	86 96 98 29 06
58 71 96 30 24	18 46 23 34 27	85 13 99 24 44	49 18 09 79 49	74 16 32 23 02
93 22 53 64 39	07 10 63 76 35	87 03 04 79 88	08 13 13 85 51	55 34 57 72 69
78 76 58 54 74	92 38 70 96 92	52 06 79 79 45	82 63 18 27 44	69 66 92 19 09
61 81 31 96 82	00 57 25 60 59	46 72 60 18 77	55 66 12 62 11	08 99 55 64 57
42 88 07 10 05	24 98 65 63 21	47 21 61 88 32	27 80 30 21 60	10 92 35 36 12
77 94 30 05 39	28 10 99 00 27	12 73 73 99 12	49 99 57 94 82	96 88 57 17 91

By repeating this process of selecting random numbers from Table 14.3 (starting anywhere in the table and moving in any direction but not repeating the same sequence) and then determining weekly demand from the random number, we can simulate demand for a period of time. For example, Table 14.4 shows demand for a period of 15 consecutive weeks.

Table 14.4
Randomly generated demand for 15 weeks

Week	r	Demand, x	Revenue
1	39	1	$ 4,300
2	73	2	8,600
3	72	2	8,600
4	75	2	8,600
5	37	1	4,300
6	02	0	0
7	87	3	12,900
8	98	4	17,200
9	10	0	0
10	47	1	4,300
11	93	4	17,200
12	21	1	4,300
13	95	4	17,200
14	97	4	17,200
15	69	2	8,600
		$\Sigma = 31$	$133,300

From Table 14.4 the manager can compute the estimated average weekly demand and revenue:

$$\text{estimated average demand} = \frac{31}{15} = 2.07 \text{ laptop PCs per week}$$

$$\text{estimated average revenue} = \frac{\$133{,}300}{15} = \$8{,}886.67$$

The manager can then use this information to help determine the number of PCs to order each week.

Although this example is convenient for illustrating how simulation works, the average demand could have more appropriately been calculated *analytically* using the formula for expected value. The *expected value* or average for weekly demand can be computed analytically from the probability distribution, $P(x)$:

$$E(x) = \sum_{i=1}^{n} P(x_i)x_i$$

where

x_i = demand value i
$P(x_i)$ = probability of demand
n = the number of different demand values

Therefore,

$$\begin{aligned} E(x) &= (.20)(0) + (.40)(1) + (.20)(2) + (.10)(3) + (.10)(4) \\ &= 1.5 \text{ PCs per week} \end{aligned}$$

Simulation results will not equal analytical results unless enough trials of the simulation have been conducted to reach steady state.

The analytical result of 1.5 PCs is close to the simulated result of 2.07 PCs, but clearly there is some difference. The margin of difference (0.57 PCs) between the simulated value and the analytical value is a result of the number of periods over which the simulation was conducted. The results of any simulation study are subject to the number of times the simulation occurred (i.e., the number of *trials*). Thus, the more periods for which the simulation is conducted, the more accurate the result. For example, if demand were simulated for

Time Out for John Von Neumann

The mathematics of the Monte Carlo method have been known for years; the British mathematician Lord Kelvin used the technique in a paper in 1901. However, it was formally identified and given this name by the Hungarian mathematician John Von Neumann while working on the Los Alamos atomic bomb project during World War II. During this project, physicists confronted a problem in determining how far neutrons would travel through various materials (i.e., neutron diffusion in fissile material). The Monte Carlo process was suggested to Von Neumann by a colleague at Los Alamos, Stanislas Ulam, as a means to solve this problem—that is, by selecting random numbers to represent the random actions of neutrons. However, the Monte Carlo method as used in simulation did not gain widespread popularity until the development of the modern electronic computer after the war. Interestingly, this remarkable man, John Von Neumann, is credited with being the key figure in the development of the computer.

1,000 weeks, in all likelihood an average value exactly equal to the analytical value (1.5 laptop PCs per week) would result.

Once a simulation has been repeated enough times that it reaches an average result that remains constant, this result is analogous to the *steady-state* result, a concept we discussed previously in our presentation of queuing. For this example, 1.5 PCs is the long-run average or steady-state result, but we have seen that the simulation might have to be repeated more than 15 times (i.e., weeks) before this result is reached.

It is often difficult to validate that the results of a simulation truly replicate reality.

Comparing our simulated result with the analytical (expected value) result for this example points out one of the problems that can occur with simulation. It is often difficult to *validate* the results of a simulation model—that is, to make sure that the true steady-state average result has been reached. In this case we were able to compare the simulated result with the expected value (which is the true steady-state result), and we found there was a slight difference. We logically deduced that the 15 trials of the simulation were not sufficient to determine the steady-state average. However, simulation most often is employed whenever analytical analysis is not possible (this is one of the reasons that simulation is generally useful). In these cases, there is no analytical standard of comparison, and validation of the results becomes more difficult. We will discuss this problem of validation in more detail later in the chapter.

Computer Simulation with Excel Spreadsheets

Simulations are normally done on the computer.

The simulation we performed manually for the ComputerWorld example was not too difficult. However, if we had performed the simulation for 1,000 weeks, it would have taken several hours. On the other hand, this simulation could be done on a computer in several seconds. Also, our simulation example was not very complex. As simulation models get progressively more complex, it becomes virtually impossible to perform them manually, thus making the computer a necessity.

Although we will not develop a simulation model in a computer language for this example, we will demonstrate how a computerized simulation model is developed by using Excel spreadsheets.

The first step in developing a simulation model is to generate a random number, r. Numerous subroutines that are available on practically every computer system generate random numbers. Most are quite easy to use and require the insertion of only a few statements in a program. These random numbers are generated by mathematical processes as opposed to a physical process, such as spinning a roulette wheel. For this reason, they are

Random numbers generated by a mathematical process instead of a physical process are ***pseudorandom numbers.***

referred to as **pseudorandom numbers.** It should be apparent from the previous discussion that random numbers play a very important part in a probabilistic simulation. Some of the random numbers we used came from Table 14.3, a table of random numbers. However, random numbers do not come just from tables, and their generation is not as simple as one might initially think. If random numbers are not truly random, the validity of simulation results can be significantly affected.

Random numbers are typically generated on the computer by using a numerical technique.

The random numbers in Table 14.3 were generated by using a *numerical technique.* Thus, they are not true random numbers but *pseudorandom numbers.* True random numbers can be produced only by a physical process, such as spinning a roulette wheel over and over. However, a physical process, such as spinning a roulette wheel, cannot be conveniently employed in a computerized simulation model. Thus, there is a need for a numerical method that artificially creates random numbers.

A table of random numbers must be uniform, efficiently generated, and absent of patterns.

To truly reflect the system being simulated, the artificially created random numbers must have the following characteristics:

1. The random numbers must be uniformly distributed. This means that each random number in the interval of random numbers (i.e., 0 to 1 or 0 to 100) has an equal chance of being selected. If this condition is not met, then the simulation results will be biased by the random numbers that have a *more likely* chance of being selected.
2. The numerical technique for generating random numbers should be efficient. This means that the random numbers should not degenerate into constant values or recycle too frequently.
3. The sequence of random numbers should not reflect any pattern. For example, the sequence of numbers 0, 1, 2, 3, 4, 5, 6, 7, 8, 9, 0, 1, 2, 3, 4, 5, 6, 7, 8, 9, 0, 1, 2, 3, 4, 5, 6, 7, 8, 9, 0, and so on, although uniform, is not random.

Random numbers between 0 and 1 can be generated in Excel by entering the formula =**RAND()** in a cell. The random numbers generated by this formula include all the necessary characteristics for randomness and uniformity that we discussed earlier. Exhibit 14.1 is an Excel spreadsheet with 100 random numbers generated by entering the formula =**RAND()** in cell A3 and copying to the cells in the range **A3:J12**. Recall that we can copy things in a range of cells in two ways. You can first cover cells **A3:J12** with the cursor and then type the formula =**RAND()** into cell A3. Then you press the "Ctrl" and "Enter" keys simultaneously. Alternatively, you can type =**RAND()** in cell A3, copy this cell (using the right mouse button), then cover cells **A3:J12** with the cursor, and (again with the right mouse button) paste this formula in these cells.

Exhibit 14.1

Microsoft Excel - Exhibit14.1.xls

A3 0.629323723538247

	A	B	C	D	E	F	G	H	I	J
1	**100 Random Numbers Generated Using RAND()**									
2										
3	0.6299	0.6922	0.4634	0.0433	0.0755	0.0641	0.3189	0.2589	0.2288	0.7371
4	0.4191	0.7927	0.6893	0.9192	0.8019	0.4114	0.3443	0.5397	0.8936	0.6944
5	0.7306	0.4966	0.5271	0.2341	0.3518	0.1129	0.7664	0.5752	0.7673	0.7338
6	0.8712	0.5170	0.8834	0.9357	0.6017	0.8175	0.9635	0.0216	0.9409	0.3832
7	0.8718	0.2347	0.3095	0.8006	0.7955	0.0621	0.3317	0.4863	0.4598	0.3011
8	0.0935	0.0287	0.1110	0.6009	0.1023	0.3886	0.3424	0.2876	0.1904	0.1980
9	0.2892	0.0149	0.5325	0.4057	0.0385	0.4983	0.8288	0.1043	0.3955	0.1855
10	0.4016	0.8078	0.0856	0.2995	0.5729	0.5776	0.8871	0.4656	0.9582	0.6215
11	0.4508	0.3710	0.1533	0.9799	0.4267	0.7611	0.2242	0.8883	0.7665	0.5268
12	0.6573	0.4849	0.6997	0.4905	0.8855	0.9194	0.5891	0.0643	0.2703	0.9780
13										

If you attempt to replicate this spreadsheet, you will generate different random numbers from those shown in Exhibit 14.1. Every time you generate random numbers, they will be different. In fact, any time you recalculate anything on your spreadsheet, the random numbers will change. You can see this by pressing the F9 key and observing that all the random numbers change. However, sometimes it is useful in a simulation model to be able to use the same set (or stream) of random numbers over and over. You can freeze the random numbers you are using on your spreadsheet by first covering the cells with random numbers in them with the cursor—for example, cells **A3:J12** in Exhibit 14.1. Next, you copy these cells (using the right mouse button); then you click on the "Edit" menu at the top of your spreadsheet and select "Paste Special" from this menu. Next, you select the "Values" option and click on "OK." This procedure pastes a copy of the numbers in these cells over the same cells with =**RAND**() formulas in them, thus freezing the numbers in place.

Notice one more thing from Exhibit 14.1: The random numbers are all between 0 and 1, whereas the random numbers in Table 14.3 are whole numbers between 0 and 100. We used whole random numbers previously for illustrative purposes; however, computer programs such as Excel generally provide random numbers between 0 and 1.

Now we are ready to duplicate our example simulation model for the ComputerWorld store by using Excel. The spreadsheet in Exhibit 14.2 includes the simulation model originally developed in Table 14.4.

Exhibit 14.2

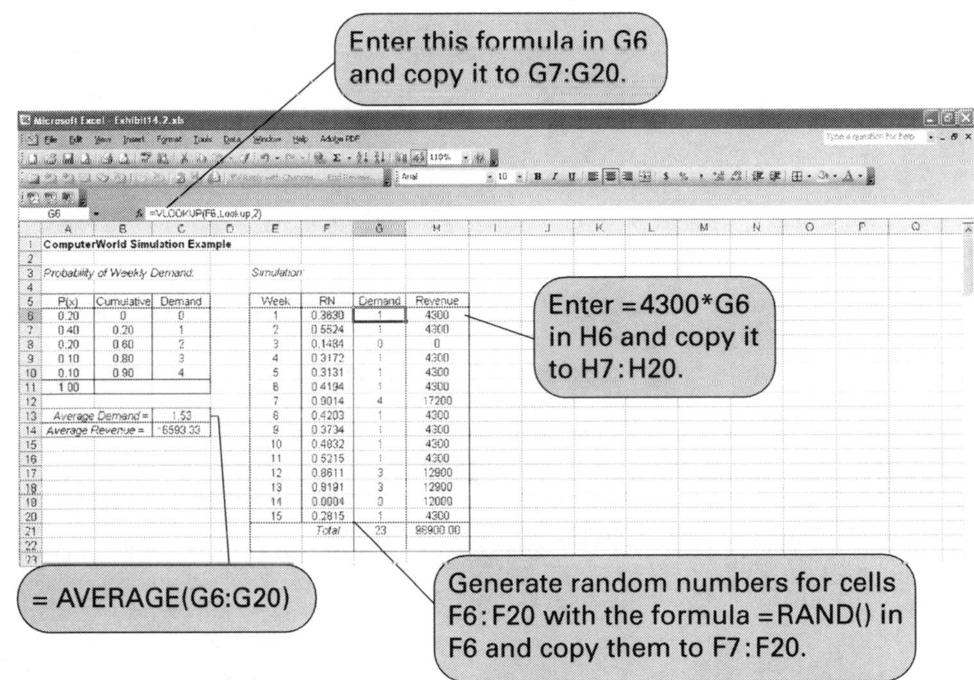

Note that the probability distribution for the weekly demand for laptops has been entered in cells **A6:C10**. Also notice that we have entered a new set of cumulative probability values in column B. We generated these cumulative probabilities by first entering 0 in cell B6, then entering the formula **=A6+B6** in cell B7, and copying this formula to cells **B8:B10**. This cumulative probability creates a range of random numbers for each demand value. For example, any random number less than 0.20 will result in a demand value of 0, and any random number greater than 0.20 but less than 0.60 will result in a demand value of 1, and so on. (Notice that there is no value of 1.00 in cell B11; the last demand value, 4, will be selected for any random number equal to or greater than .90.)

Random numbers are generated in cells **F6:F20** by entering the formula =**RAND**() in cell F6 and copying it to the range of cells in **F7:F20**.

Now we need to be able to generate demand values for each of these random numbers in column F. We accomplish this by first covering the cumulative probabilities and the demand values in cells **B6:C10** with the cursor. Then we give this range of cells the name "Lookup." This can be done by typing "Lookup" directly on the formula bar in place of B6 or by clicking on the "Insert" button at the top of the spreadsheet and selecting "Name" and "Define" and then entering the name "Lookup." This has the effect of creating a table called "Lookup" with the ranges of random numbers and associated demand values in it. Next, we enter the formula **=VLOOKUP(F6,Lookup,2)** in cell G6 and copy it to the cells in the range **G7:G20**. This formula will compare the random numbers in column F with the cumulative probabilities in **B6:B10** and generate the correct demand value from cells **C6:C10**.

Once the demand values have been generated in column G, we can determine the weekly revenue values by entering the formula **=4300*G6** in H6 and copying it to cells **H7:H20**.

Average weekly demand is computed in cell C13 by using the formula **=AVERAGE (G6:G20)**, and the average weekly revenue is computed by entering a similar formula in cell C14.

Notice that the average weekly demand value of 1.53 in Exhibit 14.2 is different from the simulation result (2.07) we obtained from Table 14.4. This is because we used a different stream of random numbers. As mentioned previously, to acquire an average closer to the true steady-state value, the simulation probably needs to include more repetitions than 15 weeks. As an example, Exhibit 14.3 simulates demand for 100 weeks. The window has been "frozen" at row 16 and scrolled up to show the first 10 weeks and the last 6 weeks on the screen in Exhibit 14.3.

Exhibit 14.3

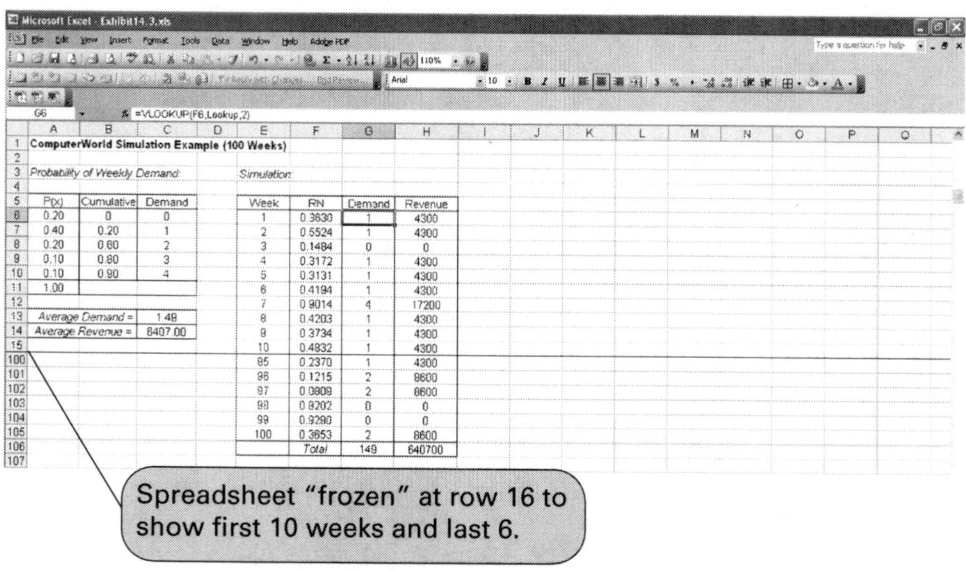

P(x)	Cumulative	Demand
0.20	0	0
0.40	0.20	1
0.20	0.60	2
0.10	0.80	3
0.10	0.90	4
1.00		
Average Demand =		1.48
Average Revenue =		6407.00

Week	RN	Demand	Revenue
1	0.3630	1	4300
2	0.5524	1	4300
3	0.1484	0	0
4	0.3172	1	4300
5	0.3131	1	4300
6	0.4194	1	4300
7	0.9014	4	17200
8	0.4203	1	4300
9	0.3734	1	4300
10	0.4832	1	4300
95	0.2370	1	4300
96	0.1215	2	8600
97	0.0808	2	8600
98	0.8202	0	0
99	0.9290	0	0
100	0.3653	2	8600
	Total	149	640700

Decision Making with Simulation

In our previous example, the manager of ComputerWorld acquired some useful information about the weekly demand and revenue for laptops that would be helpful in making a decision about how many laptops would be needed each week to meet demand. However, this example did not lead directly to a decision. Next, we will expand our ComputerWorld store example so that a possible decision will result.

From the simulation in Exhibit 14.3 the manager of the store knows that the average weekly demand for laptop PCs will be approximately 1.49; however, the manager cannot order 1.49 laptops each week. Because fractional laptops are not possible, either one or two must be ordered. Thus, the manager wants to repeat the earlier simulation with two possible order sizes, 1 and 2. The manager also wants to include some additional information in the model that will affect the decision.

If too few laptops are on hand to meet demand during the week, then not only will there be a loss of revenue, but there will also be a shortage cost of $500 per unit incurred because the customer will be unhappy. However, each laptop still in stock at the end of each week that has not been sold will incur an inventory or storage cost of $50. Thus, it costs the store money to have either too few or too many laptops on hand each week. Given this scenario, the manager wants to order either one or two laptops, depending on which order size will result in the greatest average weekly revenue.

Exhibit 14.4 shows the Excel spreadsheet for this revised example. The simulation is for 100 weeks. The columns labeled "1," "2," and "4" for "Week," "RN," and "Demand" were constructed similarly to the model in Exhibit 14.3. The array of cells **B6:C10** was given the name "Lookup," and the formula **=VLOOKUP(F6,Lookup,2)** was entered in cell H6 and copied to cells **H7:H105**.

Exhibit 14.4

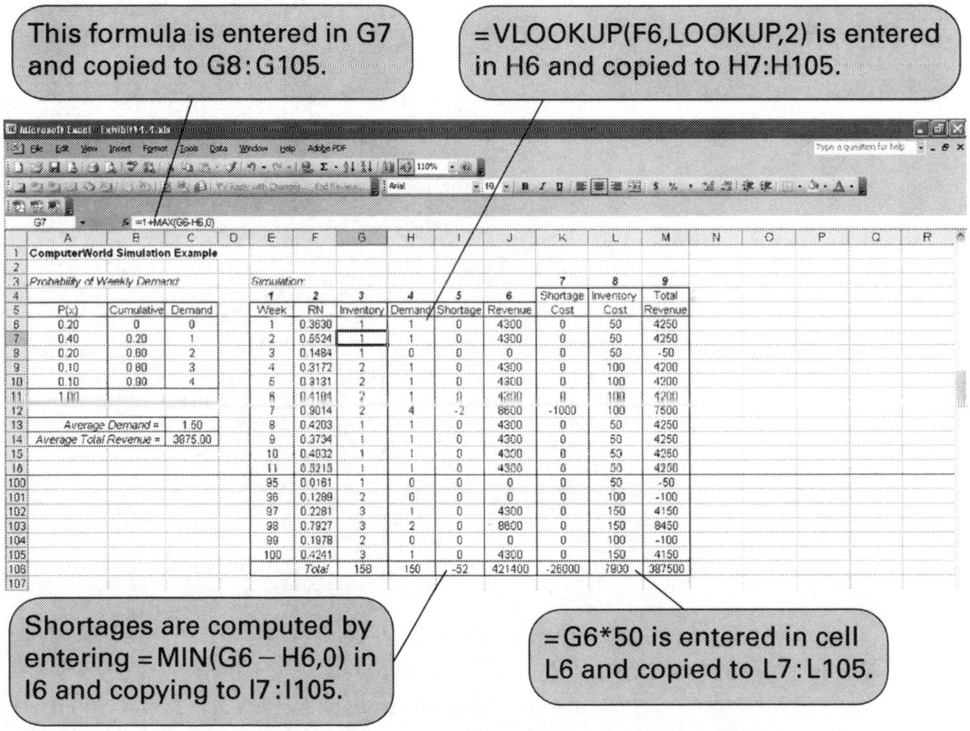

This formula is entered in G7 and copied to G8:G105.

=VLOOKUP(F6,LOOKUP,2) is entered in H6 and copied to H7:H105.

G7 =1+MAX(G6-H6,0)

ComputerWorld Simulation Example

Probability of Weekly Demand

P(x)	Cumulative	Demand
0.20	0	0
0.40	0.20	1
0.20	0.60	2
0.10	0.80	3
0.10	0.90	4
1.00		

Average Demand =	1.50
Average Total Revenue =	3875.00

Simulation:

1	2	3	4	5	6	7	8	9
Week	RN	Inventory	Demand	Shortage	Revenue	Shortage Cost	Inventory Cost	Total Revenue
1	0.3630	1	1	0	4300	0	50	4250
2	0.5524	1	1	0	4300	0	50	4250
3	0.1484	1	0	0	0	0	50	-50
4	0.3172	2	1	0	4300	0	100	4200
5	0.3131	2	1	0	4300	0	100	4200
6	0.4184	2	1	0	4300	0	100	4200
7	0.9014	2	4	-2	8600	-1000	100	7500
8	0.4203	1	1	0	4300	0	50	4250
9	0.3734	1	1	0	4300	0	50	4250
10	0.4032	1	1	0	4300	0	50	4250
11	0.3215	1	1	0	4300	0	50	4250
95	0.0161	1	0	0	0	0	50	-50
96	0.1289	2	0	0	0	0	100	-100
97	0.2281	3	1	0	4300	0	150	4150
98	0.7927	3	2	0	8600	0	150	8450
99	0.1978	2	0	0	0	0	100	-100
100	0.4241	3	1	0	4300	0	150	4150
	Total	158	150	-52	421400	-26000	7900	387500

Shortages are computed by entering =MIN(G6 – H6,0) in I6 and copying to I7:I105.

=G6*50 is entered in cell L6 and copied to L7:L105.

The simulation in Exhibit 14.4 is for an order size of one laptop each week. The "Inventory" column (3) keeps track of the amount of inventory available each week—the one laptop that comes in on order plus any laptops carried over from the previous week. The cumulative inventory is computed each week by entering the formula **=1+MAX(G6−H6,0)** in cell G7 and copying it to cells **G8:G105**. This formula adds the one laptop on order to either the number left over from the previous week (**G6-H6**) or 0, if there were not enough laptops on hand to meet demand. It does not allow for negative inventory levels, called *back orders*. In other words, if a sale cannot be made due to a shortage, then it is gone. The inventory values in column 3 are eventually multiplied by the inventory cost of $50 per unit in column 8, using the formula **=G6*50**.

If there is a shortage, it is recorded in column 5, labeled "Shortage." The shortage is computed by entering the formula **=MIN(G6-H6,0)** in cell I6 and copying it to cells **I7:I105.** Shortage costs are computed in column 7 by multiplying the shortage values in column 5 by $500 by entering the formula **=I6*500** in cell K6 and copying it to cells **K7:K105.**

Weekly revenues are computed in column 6 by entering the formula **=4300*MIN(H6,G6)** in cell J6 and copying it to cells **J7:J105**. In other words, the revenue is determined by either the inventory level in column 3 or the demand in column 4, whichever is smaller.

Total weekly revenue is computed in column 9 by subtracting shortage costs and inventory costs from revenue by entering the formula **=J6-K6-L6** in cell M6 and copying it to cells **M7:M105**.

The average weekly demand, 1.50, is shown in cell C13. The average weekly revenue, $3,875, is computed in cell C14.

Next, we must repeat this same simulation for an order size of two laptops each week. The spreadsheet for an order size of two is shown in Exhibit 14.5. Notice that the only actual difference is the use of a new formula to compute the weekly inventory level in column 3. This formula in cell G7, reflecting two laptops ordered each week, is shown on the formula bar at the top of the spreadsheet.

Exhibit 14.5

New formula for two laptops ordered per week

Microsoft Excel - Exhibit14.5.xls

G7 =2+MAX(G6-H6,0)

ComputerWorld Simulation Example

Probability of Weekly Demand:

P(x)	Cumulative	Demand
0.20	0	0
0.40	0.20	1
0.20	0.60	2
0.10	0.80	3
0.10	0.90	4
1.00		

Average Demand =	1.50
Average Total Revenue =	4927.50

Simulation:

1 Week	2 RN	3 Inventory	4 Demand	5 Shortage	6 Revenue	7 Shortage Cost	8 Inventory Cost	9 Total Revenue
1	0.3630	2	1	0	4300	0	100	4200
2	0.5524	3	1	0	4300	0	150	4150
3	0.1484	4	0	0	0	0	200	-200
4	0.3172	6	1	0	4300	0	300	4000
5	0.3131	7	1	0	4300	0	350	3950
6	0.4194	8	1	0	4300	0	400	3900
7	0.9014	9	4	0	17200	0	450	16750
8	0.4203	7	1	0	4300	0	350	3950
9	0.3734	8	1	0	4300	0	400	3900
10	0.4832	9	1	0	4300	0	450	3850
11	0.5215	10	1	0	4300	0	500	3800
95	0.0161	44	0	0	0	0	2200	-2200
96	0.1289	46	0	0	0	0	2300	-2300
97	0.2281	48	1	0	4300	0	2400	1900
98	0.7927	49	2	0	8600	0	2450	6150
99	0.1878	49	0	0	0	0	2450	-2450
100	0.4241	51	1	0	4300	0	2550	1750
	Total	3045	150	0	645000	0	152250	492750

This second simulation, in Exhibit 14.5, results in an average weekly demand of 1.50 laptops and an average weekly total revenue of $4,927.50. This is higher than the total weekly revenue of $3,875 achieved in the first simulation run in Exhibit 14.4, even though the store would incur significantly higher inventory costs. Thus, the correct decision—based on weekly revenue—would be to order two laptops per week. However, there are probably additional aspects of this problem the manager would want to consider in the decision-making process, such as the increasingly high inventory levels as the simulation progresses. For example, there may not be enough storage space to accommodate this much inventory. Such questions as this and others can also be analyzed with simulation. In fact, one of the main attributes of simulation is its usefulness as a model for experimenting, called **what-if? analysis.**

This example briefly demonstrates how simulation can be used to make a decision (i.e., to "optimize"). In this example we experimented with two order sizes and determined the one that resulted in the greater revenue. The same basic modeling principles can be used to solve larger problems with hundreds of possible order sizes and a probability distribution for demand with many more values plus variable lead times (i.e., the time it takes to receive an order), the ability to back order, and other complicating factors. These factors make the simulation model larger and more complex, but such models are frequently developed and used in business.

Simulation of a Queuing System

To demonstrate the simulation of a queuing system, we will use an example. Burlingham Mills produces denim, and one of the main steps in the production process is dyeing the cotton yarn that is subsequently woven into denim cloth. The yarn is dyed in a large concrete vat like a narrow swimming pool. The yarn is strung over a series of rollers so that it passes through the vat, up over a set of rollers, back down into the vat, back up and over another set of rollers, and so on. Yarn is dyed in batches that arrive at the dyeing vat in 1-, 2-, 3-, or 4-day intervals, according to the probability distribution shown in Table 14.5. Once a batch of yarn arrives at the dyeing facility, it takes either 0.5, 1.0, or 2.0 days to complete the dyeing process, according to the probability distribution shown in Table 14.6.

Table 14.5
Distribution of arrival intervals

Arrival Interval (days), x	Probability, $P(x)$	Cumulative Probability	Random Number Range, r_1
1.0	.20	.20	1–20
2.0	.40	.60	21–60
3.0	.30	.90	61–90
4.0	.10	1.00	91–99, 00

Table 14.6
Distribution of service times

Service Time (days), y	Probability, $P(y)$	Cumulative Probability	Random Number Range, r_2
0.5	.20	.20	1–20
1.0	.50	.70	21–70
2.0	.30	1.00	71–99, 00

Developing the cumulative probability distribution helps to determine random number ranges.

Table 14.5 defines the interarrival time, or how often batches arrive at the dyeing facility. For example, there is a .20 probability of a batch arriving *1 day* after the previous batch. Table 14.6 defines the service time for a batch. Notice that cumulative probabilities have been included in Tables 14.5 and 14.6. The cumulative probability provides a means for determining the ranges of random numbers associated with each probability, as we demonstrated with our Excel example in the previous section. For example, in Table 14.5 the first random number range for r_1 is from 1 to 20, which corresponds to the cumulative probability of .20. The second range of random numbers is from 21 to 60, which corresponds to a cumulative probability of .60. Although the cumulative probability goes up to 1.00, Table 14.3 contains only random number values from 0 to 99. Thus, the number 0 is used in place of 100 in the last random number range of each table.

Table 14.7 illustrates the simulation of 10 batch arrivals at the dyeing vat. The manual simulation process illustrated in Table 14.7 can be interpreted as follows:

Table 14.7 Simulation at the Burlingham Mills Dyeing Facility

Batch	r_1	Arrival Interval, x	Arrival Clock	Enter Facility Clock	Waiting Time	r_2	Service Time, y	Departure Clock	Time in System
1	—	—	0.0	0.0	0.0	65	1.0	1.0	1.0
2	71	3.0	3.0	3.0	0.0	18	0.5	3.5	0.5
3	12	1.0	4.0	4.0	0.0	17	0.5	4.5	0.5
4	48	2.0	6.0	6.0	0.0	89	2.0	8.0	2.0
5	18	1.0	7.0	8.0	1.0	83	2.0	10.0	3.0
6	08	1.0	8.0	10.0	2.0	90	2.0	12.0	4.0
7	05	1.0	9.0	12.0	3.0	89	2.0	14.0	5.0
8	18	1.0	10.0	14.0	4.0	08	0.5	14.5	4.5
9	26	2.0	12.0	14.5	2.5	47	1.0	15.5	3.5
10	94	4.0	16.0	16.0	0.0	06	0.5	16.5	0.5
					12.5				24.5

1. Batch 1 arrives at time 0, which is recorded on an *arrival clock*. Because there are no batches in the system, batch 1 approaches the dyeing facility immediately, also at time 0. The waiting time is 0.
2. Next, a random number, $r_2 = 65$, is selected from the second column in Table 14.3. Observing Table 14.6, we see that the random number 65 results in a service time, y, of 1 day. After leaving the dyeing vat, the batch departs at time 1 day, having been in the queuing system a total of 1 day.
3. The next random number, $r_1 = 71$, is selected from Table 14.3, which specifies that batch 2 arrives 3 days after batch 1, or at time 3.0, as shown on the arrival clock. Because batch 1 departed the service facility at time 1.0, batch 2 can be served immediately and thus incurs no waiting time.
4. The next random number, $r_2 = 18$, is selected from Table 14.3, which indicates that batch 2 will spend 0.5 days being served and will depart at time 3.5.

This process of selecting random numbers and generating arrival intervals and service times continues until 10 batch arrivals have been simulated, as shown in Table 14.7.

Once the simulation is complete, we can compute operating characteristics from the simulation results, as follows:

$$\text{average waiting time} = \frac{12.5 \text{ days}}{10 \text{ batches}} = 1.25 \text{ days per batch}$$

$$\text{average time in the system} = \frac{24.5 \text{ days}}{10 \text{ batches}} = 2.45 \text{ days per batch}$$

However, as in our previous example, these results must be viewed with skepticism. Ten trials of the system do not ensure steady-state results. In general, we can expect a considerable difference between the true average values and the values estimated from only 10 random draws. One reason is that we cannot be sure that the random numbers we selected in this example replicated the actual probability distributions because we used so few random numbers. The stream of random numbers that was used might have had a preponderance of high or low values, thus biasing the final model results. For example, of nine arrivals, five had interarrival times of 1 day. This corresponds to a probability of .55 (i.e., 5/9); however, the actual probability of an arrival interval of 1 day is .20 (from Table 14.5). This excessive number of short interarrival times (caused by the sequence of random numbers) has probably artificially inflated the operating statistics of the system.

As the number of random trials is increased, the probabilities in the simulation will more closely conform to the actual probability distributions. That is, if we simulated the queuing system for 1,000 arrivals, we could more reasonably expect that 20% of the arrivals would have an interarrival time of 1 day.

A factor that can affect simulation results is the starting conditions.

An additional factor that can affect simulation results is the starting conditions. If we start our queuing system with no batches in the system, we must simulate a length of time before the system replicates normal operating conditions. In this example, it is logical to start simulating at the time the vat starts operating in the morning, especially if we simulate an entire working day. Some queuing systems, however, start with items already in the system. For example, the dyeing facility might logically start each day with partially completed batches from the previous day. In this case, it is necessary to begin the simulation with batches already in the system.

By adding a second random variable to a simulation model, such as the one just shown, we increase the complexity and therefore the manual operations. To simulate the example in Table 14.7 manually for 1,000 trials would require several hours. It would be far preferable to perform this type of simulation on a computer. A number of mathematical computations would be required to determine the various column values of Table 14.7, as we will demonstrate in the Excel spreadsheet simulation of this example in the next section.

Computer Simulation of the Queuing Example with Excel

The simulation of the dyeing process at Burlingham Mills shown in Table 14.7 can also be done in Excel. Exhibit 14.6 shows the spreadsheet simulation model for this example.

Exhibit 14.6

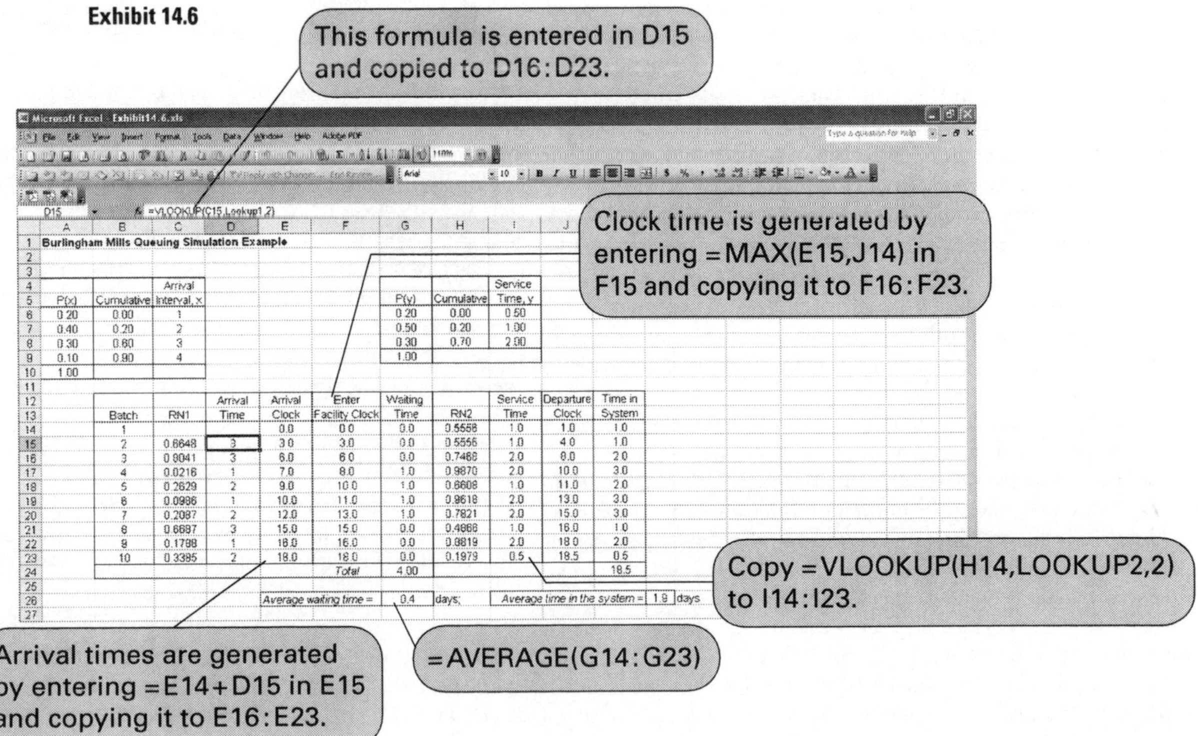

P(x)	Cumulative	Arrival Interval, x
0.20	0.00	1
0.40	0.20	2
0.30	0.60	3
0.10	0.90	4
1.00		

P(y)	Cumulative	Service Time, y
0.20	0.00	0.50
0.50	0.20	1.00
0.30	0.70	2.00
1.00		

Batch	RN1	Arrival Time	Arrival Clock	Enter Facility Clock	Waiting Time	RN2	Service Time	Departure Clock	Time in System
1			0.0	0.0	0.0	0.5558	1.0	1.0	1.0
2	0.6648	3	3.0	3.0	0.0	0.5556	1.0	4.0	1.0
3	0.8041	3	6.0	6.0	0.0	0.7488	2.0	8.0	2.0
4	0.0216	1	7.0	8.0	1.0	0.9870	2.0	10.0	3.0
5	0.2629	2	9.0	10.0	1.0	0.6608	1.0	11.0	2.0
6	0.0986	1	10.0	11.0	1.0	0.9618	2.0	13.0	3.0
7	0.2087	2	12.0	13.0	1.0	0.7821	2.0	15.0	3.0
8	0.6697	3	15.0	15.0	0.0	0.4866	1.0	16.0	1.0
9	0.1788	1	16.0	16.0	0.0	0.8819	2.0	18.0	2.0
10	0.3385	2	18.0	18.0	0.0	0.1979	0.5	18.5	0.5
				Total	4.00				18.5

Average waiting time = 0.4 days; *Average time in the system =* 1.9 days

The stream of random numbers in column C is generated by the formula **=RAND()**, used in the ComputerWorld examples in Exhibits 14.2 through 14.5. (Notice that for this computer simulation, we have changed our random numbers from whole numbers to numbers between 0.0 and 1.0.) The arrival times are generated from the cumulative probability distribution of arrival intervals in cells **B6:C9**. This array of cells is renamed "Lookup1" because there are two probability distributions in the model. The formula **=VLOOKUP(C15, Lookup1,2)** is entered in cell D15 and copied to cells **D16:D23** to generate the arrival times in column D. The arrival clock times are computed by entering the formula **=E14+D15** in cell E15 and copying it to cells **E16:E23**.

Management Science Application

Simulating the Israeli Army Recruitment Process

Israel has compulsory army service starting at age 18. Candidates are examined while they are still in high school, a year before their recruitment. Prior to 1995 the examinations were conducted at six recruitment offices around the country. Each office included five major testing stations, where candidates were required to go through 2 days of examinations. The first day a candidate went through an admissions station, a premed station, and then a psychometric exam. Several weeks later the candidate would be scheduled for a second visit that included a personal interview and standard medical exam. More than 70% of the candidates did not finish the examination process during the 2 scheduled days and had to return for additional visits to finish all the tests. The recruitment offices were overcrowded, and staff worked at 100% capacity. Candidates spent over 40% of their time in the recruitment offices waiting in lines, and the average station waiting time was 30 minutes. This problem of overcrowding and delays was expected to get worse because of Israel's population growth from immigration (about 20%) during the 1990s. Possible solutions being considered included building an additional recruitment office and adding more personnel and staff.

A team was assigned to examine the recruitment process and overcrowding problem, with goals of finding a more cost-effective solution than building new facilities and adding personnel, and providing candidates with faster service, specifically reducing the number of extra visits. Preliminary analysis indicated that areas of improvement included the sequencing of the stations and the scheduling of the psychometric exam. The team created a simulation model to examine the various queuing situations that existed and the candidate flows through the system. The simulation model was used to analyze bottleneck situations and to evaluate possible alternatives, including changing the arrival patterns at stations, changing the way the psychometric test was administered, and looking at different possible routes through the process. After a year, a new recruiting configuration was developed, using the simulation model. A new computer system was installed that eliminated the use of personal files and thus saved wasted time for files to be physically transported between stations. A computerized routing system using bar codes assigned to candidates upon admission routed candidates to the stations with the shortest waiting times. The psychometric exam was computerized, thus eliminating the need to wait until examining rooms filled or emptied and to collect paper test results. Candidates' arrival times were evenly distributed during the morning.

The new system was implemented in 1995 in the Haifa office with successful results almost identical to those predicted by the simulation model. Ninety-nine percent of all candidates were able to complete all their tests in 1 day, in an average of 4 hours. Average station waiting time was reduced to 5 minutes. With the same workforce and facilities, throughput more than doubled. The new system was subsequently implemented in the five other recruiting offices with similar results. The two biggest offices in Tel Aviv were eventually merged, thus eliminating an office. This savings alone covered the cost of the entire project. Savings included $3.3 million for the closed offices plus $350,000 annually for reduced costs, including personnel and office expenses.

Source: O. Shtrichman, R. Ben-Haim, and M. Pollatschek, "Using Simulation to Increase Efficiency in an Army Recruitment Office," *Interfaces* 31, no. 4 (July–August 2001): 61–70.

A batch of yarn can enter the dyeing facility as soon as it arrives (in column E) if there is not another batch being dyed or as soon as any batches being dyed or waiting to be dyed have departed the facility (column J). This clock time is computed by entering the formula **=MAX(E15, J14)** in cell F15 and copying it to cells **F16:F23**. The waiting time is computed with the formula **=F14-E14**, copied in cells **G14:G23**.

A second set of random numbers is generated in column H by using the **RAND()** function. The service times are generated in column I from the cumulative probability distribution in cells **H6:I8**, using the "Lookup" function again. In this case the array of cells in **H6:I8** is named "Lookup2," and the service times in column I are generated by copying the formula **=VLOOKUP(H14, Lookup2,2)** in cells **I14:I23**. The departure times in column J are determined by using the formula **=F14+I14** copied in cells **J14:J23**, and the "Time in System" values are computed by using the formula **=J14-E14**, copied in cells **K14:K23**.

The operating statistic, average waiting time, is computed by using the formula **=AVERAGE(G14:G23)** in cell G26, and the average time in the system is computed with a similar formula in cell L26. Notice that both the average waiting time of 0.4 days and the average time in the system of 1.9 days are significantly lower than the simulation conducted in Table 14.7, as we speculated they might be.

Continuous Probability Distributions

In the first example in this chapter, ComputerWorld's store manager considered a probability distribution of discrete demand values. In the queuing example, the probability distributions were for discrete interarrival times and service times. However, applications of simulation models reflecting continuous distributions are more common than those of models employing discrete distributions.

We have concentrated on examples with discrete distributions because with a discrete distribution, the ranges of random numbers can be explicitly determined and are thus easier to illustrate. When random numbers are being selected according to a continuous probability distribution, a continuous function must be used. For example, consider the following continuous probability function, $f(x)$, for time (minutes), x:

$$f(x) = \frac{x}{8}, 0 \leq x \leq 4$$

The area under the curve, $f(x)$, represents the probability of the occurrence of the random variable x. Therefore, the area under the curve must equal 1.0 because the sum of all probabilities of the occurrence of a random variable must equal 1.0. By computing the area under the curve from 0 to any value of the random variable x, we can determine the cumulative probability of that value of x, as follows:

$$F(x) = \int_0^x \frac{x}{8} dx = \frac{1}{8}\int_0^x x\,dx = \frac{1}{8}\left(\frac{1}{2}x^2\right)\Bigg]_0^x$$

$$F(x) = \frac{x^2}{16}$$

Cumulative probabilities are analogous to the discrete ranges of random numbers we used in previous examples. Thus, we let this function, $F(x)$, equal the random number, r,

$$r = \frac{x^2}{16}$$

and solve for x,

$$x = 4\sqrt{r}$$

By generating a random number, r, and substituting it into this function, we determine a value for x, "time." (However, for a continuous function, the range of random numbers must be between zero and one to correspond to probabilities between 0.0 and 1.00.) For example, if $r = .25$, then

$$x = 4\sqrt{.25} = 2 \text{ min.}$$

The purpose of briefly presenting this example is to demonstrate the difference between discrete and continuous functions. This continuous function is relatively simple; as functions become more complex, it becomes more difficult to develop the equation for determining the random variable x from r. Even this simple example required some calculus, and developing more complex models would require a higher level of mathematics.

Simulation of a Machine Breakdown and Maintenance System

A continuous probability distribution of the time between machine breakdowns.

In this example we will demonstrate the use of a continuous probability distribution. The Bigelow Manufacturing Company produces a product on a number of machines. The elapsed time between breakdowns of the machines is defined by the following continuous probability distribution:

$$f(x) = \frac{x}{8}, 0 \leq x \leq 4 \text{ weeks}$$

where

x = weeks between machine breakdowns

As indicated in the previous section on continuous probability distributions, the equation for generating x, given the random number r_1, is

$$x = 4\sqrt{r_1}$$

When a machine breaks down, it must be repaired, and it takes either 1, 2, or 3 days for the repair to be completed, according to the discrete probability distribution shown in Table 14.8. Every time a machine breaks down, the cost to the company is an estimated $2,000 per day in lost production until the machine is repaired.

Table 14.8
Probability distribution of machine repair time

Machine Repair Time, y (days)	Probability of Repair Time, $P(y)$	Cumulative Probability	Random Number Range, r_2
1	.15	.15	0.00–.15
2	.55	.70	.16–.70
3	.30	1.00	.71–1.00

The company would like to know whether it should implement a machine maintenance program at a cost of $20,000 per year that would reduce the frequency of breakdowns and thus the time for repair. The maintenance program would result in the following continuous probability function for time between breakdowns:

$$f(x) = x/18, \quad 0 \leq x \leq 6 \text{ weeks}$$

where

x = weeks between machine breakdowns

The equation for generating x, given the random number r_1, for this probability distribution is

$$x = 6\sqrt{r_1}$$

The reduced repair time resulting from the maintenance program is defined by the discrete probability distribution shown in Table 14.9.

Table 14.9
Revised probability distribution of machine repair time with the maintenance program

Machine Repair Time, y (days)	Probability of Repair Time, $P(y)$	Cumulative Probability	Random Number Range, r_2
1	.40	.40	0.00–.40
2	.50	.90	.41–.90
3	.10	1.00	.91–1.00

To solve this problem, we must first simulate the existing system to determine an estimate of the average annual repair costs. Then we must simulate the system with the maintenance program installed to see what the average annual repair costs will be with the maintenance program. We will then compare the average annual repair cost with and without the maintenance program and compute the difference, which will be the average annual savings in repair costs with the maintenance program. If this savings is more than the annual cost of the maintenance program ($20,000), we will recommend that it be implemented; if it is less, we will recommend that it not be implemented.

First, we will manually simulate the existing breakdown and repair system without the maintenance program, to see how the simulation model is developed. Table 14.10 illustrates the simulation of machine breakdowns and repair for 20 breakdowns, which occur over a period of approximately 1 year (i.e., 52 weeks).

Table 14.10
Simulation of machine breakdowns and repair times

Breakdowns	r_1	Time Between Breakdowns, x (weeks)	r_2	Repair Time, y (days)	Cost, $2,000$y$	Cumulative Time, Σx (weeks)
1	.45	2.68	.19	2	$ 4,000	2.68
2	.90	3.80	.65	2	4,000	6.48
3	.84	3.67	.51	2	4,000	10.15
4	.17	1.65	.17	2	4,000	11.80
5	.74	3.44	.63	2	4,000	15.24
6	.94	3.88	.85	3	6,000	19.12
7	.07	1.06	.37	2	4,000	20.18
8	.15	1.55	.89	3	6,000	21.73
9	.04	0.80	.76	3	6,000	22.53
10	.31	2.23	.71	3	6,000	24.76
11	.07	1.06	.34	2	4,000	25.82
12	.99	3.98	.11	1	2,000	29.80
13	.97	3.94	.27	2	4,000	33.74
14	.73	3.42	.10	1	2,000	37.16
15	.13	1.44	.59	2	4,000	38.60
16	.03	0.70	.87	3	6,000	39.30
17	.62	3.15	.08	1	2,000	42.45
18	.47	2.74	.08	1	2,000	45.19
19	.99	3.98	.89	3	6,000	49.17
20	.75	3.46	.42	2	4,000	52.63
					$84,000	

The simulation in Table 14.10 results in a total annual repair cost of $84,000. However, this is for only 1 year, and thus it is probably not very accurate.

The next step in our simulation analysis is to simulate the machine breakdown and repair system with the maintenance program installed. We will use the revised continuous probability distribution for time between breakdowns and the revised discrete probability distribution for repair time shown in Table 14.9. Table 14.11 illustrates the manual simulation of machine breakdowns and repair for 1 year.

Table 14.11
Simulation of machine breakdowns and repair with the maintenance program

Breakdowns	r_1	Time Between Breakdowns, x (weeks)	r_2	Repair Time, y (days)	Cost, $2,000$y$	Cumulative Time, Σx (weeks)
1	.45	4.03	.19	1	$ 2,000	4.03
2	.90	5.69	.65	2	4,000	9.72
3	.84	5.50	.51	2	4,000	15.22
4	.17	2.47	.17	1	2,000	17.69
5	.74	5.16	.63	2	4,000	22.85
6	.94	5.82	.85	2	4,000	28.67
7	.07	1.59	.37	1	2,000	30.29
8	.15	2.32	.89	2	4,000	32.58
9	.04	1.20	.76	2	4,000	33.78
10	.31	3.34	.71	2	4,000	37.12
11	.07	1.59	.34	1	2,000	38.71
12	.99	5.97	.11	1	2,000	44.68
13	.97	5.91	.27	1	2,000	50.59
14	.73	5.12	.10	1	2,000	55.71
					$42,000	

Table 14.11 shows that the annual repair cost with the maintenance program totals $42,000. Recall that in the manual simulation shown in Table 14.10, the annual repair cost was $84,000 for the system without the maintenance program. The difference between the two annual repair costs is $84,000 − 42,000 = $42,000. This figure represents the savings in average annual repair cost with the maintenance program. Because the maintenance program will cost $20,000 per year, it would seem that the recommended decision would be to implement the maintenance program and generate an expected annual savings of $22,000 per year (i.e., $42,000 − 20,000 = $22,000).

Manual simulation is limited because of the amount of real time required to simulate even one trial.

However, let us now concern ourselves with the potential difficulties caused by the fact that we simulated each system (the existing one and the system with the maintenance program) only *once*. Because the time between breakdowns and the repair times are probabilistic, the simulation results could exhibit significant variation. The only way to be sure of the accuracy of our results is to simulate each system many times and compute an average result. Performing these many simulations manually would obviously require a great deal of time and effort. However, Excel can be used to accomplish the required simulation analysis.

Computer Simulation of the Machine Breakdown Example Using Excel

Exhibit 14.7 shows the Excel spreadsheet model of the simulation of our original machine breakdown example simulated manually in Table 14.10. The Excel simulation is for 100 breakdowns. The random numbers in **C14:C113** are generated using the **RAND()** function, which was used in our previous Excel examples. The "Time Between Breakdowns" values in column D are developed using the formula for the continuous cumulative probability function, **=4*SQRT(C14)**, typed in cell D14 and copied in cells **D15:D113**.

Exhibit 14.7

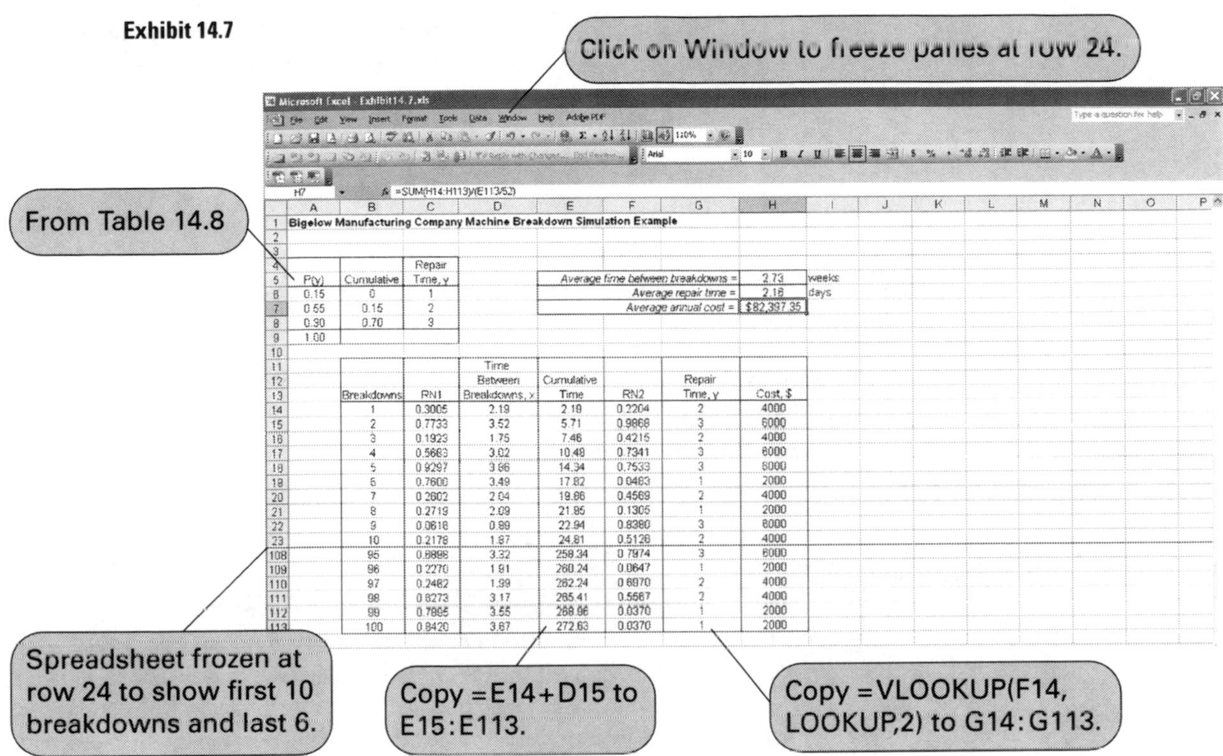

P(y)	Cumulative	Repair Time, y
0.15	0	1
0.55	0.15	2
0.30	0.70	3
1.00		

Breakdowns	RN1	Time Between Breakdowns, x	Cumulative Time	RN2	Repair Time, y	Cost, $
1	0.3005	2.18	2.18	0.2204	2	4000
2	0.7733	3.52	5.71	0.9868	3	6000
3	0.1923	1.75	7.46	0.4215	2	4000
4	0.5683	3.02	10.48	0.7341	3	6000
5	0.9297	3.86	14.34	0.7533	3	6000
6	0.7600	3.49	17.82	0.0483	1	2000
7	0.2602	2.04	19.86	0.4569	2	4000
8	0.2719	2.09	21.85	0.1305	1	2000
9	0.0618	0.89	22.94	0.8380	3	6000
10	0.2178	1.87	24.81	0.5126	2	4000
95	0.8898	3.32	258.34	0.7974	3	6000
96	0.2270	1.91	260.24	0.0647	1	2000
97	0.2482	1.99	262.24	0.6970	2	4000
98	0.8273	3.17	265.41	0.5567	2	4000
99	0.7895	3.55	268.96	0.0370	1	2000
100	0.8420	3.67	272.63	0.0370	1	2000

The "Cumulative Time" in column E is computed by copying the formula **=E14+D15** in cells **E15:E113.** The second stream of random numbers in column F is generated using the **RAND**() function. The "Repair Time" values in column G are generated from the cumulative probability distribution in the array of cells **B6:C8**. As in our previous examples, we

Exhibit 14.8

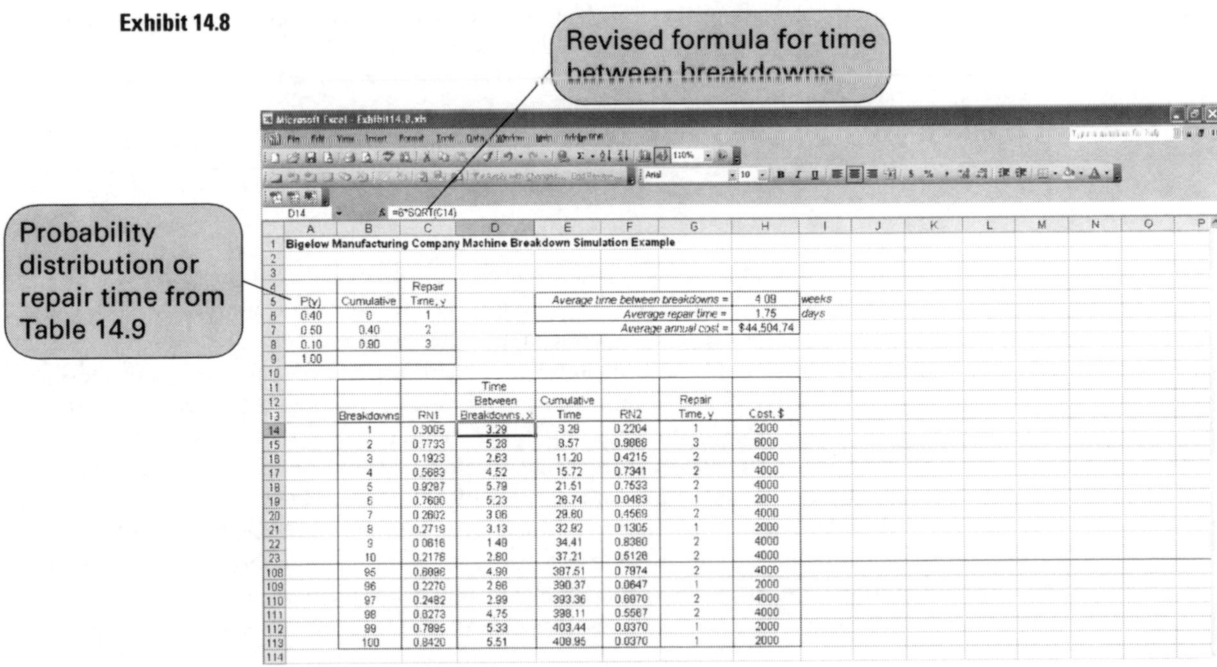

P(y)	Cumulative	Repair Time, y
0.40	0	1
0.50	0.40	2
0.10	0.90	3
1.00		

Breakdowns	RN1	Time Between Breakdowns, x	Cumulative Time	RN2	Repair Time, y	Cost, $
1	0.3005	3.29	3.29	0.2204	1	2000
2	0.7733	5.28	8.57	0.9868	3	6000
3	0.1923	2.63	11.20	0.4215	2	4000
4	0.5683	4.52	15.72	0.7341	2	4000
5	0.9297	5.79	21.51	0.7533	2	4000
6	0.7600	5.23	26.74	0.0483	1	2000
7	0.2602	3.06	29.80	0.4569	2	4000
8	0.2719	3.13	32.92	0.1305	1	2000
9	0.0616	1.49	34.41	0.8380	2	4000
10	0.2178	2.80	37.21	0.5126	2	4000
95	0.6698	4.90	387.51	0.7974	2	4000
96	0.2270	2.86	390.37	0.0647	1	2000
97	0.2482	2.99	393.36	0.6970	2	4000
98	0.6273	4.75	398.11	0.5567	2	4000
99	0.7895	5.33	403.44	0.0370	1	2000
100	0.8420	5.51	408.95	0.0370	1	2000

name this array "Lookup" and copy the formula **=VLOOKUP(F14,Lookup,2)** in cells **G14:G113**. The cost values in column H are computed by entering the formula **=2000*G14** in cell H14 and copying it to cells **H15:H113**.

The "Average Annual Cost" in cell H7 is computed with the formula **=SUM (H14:H113)/(E113/52)**. For this, the original problem, the annual cost is $82,397.35, which is not too different from the manual simulation in Table 14.10.

Exhibit 14.8 shows the Excel spreadsheet simulation for the modified breakdown system with the new maintenance program, which was simulated manually in Table 14.11. The two differences in this simulation model are the cumulative probability distribution formulas for the time between breakdowns and the reduced repair time distributions from Table 14.9 in cells **A6:C8**.

The average annual cost for this model, shown in cell H8, is $44,504.74. This annual cost is only slightly higher than the $42,000 obtained from the manual simulation in Table 14.11. Thus, as before, the decision should be to implement the new maintenance system.

Statistical Analysis of Simulation Results

In general, the outcomes of a simulation model are statistical measures such as averages, as in the examples presented in this chapter. In our ComputerWorld example, we generated average revenue as a measure of the system we simulated; in the Burlingham Mills queuing example, we generated the average waiting time for batches to be dyed; and in the Bigelow Manufacturing Company machine breakdown example, the system was measured in terms of average repair costs. However, we also discussed the care that must be taken in accepting the accuracy of these statistical results because they were frequently based on relatively few observations (i.e., simulation replications). Thus, as part of the simulation process, these statistical results are typically subjected to additional statistical analysis to determine their degree of accuracy.

One of the most frequently used tools for the analysis of the statistical validity of simulations results is confidence limits. Confidence limits can be developed within Excel for the averages resulting from simulation models in several different ways. Recall that the statistical formulas for 95% confidence limits are

$$\text{upper confidence limit} = \bar{x} + (1.96)(s/\sqrt{n})$$
$$\text{lower confidence limit} = \bar{x} - (1.96)(s/\sqrt{n})$$

where $\bar{x}$ is the mean and s is the sample standard deviation from a sample of size n from any population. Although we cannot be sure that the sample mean will exactly equal the population mean, we can be 95% confident that the true population mean will be between the upper confidence limit (UCL) and lower confidence limit (LCL) computed using these formulas.

Exhibit 14.9 shows the Excel spreadsheet for our machine breakdown example (from Exhibit 14.8), with the upper and lower confidence limits for average repair cost in cells L13 and L14. Cell L11 contains the average repair cost (for each incidence of a breakdown), computed by using the formula **=AVERAGE(H14:H113)**. Cell L12 contains the sample standard deviation, computed by using the formula **=STDEV(H14:H113)**. The upper confidence limit is computed in cell L13 by using the formula shown on the formula bar at the top of the spreadsheet, and the lower control limit is computed similarly. Thus, we can be 95% confident that the true average repair cost for the population is between $3,248.50 and $3,751.50.

Exhibit 14.9

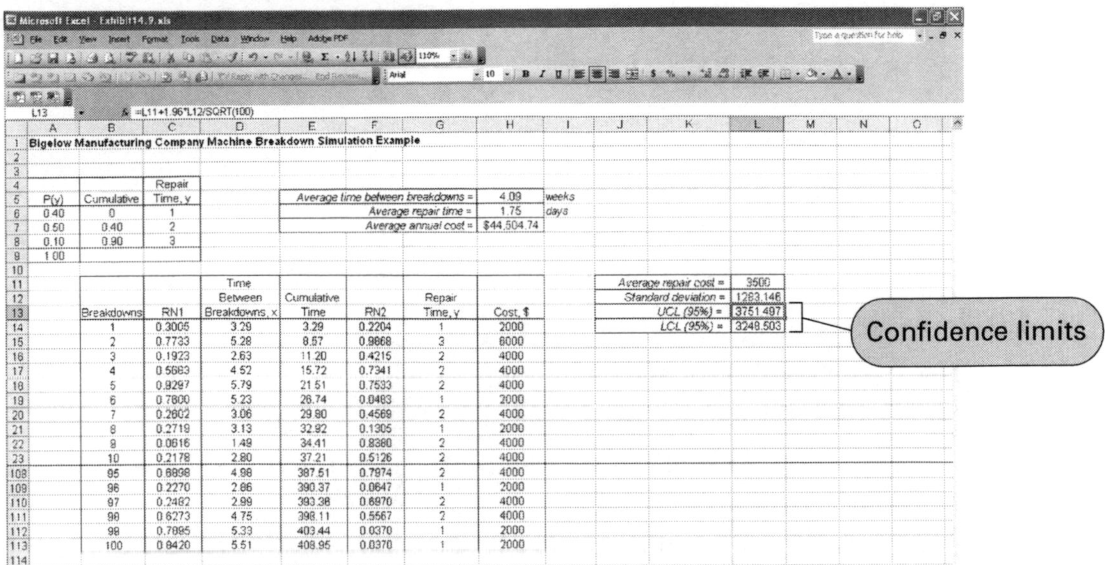

L13 f_x =L11+1.96*L12/SQRT(100)

Bigelow Manufacturing Company Machine Breakdown Simulation Example

P(y)	Cumulative	Repair Time, y
0.40	0	1
0.50	0.40	2
0.10	0.90	3
1.00		

Average time between breakdowns =	4.09	weeks
Average repair time =	1.75	days
Average annual cost =	$44,504.74	

Breakdowns	RN1	Time Between Breakdowns, x	Cumulative Time	RN2	Repair Time, y	Cost, $
1	0.3005	3.29	3.29	0.2204	1	2000
2	0.7733	5.28	8.57	0.9868	3	6000
3	0.1923	2.63	11.20	0.4215	2	4000
4	0.5663	4.52	15.72	0.7341	2	4000
5	0.8297	5.79	21.51	0.7533	2	4000
6	0.7600	5.23	26.74	0.0483	1	2000
7	0.2602	3.06	29.80	0.4569	2	4000
8	0.2719	3.13	32.92	0.1305	1	2000
9	0.0616	1.49	34.41	0.8380	2	4000
10	0.2178	2.80	37.21	0.5126	2	4000
95	0.6898	4.98	387.51	0.7974	2	4000
96	0.2270	2.86	390.37	0.0647	1	2000
97	0.2482	2.99	393.36	0.6970	2	4000
98	0.6273	4.75	398.11	0.5567	2	4000
99	0.7895	5.33	403.44	0.0370	1	2000
100	0.8420	5.51	408.95	0.0370	1	2000

Average repair cost =	3500
Standard deviation =	1283.146
UCL (95%) =	3751.497
LCL (95%) =	3248.503

Confidence limits plus several additional statistics can also be obtained by using the "Data Analysis" option from the "Tools" menu. (If this option is not available on your "Tools" menu, select the "Add-ins" option from the "Tools" menu and then select the "Analysis ToolPak" option.) Select the "Data Analysis" option from the "Tools" menu at the top of the spreadsheet, and then from the resulting menu select "Descriptive Statistics." This will result in a dialog box like the one shown in Exhibit 14.10. This box, completed as shown, results in the summary statistics for repair costs shown in cells **J8:K23** in Exhibit 14.11. These summary statistics include the mean, standard deviation, and confidence limits we computed in Exhibit 14.9, plus several other statistics.

Exhibit 14.10

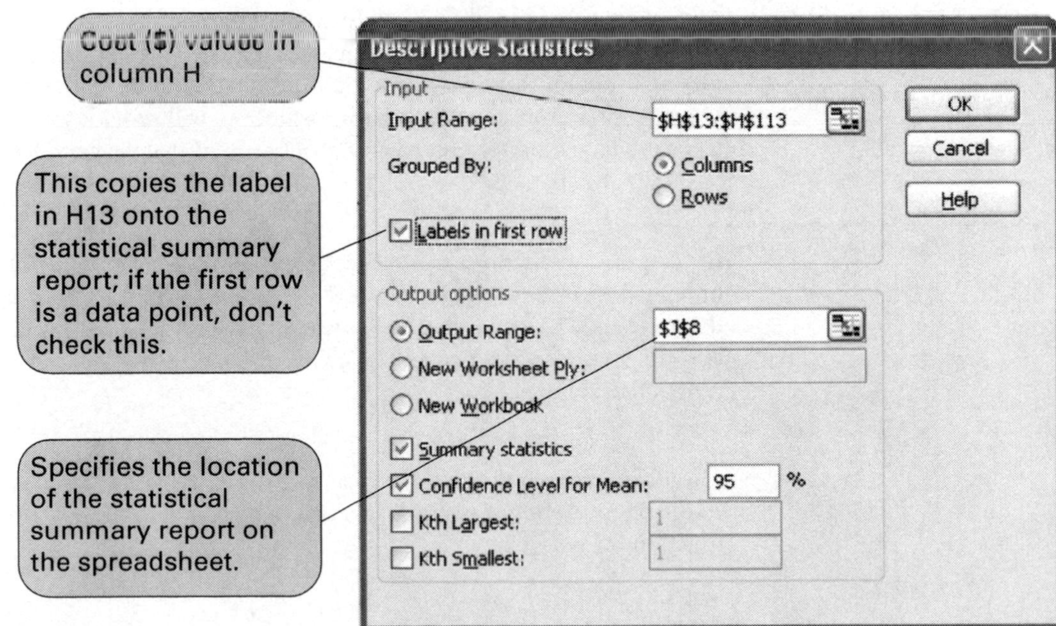

Exhibit 14.11

Microsoft Excel - Exhibit14.11.xls

H7 =SUM(H14:H113)/(E113/52)

Bigelow Manufacturing Company Machine Breakdown Simulation Example

P(y)	Cumulative	Repair Time, y
0.40	0	1
0.50	0.40	2
0.10	0.90	3
1.00		

Average time between breakdowns =	4.09	*weeks*
Average repair time =	1.75	*days*
Average annual cost = $	44504.74	

Breakdowns	RN1	Time Between Breakdowns, x	Cumulative Time	RN2	Repair Time, y	Cost, $
1	0.3005	3.29	3.29	0.2204	1	2000
2	0.7733	5.28	8.57	0.8868	3	6000
3	0.1923	2.63	11.20	0.4215	2	4000
4	0.5683	4.52	15.72	0.7341	2	4000
5	0.9287	5.79	21.51	0.7533	2	4000
6	0.7600	5.23	26.74	0.0483	1	2000
7	0.2602	3.06	29.80	0.4569	2	4000
8	0.2719	3.13	32.92	0.1305	1	2000
9	0.0616	1.49	34.41	0.8980	2	4000
10	0.2178	2.80	37.21	0.5126	2	4000
95	0.6898	4.98	387.51	0.7974	2	4000
96	0.2270	2.86	390.37	0.0647	1	2000
97	0.2482	2.99	393.36	0.6870	2	4000
98	0.6273	4.75	398.11	0.5567	2	4000
99	0.7895	5.33	403.44	0.0370	1	2000
100	0.8420	5.51	408.95	0.0370	1	2000

Cost, $	
Mean	3500
Standard Error	128.31484
Median	4000
Mode	4000
Standard Deviation	1283.1484
Sample Variance	1646464.6
Kurtosis	-0.6573353
Skewness	0.2780897
Range	4000
Minimum	2000
Maximum	6000
Sum	350000
Count	100
Confidence Level(95.0%)	251.4971

Statistical summary report

Crystal Ball

So far in this chapter we have used simulation examples that included mostly discrete probability distributions that we set up on an Excel spreadsheet. These are the easiest types of probability distributions to work with in spreadsheets. However, many realistic problems contain more complex probability distributions, like the normal distribution, which are not discrete but are continuous, or they include discrete probability distributions that are more difficult to work with than the simple ones we have used. However, there are several simulation add-ins for Excel that provide the user with the capability to perform simulation analysis, using a variety of different probability distributions in a spreadsheet environment. One of these add-ins is Crystal Ball, published by Decisioneering; it is available for download from the CD that accompanies this text. Crystal Ball is a risk analysis and forecasting program that uses Monte Carlo simulation to forecast a statistical range of results possible for a given situation. In this section we will provide an overview of how to apply Crystal Ball to a simple example for profit analysis that we first introduced in Chapter 1.

Simulation of a Profit Analysis Model

In Chapter 1 we used a simple example for the Western Clothing Company to demonstrate break-even and profit analysis. In that example, Western Clothing Company produced denim jeans. The price (p) for jeans was \$23, the variable cost (c_v) was \$8 per pair of jeans, and the fixed cost (c_f) was \$10,000. Given these parameters, we formulated a profit (Z) function as follows:

$$Z = vp - c_f - vc_v$$

Our objective in that analysis was to determine the break-even volume, v, that would result in no profit or loss. This was accomplished by setting $Z = 0$ and solving the profit function for v, as follows:

$$v = \frac{c_f}{p - c_v}$$

Substituting the values for p, c_f, and c_v into this formula resulted in the break-even volume:

$$v = \frac{10{,}000}{23 - 8}$$
$$= 666.7 \text{ pairs of jeans}$$

To demonstrate the use of Crystal Ball, we will modify that example. First, we will assume that volume is actually volume *demanded* and that it is a random variable defined by a normal probability distribution, with a mean value of 1,050 pairs of jeans and a standard deviation of 410.

Furthermore, we will assume that the price is not fixed but is also uncertain and defined by a uniform probability distribution (from \$20 to \$26) and that variable cost is not a constant value but defined by a triangular probability distribution. Instead of seeking to determine the break-even volume, we will simulate the profit model, given probabilistic demand, price, and variable costs to determine average profit and the probability that Western Clothing will break even.

The first thing we need to do is access Crystal Ball, which you can download from the CD that comes with this text.

Exhibit 14.12 shows the Excel spreadsheet for our example.[1] We have described the parameters of each probability distribution in our profit model next to its corresponding cell. For example, cell C4 contains the probability distribution for demand. What we want to do is generate demand values in this cell according to the probability distribution for demand (i.e., Monte Carlo simulation). We also want to do this in cell C5 for price and in cell C7 for variable cost. This is the same process we used in our earlier ComputerWorld example to generate demand values from a discrete probability distribution, using random numbers. Notice that cell C9 contains our formula for profit, **=C4*C5-C6-(C4*C7)**. This is the only cell formula in our spreadsheet.

Exhibit 14.12

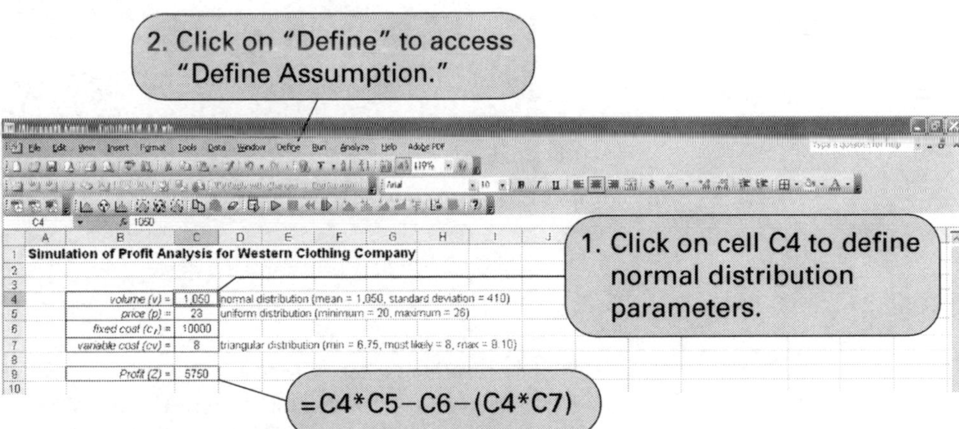

To set up the normal probability distribution for demand, we first enter the mean value 1,050 in cell C4. Cells require some initial value to start with. Next we click on "Define" from the top of the spreadsheet, as shown in Exhibit 14.12, which will result in the menu shown in Exhibit 14.13. We select "Define Assumption" from this menu, which will result in the Distribution Gallery window shown in Exhibit 14.14.

[1]This simulation example is located on the CD accompanying this text. It is in a file titled "Exhibit 14.12," located in the Crystal Ball folder on the accompanying text CD and created when Crystal Ball is loaded from the CD.

Exhibit 14.13

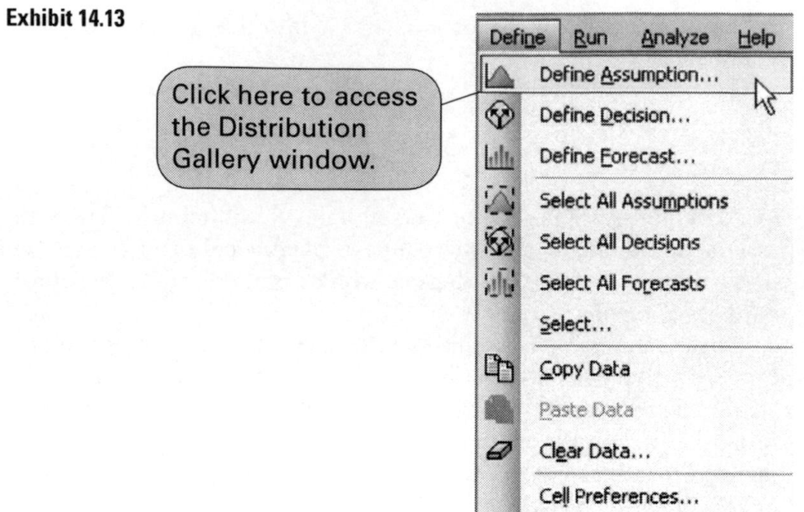

Exhibit 14.14

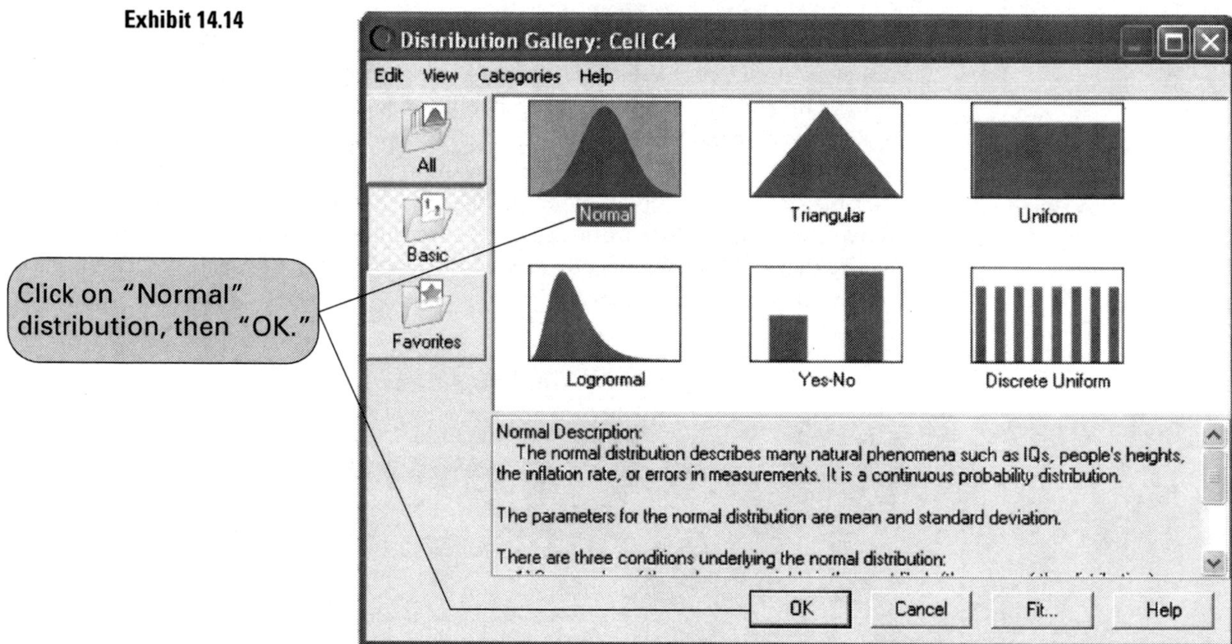

The Distribution Gallery window includes several different probability distributions we can use. Because we have indicated that demand is defined by a normal distribution, we click on this box and then on "OK." This will result in the window for the normal distribution shown in Exhibit 14.15.

The "Name" value in the box at the top of the window in Exhibit 14.15 was automatically pulled from the spreadsheet, where it is the heading "volume (v) ="; however, a new or different name could be typed in. Next, we click on "Mean" or use the Tab key to toggle down to the "Mean" display in the lower-left-hand corner of this window. Because we entered the mean value of 1,050 in cell C4 on our spreadsheet, this value will already be shown in this window. Next, we click on "Std Dev" or use the Tab key to move to the "Std Dev" window and enter the standard deviation of 410. Then we click on the Enter button, which will configure the normal distribution figure in the window, and then we click on "OK."

Exhibit 14.15

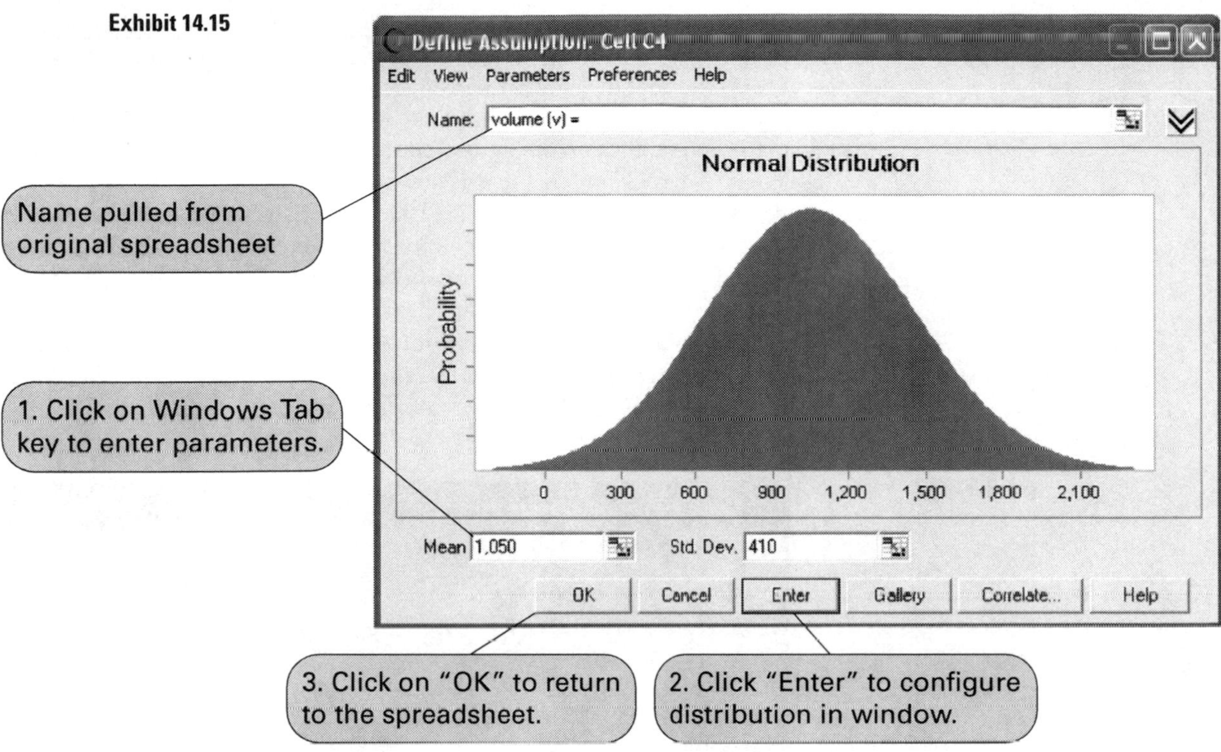

We will repeat this same process to enter the parameters for the uniform distribution for price in cell C5. First, we enter the value for price, 23, in cell C5. Next (with cell C5 activated), we click on "Define" at the top of the spreadsheet and then select "Define Assumption" from the menu, as shown earlier in Exhibit 14.13. The Distribution Gallery window will again appear, and this time you should click on "Uniform Distribution" and then "OK." This will result in the "Uniform Distribution" window shown in Exhibit 14.16.

Exhibit 14.16

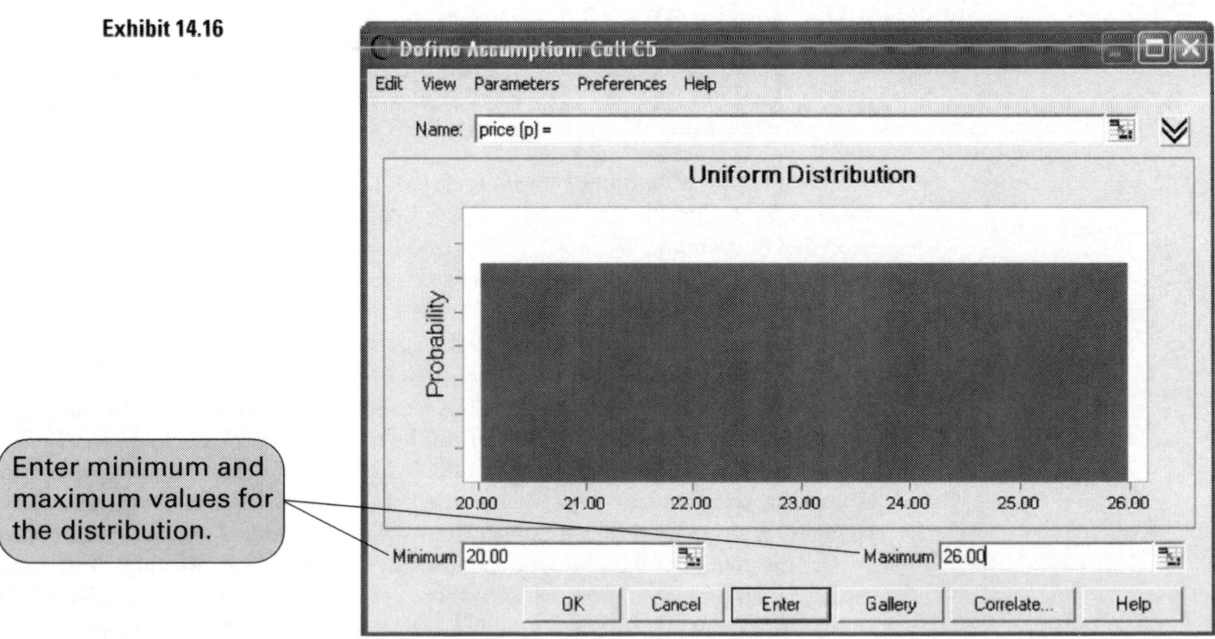

As before, the "Name" value, "price (p)," was pulled from the original spreadsheet in Exhibit 14.12. Next, we click on "Minimum" or use the Tab key to move to the "Minimum" display at the bottom of the window and enter 20, the lower limit of the uniform distribution specified in the problem statement. Next, we activate the "Maximum" display window and enter 26. Then we click on the "Enter" button to configure the distribution graph in the window. Finally, we click on "OK" to exit this window.

We repeat the same process to enter the triangular distribution parameters in cell C7. A triangular probability distribution is defined by three estimated values—a minimum, a most likely, and a maximum. It is a very useful approximation when enough data points do not exist to allow for the construction of a distribution, but the user can estimate what the endpoints and the midpoint of the distribution might be. Clicking on "Define Assumption" from the cell menu and then selecting the triangular distribution from the distribution gallery results in the window shown in Exhibit 14.17.

Exhibit 14.17

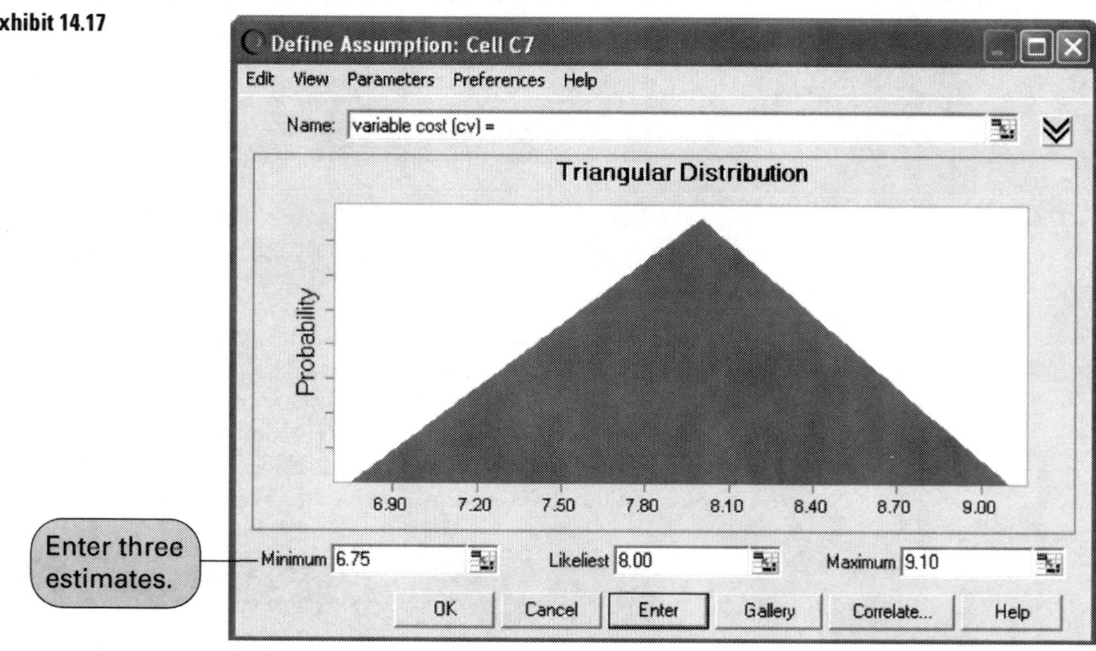

We enter the "Minimum" value of 6.75, the "Likeliest" value of 8.00, and the "Maximum" value of 9.10. Clicking on "Enter" will configure the graph of the triangular distribution shown in the window. We click on "OK" to exit this window and return to the spreadsheet.

Next, we click on cell C9 on our original spreadsheet. Recall that this is the cell in which we entered our profit formula in Exhibit 14.12. The profit value of 5,750, computed from the other cell values entered on the original spreadsheet, will be shown in cell C9. We click on the "Define" menu at the top of the spreadsheet and select "Define Forecast," as shown in Exhibit 14.18. This will result in the window shown in Exhibit 14.19. The heading "Profit(Z) =" will already be entered from the spreadsheet. We click on the "Units" display and enter "dollars." We then click on "OK" to exit this window. This completes the process of entering our simulation parameters and data. Exhibit 14.20 shows the spreadsheet with changes resulting from the parameter inputs. The next step is to run the simulation.

The mechanics of the simulation are similar to those of our previous Excel spreadsheet models. Using random numbers, we want to generate a value for demand in cell C4, then a value for price in C5, and then a value for variable cost in C7. These three values are then

Exhibit 14.18

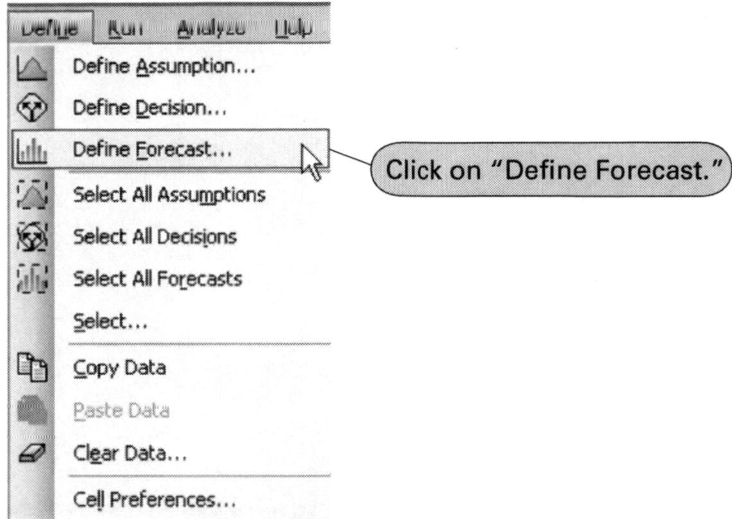

Exhibit 14.19

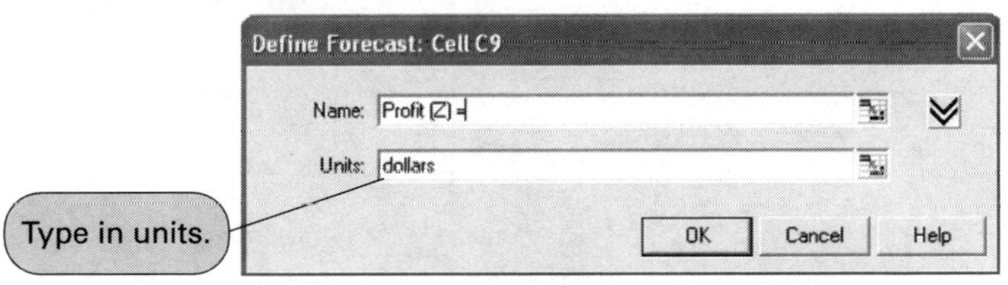

Exhibit 14.20

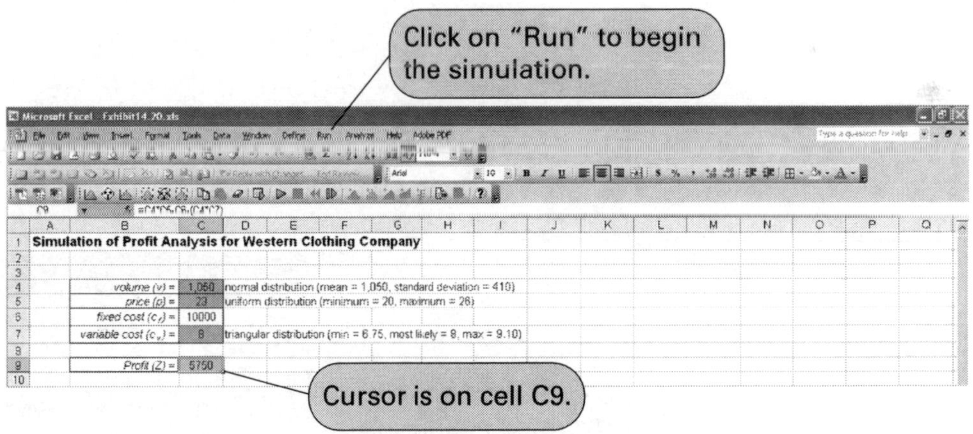

substituted into the profit formula in cell C9 to compute a profit value. This represents one repetition, or *trial*, of the simulation. The simulation is run for many trials in order to develop a distribution for profit.

To run the simulation, we access the "Run" menu at the top of the spreadsheet. This will result in the menu shown in Exhibit 14.21. We click on "Run Preferences," which will activate the window shown in Exhibit 14.22. We then enter the number of simulations for the simulation run. For this example we will run the simulation for 5,000 trials. Next, we click on "Sampling" at the top of this window to activate the window shown in Exhibit 14.23. In this

Exhibit 14.21

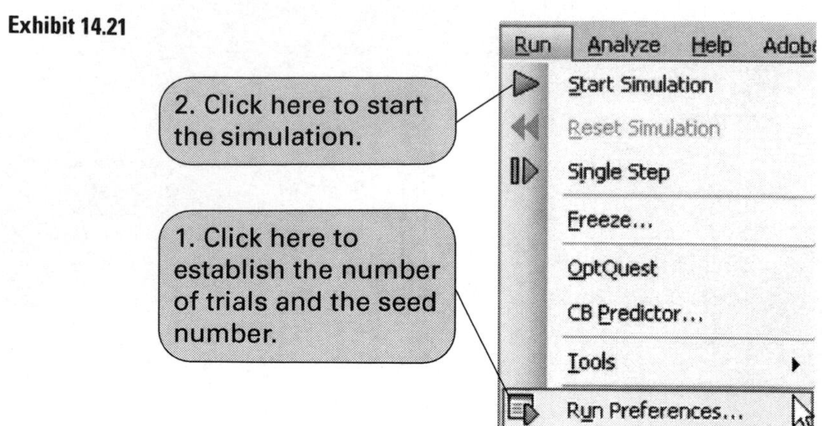

Exhibit 14.22

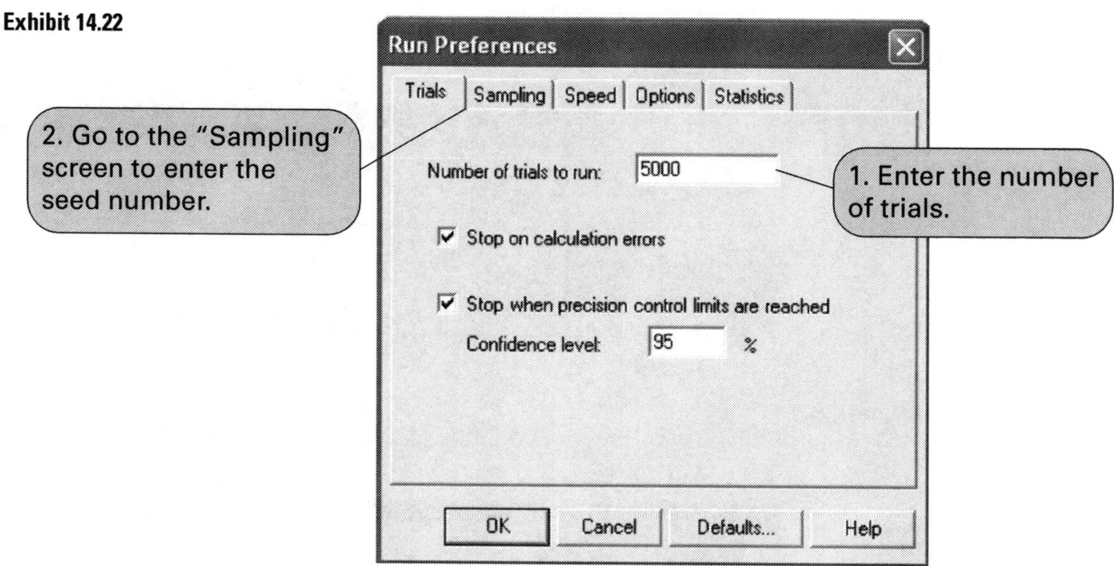

Exhibit 14.23

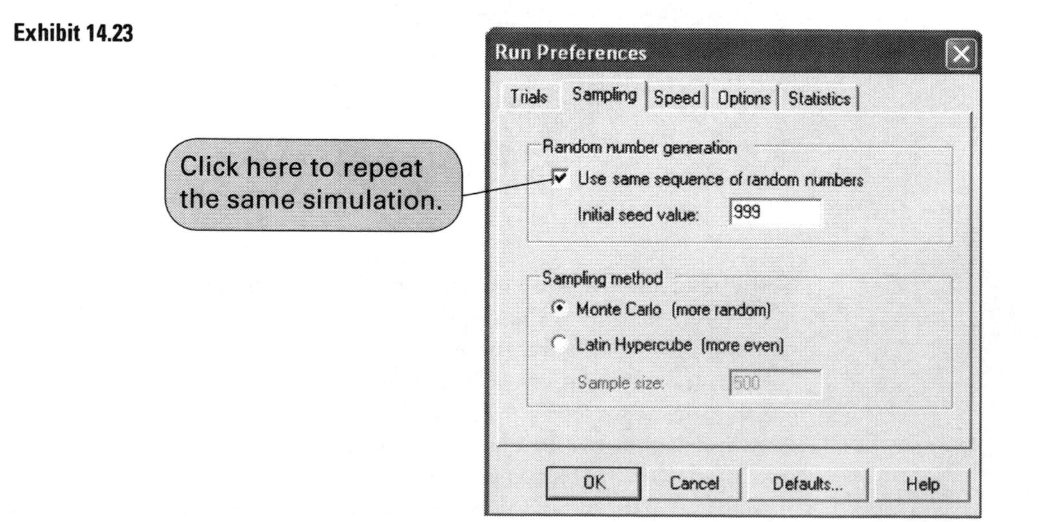

window we must enter the seed value for a sequence of random numbers for the simulation, which is always 999. We click on "OK" and then go back to the "Run" menu. From the "Run" menu (Exhibit 14.21), we click on "Start Simulation," which will run the simulation. Exhibit 14.24 shows the simulation window with the simulation completed for 5,000 trials and the frequency distribution for this simulation.

Exhibit 14.24

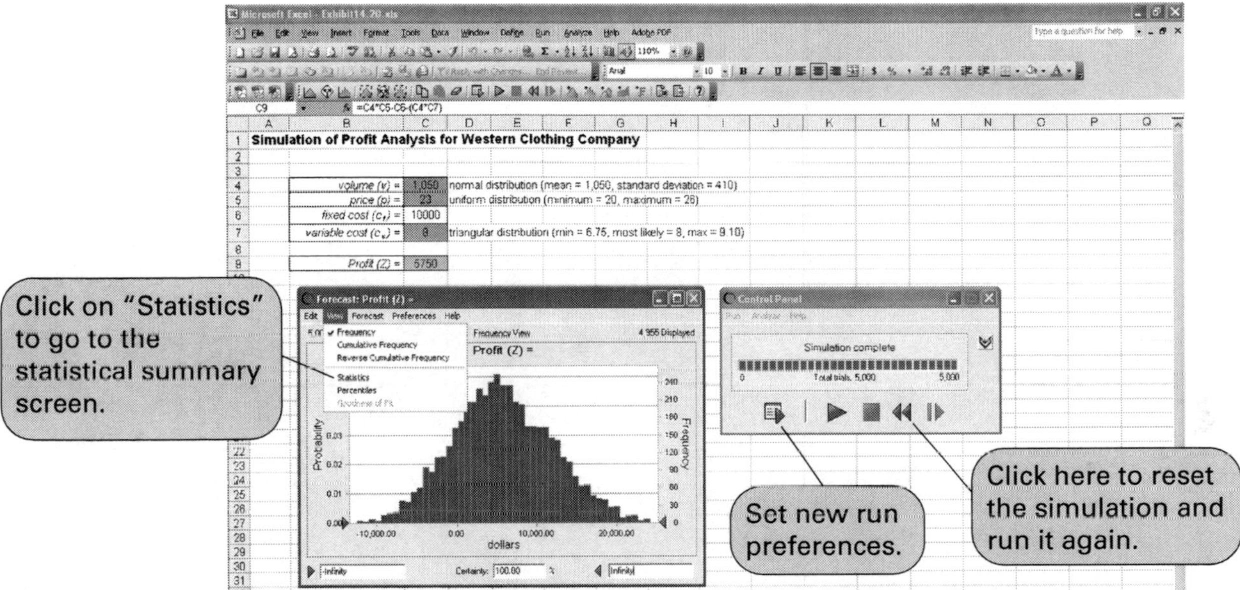

A statistical summary report for this simulation can be obtained by clicking on "View" at the top of the forecast window and then selecting "Statistics" from the drop-down menu. This results in the window shown in Exhibit 14.25. You can return to the forecast window by selecting "Frequency" from the "View" menu at the top of the statistics window.

In our original example formulated in Chapter 1, we wanted to determine the break-even volume. In this revised example, Western Clothing Company wants to know the average profit and the probability that it will break even from this simulation analysis. The mean profit (from the Statistics window in Exhibit 14.25) is $5,833.78. The probability of breaking even is determined by clicking on the arrow on the left side of the horizontal axis of the window shown in Exhibit 14.26 and "grabbing" it and moving it to "0.00," or by clicking on the lower limit, currently set at "Infinity"; we change this to 0 and press the Enter key. This will shift the lower limit to zero, the break-even point. The frequency chart that shows the location of the new lower limit and the "Certainty" of zero profit is shown as 81.73% at the bottom of the window as shown in Exhibit 14.26. Thus, there is a .8173 probability that the company will break even.

We have demonstrated using Crystal Ball with a straightforward example that was not very complex or detailed. Crystal Ball has the capability to perform much more sophisticated simulation analyses than what we have shown in this section. However, the demonstration of these capabilities and other features of Crystal Ball would require more space and in-depth coverage than is possible here. However, although using Crystal Ball to simulate more complex situations requires a greater degree of knowledge than we have provided, this basic introduction to and demonstration of Crystal Ball provide a good starting point to understanding the basic features of Crystal Ball and its use for simulation analysis.

Exhibit 14.25

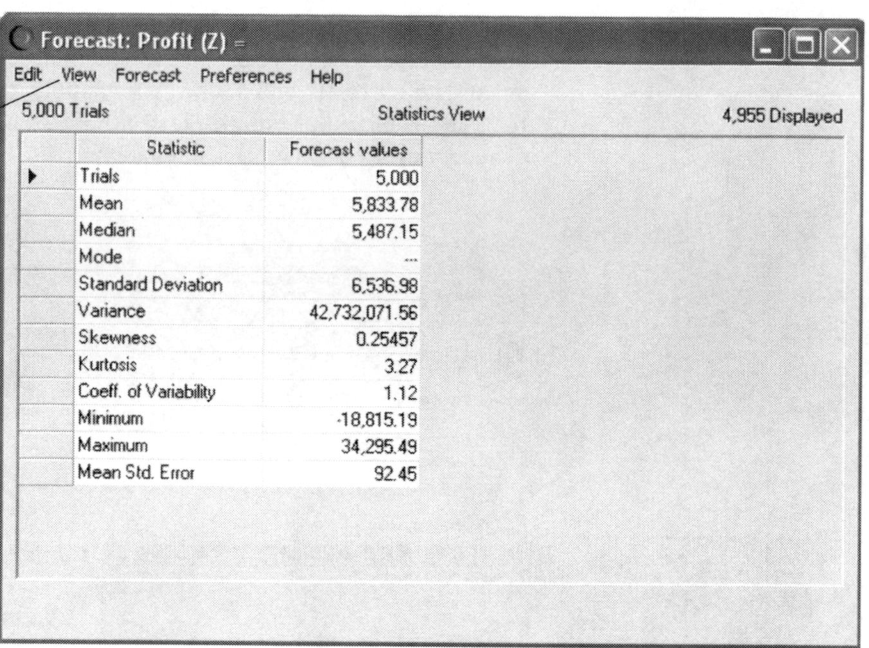

Statistic	Forecast values
Trials	5,000
Mean	5,833.78
Median	5,487.15
Mode	---
Standard Deviation	6,536.98
Variance	42,732,071.56
Skewness	0.25457
Kurtosis	3.27
Coeff. of Variability	1.12
Minimum	-18,815.19
Maximum	34,295.49
Mean Std. Error	92.45

Exhibit 14.26

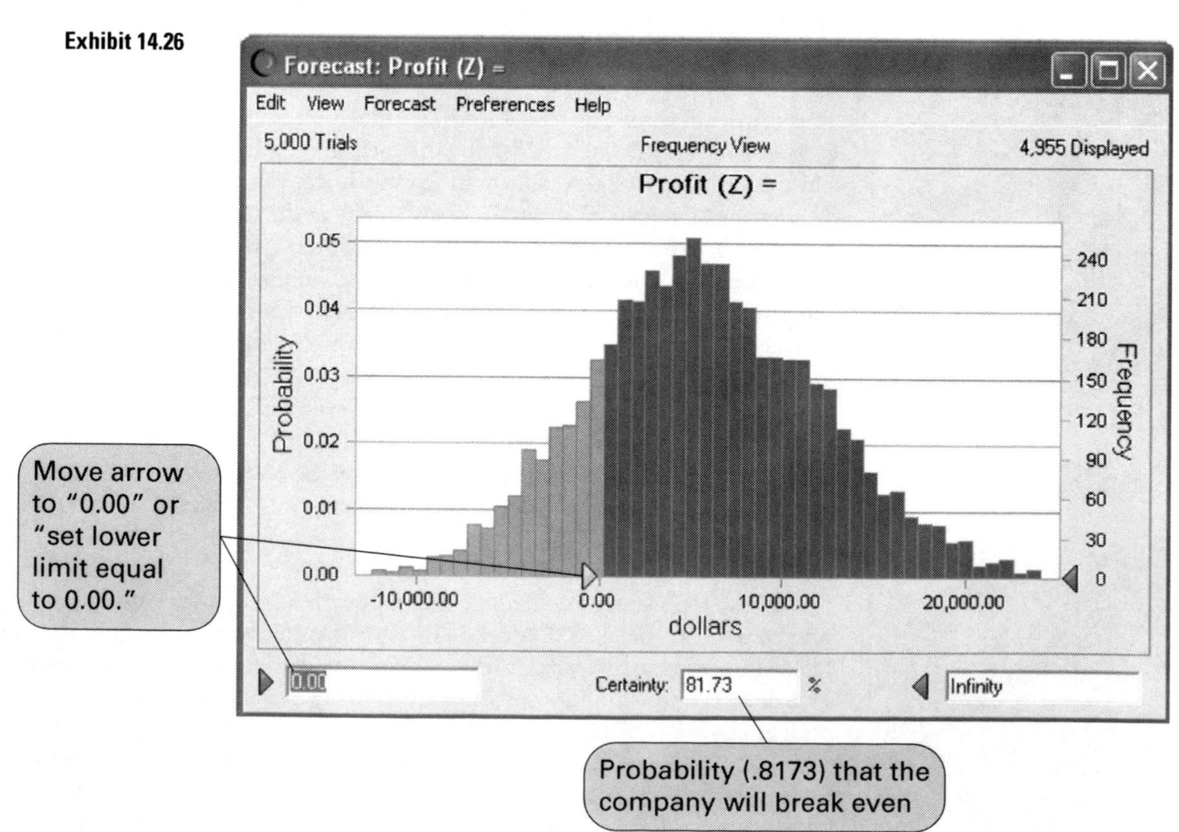

Verification of the Simulation Model

Simulation models must be validated to make sure they are accurately replicating the system being simulated.

Even though we may be able to verify the statistical results of a simulation model, we still may not know whether the model actually replicates what is going on in the real world. The user of simulation generally wants to be certain that the model is internally correct and that all the operations performed in the simulation are logical and mathematically correct. An old adage often associated with computer simulation is "garbage in, garbage out." To gain some assurances about the validity of simulation results, there are several testing procedures that the user of a simulation model can apply.

Sometimes manual simulation of several trials is a good way to validate a simulation.

First, the simulation model can be run for short periods of time or for only a few simulation trials. This allows the user to compare the results with manually derived solutions (as we did in the examples in this chapter) to check for discrepancies. Another means of testing is to divide the model into parts and simulate each part separately. This reduces the complexity of seeking out errors in the model. Similarly, the mathematical relationships in the simulation model can be simplified so that they can more easily be tested to see if the model is operating correctly.

To determine whether the model reliably represents the system being simulated, the simulation results can sometimes be compared with actual real-world data. Several statistical tests are available for performing this type of analysis. However, when a model is developed to simulate a *new* or *unique* system, there is no realistic way to ensure that the results are valid.

An additional problem in determining whether a simulation model is a valid representation of the system under analysis relates to starting conditions. Should the simulation be started with the system empty (e.g., should we start by simulating a queuing system with no customers in line), or should the simulation be started as close as possible to normal operating conditions? Another problem, as we have already seen, is the determination of how long the simulation should be run to reach true steady-state conditions, if indeed a steady state exists.

In general, a standard, foolproof procedure for validation is simply not possible. In many cases, the user of a simulation model must rely on the expertise and experience of whoever develops the model.

Areas of Simulation Application

Simulation is one of the most useful of all management science techniques. The reason for this popularity is that simulation can be applied to a number of problems that are too difficult to model and solve analytically. Some analysts feel that complex systems should be studied via simulation whether or not they can be analyzed analytically because simulation provides such an easy vehicle for experimenting on the system. As a result, simulation has been applied to a wide range of problems. Surveys conducted during the 1990s indicated that a large majority of major corporations use simulation in such functional areas as production, corporate planning, engineering, financial analysis, research and development, marketing, information systems, and personnel. Following are descriptions of some of the most common applications of simulation.

Queuing

A major application of simulation has been in the analysis of queuing systems. As indicated in Chapter 13, the assumptions required to solve the operating characteristic formulas are relatively restrictive. For the more complex queuing systems (which result from a relaxation of these assumptions), it is not possible to develop analytical formulas, and simulation is often the only available means of analysis.

Inventory Control

Most people are aware that product demand is an essential component in determining the amount of inventory a commercial enterprise should keep. Most of the mathematical formulas used to analyze inventory systems make the assumption that this demand is certain (i.e., not a random variable). In practice, however, demand is rarely known with certainty. Simulation is one of the few means for analyzing inventory systems in which demand is a random variable, reflecting demand uncertainty. Inventory control is discussed in Chapter 16.

Production and Manufacturing

Simulation is often applied to production problems, such as production scheduling, production sequencing, assembly line balancing (of work-in-process inventory), plant layout, and plant location analysis. It is surprising how often various production processes can be viewed as queuing systems that can only be analyzed using simulation. Because machine breakdowns typically occur according to some probability distributions, maintenance problems are also frequently analyzed using simulation.

Finance

Capital budgeting problems require estimates of cash flows, which are often a result of many random variables. Simulation has been used to generate values of the various contributing factors to derive estimates of cash flows. Simulation has also been used to determine the inputs into rate of return calculations in which the inputs are random variables, such as market size, selling price, growth rate, and market share.

Marketing

Marketing problems typically include numerous random variables, such as market size and type, and consumer preferences. Simulation can be used to ascertain how a particular market might react to the introduction of a product or to an advertising campaign for an existing product. Another area in marketing where simulation is applied is the analysis of distribution channels to determine the most efficient distribution system.

Public Service Operations

The operations of police departments, fire departments, post offices, hospitals, court systems, airports, and other public systems have all been analyzed by using simulation. Typically, such operations are so complex and contain so many random variables that no technique except simulation can be employed for analysis.

Environmental and Resource Analysis

Some of the more recent innovative applications of simulation have been directed at problems in the environment. Simulation models have been developed to ascertain the impact on the environment of projects such as nuclear power plants, reservoirs, highways, and dams. In many cases, these models include measures to analyze the financial feasibility of

Management Science Application

Simulating a 10-km Race in Boulder, Colorado

The Bolder Boulder, a popular 10-kilometer race held each Memorial Day in Colorado, attracts many of the world's best runners among its 20,000 participants. The race starts at the Bank of Boulder at the northeastern corner of the city, winds through the city streets, and ends at the University of Colorado's football stadium in the center of the city. As the race grew in size (from 2,200 participants in 1979 to 20,000 in 1985), its quality suffered from overcrowding problems, especially at the finish line, where runners are individually tagged as they finish. Large waiting lines built up at the finish line, causing many complaints from the participants.

To correct this problem, race management implemented an interval-start system in 1986, wherein 24 groups of up to 1,000 runners each were started at 1-minute intervals. While this solution alleviated the problem of street crowding, it did not solve the queuing problem at the finish line.

A simulation model of the race was then developed to evaluate several possible solutions—specifically, increasing the number of finish line chutes from the 8 used previously to either 12 or 15. The model was also used to identify a set of block-start intervals that would eliminate finish line queuing problems with either chute scenario. Recommendations based on the simulation model were for a 12-chute finish line configuration and specific block-start intervals. The race conducted using the recommendations from the simulation model was flawless. The actual race behavior was almost identical to the simulation results. No overcrowding or queuing problems occurred at the finish line. The simulation model was used to fine-tune the 1986 and 1987 races, which were also conducted with virtually no problems.

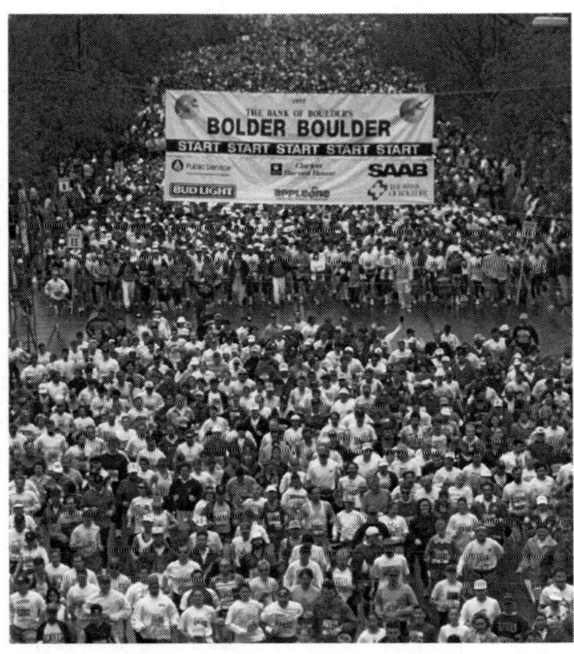

Source: R. Farina, et al., "The Computer Runs the Bolder Boulder: A Simulation of a Major Running Race," *Interfaces* 19, no. 2 (March–April 1989): 48–55.

such projects. Other models have been developed to simulate pollution conditions. In the area of resource analysis, numerous models have been developed in recent years to simulate energy systems and the feasibility of alternative energy sources.

Summary

Simulation has become an increasingly important management science technique in recent years. Various surveys have shown simulation to be one of the techniques most widely applied to real-world problems. Evidence of this popularity is the number of specialized simulation languages that have been developed by the computer industry and academia to deal with complex problem areas.

Simulation is one of the most important and widely used management science techniques.

Simulation provides a laboratory for experimentation on a real system.

The popularity of simulation is due in large part to the flexibility it allows in analyzing systems, compared to more confining analytical techniques. In other words, the problem does not have to fit the model (or technique)—the simulation model can be constructed to fit the problem. A primary benefit of simulation analysis is that it enables us to experiment with the model. For example, in our queuing example we could expand the model to represent more service facilities, more queues, and different arrival and service times; and we could observe their effects on the results. In many analytical cases, such experimentation is limited by the availability of an applicable formula. That is, by changing various parts of the problem, we may create a problem for which we have no specific analytical formula. Simulation, however, is not subject to such limitations. Simulation is limited only by one's ability to develop a computer program.

Simulation does not usually provide a recommended decision as does an optimization model; it provides ***operating characteristics****.*

Simulation is a management science technique that does not usually result in an optimal solution. Generally, a simulation model reflects the *operation of a system*, and the results of the model are in the form of operating statistics, such as averages. However, optimal solutions can sometimes be obtained for simulation models by employing *search techniques*.

Simulation has certain limitations.

However, in spite of its versatility, simulation has limitations and must be used with caution. One limitation is that simulation models are typically unstructured and must be developed for a system or problem that is also unstructured. Unlike some of the structured techniques presented in this text, they cannot simply be applied to a specific type of problem. As a result, developing simulation models often requires imagination and intuitiveness that are not required by some of the more straightforward solution techniques we have presented. In addition, the validation of simulation models is an area of serious concern. It is often impossible realistically to validate simulation results, to know if they accurately reflect the system under analysis. This problem has become an area of such concern that "output analysis" of simulation results is developing into a new field of study. Another limiting factor in simulation is the cost in money and time of model building. Because simulation models are developed for unstructured systems, they often take large amounts of staff time, computer time, and money to develop and run. For many business companies, these costs can be prohibitive.

References

Hammersly, J. M., and Handscomb, D. C. *Monte Carlo Methods*. New York: John Wiley & Sons, 1964.

Markowitz, H. M., Karr, H. W., and Hausner, B. *SIMSCRIPT: A Simulation Programming Language*. Upper Saddle River, NJ: Prentice Hall, 1963.

Meier, R. C., Newell, W. T., and Pazer, H. L. *Simulation in Business and Economics*. Upper Saddle River, NJ: Prentice Hall, 1969.

Mize, J., and Cox, G. *Essentials of Simulation*. Upper Saddle River, NJ: Prentice Hall, 1968.

Naylor, T. H., Balintfy, J. L., Burdinck, D. S., and Chu, K. *Computer Simulation Techniques*. New York: John Wiley & Sons, 1966.

Pritsker, A. A. B. *Modeling and Analysis Using Q-GERT Networks*, 2nd ed. New York: John Wiley & Sons, 1977.

———. *The GASP IV Simulation Language*. New York: John Wiley & Sons, 1974.

Schriber, T. J. *Simulation Using GPSS*. New York: John Wiley & Sons, 1974.

Tocher, K. D. "Review of Computer Simulation." *Operational Research Quarterly* 16 (June 1965): 189–217.

Van Horne, R. L. "Validation of Simulation Results." *Management Science* 17 (January 1971): 247–57.

Example Problem Solution

The following example problem demonstrates a manual simulation using discrete probability distributions.

Problem Statement

Members of the Willow Creek Emergency Rescue Squad know from past experience that they will receive between zero and six emergency calls each night, according to the following discrete probability distribution:

Calls	Probability
0	.05
1	.12
2	.15
3	.25
4	.22
5	.15
6	.06
	1.00

The rescue squad classifies each emergency call into one of three categories: minor, regular, or major emergency. The probability that a particular call will be each type of emergency is as follows:

Emergency Type	Probability
Minor	.30
Regular	.56
Major	.14
	1.00

The type of emergency call determines the size of the crew sent in response. A minor emergency requires a two-person crew, a regular call requires a three-person crew, and a major emergency requires a five-person crew.

Simulate the emergency calls received by the rescue squad for 10 nights, compute the average number of each type of emergency call each night, and determine the maximum number of crew members that might be needed on any given night.

Solution

Step 1: Develop Random Number Ranges for the Probability Distributions

Calls	Probability	Cumulative Probability	Random Number Range, r_1
0	.05	.05	1–5
1	.12	.17	6–17
2	.15	.32	18–32
3	.25	.57	33–57
4	.22	.79	58–79
5	.15	.94	80–94
6	.06	1.00	95–99, 00
	1.00		

Emergency Type	Probability	Cumulative Probability	Random Number Range, r_2
Minor	.30	.30	1–30
Regular	.56	.86	31–86
Major	.14	1.00	87–99, 00
	1.00		

Step 2: Set Up a Tabular Simulation

Use the second column of random numbers in Table 14.3:

Night	r_1	Number of Calls	r_2	Emergency Type	Crew Size	Total per Night
1	65	4	71	Regular	3	
			18	Minor	2	
			12	Minor	2	
			17	Minor	2	9
2	48	3	89	Major	5	
			18	Minor	2	
			83	Regular	3	10
3	08	1	90	Major	5	5
4	05	0	—	—	—	—
5	89	5	18	Minor	2	
			08	Minor	2	
			26	Minor	2	
			47	Regular	3	
			94	Major	5	14
6	06	1	72	Regular	3	3
7	62	4	47	Regular	3	
			68	Regular	3	
			60	Regular	3	
			88	Major	5	14
8	17	1	36	Regular	3	3
9	77	4	43	Regular	3	
			28	Minor	2	
			31	Regular	3	
			06	Minor	2	10
10	68	4	39	Regular	3	
			71	Regular	3	
			22	Minor	2	
			76	Regular	3	11

Step 3: Compute Results

$$\text{average number of minor emergency calls per night} = \frac{10}{10} = 1.0$$

$$\text{average number of regular emergency calls per night} = \frac{13}{10} = 1.3$$

$$\text{average number of major emergency calls per night} = \frac{4}{10} = 0.40$$

If all the calls came in at the same time, the maximum number of squad members required during any 1 night would be 14.

Problems

1. The Hoylake Rescue Squad receives an emergency call every 1, 2, 3, 4, 5, or 6 hours, according to the following probability distribution. The squad is on duty 24 hours per day, 7 days per week:

Time Between Emergency Calls (hr.)	Probability
1	.05
2	.10
3	.30
4	.30
5	.20
6	.05
	1.00

   a. Simulate the emergency calls for 3 days (note that this will require a "running," or cumulative, hourly clock), using the random number table.
   b. Compute the average time between calls and compare this value with the expected value of the time between calls from the probability distribution. Why are the results different?
   c. How many calls were made during the 3-day period? Can you logically assume that this is an average number of calls per 3-day period? If not, how could you simulate to determine such an average?

2. The time between arrivals of cars at the Petroco Service Station is defined by the following probability distribution:

Time Between Arrivals (min.)	Probability
1	.15
2	.30
3	.40
4	.15
	1.00

   a. Simulate the arrival of cars at the service station for 20 arrivals and compute the average time between arrivals.
   b. Simulate the arrival of cars at the service station for 1 hour, using a different stream of random numbers from those used in (a) and compute the average time between arrivals.
   c. Compare the results obtained in (a) and (b).

3. The Dynaco Manufacturing Company produces a product in a process consisting of operations of five machines. The probability distribution of the number of machines that will break down in a week follows:

Machine Breakdowns per Week	Probability
0	.10
1	.10
2	.20
3	.25
4	.30
5	.05
	1.00

a. Simulate the machine breakdowns per week for 20 weeks.
b. Compute the average number of machines that will break down per week.

4. Solve Problem 19 at the end of Chapter 12 by using simulation.

5. Simulate the decision situation described in Problem 16(a) at the end of Chapter 12 for 20 weeks, and recommend the best decision.

6. Every time a machine breaks down at the Dynaco Manufacturing Company (Problem 3), either 1, 2, or 3 hours are required to fix it, according to the following probability distribution:

Repair Time (hr.)	Probability
1	.30
2	.50
3	.20
	1.00

a. Simulate the repair time for 20 weeks and then compute the average weekly repair time.
b. If the random numbers that are used to simulate breakdowns per week are also used to simulate repair time per breakdown, will the results be affected in any way? Explain.
c. If it costs $50 per hour to repair a machine when it breaks down (including lost productivity), determine the average weekly breakdown cost.
d. The Dynaco Company is considering a preventive maintenance program that would alter the probabilities of machine breakdowns per week as shown in the following table:

Machine Breakdowns per Week	Probability
0	.20
1	.30
2	.20
3	.15
4	.10
5	.05
	1.00

The weekly cost of the preventive maintenance program is $150. Using simulation, determine whether the company should institute the preventive maintenance program.

7. Sound Warehouse in Georgetown sells CD players (with speakers), which it orders from Fuji Electronics in Japan. Because of shipping and handling costs, each order must be for five CD players.

Because of the time it takes to receive an order, the warehouse outlet places an order every time the present stock drops to five CD players. It costs $100 to place an order. It costs the warehouse $400 in lost sales when a customer asks for a CD player and the warehouse is out of stock. It costs $40 to keep each CD player stored in the warehouse. If a customer cannot purchase a CD player when it is requested, the customer will not wait until one comes in but will go to a competitor. The following probability distribution for demand for CD players has been determined:

Demand per Month	Probability
0	.04
1	.08
2	.28
3	.40
4	.16
5	.02
6	.02
	1.00

The time required to receive an order once it is placed has the following probability distribution:

Time to Receive an Order (mo.)	Probability
1	.60
2	.30
3	.10
	1.00

The warehouse has five CD players in stock. Orders are always received at the beginning of the week. Simulate Sound Warehouse's ordering and sales policy for 20 months, using the first column of random numbers in Table 14.3. Compute the average monthly cost.

8. First American Bank is trying to determine whether it should install one or two drive-through teller windows. The following probability distributions for arrival intervals and service times have been developed from historical data:

Time Between Automobile Arrivals (min.)	Probability
1	.20
2	.60
3	.10
4	.10
	1.00

Service Time (min.)	Probability
2	.10
3	.40
4	.20
5	.20
6	.10
	1.00

Assume that in the two-server system, an arriving car will join the shorter queue. When the queues are of equal length, there is a 50–50 chance the driver will enter the queue for either window.

a. Simulate both the one- and two-teller systems. Compute the average queue length, waiting time, and percentage utilization for each system.
b. Discuss your results in (a) and suggest the degree to which they could be used to make a decision about which system to employ.

9. The time between arrivals of oil tankers at a loading dock at Prudhoe Bay is given by the following probability distribution:

Time Between Ship Arrivals (days)	Probability
1	.05
2	.10
3	.20
4	.30
5	.20
6	.10
7	.05
	1.00

The time required to fill a tanker with oil and prepare it for sea is given by the following probability distribution:

Time to Fill and Prepare (days)	Probability
3	.10
4	.20
5	.40
6	.30
	1.00

a. Simulate the movement of tankers to and from the single loading dock for the first 20 arrivals. Compute the average time between arrivals, average waiting time to load, and average number of tankers waiting to be loaded.
b. Discuss any hesitation you might have about using your results for decision making.

10. The Saki automobile dealer in the Minneapolis–St. Paul area orders the Saki sport compact, which gets 50 miles per gallon of gasoline, from the manufacturer in Japan. However, the dealer never knows for sure how many months it will take to receive an order once it is placed. It can take 1, 2, or 3 months, with the following probabilities:

Months to Receive an Order	Probability
1	.50
2	.30
3	.20
	1.00

The demand per month is given by the following distribution:

Demand per Month (cars)	Probability
1	.10
2	.30
3	.40
4	.20
	1.00

The dealer orders when the number of cars on the lot gets down to a certain level. To determine the appropriate level of cars to use as an indicator of when to order, the dealer needs to know how many cars will be demanded during the time required to receive an order. Simulate the demand for 30 orders and compute the average number of cars demanded during the time required to receive an order. At what level of cars in stock should the dealer place an order?

11. State University is playing Tech in their annual football game on Saturday. A sportswriter has scouted each team all season and accumulated the following data: State runs four basic plays—a sweep, a pass, a draw, and an off tackle; Tech uses three basic defenses—a wide tackle, an Oklahoma, and a blitz. The number of yards State will gain for each play against each defense is shown in the following table:

	Tech Defense		
State Play	Wide Tackle	Oklahoma	Blitz
Sweep	–3	5	12
Pass	12	4	–10
Draw	2	1	20
Off tackle	7	3	–3

The probability that State will run each of its four plays is shown in the following table:

Play	Probability
Sweep	.10
Pass	.20
Draw	.20
Off tackle	.50

The probability that Tech will use each of its defenses follows:

Defense	Probability
Wide tackle	.30
Oklahoma	.50
Blitz	.20

The sportswriter estimates that State will run 40 plays during the game. The sportswriter believes that if State gains 300 or more yards, it will win; however, if Tech holds State to fewer than 300 yards, it will win. Use simulation to determine which team the sportswriter will predict to win the game.

12. Each semester, the students in the college of business at State University must have their course schedules approved by the college adviser. The students line up in the hallway outside the adviser's office. The students arrive at the office according to the following probability distribution:

Time Between Arrivals (min.)	Probability
4	.20
5	.30
6	.40
7	.10
	1.00

The time required by the adviser to examine and approve a schedule corresponds to the following probability distribution:

Schedule Approval (min.)	Probability
6	.30
7	.50
8	.20
	1.00

Simulate this course approval system for 90 minutes. Compute the average queue length and the average time a student must wait. Discuss these results.

13. A city is served by two newspapers—the *Tribune* and the *Daily News*. Each Sunday readers purchase one of the newspapers at a stand. The following matrix contains the probabilities of a customer's buying a particular newspaper in a week, given the newspaper purchased the previous Sunday:

This Sunday	***Next Sunday***	
	Tribune	*Daily News*
Tribune	.65	.35
Daily News	.45	.55

Simulate a customer's purchase of newspapers for 20 weeks to determine the steady-state probabilities of a customer buying each newspaper in the long run.

14. Loebuck Grocery orders milk from a dairy on a weekly basis. The manager of the store has developed the following probability distribution for demand per week (in cases):

Demand (cases)	Probability
15	.20
16	.25
17	.40
18	.15
	1.00

The milk costs the grocery \$10 per case and sells for \$16 per case. The carrying cost is \$0.50 per case per week, and the shortage cost is \$1 per case per week. Simulate the ordering system for Loebuck

Grocery for 20 weeks. Use a weekly order size of 16 cases of milk and compute the average weekly profit for this order size. Explain how the complete simulation for determining order size would be developed for this problem.

15. The Paymore Rental Car Agency rents cars in a small town. It wants to determine how many rental cars it should maintain. Based on market projections and historical data, the manager has determined probability distributions for the number of rentals per day and rental duration (in days only) as shown in the following tables:

Number of Customers/Day	Probability
0	.20
1	.20
2	.50
3	.10
	1.00

Rental Duration (days)	Probability
1	.10
2	.30
3	.40
4	.10
5	.10
	1.00

Design a simulation experiment for the car agency and simulate using a fleet of four rental cars for 10 days. Compute the probability that the agency will not have a car available upon demand. Should the agency expand its fleet? Explain how a simulation experiment could be designed to determine the optimal fleet size for the Paymore Agency.

16. A CPM/PERT project network has probabilistic activity times (x) as shown on each branch of the network; for example, activity 1–3 has a .40 probability that it will be completed in 6 weeks and a .60 probability it will be completed in 10 weeks:

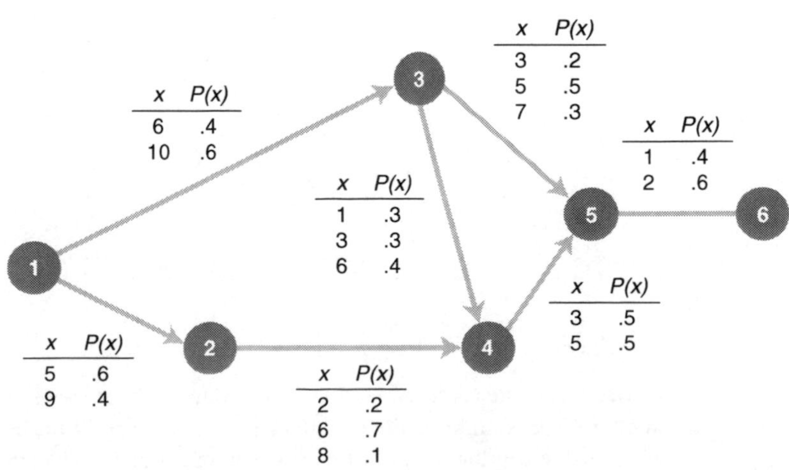

Simulate the project network 10 times and determine the critical path each time. Compute the average critical path time and the frequency at which each path is critical. How does this simulation analysis of the critical path method compare with regular CPM/PERT analysis?

17. A robbery has just been committed at the Corner Market in the downtown area of the city. The market owner was able to activate the alarm, and the robber fled on foot. Police officers arrived a few minutes later and asked the owner, "How long ago did the robber leave?" "He left only a few minutes ago," the store owner responded. "He's probably 10 blocks away by now," one of the officers said to the other. "Not likely," said the store owner. "He was so stoned on drugs that I bet even if he has run 10 blocks, he's still only within a few blocks of here! He's probably just running in circles!"

    Perform a simulation experiment that will test the store owner's hypothesis. Assume that at each corner of a city block there is an equal chance that the robber will go in any one of the four possible directions: north, south, east, or west. Simulate for five trials and then indicate in how many of the trials the robber is within 2 blocks of the store.

18. Compcomm, Inc., is an international communications and information technology company that has seen the value of its common stock appreciate substantially in recent years. A stock analyst would like to use simulation to predict the stock prices of Compcomm for an extended period. Based on historical data, the analyst has developed the following probability distribution for the movement of Compcomm stock prices per day:

Stock Price Movement	Probability
Increase	.45
Same	.30
Decrease	.25
	1.00

The analyst has also developed the following probability distributions for the amount of the increases or decreases in the stock price per day:

	Probability	
Stock Price Change	Increase	Decrease
1/8	.40	.12
1/4	.17	.15
3/8	.12	.18
1/2	.10	.21
5/8	.08	.14
3/4	.07	.10
7/8	.04	.05
1	.02	.05
	1.00	1.00

The price of the stock is currently 62.

Develop a Monte Carlo simulation model to track the stock price of Compcomm stock and simulate for 30 days. Indicate the new stock price at the end of the 30 days. How would this model be expanded to conduct a complete simulation of 1 year's stock price movement?

19. The emergency room of the community hospital in Farmburg has one receptionist, one doctor, and one nurse. The emergency room opens at time zero, and patients begin to arrive some time later. Patients arrive at the emergency room according to the following probability distribution:

Time Between Arrivals (min.)	Probability
5	.06
10	.10
15	.23
20	.29
25	.18
30	.14
	1.00

The attention needed by a patient who comes to the emergency room is defined by the following probability distribution:

Patient Needs to See	Probability
Doctor alone	.50
Nurse alone	.20
Both	.30
	1.00

If a patient needs to see both the doctor and the nurse, he or she cannot see one before the other—that is, the patient must wait to see both together.

The length of the patient's visit (in minutes) is defined by the following probability distributions:

Doctor	Probability	Nurse	Probability	Both	Probability
10	.22	5	.08	15	.07
15	.31	10	.24	20	.16
20	.25	15	.51	25	.21
25	.12	20	.17	30	.28
30	.10		1.00	35	.17
	1.00			40	.11
					1.00

Simulate the arrival of 20 patients to the emergency room and compute the probability that a patient must wait and the average waiting time. Based on this one simulation, does it appear that this system provides adequate patient care?

20. The Western Outfitters Store specializes in denim jeans. The variable cost of the jeans varies according to several factors, including the cost of the jeans from the distributor, labor costs, handling, packaging, and so on. Price also is a random variable that varies according to competitors' prices.

Sales volume also varies each month. The probability distributions for volume, price, and variable costs each month are as follows:

Sales Volume	Probability
300	.12
400	.18
500	.20
600	.23
700	.17
800	.10
	1.00

Price	Probability
$22	.07
23	.16
24	.24
25	.25
26	.18
27	.10
	1.00

Variable Cost	Probability
$ 8	.17
9	.32
10	.29
11	.14
12	.08
	1.00

Fixed costs are $9,000 per month for the store.

Simulate 20 months of store sales and compute the probability that the store will at least break even and the average profit (or loss).

21. Randolph College and Salem College are within 20 miles of each other, and the students at each college frequently date each other. The students at Randolph College are debating how good their dates are at Salem College. The Randolph students have sampled several hundred of their fellow students and asked them to rate their dates from 1 to 5 (in which 1 is excellent and 5 is poor) according to physical attractiveness, intelligence, and personality. Following are the resulting probability distributions for these three traits for students at Salem College:

Physical Attractiveness	Probability
1	.27
2	.35
3	.14
4	.09
5	.15
	1.00

Intelligence	Probability
1	.10
2	.16
3	.45
4	.17
5	.12
	1.00

Personality	Probability
1	.15
2	.30
3	.33
4	.07
5	.15
	1.00

Simulate 20 dates and compute an average overall rating of the Salem students.

22. In Problem 21 discuss how you might assess the accuracy of the average rating for Salem College students based on only 20 simulated dates.

23. Burlingham Mills produces denim cloth that it sells to jeans manufacturers. It is negotiating a contract with Troy Clothing Company to provide denim cloth on a weekly basis. Burlingham has established its monthly available production capacity for this contract to be between 0 and 600 yards, according to the following probability distribution:

$$f(x) = \frac{x}{180{,}000}, \quad 0 \le x \le 600 \text{ yd.}$$

Troy Clothing's weekly demand for denim cloth varies according to the following probability distribution:

Demand (yd.)	Probability
0	.03
100	.12
200	.20
300	.35
400	.20
500	.10
	1.00

Simulate Troy Clothing's cloth orders for 20 weeks and determine the average weekly capacity and demand. Also determine the probability that Burlingham will have sufficient capacity to meet demand.

24. A baseball game consists of plays that can be described as follows.

Play	Description
No advance	An out where no runners can advance. This includes strikeouts, pop-ups, short flies, and the like.
Groundout	Each runner can advance one base.
Possible double play	Double play if there is a runner on first base and fewer than two outs. The lead runner who can be forced is out; runners not out advance one base. If there is no runner on first or there are two outs, this play is treated as a "no advance."
Long fly	A runner on third base can score.
Very long fly	Runners on second and third base advance one base.
Walk	Includes a hit batter.
Infield single	All runners advance one base.
Outfield single	A runner on first base advances one base, but a runner on second or third base scores.
Long single	All runners can advance a maximum of two bases.
Double	Runners can advance a maximum of two bases.
Long double	All runners score.
Triple	
Home run	

Note: Singles also include a factor for errors, allowing the batter to reach first base.

Distributions for these plays for two teams, the White Sox (visitors) and the Yankees (home), are as follows:

Team: White Sox

Play	Probability
No advance	.03
Groundout	.39
Possible double play	.06
Long fly	.09
Very long fly	.08
Walk	.06
Infield single	.02
Outfield single	.10
Long single	.03
Double	.04
Long double	.05
Triple	.02
Home run	.03
	1.00

Team: Yankees

Play	Probability
No advance	.04
Groundout	.38
Possible double play	.04
Long fly	.10
Very long fly	.06
Walk	.07
Infield single	.04
Outfield single	.10
Long single	.04
Double	.05
Long double	.03
Triple	.01
Home run	.04
	1.00

Simulate a nine-inning baseball game using the preceding information.[2]

[2]This problem was adapted from R. E. Trueman, "A Computer Simulation Model of Baseball: With Particular Application to Strategy Analysis," in R. E. Machol, S. P. Ladany, and D. G. Morrison, eds., *Management Science in Sports* (New York: North Holland Publishing Co., 1976), 1–14.

25. Tracy McCoy is shopping for a new car. She has identified a particular sports utility vehicle she likes but has heard that it has high maintenance costs. Tracy has decided to develop a simulation model to help her estimate maintenance costs for the life of the car. Tracy estimates that the projected life of the car with the first owner (before it is sold) is uniformly distributed with a minimum of 2.0 years and a maximum of 8.0 years. Furthermore, she believes that the miles she will drive the car each year can be defined by a triangular distribution with a minimum value of 3,700 miles, a maximum value of 14,500 miles, and a most likely value of 9,000 miles. She has determined from automobile association data that the maintenance cost per mile driven for the vehicle she is interested in is normally distributed, with a mean of $0.08 per mile and a standard deviation of $0.02 per mile. Using Crystal Ball, develop a simulation model (using 1,000 trials) and determine the average maintenance cost for the life of the car with Tracy and the probability that the cost will be less than $3,000.

26. In Problem 20, assume that the sales volume for Western Outfitters Store is normally distributed, with a mean of 600 pairs of jeans and a standard deviation of 200; the price is uniformly distributed, with a minimum of $22 and a maximum of $28; and the variable cost is defined by a triangular distribution with a minimum value of $6, a maximum of $11, and a most likely value of $9. Develop a simulation model by using Crystal Ball (with 1,000 trials) and determine the average profit and the probability that Western Outfitters will break even.

27. In Problem 21, assume that the students at Randolph College have redefined the probability distributions of their dates at Salem College as follows: Physical attractiveness is uniformly distributed from 1 to 5; intelligence is defined by a triangular distribution with a minimum rating of 1, a maximum of 5, and a most likely of 2; and personality is defined by a triangular distribution with a minimum of 1, a maximum of 5, and a most likely rating of 3. Develop a simulation model by using Crystal Ball and determine the average date rating (for 1,000 trials). Also compute the probability that the rating will be "better" than 3.0.

28. In Problem 23, assume that production capacity at Burlingham Mills for the Troy Clothing Company contract is normally distributed, with a mean of 320 yards per month and a standard deviation of 120 yards, and that Troy Clothing's demand is uniformly distributed between 0 and 500 yards. Develop a simulation model by using Crystal Ball and determine the average monthly shortage or surplus for denim cloth (for 1,000 trials). Also determine the probability that Burlingham will always have sufficient production capacity.

29. Erin Jones has $100,000 and, to diversify, she wants to invest equal amounts of $50,000 each in two mutual funds selected from a list of four possible mutual funds. She wants to invest for a 3-year period. She has used historical data from the four funds plus data from the market to determine the mean and standard deviation (normally distributed) of the annual return for each fund, as follows:

	Return (r)	
Fund	μ	σ
1. Internet	.20	.09
2. Index	.12	.04
3. Entertainment	.16	.10
4. Growth	.14	.06

The possible combinations of two investment funds are (1,2), (1,3), (1,4), (2,3), (2,4), and (3,4).

a. Use Crystal Ball to simulate each of the investment combinations to determine the expected return in 3 years. (Note that the formula for the future value, FV, of a current investment, P, with return, r, for n years in the future is $FV_n = P_r(1 + r)^n$.) Indicate which investment combination has the highest expected return.

b. Erin wants to reduce her risk as much as possible. She knows that if she invests her $100,000 in a CD at the bank, she is guaranteed a return of $20,000 after 3 years. Using the frequency charts for the simulation runs in Crystal Ball, determine which combination of investments would result in the greatest probability of receiving a return of $120,000 or greater.

30. In Chapter 16, the formula for the optimal order quantity of an item, Q, given its demand, D, order cost, C_o, and the cost of holding, or carrying, an item in inventory, C_c, is as follows:

$$Q = \sqrt{\frac{2C_o D}{C_c}}$$

The total inventory cost formula is

$$TC = \frac{C_o D}{Q} + C_c \frac{Q}{2}$$

Order cost, C_o, and carrying cost, C_c, are generally values that the company is often able to determine with certainty because they are internal costs, whereas demand, D, is usually not known with certainty because it is external to the company. However, in the order quantity formula given here, demand is treated as if it were certain. To consider the uncertainty of demand, it must be simulated.

Using Crystal Ball, simulate the preceding formulas for Q and TC to determine their average values for an item, with C_o = $150, C_c = $0.75, and demand, D, that is normally distributed with a mean of 10,000 and a standard deviation of 4,000.

31. The Management Science Association (MSA) has arranged to hold its annual conference at the Riverside Hotel in Orlando next year. Based on historical data, the MSA believes the number of rooms it will need for its members attending the conference is normally distributed, with a mean of 800 and a standard deviation of 270. The MSA can reserve rooms now (1 year prior to the conference) for $80; however, for any rooms not reserved now, the cost will be at the hotel's regular room rate of $120. The MSA guarantees the room rate of $80 to its members. If its members reserve fewer than the number of rooms it reserves, MSA must pay the hotel for the difference, at the $80 room rate. If MSA does not reserve enough rooms, it must pay the extra cost—that is, $40 per room.
    a. Using Crystal Ball, determine whether the MSA should reserve 600, 700, 800, 900, or 1,000 rooms in advance to realize the lowest total cost.
    b. Can you determine a more exact value for the number of rooms to reserve to minimize cost?

32. In Chapter 8, Figure 8.6 shows a simplified project network for building a house, as follows:

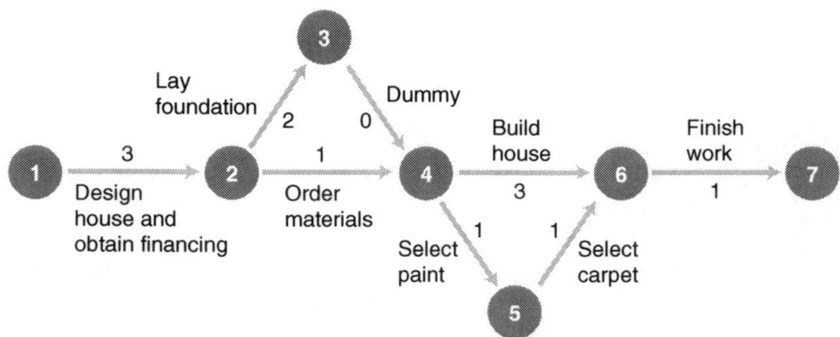

There are four paths through this network:

Path A: 1–2–3–4–6–7
Path B: 1–2–3–4–5–6–7
Path C: 1–2–4–6–7
Path D: 1–2–4–5–6–7

The time parameters (in weeks) defining a triangular probability distribution for each activity are provided as follows:

	Time Parameters		
Activity	Minimum	Likeliest	Maximum
1–2	1	3	5
2–3	1	2	4
2–4	.5	1	2
3–4	0	0	0
4–5	1	2	3
4–6	1	3	6
5–6	1	2	4
6–7	1	2	4

a. Using Crystal Ball, simulate each path in the network and identify the longest path (i.e., the critical path).
b. Observing the simulation run frequency chart for path A, determine the probability that this path will exceed the critical path time. What does this tell you about the simulation results for a project network versus an analytical result?

Case Problem

JET Copies

James Banks was standing in line next to Robin Cole at Klecko's Copy Center, waiting to use one of the copy machines. "Gee, Robin, I hate this," he said. "We have to drive all the way over here from Southgate and then wait in line to use these copy machines. I hate wasting time like this."

"I know what you mean," said Robin. "And look who's here. A lot of these students are from Southgate Apartments or one of the other apartments near us. It seems as though it would be more logical if Klecko's would move its operation over to us, instead of all of us coming over here."

James looked around and noticed what Robin was talking about. Robin and he were students at State University, and most of the customers at Klecko's were also students. As Robin suggested, a lot of the people waiting were State students who lived at Southgate Apartments, where James also lived with Ernie Moore. This gave James an idea, which he shared with Ernie and their friend Terri Jones when he got home later that evening.

"Look, you guys, I've got an idea to make some money," James started. "Let's open a copy business! All we have to do is buy a copier, put it in Terri's duplex next door, and sell copies. I know we can get customers because I've just seen them all at Klecko's. If we provide a copy service right here in the Southgate complex, we'll make a killing."

Terri and Ernie liked the idea, so the three decided to go into the copying business. They would call it JET Copies, named for James, Ernie, and Terri. Their first step was to purchase a copier. They bought one like the one used in the college of business office at State for $18,000. (Terri's parents provided a loan.) The company that sold them the copier touted the copier's reliability, but after they bought it, Ernie talked with someone in the dean's office at State, who told him that the University's copier broke down frequently and when it did, it often took between 1 and 4 days to get it repaired. When Ernie told this to Terri and James, they became worried. If the copier broke down frequently and was not in use for long periods while they waited for a repair person to come fix it, they could lose a lot of revenue. As a result, James, Ernie, and Terri thought they might need to purchase a smaller backup copier for $8,000 to use when the main copier broke down. However, before they approached Terri's parents for another loan, they wanted to have an estimate of just how much money they might lose if they did not have a backup copier. To get this estimate, they decided to develop a simulation model because they were studying simulation in one of their classes at State.

To develop a simulation model, they first needed to know how frequently the copier might break down—specifically, the time between breakdowns. No one could provide them with an exact probability distribution, but from talking to staff members in the college of business, James estimated that the time between breakdowns was probably between 0 and 6 weeks, with the probability increasing the longer the copier went without breaking down. Thus, the probability distribution of breakdowns generally looked like the following:

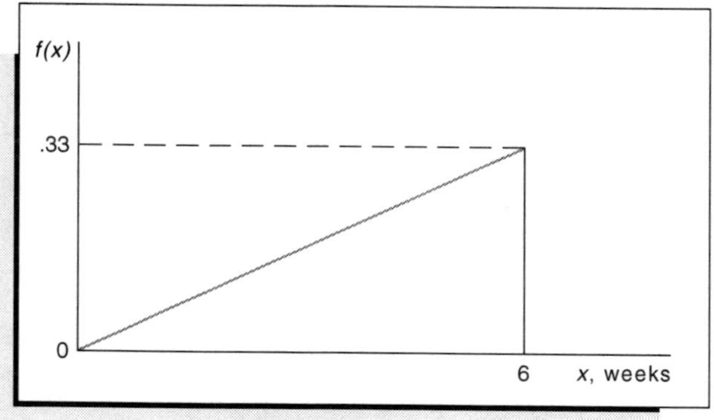

Next, they needed to know how long it would take to get the copier repaired when it broke down. They had a service contract with the dealer that "guaranteed" prompt repair service. However, Terri gathered some data from the college of business from which she developed the following probability distribution of repair times:

Repair Time (days)	Probability
1	.20
2	.45
3	.25
4	.10
	1.00

Finally, they needed to estimate how much business they would lose while the copier was waiting for repair. The three of them had only a vague idea of how much business they would do but finally estimated that they would sell between 2,000 and 8,000 copies per day at $0.10 per copy. However, they had no idea about what kind of probability distribution to use for this range of values. Therefore, they decided to use a uniform probability distribution between 2,000 and 8,000 copies to estimate the number of copies they would sell per day.

James, Ernie, and Terri decided that if their loss of revenue due to machine downtime during 1 year was $12,000 or more, they should purchase a backup copier. Thus, they needed to simulate the breakdown and repair process for a number of years to obtain an average annual loss of revenue. However, before programming the simulation model, they decided to conduct a manual simulation of this process for 1 year to see if the model was working correctly. Perform this manual simulation for JET Copies and determine the loss of revenue for 1 year.

CASE PROBLEM

BENEFIT–COST ANALYSIS OF THE SPRADLIN BLUFF RIVER PROJECT

The U.S. Army Corps of Engineers has historically constructed dams on various rivers in the southeastern United States. Its primary instrument for evaluating and selecting among many projects under consideration is benefit–cost analysis. The Corps estimates both the annual benefits deriving from a project in several different categories and the annual costs and then divides the total benefits by the total costs to develop a benefit–cost ratio. This ratio is then used by the Corps and Congress to compare numerous projects under consideration and select those for funding. A benefit–cost ratio greater than 1.0 indicates that the benefits are greater than the costs; and the higher a project's benefit–cost ratio, the more likely it is to be selected over projects with lower ratios.

The Corps is evaluating a project to construct a dam over the Spradlin Bluff River in southwest Georgia. The Corps has identified six traditional areas in which benefits will accrue: flood control, hydroelectric power, improved navigation, recreation, fish and wildlife, and area commercial redevelopment. The Corps has made three estimates (in dollars) for each benefit—a minimum possible value, a most likely value, and a maximum benefit value. These benefit estimates are as follows:

	Estimate		
Benefit	*Minimum*	*Most Likely*	*Maximum*
Flood control	$ 1,695,200	$ 2,347,800	$ 3,570,600
Hydroelectric power	8,068,250	11,845,000	14,845,000
Navigation	50,400	64,000	109,500
Recreation	6,404,000	9,774,000	14,566,000
Fish and wildlife	104,300	255,000	455,300
Area redevelopment	0	1,630,000	2,385,000

There are two categories of costs associated with a construction project of this type—the total capital cost, annualized over 100 years (at a rate of interest specified by the government), and annual operation and maintenance costs. The cost estimates for this project are as follows:

	Estimate		
Cost	*Minimum*	*Most Likely*	*Maximum*
Annualized capital cost	$12,890,750	$14,150,500	$19,075,900
Operation and maintenance	3,483,500	4,890,000	7,350,800

Using Crystal Ball, determine a simulated mean benefit–cost ratio and standard deviation.

What is the probability that this project will have a benefit–cost ratio greater than 1.0?

Topic 20

Estimation: Additional Topics

Chapter 9

Estimation: Additional Topics

Chapter Outline

Introduction

In this chapter we consider certain additional topics in estimation. In Chapter 8 we presented confidence interval procedures to estimate certain parameters of a *single* population. In this chapter we consider confidence interval procedures to estimate certain parameters of *two* populations. An important problem in statistical inference deals with the comparison of *two means* from normally distributed populations or the comparison of *two proportions* from large populations. For example:

1. Corporate executives employed by retail distributors may want to estimate the difference between mean daily sales of two retail stores.
2. Manufacturers may want to compare the average productivity, in units per hour, of day shift workers and night shift workers in a plant.

3. The campaign manager for a presidential candidate may want to compare the popularity rating of this candidate in two different regions of the country.
4. The North American Fareston versus Tamoxifen Adjuvant Trial for Breast Cancer (Reference 5) is comparing carcinoma recurrence rates of breast cancer survivors who take a new drug, Fareston, with the recurrence rates of those survivors who take Tamoxifen.
5. A chemical company receives shipments from two suppliers. Independent random samples of batches from each supplier are selected, and a comparison of impurity levels of the two batches is made.

We also present in this chapter procedures to estimate the variance of a population, as well as an introduction to sample size determination, with more extensive focus on sample size in Chapter 20.

9.1 Confidence Intervals for the Difference Between Two Normal Population Means

To compare population means, random samples are drawn from the two populations. The procedure that we use to select the samples determines the appropriate method that we use to analyze inferences based on the sample results. In this section we present two sampling schemes. The first is for *dependent* samples. The second sampling scheme is for *independent* samples with *known* population variances. In Section 9.2 we will focus our attention on sampling schemes for independent samples when we cannot assume that the population variances are equal.

Dependent Samples

We consider samples to be *dependent* if the values in one sample are influenced by the values in the other sample. In this scheme the sample members are chosen in pairs, one from each population. Thus, this procedure is often known as *matched pairs*.

The idea is that, apart from the factor under study, the members of these pairs should resemble one another as closely as possible so that the comparison of interest can be made directly. Suppose that the effectiveness of a speed-reading course is to be measured. One possible approach would be to record the number of words per minute read by a sample of students *before* taking the course and compare these speeds with results for the same students *after* completing the course. In this case each pair of observations consists of "before" and "after" measurements on a single student.

An interval estimate for the general case of n matched pairs of observations, denoted $(x_1, y_1), (x_2, y_2), \ldots, (x_n, y_n)$, selected from populations with means μ_X and μ_Y follows.

Confidence Intervals for Two Means: Dependent Samples (Matched Pairs)

Suppose that there is a random sample of n matched pairs of observations from normal distributions with means μ_X and μ_Y. That is, let x_1, $x_2, \ldots, x_n$ denote the values of the observations from the population with mean μ_X; and $y_1, y_2, \ldots, y_n$ the matched sampled values from the population with the mean μ_Y. Let $\bar{d}$ and s_d denote the observed sample mean and standard deviation for the n differences $d_i = x_i - y_i$. If the population distribution of the differences is assumed to be normal, then a $100(1-\alpha)\%$ **confidence interval for the difference between means** ($\mu_d = \mu_X - \mu_Y$) is given by

$$\bar{d} - t_{n-1,\alpha/2}\frac{s_d}{\sqrt{n}} < \mu_d < \bar{d} + t_{n-1,\alpha/2}\frac{s_d}{\sqrt{n}} \tag{9.1}$$

or equivalently

$$\bar{d} \pm ME$$

The standard deviation of the differences, s_d, and the margin of error, ME, are

$$s_d = \sqrt{\frac{\sum(d_i - \bar{d})^2}{n_d}}$$

$$ME = t_{n-1,\alpha/2}\frac{s_d}{\sqrt{n}} \tag{9.2}$$

and $t_{n-1,\alpha/2}$ is the number for which

$$P(t_{n-1} > t_{n-1,\alpha/2}) = \frac{\alpha}{2}$$

The random variable, t_{n-1}, has a Student's t distribution with $(n-1)$ degrees of freedom.

Example 9.1 Cholesterol Reduction Study (Confidence Interval)

A medical study was conducted to compare the difference in effectiveness of two particular drugs in lowering cholesterol levels. The research team used a paired sample approach to control variation in reduction that might be due to factors other than the drug itself. Each member of a pair was matched by age, weight, lifestyle, and other pertinent factors. Drug X was given to one person randomly selected in each pair, and drug Y was given to the other individual in the pair. After a specified amount of time each person's cholesterol level was measured again. Suppose that a random sample of eight pairs of patients with known cholesterol problems is selected from the large populations of participants. Table 9.1 gives the number of points by which each person's cholesterol level was reduced, as well as the differences, $d_i = x_i - y_i$, for each pair. Estimate with a 99% confidence level the mean difference in the effectiveness of the two drugs, X and Y, to lower cholesterol.

Table 9.1 Cholesterol Reduction

PAIR	DRUG X	DRUG Y	DIFFERENCE ($d_i = x_i - y_i$)
1	29	26	3
2	32	27	5
3	31	28	3
4	32	27	5
5	32	30	2
6	29	26	3
7	31	33	−2
8	30	36	−6

Solution From Table 9.1 we compute the sample mean, $\bar{d}$, and the observed sample standard deviation, s_d, of the differences in cholesterol reduction as

$$\bar{d} = 1.625 \quad \text{and} \quad s_d = 3.777$$

From the Student's t distribution table, $t_{n-1,\alpha/2} = t_{7,0.005} = 3.499$. We use Equation 9.1 and find the 99% confidence interval for the difference between the population means:

$$\bar{d} - \frac{t_{n-1,\alpha/2}s_d}{\sqrt{n}} < \mu_x - \mu_y < \bar{d} + \frac{t_{n-1,\alpha/2}s_d}{\sqrt{n}}$$

$$1.625 - \frac{(3.499)(3.777)}{\sqrt{8}} < \mu_x - \mu_y < 1.625 + \frac{(3.499)(3.777)}{\sqrt{8}}$$

$$-3.05 < \mu_x - \mu_y < 6.30$$

Since the confidence interval contains the value of zero, we can conclude that $\mu_x - \mu_y$ could be positive, suggesting that drug X is more effective; that $\mu_x - \mu_y$ could be negative, suggesting that drug Y is more effective; or that $\mu_x - \mu_y$ could be zero, suggesting that drug X and drug Y are equally effective. Thus, it is not possible to determine if either drug is more effective in reducing one's cholesterol level. A brief discussion of matched pairs with missing values is presented in the chapter Appendix.

Independent Samples, Known Population Variances

In this scheme, samples are drawn *independently* from the two normally distributed populations with *known population variances* so that the membership of one sample is not influenced by the membership of the other sample.

Consider the case where independent samples, not necessarily of equal size, are taken from the two populations of interest. Suppose that there is a random sample of n_x observations from a population with mean μ_X and variance σ_X^2 and an independent random sample of n_y observations from a population with mean μ_Y and variance σ_Y^2 Let the respective sample means be $\bar{x}$ and $\bar{y}$.

As a first step, examine the situation where the two population distributions are normal with known variances. Since the object of interest is the difference between the two population means, it is natural to base an inference on the difference between the corresponding sample means. This random variable has mean

$$E(\overline{X} - \overline{Y}) = E(\overline{X}) - E(\overline{Y}) = \mu_x - \mu_y$$

and since the samples are independent,

$$\text{Var}(\overline{X} - \overline{Y}) = \text{Var}(\overline{X}) + \text{Var}(\overline{Y}) = \frac{\sigma_X^2}{n_X} + \frac{\sigma_Y^2}{n_Y}$$

Furthermore, it can be shown that its distribution is normal. It therefore follows that the random variable

$$Z = \frac{(\overline{x} - \overline{y}) - (\mu_X - \mu_Y)}{\sqrt{\dfrac{\sigma_X^2}{n_x} + \dfrac{\sigma_Y^2}{n_y}}}$$

has a standard normal distribution. An argument parallel to that in Chapter 8 can then be used to obtain the confidence interval for the difference between the population means.

Confidence Intervals for Difference Between Means: Independent Samples (Normal Distributions and Known Population Variances)

Suppose that there are two **independent random samples** of n_x and n_y observations from normally distributed populations with means μ_X and μ_Y and variances σ_x^2 and σ_y^2. If the observed sample means are $\overline{x}$ and $\overline{y}$, then a $100(1 - \alpha)\%$ confidence interval for $(\mu_X - \mu_Y)$ is given by

$$(\overline{x} - \overline{y}) - z_{\alpha/2}\sqrt{\frac{\sigma_x^2}{n_x} + \frac{\sigma_y^2}{n_y}} < \mu_X - \mu_Y < (\overline{x} - \overline{y}) + z_{\alpha/2}\sqrt{\frac{\sigma_x^2}{n_x} + \frac{\sigma_y^2}{n_y}} \qquad (9.3)$$

or equivalently

$$(\overline{x} - \overline{y}) \pm ME$$

where the margin of error, *ME*, is given by

$$ME = z_{\alpha/2}\sqrt{\frac{\sigma_x^2}{n_x} + \frac{\sigma_y^2}{n_y}} \qquad (9.4)$$

In some applications, historical variances from similar studies can be used as the true population variances.

Example 9.2 Relevance of Strategic Management Research (Confidence Interval)

Independent random samples of accounting professors and information systems (IS) professors were asked to provide the number of hours they spend in preparation for each class. The sample of 321 IS professors had a mean time of 3.01 preparation hours, and the sample of 94 accounting professors had a mean time of 2.88 hours. From similar past studies the population standard deviation for the IS professors is assumed to be 1.09, and, similarly, the population standard deviation for the accounting professors is 1.01. Denoting by μ_X the population mean for IS professors and by μ_Y the population mean for accounting professors, find a 95% confidence interval for $(\mu_X - \mu_Y)$.

Solution We use Equation 9.3,

$$(\bar{x} - \bar{y}) - z_{\alpha/2}\sqrt{\frac{\sigma_x^2}{n_x} + \frac{\sigma_y^2}{n_y}} < \mu_x - \mu_y < (\bar{x} - \bar{y}) + z_{\alpha/2}\sqrt{\frac{\sigma_x^2}{n_x} + \frac{\sigma_y^2}{n_y}}$$

with

$$n_x = 321 \quad \bar{x} = 3.01 \quad \sigma_x = 1.09$$
$$n_y = 94 \quad \bar{y} = 2.88 \quad \sigma_y = 1.01$$

and for a 95% confidence interval

$$z_{\alpha/2} = z_{0.025} = 1.96$$

The confidence interval is then

$$(3.01 - 2.88) - 1.96\sqrt{\frac{(1.09)^2}{321} + \frac{(1.01)^2}{94}} < \mu_x - \mu_y < (3.01 - 2.88) + 1.96\sqrt{\frac{(1.09)^2}{321} + \frac{(1.01)^2}{94}}$$

or

$$-0.11 < \mu_x - \mu_y < 0.37$$

This interval includes zero, indicating an absence of strong evidence that the population means are different.

Exercises

Basic Exercises

9.1 A dependent random sample from two normally distributed populations gives the following results:

$$n = 15 \quad \bar{d} = 25.4 \quad s_d = 2.8$$

a. Find the 95% confidence interval for the difference in the means of the two populations.
b. Find the margin of error for a 95% confidence interval for the difference in the means of the two populations

9.2 A confidence interval for the difference between the means of two normally distributed populations based on the following dependent samples is desired:

Before	After
6	8
12	14
8	9
10	13
6	7

a. Find the margin of error for a 90% confidence level.
b. Find the *UCL* and the *LCL* for a 90% confidence level.
c. Find the width of a 95% confidence interval.

9.3 Independent random sampling from two normally distributed populations gives the following results:

$$n_x = 64 \quad \bar{x} = 400 \quad \sigma_x = 20$$
$$n_y = 36 \quad \bar{y} = 360 \quad \sigma_y = 25$$

Find a 90% confidence interval estimate of the difference in the means of the two populations.

Application Exercises

9.4 A random sample of 10 pairs of identical houses was chosen in a large midwestern city, and a passive solar heating system was installed in one member of each pair. The total fuel bills (in dollars) for three winter months for these homes were then determined, as shown in the accompanying table. Assuming normal population distributions, find a 90% confidence interval for the difference between the two population means.

Pair	Without Passive Solar	With Passive Solar	Pair	Without Passive Solar	With Passive Solar
1	485	452	6	386	380
2	423	386	7	426	395
3	515	502	8	473	411
4	425	376	9	454	415
5	653	605	10	496	441

9.5 A random sample of six salespersons that attended a motivational course on sales techniques was monitored in the three months before and the three months after the course. The table shows the values of sales (in thousands of dollars) generated by these six salespersons in the two periods. Assume that the population distributions are normal. Find an 80% confidence interval for the difference between the two population means.

Salesperson	Before Course	After Course
1	212	237
2	282	291
3	203	191
4	327	341
5	165	192
6	198	180

9.6 A manufacturer knows that the numbers of items produced per hour by machine A and by machine B are normally distributed with a standard deviation of 8.4 items for machine A and a standard deviation of 11.3 items for machine B. The mean hourly amount produced by machine A for a random sample of 40 hours was 130 units; the mean hourly amount produced by machine B for a random sample of 36 hours was 120 units. Find the 95% confidence interval for the difference in mean parts produced per hour by these two machines.

9.2 Confidence Intervals for the Difference Between Two Normal Population Means with Population Variances Unknown

It seems reasonable that if we do not know the population means, we most likely do not know the population variances either. So we turn our attention in this section to this more common situation. Two possibilities arise: Either the unknown population variances are assumed to be equal, or they are *not* assumed to be equal. We present both of the situations but defer discussion of how to determine whether population variances are equal to Chapter 11.

Independent Samples, Population Variances Assumed to Be Equal

Suppose again that there are two independent random samples of n_x and n_y observations from normally distributed populations with means μ_X and μ_Y and that the populations have a common (unknown) variance σ^2— that is, $\sigma_x^2 = \sigma_y^2 = \sigma^2$. Inference about the population means is based on the difference $(\bar{x} - \bar{y})$ between the two sample means. This random variable has a normal distribution with mean $(\mu_x - \mu_y)$ and variance

$$\text{Var}(\bar{X} - \bar{Y}) = \text{Var}(\bar{X}) + \text{Var}(\bar{Y}) = \frac{\sigma^2}{n_x} + \frac{\sigma^2}{n_y}$$

It therefore follows that the random variable,

$$Z = \frac{(\bar{x} - \bar{y}) - (\mu_x - \mu_y)}{\sqrt{\dfrac{\sigma^2}{n_x} + \dfrac{\sigma^2}{n_y}}}$$

has a standard normal distribution. However, this result cannot be used as it stands because the unknown population variance is involved.

Since $\sigma_x^2 = \sigma_y^2 = \sigma^2$, then both s_x^2 and s_y^2 are estimators of the common population variance σ^2. To use only s_x^2 or only s_y^2 to estimate the common variance would ignore information from the other sample. If the sample sizes are the same $(n_x = n_y)$, then the average of s_x^2 and s_y^2 could be used to estimate the common variance. However, in the more general situation of unequal sample sizes, an estimate is needed that acknowledges the fact that more information about the common variance is obtained from the sample with the larger sample size. Thus, a weighted average of s_x^2 and s_y^2 is used. This estimator, s_p^2, pools the two sets of sample information and is given in Equation 9.7.

Confidence Intervals for Two Means: Unknown Population Variances That Are Assumed to Be Equal

Suppose that there are two independent random samples with n_X and n_Y observations from **normally** distributed populations with means μ_X and μ_Y and a **common, but unknown, population variance.** If the observed sample means are $\bar{x}$ and $\bar{y}$, and the observed sample variances are s_x^2 and s_y^2, then a $100(1 - \alpha)\%$ confidence interval for $(\mu_x - \mu_y)$ is given by

$$(\bar{x} - \bar{y}) - t_{n_x+n_y-2,\alpha/2}\sqrt{\frac{s_p^2}{n_x} + \frac{s_p^2}{n_y}} < \mu_x - \mu_y < (\bar{x} - \bar{y}) + t_{n_x+n_y-2,\alpha/2}\sqrt{\frac{s_p^2}{n_x} + \frac{s_p^2}{n_y}} \quad (9.5)$$

or equivalently

$$(\bar{x} - \bar{y}) \pm ME$$

where the **margin of error,** *ME*, is

$$ME = t_{n_x+n_y-2,\alpha/2}\sqrt{\frac{s_p^2}{n_x} + \frac{s_p^2}{n_y}} \quad (9.6)$$

and the **pooled sample variance,** s_p^2, is given by

$$s_p^2 = \frac{(n_x - 1)s_x^2 + (n_y - 1)s_y^2}{n_x + n_y - 2} \quad (9.7)$$

$t_{n_x+n_y-2,\alpha/2}$ is the number for which

$$P(t_{n_x+n_y-2} > t_{n_x+n_y-2,\alpha/2}) = \frac{\alpha}{2}$$

The random variable, t, is approximately a Student's t distribution with $n_x + n_y - 2$ degrees of freedom and t is given by

$$t = \frac{(\bar{x} - \bar{y}) - (\mu_x - \mu_y)}{s_p\sqrt{\frac{1}{n_x} + \frac{1}{n_y}}}$$

Example 9.3 Traffic Fines (Confidence Interval)

The residents of Orange City complain that traffic speeding fines given in their city are higher than the traffic speeding fines that are given in nearby DeLand. The assistant to the county manager agreed to study the problem and to indicate if the complaints were reasonable. Independent random samples of the amounts paid by residents for speeding tickets in each of two cities over the last three months were obtained. These amounts were

Orange City	100	125	135	128	140	142	128	137	156	142
DeLand	95	87	100	75	110	105	85	95		

Assuming an equal population variance, find a 95% confidence interval for the difference in the mean costs of speeding tickets in these two cities.

Solution Let the X population be Orange City and the Y population be DeLand. First, we use a statistical package such as Minitab and conclude that normal probability plots for both samples do not indicate evidence of non-normality.

$$n_x = 10 \quad \bar{x} = \$133.30 \quad s_x^2 = 218.0111$$
$$n_y = 8 \quad \bar{y} = \$94.00 \quad s_y^2 = 129.4286$$

The pooled sample variance is found by Equation 9.7 to be

$$s_p^2 = \frac{(n_x - 1)s_x^2 + (n_y - 1)s_y^2}{n_x + n_y - 2} = \frac{(10 - 1)(218.011) + (8 - 1)(129.4286)}{10 + 8 - 2} = 179.2562$$

and

$$(\bar{x} - \bar{y}) = (133.30 - 94.00) = \$39.30$$

The degrees of freedom result is $n_x + n_y - 2 = 16$ and $t_{(16,0.025)} = 2.12$.

The confidence interval is obtained by Equation 9.5:

$$(\bar{x} - \bar{y}) - t_{n_x+n_y-2,\alpha/2}\sqrt{\frac{s_p^2}{n_x} + \frac{s_p^2}{n_y}} < \mu_x - \mu_y < (\bar{x} - \bar{y}) + t_{n_x+n_y-2,\alpha/2}\sqrt{\frac{s_p^2}{n_x} + \frac{s_p^2}{n_y}}$$

$$39.3 - (2.12)\sqrt{\frac{179.2562}{10} + \frac{179.2562}{8}} < \mu_x - \mu_y < 39.3 + (2.12)\sqrt{\frac{179.2562}{10} + \frac{179.2562}{8}}$$

$$39.3 \pm 13.46$$

Figure 9.1 Traffic Fines (Minitab Output)

	N	Mean	StDev	SE Mean
Orange City	10	133.3	14.8	4.7
DeLand	8	94.0	11.4	4.0

Difference = mu Orange City - mu DeLand
Estimate for difference: 39.30
95% CI for difference: (25.84, 52.76)

Figure 9.1 is the Minitab output for this example.

In the long run there is a difference in the cost of speeding tickets given in Orange City and those tickets given in DeLand. The mean cost of a speeding ticket in Orange City is as little as \$25.84 or as much as \$52.76 higher than the mean cost of a similar ticket in DeLand.

Independent Samples, Population Variances Not Assumed to Be Equal

In many applications it is not reasonable to assume equality of population variances. In that case we have not have need for a pooled sample variance. When the population variances are unknown and not assumed to be equal, the approximate degrees of freedom is given in Equation 9.9 and is known as Satterthwaite's approximation (References 6 and 7). Most statistical packages provide both procedures (with and without equal variances) for finding confidence intervals for differences in means of independent samples.

Confidence Intervals for Two Means: Unknown Population Variances, Not Assumed to Be Equal

Suppose that there are two **independent random samples** of n_x and n_y observations from **normally** distributed populations with means μ_X and μ_Y, and it is assumed that the population variances are not equal. If the observed sample means and variances are $\bar{x}$, $\bar{y}$ and s_X^2, s_Y^2, then a $100(1-\alpha)\%$ confidence interval for $(\mu_x - \mu_y)$ is given by

$$(\bar{x}-\bar{y}) - t_{(v,\alpha/2)}\sqrt{\frac{s_x^2}{n_x}+\frac{s_y^2}{n_y}} < \mu_x - \mu_y < (\bar{x}-\bar{y}) + t_{(v,\alpha/2)}\sqrt{\frac{s_x^2}{n_x}+\frac{s_y^2}{n_y}} \quad (9.8)$$

where the **margin of error, *ME***, is

$$ME = t_{(v,\alpha/2)}\sqrt{\frac{s_x^2}{n_x}+\frac{s_y^2}{n_y}} \quad (9.9)$$

and the degrees of freedom, v, is given by

$$v = \frac{\left[\left(\frac{s_x^2}{n_x}\right)+\left(\frac{s_y^2}{n_y}\right)\right]^2}{\left(\frac{s_x^2}{n_x}\right)^2/(n_x-1)+\left(\frac{s_y^2}{n_y}\right)^2/(n_y-1)} \quad (9.10)$$

If the sample sizes are equal, then the degrees of freedom reduces to

$$v = \left(1 + \frac{2}{\frac{s_x^2}{s_y^2} + \frac{s_y^2}{s_x^2}}\right) \times (n - 1) \tag{9.11}$$

Example 9.4 Auditors (Confidence Interval)

Master's Accounting Firm conducted a random sample of the accounts payable for the east and the west offices of Amalgamated Distributors. From these two independent samples they wanted to estimate the difference between the population mean values of the payables. The sample statistics obtained were as follows:

	EAST OFFICE (POPULATION X)	WEST OFFICE (POPULATION Y)
Sample mean	\$290	\$250
Sample size	16	11
Sample standard deviation	15	50

We do not assume that the unknown population variances are equal. Estimate the difference between the mean values of the payables for the two offices. Use a 95% confidence level.

Solution First, we calculate the degrees of freedom by use of Equation 9.10:

$$v = \frac{\left[\left(\frac{s_x^2}{n_x}\right) + \left(\frac{s_y^2}{n_y}\right)\right]^2}{\left(\frac{s_x^2}{n_x}\right)^2 /(n_x - 1) + \left(\frac{s_y^2}{n_y}\right)^2 /(n_y - 1)} = \frac{[(225/16 + 2,500/11]^2}{\left(\frac{225}{16}\right)^2 /15 + \left(\frac{2,500}{11}\right)^2 /10} \approx 11$$

The margin of error is now found by use of Equation 9.9:

$$ME = t_{(v,\alpha/2)}\sqrt{\frac{s_x^2}{n_x} + \frac{s_y^2}{n_y}} = t_{(11,0.025)}\sqrt{\frac{225}{16} + \frac{2,500}{11}} = 2.201(15.534967) = 34.19$$

Using Equation 9.8, the 95% confidence interval is

$$(290 - 250) \pm 34.19 =$$
$$\$5.81 < \mu_x - \mu_y < \$74.19$$

Figure 9.2 Difference in Accounts Payable Between East and West Offices (Minitab Output)

Two-Sample T-Test and CI

```
Sample       N      Mean      StDev       SE Mean
1           16     290.0       15.0           3.8
2           11     250.0       50.0            15

Difference = mu (1) - mu (2)
Estimate for difference: 40.000
95% CI for difference: (5.8078, 74.1922)
T-Test of difference = 0 (vs not =): T-Value-3.57  P-Value = 0.026  DF = 11
```

Figure 9.2 is the Minitab output for this data.
In the long run, the mean accounts payable for the east office exceeds the mean accounts payable for the west office by as little as \$5.81 or by as much as \$74.19.

Exercises

Basic Exercises

9.7 Assuming equal population variances, determine the number of degrees of freedom for each of the following:

a. $n_1 = 12, \quad s_1^2 = 30; \quad n_2 = 14, \quad s_2^2 = 36$
b. $n_1 = 6, \quad s_1^2 = 30; \quad n_2 = 7, \quad s_2^2 = 36$
c. $n_1 = 9, \quad s_1^2 = 16; \quad n_2 = 12, \quad s_2^2 = 25$

9.8 Assuming equal population variances, compute the pooled sample variance, s_p^2, for part (a) through part (c) of Exercise 9.7.

9.9 Assuming unequal population variances, determine the number of degrees of freedom for each of the following:

a. $n_1 = 12, \quad s_1^2 = 6; \quad n_2 = 14, \quad s_2^2 = 10$
b. $n_1 = 6, \quad s_1^2 = 30; \quad n_2 = 10, \quad s_2^2 = 36$
c. $n_1 = 9, \quad s_1^2 = 16; \quad n_2 = 12, \quad s_2^2 = 25$
d. $n_1 = 6, \quad s_1^2 = 30; \quad n_2 = 7, \quad s_2^2 = 36$

9.10 Determine the margin of error for a 95% confidence interval for the difference in population means for each of the following (assume equal population variances):

a. $n_1 = 12, \quad s_1^2 = 6; \quad \bar{x}_1 = 200$
$n_2 = 14, \quad s_2^2 = 10; \quad \bar{x}_2 = 160$
b. $n_1 = 6, \quad s_1^2 = 6; \quad \bar{x}_1 = 200$
$n_2 = 7, \quad s_2^2 = 10; \quad \bar{x}_2 = 160$
c. The sample sizes in part (a) are double the sample sizes in part (b). Comment on your answers to part (a) compared to your answers to part (b).

Application Exercises

9.11 From a random sample of six students in an introductory finance class that uses group-learning techniques, the mean examination score was found to be 76.12 and the sample standard deviation was 2.53. For an independent random sample of nine students in another introductory finance class that does not use group-learning techniques, the sample mean and standard deviation of exam scores were 74.61 and 8.61, respectively. Estimate with 95% confidence the difference between the two population mean scores; do not assume equal population variances.

9.12 Prairie Flower Cereal Inc. is a small, but growing, producer of hot and ready-to-eat breakfast cereals. Gordon Thorson, a successful grain farmer, started the company in 1910 (Reference 3). Two machines are used for packaging 18-ounce (510-gram) boxes of sugar-coated wheat cereal. Estimate the difference in the mean weights of boxes of this type of cereal packaged by the two machines. Use a 95% confidence level and the data file **Sugar Coated Wheat**. Explain your findings.

9.13 Recent business graduates currently employed in full-time positions were surveyed. Family backgrounds were self-classified as relatively high or low socioeconomic status. For a random sample of 16 high-socioeconomic-status recent business graduates, mean total compensation was \$34,500 and the sample standard deviation was \$8,520. For an independent random sample of 9 low-socioeconomic-status recent business graduates, mean total compensation was \$31,499 and the sample standard deviation was \$7,521. Find a 90% confidence interval for the difference between the two population means.

9.14 Suppose, for a random sample of 200 firms that revalued their fixed assets, the mean ratio of debt to tangible assets was 0.517 and the sample standard deviation was 0.148. For an independent random sample of 400 firms that did not revalue their fixed assets, the mean ratio of debt to tangible assets was 0.489 and the sample standard deviation was 0.159. Find a 99% confidence interval for the difference between the two population means.

9.15 A researcher intends to estimate the effect of a drug on the scores of human subjects performing a task of psychomotor coordination. The members of a random sample of 9 subjects were given the drug prior to testing. Their mean score was 9.78, and the sample variance was 17.64. An independent random sample of 10 subjects was used as a control group and given a placebo prior to testing. The mean score in this control group was 15.10, and the sample variance was 27.01. Assuming that the population distributions are normal with equal variances, find a 90% confidence interval for the difference between the population mean scores.

9.3 Confidence Intervals for the Difference Between Two Population Proportions (Large Samples)

Confidence intervals for a single population proportion were derived in Chapter 8. Often a comparison of two population proportions is of interest. For instance, one might want to compare the proportion of residents in one city who indicate that they will vote for a particular presidential candidate with the proportion of residents in another city who indicate the same candidate preference. Confidence intervals for the difference between two population proportions with independent large samples taken from these two populations are considered in this section.

Suppose that a random sample of n_x observations from a population with proportion P_x of "successes" yields sample proportion $\hat{p}_x$ and that an independent random sample of n_y observations from a population with proportion P_y of "successes" produces sample proportion $\hat{p}_y$. Since our concern is with the population difference $(P_x - P_y)$, it is natural to examine the random variable $(\hat{p}_X - \hat{p}_Y)$. This has mean

$$E(\hat{p}_X - \hat{p}_Y) = E(\hat{p}_X) - E(\hat{p}_Y) = P_X - P_Y$$

and, since the samples are taken independently, variance

$$\begin{aligned}\text{Var}(\hat{p}_X - \hat{p}_Y) &= \text{Var}(\hat{p}_X) + \text{Var}(\hat{p}_Y)\\ &= \frac{P_X(1-P_X)}{n_x} + \frac{P_Y(1-P_Y)}{n_y}\end{aligned}$$

Furthermore, if the sample sizes are large, the distribution of this random variable is approximately normal, so subtracting its mean and dividing by its standard deviation gives a standard normally distributed random variable. Moreover, for large sample sizes this approximation remains valid when the unknown population proportions P_x and P_y are replaced by the corresponding sample quantities. Thus, to a good approximation, the random variable

$$Z = \frac{(\hat{p}_x - \hat{p}_y) - (P_x - P_y)}{\sqrt{\dfrac{\hat{p}_x(1-\hat{p}_x)}{n_x} + \dfrac{\hat{p}_y(1-\hat{p}_y)}{n_y}}}$$

has a standard normal distribution. This result allows the derivation of confidence intervals for the difference between the two population proportions when the same sample sizes are large.

Confidence Intervals for the Difference Between Population Proportions (Large Samples)

Let $\hat{p}_x$ denote the observed proportion of successes in a random sample of n_x observations from a population with proportion P_X of successes, and let $\hat{p}_y$ denote the proportion of successes observed in an independent random sample of n_y observations from a population with proportion P_Y of successes. Then, if the sample sizes are large (generally at least 40 observations in each sample), a $100(1-\alpha)\%$ **confidence interval**

for the difference between population proportions, $(P_X - P_Y)$, is given by

$$(\hat{p}_x - \hat{p}_y) \pm ME \tag{9.12}$$

where the **margin of error, *ME*,** is

$$ME = z_{\alpha/2}\sqrt{\frac{\hat{p}_x(1-\hat{p}_x)}{n_x} + \frac{\hat{p}_y(1-\hat{p}_y)}{n_y}} \tag{9.13}$$

Example 9.5 Precinct Preference (Confidence Interval)

During a presidential election year many forecasts are made to determine how voters perceive a particular candidate. In a random sample of 120 registered voters in precinct A, 107 indicated that they supported the candidate in question. In an independent random sample of 141 registered voters in precinct B, only 73 indicated support for the same candidate. If the respective population proportions are denoted P_A and P_B, find a 95% confidence interval for the population difference, $(P_A - P_B)$.

Solution From the sample information it follows that

$$n_A = 120 \quad \text{and} \quad \hat{p}_A = 107/120 = 0.892; \qquad n_B = 141 \quad \text{and} \quad \hat{p}_B = 73/141 = 0.518$$

For a 95% confidence interval, $\alpha = .05$, and so

$$z_{\alpha/2} = z_{0.025} = 1.96$$

The required interval is therefore

$$(0.892 - 0.518) - 1.96\sqrt{\frac{(0.892)(0.108)}{120} + \frac{(0.518)(0.482)}{141}}$$
$$< P_A - P_B < (0.892 - 0.518) + 1.96\sqrt{\frac{(0.892)(0.108)}{120} + \frac{(0.518)(0.482)}{141}}, \text{ or}$$
$$0.275 < P_A - P_B < 0.473$$

The fact that zero is well outside this range suggests that there is a difference in the population proportions of registered voters in precinct A and precinct B who support this presidential candidate. In the long run the difference is estimated to be as little as 27.5% or as high as 47.3%.

Figure 9.3 is the Minitab output for Example 9.5. The data suggest that there is a difference in the population proportions of registered voters in precinct A and precinct B who support this presidential candidate. In the long run about 95% of all such intervals would contain the true value of the difference.

Figure 9.3 Precinct Preference for Example 9.5 (Minitab Output)

Sample	X	N	Sample p
1	107	120	0.891667
2	73	141	0.517730

Estimate for p(1) - p(2): 0.373936
95% CI for p(1) - p(2): (0.274463, 0.473409)

Exercises

Basic Exercises

9.16 Calculate the margin of error for each of the following:

a. $n_1 = 260, \quad \hat{p}_1 = 0.75; \quad n_2 = 200, \quad \hat{p}_2 = 0.68$

b. $n_1 = 400, \quad \hat{p}_1 = 0.60; \quad n_2 = 500, \quad \hat{p}_2 = 0.68$

c. $n_1 = 500, \quad \hat{p}_1 = 0.20; \quad n_2 = 375, \quad \hat{p}_2 = 0.25$

9.17 Calculate the 95% confidence interval for the difference in population proportions for each of the following:

a. $n_1 = 370, \quad \hat{p}_1 = 0.65; \quad n_2 = 200, \quad \hat{p}_2 = 0.68$

b. $n_1 = 220, \quad \hat{p}_1 = 0.48; \quad n_2 = 270, \quad \hat{p}_2 = 0.52$

c. $n_1 = 500, \quad \hat{p}_1 = 0.30; \quad n_2 = 325, \quad \hat{p}_2 = 0.25$

Application Exercises

9.18 In a random sample of 120 large retailers, 85 used regression as a method of forecasting. In an independent random sample of 163 small retailers, 78 used regression as a method of forecasting. Find a 98% confidence interval for the difference between the two population proportions.

9.19 Do seniors and freshmen have different views concerning the university's library collection? Using the data file **Library**, estimate the difference in proportions of seniors and freshmen who think that the school's library has an adequate collection of books. Use a confidence level of 90%.

9.20 "Would you use the library more if the hours were extended?" From a random sample of 138 freshmen, 80 indicated that they would use the school's library more if the hours were extended. In an independent random sample of 96 sophomores, 73 responded that they would use the library more if the hours were extended. Estimate the difference in proportion of first-year and second-year students responding affirmatively to this question. Use a 95% confidence level.

9.21 A random sample of 100 men contained 61 in favor of a state constitutional amendment to retard the rate of growth of property taxes. An independent random sample of 100 women contained 54 in favor of this amendment. The confidence interval

$$0.04 < P_x - P_y < 0.10$$

was calculated for the difference between the population proportions. What is the confidence level of this interval?

9.22 Supermarket shoppers were observed and questioned immediately after putting an item in their cart. Of a random sample of 510 choosing a product at the regular price, 320 claimed to check price at the point of choice. Of an independent random sample of 332 choosing a product at a special price, 200 made this claim. Find a 90% confidence interval for the difference between the two population proportions.

9.4 Confidence Intervals for the Variance of a Normal Distribution

On occasion, interval estimates are required for the variance of a population. As might be expected, such estimates are based on the sample variance.

Suppose a random sample of n observations from a normally distributed population with variance σ^2 and sample variance s^2 is taken. The random variable

$$\chi^2_{n-1} = \frac{(n-1)s^2}{\sigma^2}$$

follows a chi-square distribution with $(n - 1)$ degrees of freedom. This result forms the basis for the derivation of confidence intervals for the population variance when sampling from a normal distribution.

In order to develop the formula for calculating confidence intervals for the variance, an additional notation is needed. We illustrate this notation in Figure 9.4.

Notation

A random variable having the chi-square distribution with $v = n - 1$ degrees of freedom will be denoted by χ_v^2 or simply χ_{n-1}^2. Define as $\chi_{n-1,\alpha}^2$ the number for which

$$P(\chi_{n-1}^2 > \chi_{n-1,\alpha}^2) = \alpha$$

For a specified probability α, a chi-square number for $n - 1$ degrees of freedom is needed—that is, $\chi_{n-1,\alpha}^2$. This can be found from values of the cumulative distribution function of a chi-square random variable. For instance, suppose the number that is exceeded with probability 0.05 by a chi-square random variable with 6 degrees of freedom is needed; that is

$$P(\chi_6^2 > \chi_{6,0.05}^2) = 0.05$$

From Appendix Table 7, $\chi_{6,0.05}^2 = 12.59$. Similarly,

$$P(\chi_{n-1}^2 > \chi_{n-1,\alpha/2}^2) = \frac{\alpha}{2}$$

It follows that $\chi_{n-1,1-\alpha/2}^2$ is given by

$$P(\chi_{n-1}^2 > \chi_{n-1,1-\alpha/2}^2) = 1 - \frac{\alpha}{2}$$

and hence

$$P(\chi_{n-1}^2 < \chi_{n-1,1-\alpha/2}^2) = \frac{\alpha}{2}$$

Finally,

$$P(\chi_{n-1,1-\alpha/2}^2 < \chi_{n-1}^2 < \chi_{n-1,\alpha/2}^2) = 1 - \frac{\alpha}{2} - \frac{\alpha}{2} = 1 - \alpha$$

This probability is illustrated in Figure 9.5.

Figure 9.4 Chi-Square Distribution

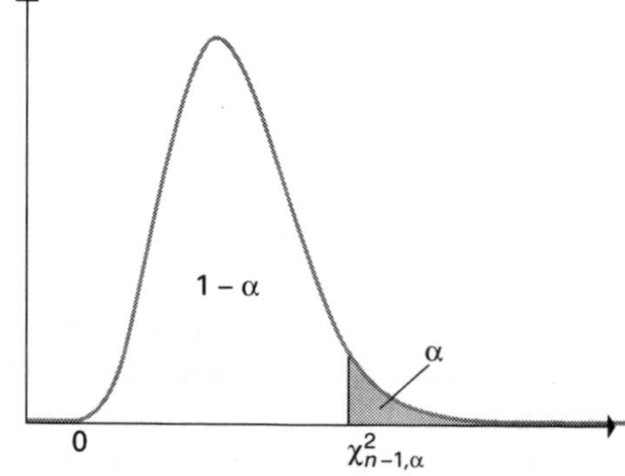

Figure 9.5 Chi-Square Distribution for $n - 1$ Degrees of Freedom and $(1 - \alpha)$% Confidence Level

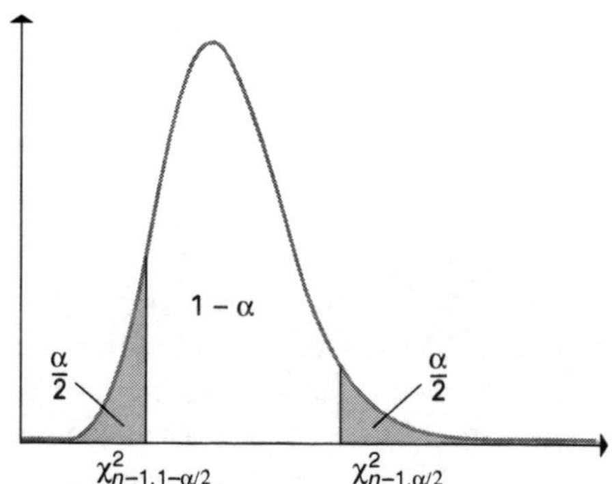

Suppose a pair of numbers is needed such that the probability that a chi-square random variable with 6 degrees of freedom lying between these numbers is 0.90. Then $\alpha = 0.10$ and

$$P(\chi^2_{6,0.95} < \chi^2_6 < \chi^2_{6,0.05}) = 0.90$$

Previously, it was found that $\chi^2_{6,0.05} = 12.59$. From Appendix Table 7 we find that $\chi^2_{6,0.95} = 1.64$. The probability is 0.90 that this chi-square random variable falls between 1.64 and 12.59.

To find confidence intervals for the population variance,

$$\begin{aligned} 1-\alpha &= P(\chi^2_{n-1,1-\alpha/2} < \chi^2_{n-1} < \chi^2_{n-1,\alpha/2}) \\ &= P\left(\chi^2_{n-1,1-\alpha/2} < \frac{(n-1)s^2}{\sigma^2} < \chi^2_{n-1,\alpha/2}\right) \\ &= P\left(\frac{(n-1)s^2}{\chi^2_{n-1,\alpha/2}} < \sigma^2 < \frac{(n-1)s^2}{\chi^2_{n-1,1-\alpha/2}}\right) \end{aligned}$$

Confidence Intervals for the Variance of a Normal Population

Suppose that there is a random sample of n observations from a normally distributed population with variance σ^2. If the observed sample variance is s^2, then a $100(1-\alpha)\%$ **confidence interval for the population variance** is given by

$$\frac{(n-1)s^2}{\chi^2_{n-1,\alpha/2}} < \sigma^2 < \frac{(n-1)s^2}{\chi^2_{n-1,1-\alpha/2}} \tag{9.14}$$

where $\chi^2_{n-1,\alpha/2}$ is the number for which

$$P(\chi^2_{n-1} > \chi^2_{n-1,\alpha/2}) = \frac{\alpha}{2}$$

and $\chi^2_{n-1,1-\alpha/2}$ is the number for which

$$P(\chi^2_{n-1} < \chi^2_{n-1,1-\alpha/2}) = \frac{\alpha}{2}$$

and the random variable χ^2_{n-1} follows a chi-square distribution with $(n-1)$ degrees of freedom.

Although it is assumed throughout this section that the population is normally distributed, we should always check for any evidence that this assumption fails. Notice that the confidence interval in Equation 9.14 is not of the usual form of sample point estimator ± margin of error.

Example 9.6 Comparing Temperature Variances (Confidence Interval)

The manager of Northern Steel, Inc., wants to assess the temperature variation in the firm's new electric furnace. A random sample of 25 temperatures over a 1-week period is obtained, and the sample variance is found to be $s^2 = 100$. Find a 95% confidence interval for the population variance temperature.

Solution Here, $n = 25$ and $s^2 = 100$, and for a 95% confidence interval, $\alpha = 0.05$. It follows from the chi-square distribution in Appendix Table 7 Figure 9.6 that

$$\chi^2_{n-1,1-\alpha/2} = \chi^2_{24,0.975} = 12.40 \quad \text{and} \quad \chi^2_{n-1,\alpha/2} = \chi^2_{24,0.025} = 39.36$$

The 95% confidence interval for the population variance is given by

$$\frac{(n-1)s^2}{\chi^2_{n-1,\alpha/2}} < \sigma^2 < \frac{(n-1)s^2}{\chi^2_{n-1,1-\alpha/2}}$$

Substitution yields

$$\frac{(24)(100)}{39.36} < \sigma^2 < \frac{(24)(100)}{12.40} =$$
$$60.97 < \sigma^2 < 193.53$$

Figure 9.6 Chi-Square Distribution for $n = 25$ and 95% Confidence Level

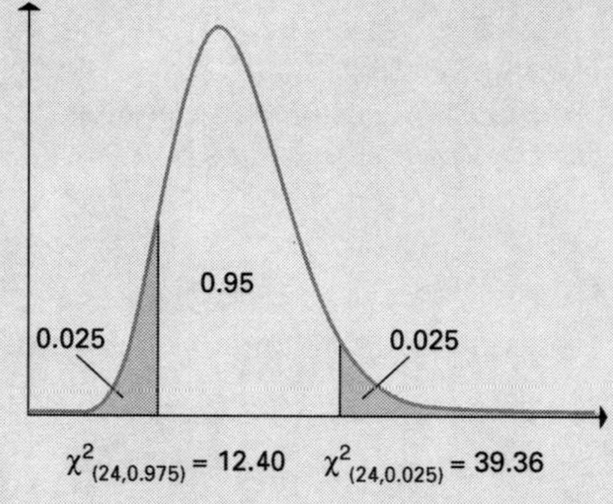

It is dangerous to follow the procedure just demonstrated when the population distribution is not normal. The validity of the interval estimator for the variance depends far more critically on the assumption of normality than does that of the interval estimator for the population mean.

EXERCISES

Basic Exercises

9.23 Find the lower confidence limit for each of the following normal populations:

a. $n = 21$; $\alpha = 0.025$; $s^2 = 16$
b. $n = 16$; $\alpha = 0.05$; $s = 8$
c. $n = 28$; $\alpha = 0.01$; $s = 15$

9.24 Find the upper confidence limit for parts (a) through (c) of Exercise 9.23.

9.25 Consider the following random sample from a normal population:

12 16 8 10 9

a. Find the 90% confidence interval for population variance.
b. Find the 95% confidence interval for population variance.

Application Exercises

9.26 LDS wants to be sure that the leak rate (in cubic centimeters per second) of transmission oil coolers (TOCs) meets the established specification limits. A random sample 50 TOCs is tested, and the leak rates are recorded in the data file **TOC** (Reference 4). Estimate the variance in leak rate with a 95% confidence level (check normality).

9.27 A clinic offers a weight-reduction program. A review of its records found the following weight losses, in pounds, for a random sample of 10 clients at the conclusion of the program:

18.2 25.9 6.3 11.8 15.4 20.3 16.8 19.5 12.3 17.2

Find a 90% confidence interval for the population variance of weight losses for clients of this weight-reduction program.

9.28 The quality control manager of a chemical company randomly sampled twenty 100-pound bags of fertilizer to estimate the variance in the pounds of impurities. The sample variance was found to be 6.62. Find a 95% confidence interval for the population variance in the pounds of impurities.

9.29 A psychologist wants to estimate the variance of employee test scores. A random sample of 18 scores had a sample standard deviation of 10.4. Find a 90% confidence interval for the population variance. What are the assumptions, if any, to calculate this interval estimate?

9.30 A manufacturer is concerned about the variability of the levels of impurity contained in consignments of raw material from a supplier. A random sample of 15 consignments showed a standard deviation of 2.36 in the concentration of impurity levels. Assume normality.

a. Find a 95% confidence interval for the population variance.
b. Would a 99% confidence interval for this variance be wider or narrower than that found in part (a)?

9.31 A manufacturer bonds a plastic coating to a metal surface. A random sample of nine observations on the thickness of this coating is taken from a week's output, and the thicknesses (in millimeters) of these observations are as follows:

19.8 21.2 18.6 20.4 21.6 19.8 19.9 20.3 20.8

Assuming normality, find a 90% confidence interval for the population variance.

9.5 Sample Size Determination

We have developed confidence intervals for population parameters on the basis of the information contained in a given sample. Following such a process, we may believe that the resulting confidence interval is too wide, reflecting an undesirable amount of uncertainty about the parameter being estimated. Typically, one way to obtain a narrower interval with a given confidence level is to take a larger sample.

In some circumstances we may be able to fix in advance the width of the confidence interval, choosing a sample size big enough to guarantee that width. In this section consideration of how sample size can be chosen in this way for two interval estimation problems is given. Similar procedures can be employed to solve other problems. We will concentrate on populations that are not necessarily large in Chapter 20.

Mean of a Normally Distributed Population, Known Population Variance

If a random sample of n observations is taken from a normally distributed population with mean μ and known variance σ^2, it was seen in Chapter 8 that a $100(1-\alpha)\%$ confidence interval for the population mean is provided by

$$\bar{x} - \frac{z_{\alpha/2}\sigma}{\sqrt{n}} < \mu < \bar{x} + \frac{z_{\alpha/2}\sigma}{\sqrt{n}}$$

where $\bar{x}$ is the observed sample mean and $Z_{\alpha/2}$ is the appropriate cutoff point of the standard normal distribution. This interval is centered on the sample mean and extends a distance of B, the margin of error,

$$ME = \frac{z_{\alpha/2}\sigma}{\sqrt{n}}$$

on each side of the sample mean, so that ME is half the width of the interval. Suppose, now, that the investigator wants to fix the margin of error, ME, in advance. From basic algebra it follows that, if

$$ME = \frac{z_{\alpha/2}\sigma}{\sqrt{n}}$$

then

$$\sqrt{n} = \frac{z_{\alpha/2}\sigma}{ME}$$

and by squaring both sides of the equation, the sample size n is

$$n = \frac{z_{\alpha/2}^2\sigma^2}{ME^2}$$

This choice of the sample size guarantees that the confidence interval extends a distance ME on each side of the sample mean.

Sample Size for the Mean of a Normally Distributed Population with Known Population Variance

Suppose that a random sample from a normally distributed population with known variance σ^2 is selected. Then a 100(1 – α)% confidence interval for the population mean extends a distance *ME* (sometimes called the **sampling error**) on each side of the sample mean if the sample size, *n*, is

$$n = \frac{z_{\alpha/2}^2\sigma^2}{ME^2} \tag{9.15}$$

Of course, the number of sample observations must necessarily be an integer. If the number n resulting from the sample size formula is not an integer, then *round up* to the next whole number in order to guarantee that our confidence interval does not exceed the required width.

Example 9.7 Length of Metal Rods (Sample Size)

The lengths of metal rods produced by an industrial process are normally distributed with a standard deviation of 1.8 millimeters. Based on a random sample of nine observations from this population, the 99% confidence interval

$$194.65 < \mu < 197.75$$

was found for the population mean length. Suppose that a production manager believes that the interval is too wide for practical use and instead requires a 99% confidence interval extending no further than 0.50 mm on each side of the sample mean. How large a sample is needed to achieve such an interval?

Solution Since

$$ME = 0.50 \quad \sigma = 1.8 \quad and \quad z_{\alpha/2} = z_{0.005} = 2.576$$

the required sample size is

$$n = \frac{z_{\alpha/2}^2 \sigma^2}{ME^2}$$
$$= \frac{(2.576)^2 (1.8)^2}{(0.5)^2} \approx 86$$

Therefore, to satisfy the manager's requirement, a sample of at least 86 observations is needed. This large increase in the sample size represents the additional cost of achieving the higher precision in the estimate of the true value of the population mean, reflected in a narrower confidence interval. The value 2.576, rather than 2.58, was used to determine the sample size needed.

Population Proportion

In Chapter 8 we saw that for a random sample of n observations, a $100(1 \alpha)\%$ confidence interval for the population proportion P is

$$\hat{p} - z_{\alpha/2}\sqrt{\frac{\hat{p}(1-\hat{p})}{n}} < P < \hat{p} + z_{\alpha/2}\sqrt{\frac{\hat{p}(1-\hat{p})}{n}}$$

where $\hat{p}$ is the observed sample proportion. This interval is centered on the sample proportion and extends a distance (margin of error)

$$ME = z_{\alpha/2}\sqrt{\frac{\hat{p}(1-\hat{p})}{n}}$$

on each side of the sample proportion. Now, this result *cannot* be used directly to determine the sample size necessary to obtain a confidence interval of some specific width, since it involves the sample proportion, which will not be known at the outset. However, whatever the outcome, $\hat{p}(1-\hat{p})$ cannot be bigger than 0.25, its value when the sample proportion is 0.5. Thus, the *largest* possible value for the margin of error, ME, is given by

$$ME = z_{\alpha/2}\sqrt{\frac{0.25}{n}} = \frac{(0.5)z_{\alpha/2}}{\sqrt{n}}$$

Suppose, then, that a sufficiently large sample size is chosen to *guarantee* that the confidence interval extends no more than ME on each side of the sample proportion. Again using basic algebra,

$$\sqrt{n} = \frac{0.5z_{\alpha/2}}{ME}$$

and squaring yields

$$n = \frac{0.25(z_{\alpha/2})^2}{(ME)^2}$$

Sample Size for Population Proportion

Suppose that a random sample is selected from a population. Then a $100(1 - \alpha)\%$ confidence interval for the population proportion, extending a distance of at most *ME* on each side of the sample proportion, can be guaranteed if the sample size is

$$n = \frac{0.25(z_{\alpha/2})^2}{ME^2} \quad (9.16)$$

Example 9.8 Graduate Admissions Personnel (Sample Size)

In Exercise 8.33 a 95% confidence interval was calculated for the proportion of graduate admissions personnel who viewed scores on standardized exams as very important in the consideration of a candidate. Based on 142 observations the interval obtained was

$$0.533 < P < 0.693$$

Suppose, instead, that it must be ensured that a 95% confidence interval for the population proportion extends no further than 0.06 on each side of the sample proportion. How large a sample must be taken?

Solution It is given that

$$ME = 0.06 \quad \text{and} \quad z_{\alpha/2} = z_{0.025} = 1.96$$

Thus, the number of sample observations needed is

$$n = \frac{0.25z_{\alpha/2}^2}{(ME)^2} = \frac{0.25(1.96)^2}{(0.06)^2} = 266.78$$

To achieve this narrower confidence interval, a minimum of 267 sample observations is required (a significant increase over the original 142 observations).

The media frequently report the results of opinion surveys concerning issues of current interest, such as the president's rating on domestic issues or foreign policy, or people's views on some new tax proposal. These surveys generally represent the opinions of some subset of the population. Typically, these reports give estimates of the percentage of population members holding particular views. These reports often end with a statement like this: "There is a plus or minus 3% sampling error," or "The poll has a 3% margin of error." Specifically, these intervals are the sample percentage, plus or minus the advertised sampling error or margin of error. However, we stress that the margin of error does not include any errors due to biased or otherwise inadequate samples.

Example 9.9 Electoral College (Sample Size)

Suppose that an opinion survey following a presidential election reported the views of a sample of U.S. citizens of voting age concerning changing the electoral college process. The poll was said to have "a 3% margin of error." The implication is that a 95% confidence interval for the population proportion holding a particular opinion is the sample proportion plus or minus at most 3%. How many citizens of voting age need to be sampled to obtain this 3% margin of error?

Solution Using Equation 9.16,

$$n = \frac{0.25z_{\alpha/2}^2}{(ME)^2} = \frac{(0.25)(1.96)^2}{(0.03)^2} = 1{,}067.111$$

Therefore, 1,068 U.S. citizens of voting age need to be sampled to achieve the desired result.

EXERCISES

Basic Exercises

9.32 How large a sample is needed to estimate the mean of a normally distributed population for each of the following?

a. $ME = 5$; $\sigma = 40$; $\alpha = 0.01$
b. $ME = 10$; $\sigma = 40$; $\alpha = 0.01$
c. Compare and comment on your answers to parts (a) and (b).

9.33 How large a sample is needed to estimate the population proportion for each of the following?

a. $ME = 0.03$; $\alpha = 0.05$
b. $ME = 0.05$; $\alpha = 0.05$
c. Compare and comment on your answers to parts (a) and (b).

9.34 How large a sample is needed to estimate the population proportion for each of the following?

a. $ME = 0.05$; $\alpha = 0.01$
b. $ME = 0.05$; $\alpha = 0.10$
c. Compare and comment on your answers to parts (a) and (b).

Application Exercises

9.35 A research group wants to estimate the proportion of consumers who plan to buy a scanner for their PC during the next three months.

a. How many people should be sampled so that the sampling error is at most 0.04 with a 90% confidence interval?
b. What is the sample size required if the confidence is increased to 95%, keeping the sampling error the same?
c. What is the required sample size if the research group extends the sampling error to 0.05 and wants a 98% confidence level?

9.36 A politician wants to estimate the proportion of constituents favoring a controversial piece of proposed legislation. Suppose that a 99% confidence interval that extends at most 0.05 on each side of the sample proportion is required. How many sample observations are needed?

9.37 The student government association at a university wants to estimate the percentage of the student body that supports a change being considered in the academic calendar of the university for the next academic year. How many students should be surveyed if a 90% confidence interval is desired and the margin of error is to be only 3%?

Summary

In Chapter 8 we focused our attention on confidence interval estimation of parameters based on a single population. In this chapter we emphasized additional confidence intervals. Four confidence intervals were presented for the comparison of the means of two normally distributed populations based on the following sampling schemes: (1) samples were dependent (matched pairs); (2) samples were independent, and population variances were known; (3) samples were independent, and population variances were unknown, but we assumed equality of variances; and (4) samples were independent, and population variances were unknown, but we did not assume equality of variances. We also considered confidence interval estimation of the difference between two population proportions for large samples, as well as confidence interval estimation for the variance of a normally distributed population.

Generally, adding and subtracting the sampling error from the point estimator forms confidence intervals. This was not the case for the population variance, however. Three tables, the standard normal Z table, the Student's t table, and the chi-square table were used in the development of the confidence intervals in this chapter. Finally, an introduction to determining sample size for two particular interval estimates was considered. Additional sampling is discussed in Chapter 20.

Key Words

- confidence interval
  - for two means, independent
  - for two means, matched
  - for two means with variances equal
  - for two means with variances not equal
  - for two proportions
  - for variance
- interval half width
- pooled sample variance
- sample size for mean with known variance
- sample size for proportion
- sampling error
- Student's t
- width

Chapter Exercises and Applications

9.38 Independent random samples from two normally distributed populations give the following results:

$$n_x = 15 \quad \bar{x} = 400 \quad s_x = 20$$
$$n_y = 13 \quad \bar{y} = 360 \quad s_y = 25$$

Assume that the unknown population variances are equal and find a 90% confidence interval for the difference between population means.

9.39 Independent random samples from two normally distributed populations give the following results:

$$n_x = 15 \quad \bar{x} = 400 \quad s_x = 10$$
$$n_y = 13 \quad \bar{y} = 360 \quad s_y = 40$$

If we do not assume that the unknown population variances are equal, what is the 90% confidence interval for the difference between population means?

9.40 Independent random samples from two normally distributed populations give the following results:

$$n_x = 10 \quad \bar{x} = 480 \quad s_x = 30$$
$$n_y = 12 \quad \bar{y} = 520 \quad s_y = 25$$

a. If we assume that the unknown population variances are equal, what is the 90% confidence interval for the difference of population means?

b. If we assume that the unknown population variances are equal, what is the 90% confidence interval for the difference between population means?

9.41 A company sends a random sample of 12 of its salespeople to a course designed to increase their motivation and, hence, presumably their effectiveness. In the following year these people generated sales with an average value of \$435,000 and a sample standard deviation of \$56,000. During the same period, an independently chosen random sample of 15 salespeople who had not attended the course obtained sales with an average value of \$408,000 and a sample standard deviation of \$43,000. Assume that the two population distributions are normal and have the same variance. Find a 95% confidence interval for the difference between their means.

9.42 Students in an introductory economics class are assigned to quiz sections conducted by teaching assistants. For one teaching assistant the 21 students in the quiz section obtained a mean score of 72.1 on the final examination and a standard deviation of 11.3. For a second teaching assistant the 18 students in the section obtained a mean score on the final exam of 73.8 and a standard deviation of 10.6. Assume that these data can be regarded as independent random samples from normally distributed populations with a common variance. Find an 80% confidence interval for the difference between the population means.

9.43 Several drugs are used to treat diabetes. A sales specialist for a leading pharmaceutical company randomly sampled the records of 10 sales districts to estimate the number of new prescriptions that had been written during a particular month for his company's new diabetes drug. The numbers of new prescriptions were

210 240 190 275 290 265 312 284 261 243

a. Find a 90% confidence interval for the average number of new prescriptions written for this new drug among all the sales districts. What are the assumptions?
b. Assuming that the confidence level remains constant, what sample size is needed to reduce by half the margin of error of the confidence interval in part (a)?

9.44 A proposal for a new 1-cent tax increase to support cancer research is to appear on the ballot in one county's next election. The residents in two cities were questioned as to their level of support. In Sterling Heights a recent survey of 225 residents showed that 140 people supported the proposal, 35 were undecided, and the remainder was opposed to the new proposal. In a nearby community, Harrison Township, the results of a random sample of 210 residents found that 120 people supported the tax, 30 were opposed, and the remainder was undecided. Estimate the difference in the percentages of residents from these two communities who support this proposal. Use a 95% confidence level.

9.45 Is the average amount spent on textbooks per semester by accounting majors significantly different than the average amount spent on textbooks per semester by management majors? Answer this question with a 90% confidence interval using the following data from random samples of students majoring in accounting or management. Discuss assumptions.

	Accounting Majors	Management Majors
Mean	$340	$285
Standard deviation	20	30
Sample size	40	50

9.46 The supervisor of an orange juice bottling company is considering the purchase of a new machine to bottle 16 fl. oz. (473 mL) bottles of 100% pure orange juice and wants an estimate of the difference in the mean filling weights between the new machine and the old machine. Random samples of bottles of orange juice that had been filled by both machines were obtained. Do the following data indicate that there is a difference in the mean filling weights between the new and the old machines? Discuss assumptions.

	New Machine	Old Machine
Mean	470 mL	460 mL
Standard deviation	5 mL	7 mL
Sample size	15	12

9.47 Renee Payne, who is employed by a major investment firm in West Palm Beach, Florida, would like to estimate the percentage of new clients who will make a certain type of investment. If she wants a sampling error no greater than 2.5% and a confidence level of 90%, how many clients should she sample? What sample size is required for an 85% confidence level?

9.48 An agency offers students preparation courses for a graduate school admissions test. As part of an experiment to evaluate the merits of the course, 12 students were chosen and divided into six pairs in such a way that the two members of any pair had similar academic records. Before taking the test, one member of each pair was assigned at random to take the preparation course, while the other member took no course. The achievement test scores are contained in the **Student Pair** data file. Assuming that the differences in scores are normally distributed, find a 98% confidence interval for the difference in means scores between those who took the course and those who did not.

9.49 The president's policy on domestic affairs received a 65% approval rating in a recent poll. The margin of error was given as 0.035. What sample size was used for this poll if we assume a 95% confidence level?

9.50 A newspaper article reported that 400 people in one state were surveyed and 75% were opposed to a recent court decision. The same article reported that a similar survey of 500 people in another state indicated opposition by only 45%. Construct a 95% confidence interval of the difference in population proportions based on the data.

Appendix

1. Student's *t* Distribution

Gosset sought to develop a probability distribution for normally distributed random variables that did not include the population variance σ^2. As a result, he took the ratio of Z, a standard normal random variable, and the square root of χ^2 divided by its degrees of freedom, v. In mathematical notation

$$t = \frac{Z}{\sqrt{\chi^2/v}}$$

$$t = \frac{(x-\mu)/\sigma}{\sqrt{s^2(n-1)\,/\,\sigma^2(n-1)}} = \frac{(x-\mu)}{s}$$

The resulting t statistic has $n - 1$ degrees of freedom. Notice that the t probability distribution is based on normally distributed random variables. For applications, the normal Z is used when the population variance σ^2 is available, and the Student's t is used when only the sample variance s^2 is available. Statistical research using computer-generated random samples has shown that t can be used to study the distribution of sample means even if the distribution of the individual random variables is not normal.

2. Student's *t*-Test for Two Means with Unknown Population Variances Not Assumed to Be Equal

For the difference between two populations,

$$Z = \frac{(\bar{x}-\bar{y})-(\mu_X-\mu_Y)}{\sqrt{\dfrac{\sigma_X^2}{n_x}+\dfrac{\sigma_Y^2}{n_y}}} \quad \text{and} \quad \chi^2 = \chi_X^2 + \chi_Y^2$$

is the sum of two independent chi-square random variables from the two independent random samples:

$$\chi_X^2 = \frac{(n_x-1)s_x^2}{\sigma_X^2}$$

$$\chi_Y^2 = \frac{(n_y-1)s_y^2}{\sigma_Y^2}$$

with $(n_x - 1)$ and $(n_y - 1)$ degrees of freedom, respectively. The degrees of freedom for χ^2 is the sum of the component degrees of freedom, $v = (n_x - 1) + (n_y - 1) = n_x + n_y - 2$.

Bringing these pieces together,

$$t = \frac{\left[(\bar{x}-\bar{y})-(\mu_X-\mu_Y)\right]/\sqrt{\sigma_X^2/n_x+\sigma_Y^2/n_y}}{\sqrt{\left[(n_x-1)s_x^2\,/\,\sigma_x^2+(n_y-1)s_y^2\,/\,\sigma_y^2\right]/\,(n_x+n_y-2)}}$$

If $\sigma_X^2 = \sigma_Y^2$, then this reduces to

$$t = \frac{(\bar{x} - \bar{y}) - (\mu_X - \mu_Y)}{\sqrt{\frac{s_p^2}{n_x} + \frac{s_p^2}{n_y}}}$$

3. Matched Pairs with Missing Values

Consider matched pairs with missing values. Suppose that at least one value from the first sample is missing and *exactly* the same number of missing values occurs in the second sample (not from the same observations). In this one case Excel will perform the calculations giving incorrect results. First, remove all cases from either sample that contain missing values. This will also apply in Chapter 11 when hypothesis tests of matched pairs are considered.

References

1. Agresti, A., and B. A. Coull. "Approximate Is Better than 'Exact' for Interval Estimation of Binomial Proportions." *American Statistician* 52 (1998): 119–126.
2. Agresti, A., and B. Caffo. "Simple and Effective Confidence Intervals for Proportions and Differences of Proportions Result from Adding Two Successes and Two Failures." *American Statistician* 54 (2000): 280–288.
3. Carlson, William L. *Cases in Managerial Data Analysis.* (Belmont, CA: Wadsworth Publishing Company, 1997).
4. Fiedler, Alfred W., Plant Manager. "Machine Reading Leak Rate Repeatability Studies Conducted at LDS Vacuum Products." (Altamonte Springs, FL, February 1999).
5. North American Fareston versus Tamoxifen Adjuvant Trial for Breast Cancer: A Phase III Study of Tamoxifen Versus Toremifene as Adjuvant Therapy for Women with Carcinoma of the Breast, *www.naftatrial.com*, May 31, 2004.
6. Satterthwaite, F. E. (1946). An approximate distribution of estimates of variance components. *Biometrics Bulletin*, 2, 110–114.
7. Winer, B. J., *Statistical Principles in Experimental Design*, 2d ed. (New York: McGraw-Hill, 1971).

Topic 21

Hypothesis Testing

Chapter 10

Hypothesis Testing

Chapter Outline

Introduction

In this chapter we develop hypothesis-testing procedures that enable us to test the validity of some conjecture or claim by using sample data. This form of inference contrasts and complements the estimation procedures we developed in Chapters 8 and 9. The process begins with an investigator forming a hypothesis about the nature of some population. This hypothesis is stated clearly as involving two options, and then we select one option based on the results of a statistic computed from a random sample of data. Following are examples of typical problems:

1. Malt O Meal Inc., a producer of ready-to-eat cereal, claims that, on average, its cereal packages weigh at least 16 ounces. The company can test this claim by collecting a random sample of cereal packages, determining the weight of each one, and computing the sample mean package weight from the data.
2. An automobile parts factory wishes to monitor its manufacturing process to ensure that the diameter of pistons meets engineering tolerance specifications. It could obtain random samples every 2 hours from the production line and use them to determine if standards are being maintained.

These examples are based on a common theme. We state a hypothesis about some population parameter and then sample data are used to test the validity of our hypothesis.

10.1 Concepts of Hypothesis Testing

Here, we introduce a general framework to test hypotheses by using statistics computed from random samples. Since these statistics have a sampling distribution, our decision is made in the face of random variation. Thus, clear decision rules are needed for choosing between the two choices.

The process that we develop here has a direct analogy to a criminal jury trial. In a jury trial we assume that the accused is innocent, and the jury will decide that a person is guilty only if there is very strong evidence against the presumption of innocence. That criminal jury trial process for choosing between guilt and innocence has:

1. Rigorous procedures for presenting and evaluating evidence
2. A judge to enforce the rules
3. A decision process that assumes innocence unless there is evidence to prove guilt beyond a reasonable doubt

Note that this process will fail to convict a number of people who are, in fact, guilty. But if a person's innocence is rejected and the person is found guilty, we have a strong belief that the person is guilty.

We begin the hypothesis-testing procedure by considering a value for a population probability distribution parameter such as the mean, μ, the variance, σ^2, or the proportion, P. Our approach starts with a hypothesis about the parameter—called the **null hypothesis**—that will be maintained unless there is strong evidence against this null hypothesis. If we reject the null hypothesis, then the second hypothesis, named the **alternative hypothesis**, will be accepted. However, if we fail to reject the null hypothesis, we cannot necessarily conclude that the null hypothesis is correct. If we fail to reject, then either the null hypothesis is correct or the alternative hypothesis is correct but our test procedure is not strong enough to reject the null hypothesis.

Using our Malt O Meal example, we could begin by assuming that the mean package weight is equal to 16 ounces, so our null hypothesis is defined as

$$H_0 : \mu = 16$$

A hypothesis, whether null or alternative, might specify a single value—in this case, $\mu = 16$—for the population parameter μ. We define this hypothesis as a **simple hypothesis**, which is read, "The null hypothesis is that the population parameter μ is equal to a specific value of 16." For this cereal example a possible alternative hypothesis is that the population mean package weight falls in a range of values greater than 16 ounces:

$$H_1 : \mu > 16$$

We define this alternative hypothesis as a **one-sided composite alternative hypothesis**. Another possibility would be to test the null hypothesis against the general **two-sided composite alternative hypothesis**:

$$H_1 : \mu \neq 16$$

We choose these hypotheses so that one or the other must be true. In this book we will denote the null hypothesis as H_0 and the alternative hypothesis as H_1.

Similar to a jury trial our decision to choose one or the other hypothesis follows a rigorous procedure. The decision process uses a decision statistic computed from a random sample, such as a sample mean, $\bar{x}$, a sample variance, s^2, or a sample proportion, $\hat{p}$. The decision statistic will have a known sampling distribution, based on the sampling procedure and the parameter value specified by the null hypothesis. From this sampling distribution we will determine values of the decision statistic that have a small probability of occurring if the null hypothesis is true. If the decision statistic has a value that has a small probability of occurring when the null hypothesis is true, we will reject the null hypothesis and accept the alternative hypothesis. However, if the decision statistic does not have a small probability of occurring when the null hypothesis is true, then we will not reject the null hypothesis. The specification of null and alternative hypotheses depends on the problem, as indicated in the following examples.

1. Malt O Meal wants to determine if its mean package weight is above the label weight. Let μ denote the population mean weight (in ounces) of cereal per box. The composite null hypothesis is that this mean is at most 16 ounces:

   $$H_0 : \mu \leq 16$$

   and the obvious alternative is that the mean weight is greater than 16 ounces:

   $$H_1 : \mu > 16$$

   For this problem we would seek strong evidence that the mean weight of packages is greater than 16 ounces. For example, a company might wish to avoid legal action because of low package weights. The company would have confidence in its belief if it had strong evidence that results in rejecting H_0.
2. An automobile piston factory has proposed a process to monitor the diameter of pistons on a regular schedule. Every 2 hours a random sample of $n = 6$ pistons would be randomly selected from the production process and their diameters measured. The mean diameter for the 6 pistons would be computed and used to test the simple null hypothesis:

   $$H_0 : \mu = 3.800$$

   versus the alternative hypothesis:

   $$H_1 : \mu \neq 3.800$$

   In this case the company would continue to operate unless the null hypothesis was rejected in favor of the alternative hypothesis. Strong evidence that the pistons were not meeting the tolerance standards would result in an interruption of the production process.

Once we have specified null and alternative hypotheses and collected sample data, a decision concerning the null hypothesis must be made. We can either reject the null hypothesis and accept the alternative or fail to reject the null hypothesis. For good reasons many statisticians prefer not to say, "accept the null hypothesis"; instead, they say, "fail to reject the null hypothesis." When we fail to reject the null hypothesis, then either the null hypothesis is true or our test procedure was not strong enough to reject and we have committed an error. To select the hypothesis—null or alternative—we develop a decision rule based on sample evidence. Further on in this chapter we present specific decision rules for various problems. In many cases the form of the rule is fairly obvious. To test the null hypothesis that the mean weight of cereal boxes is less than 16 ounces,we obtain a random sample of boxes and compute the sample mean. If the sample mean is substantially above 16 ounces, we can reject the null hypothesis and accept the alternative hypothesis. In general, the greater the sample mean is above 16, the greater the chance is of rejecting the null hypothesis. We will develop specific decision rules below.

From our discussion of sampling distributions in Chapter 7 we know that the sample mean is different from the population mean. With only one sample mean we cannot be certain of the value of the population mean. Thus, we know that the adopted decision rule will have some chance of reaching an erroneous conclusion. Table 10.1 summarizes the possible types of error. We define **Type I error** as the probability of rejecting the null hypothesis when the null hypothesis is true. Our decision rule will be defined so that the probability of rejecting a true null hypothesis, denoted as α, is "small." We define α to be the significance level of the test. The probability of failing to reject the null hypothesis when it is true is $(1 - \alpha)$. We also have another possible error, called a **Type II error**, that arises when we fail to reject a false null hypothesis. For a particular decision rule the probability of making such an error when the null hypothesis is false will be denoted as β. Then the probability of rejecting a false null hypothesis is $(1 - \beta)$, which is called the power of the test.

We will illustrate these ideas by reference to an earlier example. A factory manager is trying to determine if the population mean package weight is greater than the package label weight. The null hypothesis is that in the population the mean package weight is less than or equal to the label weight of 16 ounces. This null hypothesis is tested against the alternative hypothesis that the mean package weight is greater than 16 ounces. To test the hypothesis, we will obtain an independent random sample of cereal packages and compute the sample mean. If the sample mean is substantially larger than 16 ounces, the null hypothesis is rejected. Otherwise, we will not reject the null hypothesis. Let $\bar{x}$ denote the sample mean. Then a possible decision rule is

$$\text{Reject } H_0 \text{ if } \quad \bar{x} > 16.13$$

Now, suppose that the null hypothesis is true. We could still find that the sample mean was greater than 16.13, and, according to our decision rule, the null hypothesis would be rejected. In that case we would have committed a Type I error. The probability of rejection when the null hypothesis is true is the significance level α. By contrast, suppose that the null hypothesis is false and that the population mean package weight is greater than 16. We could still find that the sample mean was less than 16.13,

Table 10.1 States of Nature and Decisions on the Null Hypothesis, with Probabilities of Making the Decisions, Given the States of Nature

	States of Nature	
Decisions on Null Hypothesis	Null Hypothesis Is True	Null Hypothesis Is False
Fail to reject H_0	Correct decision Probability $= 1 - \alpha$	Type II error Probability $= \beta$
Reject H_0	Type I error Probability $= \alpha$ (α is called the significance level)	Correct decision Probability $= 1 - \beta$ ($1 - \beta$ is called the power of the test)

and, according to our decision rule, the null hypothesis would not be rejected. Thus, a Type II error would have occurred. The probability of making such an error will depend on just how much the population mean exceeds 16. We will find that it is more likely that the null hypothesis would be rejected for a given sample size if the population mean was 16.5 compared to the case where the population mean was 16.1.

Ideally, we would like to have the probabilities of both types of errors be as small as possible. However, there is a trade-off between the probabilities of the two types of errors. Given a particular sample, any reduction in the probability of Type I error, α, will result in an increase in the probability of Type II error, β, and vice versa. We need to emphasize here that there is not a direct linear substitution (e.g., a reduction of 0.02 in α does not usually result in an increase of 0.02 in β). Thus, in the above example the probability of Type I error, α, could be reduced by changing the decision rule to

$$\text{Reject } H_0 \text{ if } \quad \bar{x} > 16.23$$

But failure to reject the null hypothesis is more likely even if the null hypothesis is false. As a result, the probability of Type II error, β would be increased. In practice, we select a small (e.g., less than 0.10) probability of Type I error and that probability is used to set the decision rule. The probability of Type II error is then determined, as shown in Figure 10.1.

Suppose that a plant manager wished to test whether the true mean weight of cereal boxes is greater than 16 ounces. He would begin the analysis by first fixing the probability of Type I error. In a sense this is like deciding the rules for a baseball or soccer game before the game starts instead of making up the rules as the game is played. After analyzing the nature of the decision process, he might decide that the decision rule should have a probability of 0.05 or less of rejecting the null hypothesis when it is true. He would do this by selecting an appropriate number, K, in the decision rule: "Reject the null hypothesis if the sample mean is greater than K ounces." In the following sections we indicate the procedure to choose K. Once the number K has been chosen, the probability of Type II error can be computed—for a particular value of μ included in H_1—using the procedures to be developed in Section 10.5.

Another concept used in hypothesis testing is the **power** of the test, defined as the probability of rejecting H_0 when H_1 is true. The power is computed for particular values of μ that satisfy the null hypothesis. The power is typically different for every different value of μ. Consider the cereal problem with

$$H_0: \mu = 16$$
$$H_1: \mu > 16$$

Thus, for any value of μ contained in the null hypothesis, H_1

$$\text{Power} = P\,(\text{Reject } H_0 \mid \mu, (\mu \subset H_1))$$

Since the decision rule is determined by the significance level chosen for the test, the concept of power does not directly affect the decision to reject or fail to

Figure 10.1 Consequences of Fixing the Significance Level of a Test

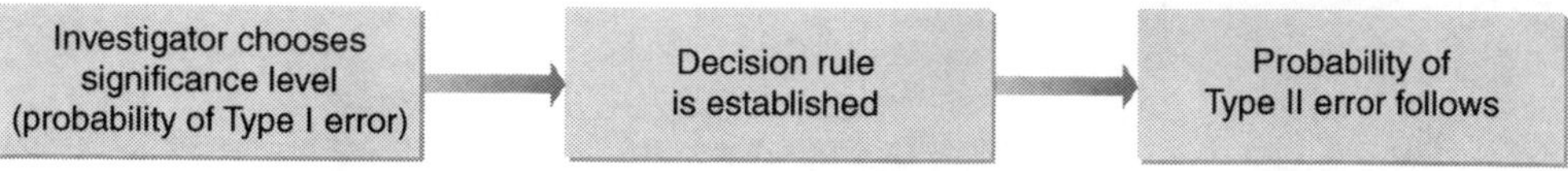

reject a null hypothesis. However, by computing the power of the test for particular significance levels and values of μ included in H_1, we will have valuable information about the properties of the decision rule. For example, we will see that, by taking a larger sample size, the power of the test will be increased for a given significance level, α. Thus, we will balance the increased costs of a larger sample size against the benefits of increasing the power of the test. Another important use of power calculations occurs when, for a given sample size, we have a choice between two or more possible tests with the same significance levels. Then it would be appropriate to choose the test that has the smallest probability of Type II error—that is, the test with the highest power.

In Sections 10.2 to 10.4, we show how, for given significance levels, decision rules can be formulated for some important classes of hypothesis-testing problems. In Section 10.5 we show how the power of a test can be computed. A summary of the important terms and ideas that have been developed thus far is given below.

Summary of Hypothesis-Testing Terminology

Null Hypothesis H_0: A maintained hypothesis that is held to be true unless sufficient evidence to the contrary is obtained.

Alternative Hypothesis H_1: A hypothesis against which the null hypothesis is tested and which will be held to be true if the null is held false.

Simple Hypothesis: A hypothesis that specifies a single value for a population parameter of interest.

Composite Hypothesis: A hypothesis that specifies a range of values for a population parameter.

One-Sided Alternative: An alternative hypothesis involving all possible values of a population parameter on either one side or the other of (that is, either greater than or less than) the value specified by a simple null hypothesis.

Two-Sided Alternative: An alternative hypothesis involving all possible values of a population parameter other than the value specified by a simple null hypothesis.

Hypothesis Test Decisions: A decision rule is formulated, leading the investigator to either reject or fail to reject the null hypothesis on the basis of sample evidence.

Type I Error: The rejection of a true null hypothesis.

Type II Error: The failure to reject a false null hypothesis.

Significance Level: The probability of rejecting a null hypothesis that is true. This probability is sometimes expressed as a percentage, so a test of significance level α is referred to as a 100α%-level test.

Power: The probability of rejecting a null hypothesis that is false.

We use the terms *reject* and *failure to reject* for possible decisions about a null hypothesis in formal summaries of the outcomes of tests. We will see that these terms do not adequately reflect the asymmetry of the status of null and alternative hypotheses or the consequences of a procedure in which the significance level is fixed and the probability of a Type II error is not controlled. The null hypothesis has the status of a maintained hypothesis—one held to be true—unless the data contain strong evidence to reject the hypothesis. By setting the significance level, α at a low level, we have a small probability of rejecting a true null hypothesis. When we reject, the probability of error is the significance level, α. But if there is only a small sample, then we will reject the null hypothesis only when it is wildly in error. As we increase the sample size, the probability of rejecting a false null hypothesis is increased. But failure to reject a null hypothesis leads to much greater uncertainty because we do not know the probability of Type II error. Thus, if we fail to reject, then either the null hypothesis is true or our procedure for detecting a false null hypothesis does not have sufficient power—for example, the sample size is too small. When we reject the null hypothesis, we have strong evidence that the null hypothesis is not true and therefore, that the alternative hypothesis is true. If we seek strong evidence in favor of a particular outcome, we define that outcome as the alternative hypothesis, H_1, and the other outcome as the null hypothesis, H_0. This is called a **counterfactual argument**. When we reject H_0, there is strong evidence in favor of H_1, and we are confident that our decision is correct. But failing to reject leads to great uncertainty. We see many applications of this idea in the following sections.

The analogy to a criminal trial is apparent. An accused defendant is presumed innocent—the null hypothesis—unless sufficient strong evidence is produced to indicate guilt beyond a reasonable doubt—rejection of the null hypothesis. The defendant may be found innocent either because he is innocent or because the evidence was not strong enough to convict. The burden of proof rests on the sample data.

EXERCISES

Basic Exercises

10.1 Mary Arnold wants to use the results of a random sample market survey to seek strong evidence that her brand of breakfast cereal has a least 20% of the total market. Formulate the null and alternative hypotheses, using P as the population proportion.

10.2 The Federal Reserve Board is meeting to decide if it should reduce interest rates in order to stimulate economic growth. State the null and alternative hypotheses regarding economic growth that the Board would formulate to guide its decision.

10.3 John Stull, senior vice president of manufacturing, is seeking strong evidence to support his hope that new operating procedures have reduced the percentage of underfilled cereal packages from the Ames production line. State his null and alternative hypotheses and indicate the results that would provide strong evidence.

Application Exercises

10.4 During 2000 and 2001 many people in Europe objected to purchasing food that was genetically modified, produced by farmers in the United States. The U.S. farmers argued that there was no scientific evidence to conclude that these products were not healthy. The Europeans argued that there still might be a problem with these foods.

a. State the null and alternative hypotheses from the perspective of the Europeans.
b. State the null and alternative hypotheses from the perspective of the U.S. farmers.

10.5 The 2000 presidential election in the United States was very close, and the decision came down to the results of the presidential voting in the state of Florida. The election was finally decided in favor of George W. Bush over Al Gore by a U.S. Supreme Court decision that stated that it was not appropriate to hand-count ballots that had been rejected by the voting machines in various counties. At that time Bush had a small lead based on the ballots that had been counted. Imagine that you were a lawyer for George W. Bush. State your null and alternative hypotheses concerning the population vote totals for each candidate. Given your hypotheses, what would you argue about the results of the proposed recount—if it had actually occurred?

10.2 Tests of the Mean of a Normal Distribution: Population Variance Known

In this and the following sections we present specific procedures for developing and implementing hypothesis tests that have applications to business and economic problems. The procedures use a random sample of n normally distributed observations x_1, $x_2, \ldots, x_n$ obtained from a population with mean μ and variance σ^2 known. We will test a hypothesis concerning the unknown population mean. Later our assumption of normality will be relaxed in many cases because of the central limit theorem.

In the discussion of hypothesis testing in Section 10.1 we noted that, if a null hypothesis is rejected using a test with significance level α, then the probability of error is known. In this case either the decision is correct or we have committed a Type I error. But if we fail to reject a null hypothesis, we do not know the probability of error. Thus, we have strong evidence to support a specific position if the null and alternative hypotheses are chosen such that rejecting the null hypothesis and accepting the alternative hypothesis lead to the support of our specific position. We demonstrate this in the following example.

Consider our previous example concerning the filling of cereal boxes. Suppose that industry regulations state that, if the population mean package weight is 16.1 ounces or less for a population of packages with label weight 16 ounces, then the manufacturer will be prosecuted. Thus, our objective is to obtain strong evidence that the mean package weight, μ, is greater than 16.1 ounces. In this case we would state our null hypothesis as

$$H_0 : \mu = \mu_0 = 16.1$$

and the alternative hypothesis would be

$$H_1 : \mu > \mu_0 = 16.1$$

By designing our testing rule with significance level α, we know that rejecting the null hypothesis provides strong evidence that the mean weight is greater than 16.1 ounces because the probability of error is a small value, α.

Our test of the population mean uses the sample mean $\bar{x}$. If the sample mean is substantially greater than $\mu_0 = 16.1$, then we reject the null hypothesis. In order to obtain the appropriate decision value we use the fact that the standardized random variable

$$Z = \frac{\overline{X} - \mu_0}{\sigma/\sqrt{n}}$$

has a standard normal distribution with mean 0 and variance 1, given that H_0 is true. If α is the probability of Type I error and Z is large such that

$$P(Z > z_\alpha) = \alpha$$

then to test the null hypothesis, we can use the decision rule

$$\text{Reject } H_0 \text{ if } \quad \frac{\bar{x} - \mu_0}{\sigma/\sqrt{n}} > z_\alpha$$

It follows that the probability of rejecting the null hypothesis, H_0, when it is true is the significance level α.

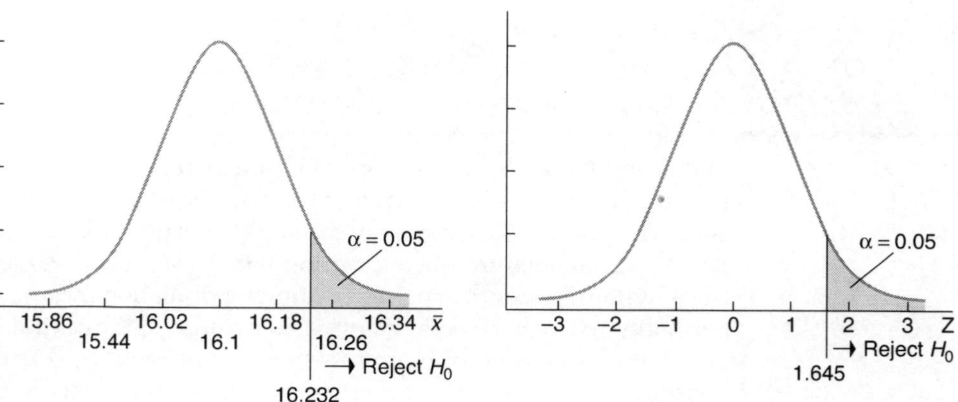

Figure 10.2 Normal Probability Density Function Showing Both Z and $\bar{X}$ Values for the Decision Rule to Test the Null Hypothesis H_0: $\mu = 16.1$ Versus H_1: $\mu > 16.1$

Note that by simple algebraic manipulation we could also state the decision rule as

$$\text{Reject } H_0 \text{ if } \quad \bar{x} > \bar{x}_c = \mu_0 + z_\alpha \sigma/\sqrt{n}$$

The value $\bar{x}_c$ is often called the **critical value** for the decision. Note that for every value z_α obtained from the standard normal distribution, there is also a value $\bar{x}_c$, and either of the above decision rules provides exactly the same result.

Suppose that for this problem the population standard deviation is $\sigma = 0.4$ and we obtain a random sample of size 25. For a one-sided hypothesis test with significance level $\alpha = 0.05$, the value of $z_\alpha = 1.645$ from the standard normal table. In this case our decision rule is

$$\text{Reject } H_0 \text{ if } \quad \frac{\bar{x} - \mu_0}{\sigma/\sqrt{n}} = \frac{\bar{x} - 16.1}{0.4/\sqrt{25}} > 1.645$$

Equivalently, the rule is

$$\text{Reject } H_0 \text{ if } \quad \bar{x} > \bar{x}_c = \mu_0 + z_\alpha \sigma/\sqrt{n} = 16.1 + 1.645 \times (0.4/\sqrt{25}) = 16.232$$

If we reject H_0 using this rule, then we accept the alternative hypothesis that the mean weight is greater than 16.1 ounces with the probability of Type I error 0.05 or less. This provides strong evidence to support our conclusion. But failure to reject the null hypothesis leads us to conclude that either H_0 is true or the selected testing procedure was not sensitive enough to reject H_0. The decision rules are illustrated in Figure 10.2. We summarize the hypothesis test for a simple null hypothesis concerning the population mean below.

A Test of the Mean of a Normal Population: Population Variance Known

A random sample of n observations was obtained from a normally distributed population with mean μ and known variance σ^2. If the observed sample mean is $\bar{x}$, then a test with significance level α of the null hypothesis

$$H_0 : \mu = \mu_0$$

against the alternative

$$H_1 : \mu > \mu_0$$

is obtained by using the decision rule

$$\text{Reject } H_0 \text{ if } \quad \frac{\bar{x} - \mu_0}{\sigma/\sqrt{n}} > z_\alpha \qquad (10.1)$$

Or, equivalently,

$$\text{Reject } H_0 \text{ if } \quad \bar{x} > \mu_0 + z_\alpha \sigma/\sqrt{n}$$

where z_α is the number for which

$$P(Z > z_\alpha) = \alpha$$

and Z is the standard normal random variable.

Let us pause to consider what is meant by the rejection of a null hypothesis. In the cereal-box problem, the hypothesis that the population mean is 16.1 would be rejected with significance level 0.05 if $\bar{x} > 16.232$. This certainly does not mean that we would have proof that the population mean weight exceeds 16.1 units. Given only sample information, we can never be certain about a population parameter. Rather, we might conclude that the data have cast doubt on the truth of the null hypothesis. If the null hypothesis were true, then we see that an observed value of the sample mean $\bar{x} = 16.3$ (e.g., 16.3 > 16.232) would represent a single unlikely observation drawn from a normal distribution with mean 16.1 and standard deviation

$$\frac{\sigma}{\sqrt{n}} = \frac{0.4}{\sqrt{25}} = 0.08$$

We are really asking how likely it would be to observe such an extreme value if the null hypothesis were, in fact, true? We saw that the probability of observing a mean value greater than 16.232 is 0.05. Hence, in rejecting the null hypothesis, either the null hypothesis is false or we have observed an unlikely event—one that would occur only with a probability of less than that specified by the significance level. This is the sense in which the sample information has aroused doubt about the null hypothesis.

p-Value

There is another popular procedure for considering the test of the null hypothesis. Notice that in our cereal problem, the null hypothesis was rejected at significance level 0.05 but would not have been rejected at the lower 0.01 level. If we used a lower significance level, we would reduce the probability of rejecting a true null hypothesis. This would modify our decision rule to make it less likely that the null hypothesis would be rejected whether or not it is true. Obviously, the lower the significance level at which we reject a null hypothesis, the greater the doubt cast on its truth. Rather than testing hypotheses at preassigned levels of significance, investigators often determine the smallest level of significance at which a null hypothesis can be rejected.

We define the p-value as the probability of obtaining a value of the test statistic as extreme as, or more extreme than, the actual value obtained when the null hypothesis is true. Thus, the p-value is the smallest significance level at which a null hypothesis can be rejected, given the observed sample statistic. For example, suppose that in the cereal-box problem with the population mean equal to 16.1, $\sigma = 0.4$, and $n = 25$ and under the null hypothesis, we had obtained a sample mean of 16.3 ounces. Then the p-value would be

$$P(\bar{x} > 16.3 \mid H_0 : \mu = 16.1) = P\left(Z > \frac{16.3 - 16.1}{0.08} = 2.5\right)$$
$$= 0.0062$$

From the normal probability table we find that the probability of obtaining a sample mean of 16.3 or greater from a normal distribution with a population mean of 16.1 and a standard deviation of the sample mean of 0.08 is equal to 0.0062. Thus, the p-value for this test is 0.0062. Now, the p-value (0.0062) represents the smallest significance level, α that would lead to rejection of the null hypothesis. When the p-value is calculated, we could test the null hypothesis by using the rule

$$\text{Reject } H_0 \text{ if } \quad p\text{-value} < \alpha$$

This rule will result in the same conclusion as obtained using Equation 10.1.

There is another, more important reason for the popularity of the p-value. The p-value provides more precise information about the strength of the rejection of the null hypothesis that results from the observed sample mean. Suppose that in the test of the cereal-box weight we had set the significance level at $\alpha = 0.05$—a popular choice. Then with a sample mean equal to 16.3 we would state that the null hypothesis was rejected at significance level 0.05. However, in fact, that sample result points to a much stronger conclusion. We could have rejected the null hypothesis at a significance level of $\alpha = 0.0063$. Alternatively, suppose that the computed p-value based on a different sample mean had been 0.07. In that case we could not reject the null hypothesis, but we would also know that we were quite close to rejecting the null hypothesis. In contrast, a p-value of 0.30 would tell us that we were quite far from rejecting the null hypothesis. The popularity of the p-value is that it provides more information than merely stating that the null hypothesis was accepted or rejected at a particular significance level. The p-value is summarized next.

Interpretation of the Probability Value or p-Value

The probability value or p-value is the smallest significance level at which the null hypothesis can be rejected. Consider a random sample of size n observations from a population that has a normal distribution with mean μ and standard deviation σ, and the resulting computed sample mean, $\bar{x}$. The null hypothesis

$$H_0 : \mu = \mu_0$$

was tested against the alternative hypothesis

$$H_1 : \mu > \mu_0$$

The p-value for the test is

$$p\text{-Value} = P\left(\frac{\bar{x} - \mu_0}{\sigma/\sqrt{n}} \geq z_p \mid H_0 : \mu = \mu_0\right) \tag{10.2}$$

where z_p is the standard normal value associated with the smallest significance level at which the null hypothesis can be rejected. The p-value is regularly computed by most statistical computer programs and provides more information about the test, based on the observed sample mean. Thus, it is a popular tool for many statistical applications.

It is important to note that the p-value is an observed random variable that will be different for each random sample obtained for a statistical test. Thus, two different analysts could obtain their own random samples and sample means from a process population, and, thus, each would compute a different p-value.

Example 10.1 Evaluating a New Production Process (Hypothesis Test)

The production manager of Northern Windows Inc. has asked you to evaluate a proposed new procedure for producing its Regal line of double-hung windows. The present process has a mean production of 80 units per hour with a population standard deviation of $\sigma = 8$. The manager indicates that she does not want to change to a new procedure unless there is strong evidence that the mean production level is higher with the new process.

Solution The manager will change to the new process only if there is strong evidence in its favor. Therefore, we will define the null hypothesis as

$$H_0 : \mu \leq 80$$

and the alternative hypothesis as

$$H_0 : \mu > 80$$

We see that, if we define the significance level $\alpha = 0.05$ and conclude that the new process has higher productivity, our probability of error is 0.05 or less. This would imply strong evidence in favor of our recommendation.

We obtain a random sample of $n = 25$ production hours using the proposed new process and compute the sample mean $\bar{x}$—often using a computer. With a significance level of $\alpha = 0.05$ the decision rule is

$$\text{Reject } H_0 \text{ if } \quad \frac{\bar{x} - 80}{8/\sqrt{25}} > 1.645$$

where $z_{0.05} = 1.645$ is obtained from the standard normal table. Alternatively, we could use the rule

$$\text{Reject } H_0 \text{ if } \quad \bar{x} > \mu_0 + z_\alpha \sigma/\sqrt{n} = 80 + 1.645 \times (8/\sqrt{25}) = 82.63$$

Suppose that the resulting sample mean was $\bar{x} = 83$. Based on that result

$$z = \frac{83 - 80}{8/\sqrt{25}} = 1.875 > 1.645$$

we would reject the null hypothesis and conclude that we have strong evidence to support the conclusion that the new process resulted in higher productivity. Given this sample mean, we could also compute the p-value as

$$p\text{-Value} = P(z_p > 1.875) = 0.03$$

Thus we could recommend the new process to the production manager.

A Test of the Mean of a Normal Distribution (Variance Known): Composite Null and Alternative Hypotheses

The appropriate procedure for testing, at significance level α, the null hypothesis

$$H_0 : \mu \leq \mu_0$$

against the alternative hypothesis

$$H_1 : \mu > \mu_0$$

is precisely the same as when the null hypothesis is H_0: $\mu = \mu_0$. In addition, the p-values are also computed in exactly the same way.

Consider our previous example concerning the filling of cereal boxes. Suppose that industry regulations state that, if the mean package weight is not 16 ounces or more for a population of packages with label weight 16 ounces, then the company will be prosecuted. In this situation we, as the regulators, could prosecute only if we found strong evidence that the mean package weight was less than 16 ounces. Thus, our objective is to prove that the mean package weight, μ, is not 16.0 ounces or more. In this case we would state the simple null hypothesis as

$$H_0 : \mu = \mu_0 = 16.0$$

or, using the composite hypothesis, as

$$H_0 : \mu \geq \mu_0 = 16.0$$

and the alternative hypothesis would be

$$H_1 : \mu < \mu_0 = 16.0$$

for either the simple or the composite hypothesis. By designing our testing rule with significance level α, we know that, if we reject the null hypothesis, then we have strong evidence that the mean weight is less than 16.0 ounces because the probability of a Type I error is a small value, α.

Our test of the population mean uses the sample mean, $\bar{x}$. If the sample mean is substantially less than $\mu_0 = 16.0$, then we reject the null hypothesis. In order to obtain the appropriate decision value, we use the fact that the standard random variable

$$Z = \frac{\bar{x} - \mu_0}{\sigma/\sqrt{n}}$$

has a standard normal distribution with mean 0 and variance 1 when the population mean is μ_0. If z has a large negative value such that

$$P(Z < -z_\alpha) = \alpha$$

then to test the null hypothesis, we can use the decision rule

$$\text{Reject } H_0 \text{ if } \quad \frac{\bar{x} - \mu_0}{\sigma/\sqrt{n}} < -z_\alpha$$

It follows that the probability of rejecting the null hypothesis, H_0, when it is true is the significance level α.

Note that by simple algebraic manipulation we could also state the decision rule as

$$\text{Reject } H_0 \text{ if } \quad \bar{x} < \bar{x}_c = \mu_0 - z_\alpha \sigma/\sqrt{n}$$

The value $\bar{x}_c$ is the "critical value" for the decision. Note that for every value $-z_\alpha$ obtained from the standard normal distribution, there is also a value $\bar{x}_c$, and either of the preceding decision rules provides exactly the same result.

Suppose that for this problem the population standard deviation is $\sigma = 0.4$ and we obtain a random sample of size 25. For a hypothesis test with significance level $\alpha = 0.05$, the value of $z_\alpha = 1.645$ from the standard normal table. In this case our decision rule is

$$\text{Reject } H_0 \text{ if } \quad \frac{\bar{x} - \mu_0}{\sigma/\sqrt{n}} = \frac{\bar{x} - 16.0}{0.4/\sqrt{25}} < -1.645$$

or we could use the decision rule

$$\text{Reject } H_0 \text{ if } \quad \bar{x} < \bar{x}_c = \mu_0 - z_\alpha \sigma / \sqrt{n} = 16.0 - 1.645 \times (0.4 / \sqrt{25}) = 15.868$$

If we reject H_0 using this rule, then we accept the alternative hypothesis that the mean weight is less than 16.0 ounces with the probability of Type I error 0.05 or less. This provides strong evidence to support our conclusion. This decision rule is illustrated in Figure 10.3.

Note that this hypothesis test is the complement of the first example. The hypothesis-testing rules for alternative hypotheses dealing with the lower tail are mirror images of those dealing with the upper tail of the distribution. Computation of p-values also follow, using the lower tail instead of the upper tail probabilities. This result is summarized in Equation 10.3.

The cereal examples presented two different objectives. In the first case we wanted strong evidence that the mean weight was greater than 16.1 ounces, and, thus, we defined the null hypothesis as

$$H_0 : \mu \le 16.1$$

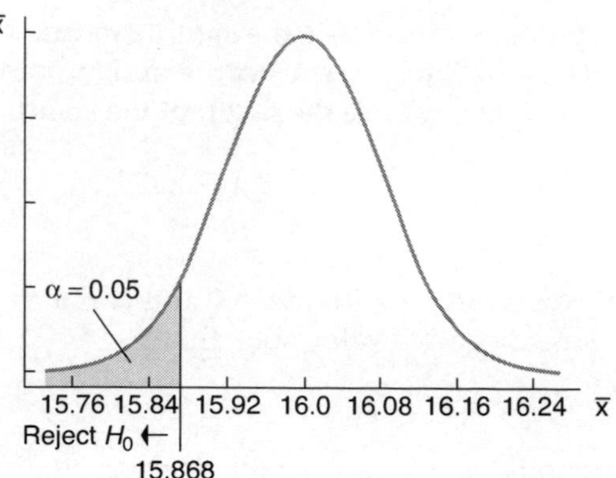

Figure 10.3 Normal Probability Density Function Showing $\bar{x}$ Values for the Decision Rule to Test the Null Hypothesis H_0: $\mu \geq 16.0$ Versus H_1: $\mu < 16.0$

In the second case we wanted strong evidence that the mean was less than 16 ounces, and, therefore, we defined the null hypothesis as

$$H_0 : \mu \geq 16$$

Possibilities of this type are present in many decision situations, and the decision maker is required to determine which option should be used in the particular problem being considered.

A Test of the Mean of a Normal Distribution (Variance Known): Composite or Simple Null and Alternative Hypotheses

The appropriate procedure for testing, at significance level α, the null hypothesis

$$H_0 : \mu = \mu_0 \quad \text{or} \quad \mu \geq \mu_0$$

against the alternative hypothesis

$$H_1 : \mu < \mu_0$$

uses the decision rule

$$\text{Reject } H_0 \text{ if} \quad Z = \frac{\bar{x} - \mu_0}{\sigma/\sqrt{n}} < -z_\alpha$$

Or, equivalently,

$$\text{Reject } H_0 \text{ if} \quad \bar{x} < \bar{x}_c = \mu_0 - z_\alpha \sigma/\sqrt{n} \tag{10.3}$$

where $-z_\alpha$ is the number for which

$$P(Z < -z_\alpha) = \alpha$$

and Z is the standard normal random variable.

In addition, the *p*-values can be computed by using the lower tail probabilities.

Example 10.2 Ball Bearing Production (Hypothesis Test)

The production manager of Twin Forks Ball Bearing Inc. has asked your assistance in evaluating a modified ball bearing production process. When the process is operating properly, the process produces ball bearings whose weights are normally distributed with a population mean of 5 ounces and a population standard deviation of 0.1 ounce. A new raw material supplier was used for a recent production run, and the manager wants to know if that change has resulted in a lowering of the mean weight of the ball bearings. There is no reason to suspect a problem with the new supplier, and the manager will continue to use the new supplier unless there is strong evidence that underweight ball bearings are being produced.

Solution In this case we are interested in knowing if there is strong evidence to conclude that lower-weight bearings are being produced. Therefore, we will test the null hypothesis

$$H_0 : \mu = \mu_0 = 5$$

against the alternative hypothesis

$$H_1 : \mu < 5$$

Note how the notion of strong evidence leads us to choose the null and alternative hypotheses. We take action only if the null hypothesis is rejected and the alternative accepted. The significance level is specified as $\alpha = 0.05$, and, thus, the corresponding lower-tail value for the standard normal random variable is $z_\alpha = -1.645$ from the normal distribution table. For this problem we obtained a random sample of $n = 16$ observations and the sample mean was 4.962. Our decision rule for this problem is

$$\text{Reject } H_0 \text{ if} \quad \frac{\bar{x} - \mu_0}{\sigma/\sqrt{n}} < -1.645$$

or

$$\text{Reject } H_0 \text{ if} \quad \bar{x} < 4.962$$
$$4.962 < 4.959$$

We see that we cannot reject the null hypothesis, H_0, since $\dfrac{4.962 - 5.0}{0.1/\sqrt{16}} = -1.52$ and $5 - 1.645\left(\dfrac{0.1}{\sqrt{16}}\right) = 4.959$ and, thus, we conclude that we do not have strong evidence that the production process is producing underweight ball bearings.

We could also compute the p-value for this sample result by noting that for the standard normal distribution

$$p\text{-Value} = P(z_p < -1.52) = 0.0643$$

Two-Sided Alternative Hypothesis

There are some problems where deviations either too high or too low are of equal importance. For example, the diameter of an automobile engine piston cannot be too large or too small. In those situations we consider the test of the null hypothesis

$$H_0 : \mu = \mu_0$$

against the alternative hypothesis

$$H_1 : \mu \neq \mu_0$$

Here, we have no strong reason for suspecting departures either above or below the hypothesized population mean, μ_0. The null hypothesis would be doubted if the sample mean was much greater or much smaller than μ_0. Again, if the random variable has a normal distribution with known variance σ, we obtain a test with significance level α by using the result that under the null hypothesis

$$P(Z > z_{\alpha/2}) = \frac{\alpha}{2} \quad \text{and} \quad P(Z < -z_{\alpha/2}) = \frac{\alpha}{2}$$

In this case we have divided the significance level α equally between the two tails of the normal distribution. Hence, the probability that Z either exceeds $z_{\alpha/2}$ or is less than $-z_{\alpha/2}$ is α. The decision rule for a test with significance level α is

$$\text{Reject } H_0 \text{ if } \quad \frac{\bar{x} - \mu_0}{\sigma/\sqrt{n}}$$

is either greater than $z_{\alpha/2}$ or less than $-z_{\alpha/2}$. These results are summarized in Equation 10.4.

A Test of the Mean of a Normal Distribution Against Two-Sided Alternative (Variance Known)

The appropriate procedure for testing, at significance level α, the null hypothesis

$$H_0 : \mu = \mu_0$$

against the alternative hypothesis

$$H_1 : \mu \neq \mu_0$$

is obtained from the decision rule

$$\text{Reject } H_0 \text{ if } \frac{\bar{x} - \mu_0}{\sigma/\sqrt{n}} < -z_{\alpha/2} \quad \text{or} \quad \text{Reject } H_0 \text{ if } \frac{\bar{x} - \mu_0}{\sigma/\sqrt{n}} > z_{\alpha/2} \tag{10.4}$$

Or, equivalently,

$$\text{Reject } H_0 \text{ if } \bar{x} < \mu_0 - z_{\alpha/2}\sigma/\sqrt{n} \quad \text{or} \quad \text{Reject } H_0 \text{ if } \bar{x} > \mu_0 - z_{\alpha/2}\sigma/\sqrt{n}$$

In addition, the *p*-values can be computed by noting that the corresponding tail probability would be doubled to reflect a *p*-value that refers to the sum of the upper and lower tail probabilities for the positive and negative values of *Z*. The *p*-value for the two-tailed test is

$$p\text{-Value} = 2P\left(\left|\frac{\bar{x} - \mu_0}{\sigma/\sqrt{n}}\right| > z_{p/2} \mid H_0 : \mu = \mu_0\right) \tag{10.5}$$

where $z_{p/2}$ is the standard normal value associated with the smallest probability of rejecting the null hypothesis at either tail of the probability distribution.

Example 10.3 Analysis of Drill Hole Diameters (Hypothesis Test)

The production manager of Circuits Unlimited has asked for your assistance in analyzing a production process. This process involves drilling holes whose diameters are normally distributed with population mean 2 inches and population standard deviation 0.06 inch. A random sample of nine measurements had a sample mean of 1.95 inches. Use a significance level of $\alpha = 0.05$ to determine if the observed sample mean is unusual and suggests that the drilling machine should be adjusted.

Solution In this case the diameter could be either too large or too small. Therefore, we perform a two-tailed hypothesis test with the null hypothesis

$$H_0 : \mu = 2.0$$

and the alternative hypothesis

$$H_1 : \mu \neq 2.0$$

The decision rule is to reject H_0 in favor of H_1 if

$$\frac{x - \mu_0}{\sigma/\sqrt{n}} < -z_{\alpha/2} \quad \text{or} \quad \frac{\bar{x} - \mu_0}{\sigma/\sqrt{n}} > z_{\alpha/2}$$

and for this problem

$$\frac{\bar{x} - \mu_0}{\sigma/\sqrt{n}} = \frac{1.95 - 2.0}{0.06/\sqrt{9}} = -2.50$$

for a 5%-level test $\alpha = 0.05$ and $z_{\alpha/2} = z_{0.05/2} = 1.96$. Thus, since –2.50 is less than –1.96, we reject the null hypothesis and conclude that the drilling machine requires adjustment.

To compute the p-value, we first find that the probability of obtaining Z less than –2.50 from the normal table is 0.0062. Here, we want the p-value for a two-tailed test, and we must double the one-tail value. Thus, the p-value for this test is 0.0124, and the null hypothesis would have been rejected for a significance level above 1.24%.

We have summarized the various hypothesis-testing alternatives discussed in this section in Figure 10.10, located in the chapter summary.

Exercises

Basic Exercises

10.6 A random sample is obtained from a population with variance $\sigma^2 = 625$, and the sample mean is computed. Test the null hypothesis $H_0 : \mu = 100$ versus the alternative hypothesis $H_1 : \mu \geq 100$ with $\alpha = 0.05$. Compute the critical value $\bar{x}_c$ and state your decision rule for the following options.

a. Sample size $n = 25$
b. Sample size $n = 16$
c. Sample size $n = 44$
d. Sample size $n = 32$

10.7 A random sample of size $n = 25$ is obtained from a population with variance σ^2, and the sample mean is computed. Test the null hypothesis $H_0 : \mu = 100$

versus the alternative hypothesis $H_1 : \mu \geq 100$ with $\alpha = 0.05$. Compute the critical value $\bar{x}_c$ and state your decision rule for the following options.

a. The population variance is $\sigma^2 = 225$.
b. The population variance is $\sigma^2 = 900$.
c. The population variance is $\sigma^2 = 400$.
d. The population variance is $\sigma^2 = 600$.

10.8 Using the results from the above two exercises, indicate how the critical value $\bar{x}_c$ is influenced by the sample size. Next, indicate how the critical value is influenced by the population variance, σ^2.

10.9 A random sample is obtained from a population with variance $\sigma^2 = 400$, and the sample mean is computed to be $\bar{x}_c = 70$. Consider the null hypothesis $H_0 : \mu = 80$ versus the alternative hypothesis $H_1 : \mu \leq 80$. Compute the p-value for the following options.

a. Sample size $n = 25$
b. Sample size $n = 16$
c. Sample size $n = 44$
d. Sample size $n = 32$

10.10 A random sample of size $n = 25$ is obtained from a population with variance σ^2, and the sample mean is computed to be $\bar{x} = 70$. Consider the null hypothesis $H_0 : \mu = 80$ versus the alternative hypothesis $H_1 : \mu \leq 80$. Compute the p-value for the following options.

a. The population variance is $\sigma^2 = 225$.
b. The population variance is $\sigma^2 = 900$.
c. The population variance is $\sigma^2 = 400$.
d. The population variance is $\sigma^2 = 600$.

Application Exercises

10.11 A manufacturer of detergent claims that the contents of boxes sold weigh on average at least 16 ounces. The distribution of weight is known to be normal, with standard deviation 0.4 ounce. A random sample of 16 boxes yielded a sample mean weight of 15.84 ounces. Test at the 10% significance level the null hypothesis that the population mean weight is at least 16 ounces.

10.12 A company that receives shipments of batteries tests a random sample of nine of them before agreeing to take a shipment. The company is concerned that the true mean lifetime for all batteries in the shipment should be at least 50 hours. From past experience it is safe to conclude that the population distribution of lifetimes is normal with standard deviation 3 hours. For one particular shipment the mean lifetime for a sample of nine batteries was 48.2 hours. Test at the 10% level the null hypothesis that the population mean lifetime is at least 50 hours.

10.13 A pharmaceutical manufacturer is concerned that the impurity concentration in pills should not exceed 3%. It is known that from a particular production run impurity concentrations follow a normal distribution with standard deviation 0.4%. A random sample of 64 pills from a production run was checked, and the sample mean impurity concentration was found to be 3.07%.

a. Test at the 5% level the null hypothesis that the population mean impurity concentration is 3% against the alternative that it is more than 3%.
b. Find the p-value for this test.
c. Suppose that the alternative hypothesis had been two-sided rather than one-sided (with null hypothesis H_0: $\mu = 3$). State, without doing the calculations, whether the p-value of the test would be higher than, lower than, or the same as that found in part (b). Sketch a graph to illustrate your reasoning.
d. In the context of this problem, explain why a one-sided alternative hypothesis is more appropriate than a two-sided alternative.

10.3 Tests of the Mean of a Normal Distribution: Population Variance Unknown

In this section we consider the same set of hypothesis tests discussed in Section 10.2. The only difference is that the population variance is unknown, and, thus, we must use tests based on the Student's t distribution. We introduced the Student's t distribution in Section 8.3 and showed its application for developing confidence intervals. Recall that the Student's t distribution depends on the degrees of freedom for computing the sample variance, $n - 1$. In addition, the Student's t distribution becomes close to the normal distribution as the sample size increases. Thus, for sample sizes over 100 the normal probability distribution can be used to approximate the Student's t distribution. Using the sample mean and variance, we know that the random variable

$$t_{n-1} = \frac{\bar{x} - \mu}{s/\sqrt{n}}$$

follows a Student's t distribution. The procedures for performing hypothesis tests using the sample variance are defined in Equations 10.6, 10.7, and 10.8.

Tests of the Mean of a Normal Distribution: Population Variance Unknown

We are given a random sample of n observations from a normal population with mean μ. Using the sample mean and sample standard deviation, $\bar{x}$ and s, respectively, we can use the following tests with significance level α.

1. To test either null hypothesis

$$H_0 : \mu = \mu_0 \quad \text{or} \quad H_0 : \mu \leq \mu_0$$

against the alternative

$$H_1 : \mu > \mu_0$$

the decision rule is

$$\text{Reject } H_0 \text{ if} \quad t = \frac{\bar{x} - \mu_0}{s/\sqrt{n}} > t_{n-1,\alpha}$$

Or, equivalently,

$$\text{Reject } H_0 \text{ if} \quad \bar{x} > \bar{x}_c = \mu_0 + t_{n-1,\alpha}\, s/\sqrt{n} \tag{10.6}$$

2. To test either null hypothesis

$$H_0 : \mu = \mu_0 \quad \text{or} \quad H_0 : \mu \geq \mu_0$$

against the alternative

$$H_1 : \mu < \mu_0$$

the decision rule is

$$\text{Reject } H_0 \text{ if} \quad \frac{\bar{x} - \mu_0}{s/\sqrt{n}} < -t_{n-1,\alpha} \tag{10.7}$$

Or, equivalently,

$$\text{Reject } H_0 \text{ if} \quad \bar{x} < \bar{x}_c = \mu_0 - t_{n-1,\alpha}\, s/\sqrt{n}$$

3. To test the null hypothesis

$$H_0 : \mu = \mu_0$$

against the alternative hypothesis

$$H_1 : \mu \neq \mu_0$$

the decision rule is

$$\text{Reject } H_0 \text{ if} \quad \frac{\bar{x} - \mu_0}{s/\sqrt{n}} < -t_{n-1,\alpha/2} \quad \text{or} \quad \text{Reject } H_0 \text{ if} \quad \frac{\bar{x} - \mu_0}{s/\sqrt{n}} > t_{n-1,\alpha/2} \tag{10.8}$$

Or, equivalently,

Reject H_0 if $\bar{x} < \mu_0 - t_{n-1,\alpha/2} s/\sqrt{n}$ or Reject H_0 if $\bar{x} > \mu_0 + t_{n-1,\alpha/2} s/\sqrt{n}$

where $t_{n-1,\alpha/2}$ is the Student's t value for $n-1$ degrees of freedom and tail probability $\alpha/2$.

The *p*-values for these tests are computed in the same way as we did for tests with known variance except that the Student's *t* value is substituted for the normal *Z* value. To obtain the *p*-value we often need to interpolate in the *t* table or use a computer package such as Minitab.

Example 10.4 Analysis of Weekly Sales of Frozen Broccoli (Hypothesis Test)

Broccoli

Grand Junction Vegetables is a producer of a wide variety of frozen vegetables. The company president has asked you to determine if the weekly sales of 16-ounce packages of frozen broccoli has increased. The weekly sales per store has had a mean of 2,400 packages over the past 6 months. You have obtained a random sample of sales data from 134 stores for your study. The data is stored in the file **Broccoli**.

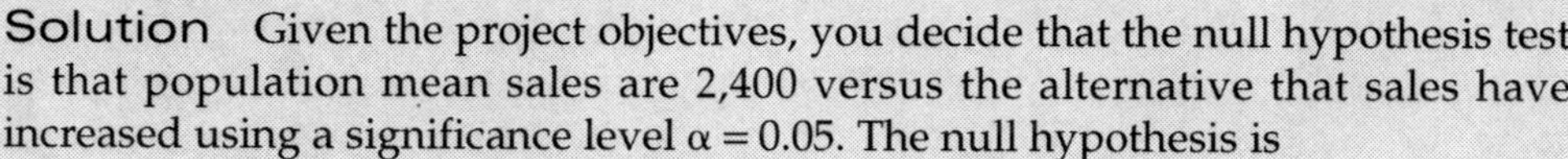

Solution Given the project objectives, you decide that the null hypothesis test is that population mean sales are 2,400 versus the alternative that sales have increased using a significance level $\alpha = 0.05$. The null hypothesis is

$$H_0 : \mu = 2{,}400$$

versus the alternative hypothesis

$$H_1 : \mu > 2{,}400$$

Figure 10.4 shows the Minitab output containing the sample mean and variance. From the Minitab output we see that the sample mean is much larger than the median and that the upper quartile has a very wide range. Thus, it is clear that the distribution of the individual observations is not a normal distribution. But the sample size is large, and, thus, by applying the central limit theorem from Chapter 7, we can assume that the sampling distribution for the sample mean is normal; therefore, a Student's t test would be appropriate for the hypothesis test. We see that the sample mean is 3,593 and the sample standard deviation is 4,919. The *test statistic* is

$$t = \frac{3{,}593 - 2{,}400}{4{,}919/\sqrt{134}} = 2.81$$

Figure 10.4 Descriptive Statistics for Broccoli Sales (Minitab Output)

Descriptive Statistics: Broccoli

Variable	N	N*	Mean	SE Mean	StDev	Minimum	Q1	Median	Q3	Maximum
Broccoli	134	0	3593	425	4919	156	707	2181	2300	27254

The value of t for $n - 1 = 133$ degrees of freedom and $\alpha = 0.05$ for the upper tail is approximately 1.645. Based on this result, we reject the null hypothesis and conclude that mean sales have increased.

The tests presented in this section are summarized in Figure 10.10, located in the chapter summary.

EXERCISES

Basic Exercises

10.14 Test the hypotheses

$$H_0: \mu \leq 100$$
$$H_1: \mu > 100$$

using a random sample of size $n = 25$, a probability of Type I error equal to 0.05, and the following sample statistics.

a. $\bar{x} = 106; s = 15$
b. $\bar{x} = 104; s = 10$
c. $\bar{x} = 95; \ s = 10$
d. $\bar{x} = 92; \ s = 18$

10.15 Test the hypotheses

$$H_0: \mu = 100$$
$$H_1: \mu < 100$$

using a random sample of size $n = 36$, a probability of Type I error equal to 0.05, and the following sample statistics.

a. $\bar{x} = 106; s = 15$
b. $\bar{x} = 104; s = 10$
c. $\bar{x} = 95; \ s = 10$
d. $\bar{x} = 92; \ s = 18$

Application Exercises

10.16 An engineering research center claims that, through the use of a new computer control system, automobiles should achieve, on average, an additional 3 miles per gallon of gas. A random sample of 100 automobiles was used to evaluate this product. The sample mean increase in miles per gallon achieved was 2.4, and the sample standard deviation was 1.8 miles per gallon. Test the hypothesis that the population mean is at least 3 miles per gallon. Find the p-value of this test, and interpret your findings.

10.17 A random sample of 1,562 undergraduates enrolled in management ethics courses was asked to respond on a scale from 1 (strongly disagree) to 7 (strongly agree) to this proposition: "Senior corporate executives are interested in social justice." The sample mean response was 4.27, and the sample standard deviation was 1.32. Test at the 1% level, against a two-sided alternative, the null hypothesis that the population mean is 4.

10.18 You have been asked to evaluate single employer plans after the establishment of the Health Benefit Guarantee Corporation. A random sample of 76 percentage changes in promised health benefits was observed. The sample mean percentage change was 0.078, and the sample standard deviation was 0.201. Find and interpret the p-value of a test of the null hypothesis that the population mean percentage change is 0 against a two-sided alternative.

10.19 A random sample of 172 marketing students was asked to rate on a scale from 1 (not important) to 5 (extremely important) health benefits as a job characteristic. The sample mean rating was 3.31, and the sample standard deviation was 0.70. Test at the 1% significance level the null hypothesis that the population mean rating is at most 3.0 against the alternative that it is bigger than 3.0.

10.20 A random sample of 170 people was provided with a forecasting problem. Each sample member was given, in two ways, the task of forecasting the next value of a retail sales variable. The previous 20 values were presented both as numbers and as points on a graph. Subjects were asked to predict the next value. The absolute forecasting errors were measured. The sample then consisted of 170 differences in absolute forecast errors (numerical minus graphical). The sample mean of these differences was −2.91, and the sample standard deviation was 11.33. Find and interpret the p-value of a test of the null hypothesis that the population mean difference is 0 against the alternative that it is negative. (The alternative can be viewed as the hypothesis that, in the aggregate, people are more successful at graphical than numerical prediction.)

10.21 The accounts of a corporation show that, on average, accounts payable are \$125.32. An auditor checked a random sample of 16 of these accounts. The sample mean was \$131.78, and the sample standard deviation was \$25.41. Assume that the population distribution is normal. Test at the 5% significance level against a two-sided alternative the null hypothesis that the population mean is \$125.32.

10.22 On the basis of a random sample the null hypothesis

$$H_0 : \mu = \mu_0$$

is tested against the alternative

$$H_1 : \mu > \mu_0$$

and the null hypothesis is not rejected at the 5% significance level.

a. Does this necessarily imply that μ_0 is contained in the 95% confidence interval for μ?
b. Does this necessarily imply that μ_0 is contained in the 90% confidence interval for μ if the observed sample mean is larger than μ_0?

10.23 A company selling licenses for new e-commerce computer software advertises that firms using this software obtain, on average during the first year, a yield of 10% on their initial investments. A random sample of 10 of these franchises produced the following yields for the first year of operation:

6.1 9.2 11.5 8.6 12.1 3.9 8.4 10.1 9.4 8.9

Assuming that population yields are normally distributed, test the company's claim.

10.24 A process that produces bottles of shampoo, when operating correctly, produces bottles whose contents weigh, on average, 20 ounces. A random sample of nine bottles from a single production run yielded the following content weights (in ounces):

21.4 19.7 19.7 20.6 20.8 20.1 19.7 20.3 20.9

Assuming that the population distribution is normal, test at the 5% level against a two-sided alternative the null hypothesis that the process is operating correctly.

10.25 A statistics instructor is interested in the ability of students to assess the difficulty of a test they have taken. This test was taken by a large group of students, and the average score was 78.5. A random sample of eight students was asked to predict this average score. Their predictions were

72 83 78 65 69 77 81 71

Assuming a normal distribution, test the null hypothesis that the population mean prediction would be 78.5. Use a two-sided alternative and a 10% significance level.

10.26 A beer distributor claims that a new display, featuring a life-size picture of a well-known rock singer, will increase product sales in supermarkets by an average of 50 cases in a week. For a random sample of 20 high-volume liquor outlets, the average sales increase was 41.3 cases, and the sample standard deviation was 12.2 cases. Test at the 5% level the null hypothesis that the population mean sales increase is at least 50 cases, stating any assumptions you make.

10.27 In contract negotiations a company claims that a new incentive scheme has resulted in average weekly earnings of at least $400 for all customer service workers. A union representative takes a random sample of 15 workers and finds that their weekly earnings have an average of $381.35 and a standard deviation of $48.60. Assume a normal distribution.

a. Test the company's claim.
b. If the same sample results had been obtained from a random sample of 50 employees, could the company's claim be rejected at a lower significance level than that used in part (a)?

10.4 Tests of the Population Proportion (Large Samples)

Another important set of business and economics problems involves population proportions. Business executives are interested in the percent market share for their products, and government officials are interested in the percentage of people that support a proposed new program. Thus, inference about the population proportion based on sample proportions is an important application of hypothesis testing.

From our work in Chapters 6 and 7 we know that the distribution of the sample proportion can be approximated quite accurately by using the normal distribution. In this approximation we denote P as the population proportion and $\hat{p}$ as the sample proportion. Thus, the sample proportion $\hat{p}$ estimated from a random sample of size n has an approximate normal distribution with mean P and variance $P(1-P)/n$. Then the standard normal statistic is

$$Z = \frac{\hat{p} - P}{\sqrt{P(1 - P)/n}}$$

If the null hypothesis is that the population proportion is

$$H_0 : P = P_0$$

it follows that, when this hypothesis is true, the random variable

$$Z = \frac{\hat{p} - P_0}{\sqrt{P_0(1 - P_0)/n}}$$

approximately follows a standard normal distribution. Using that result, we can define the tests.

Tests of the Population Proportion (Large Sample Sizes)

We begin by assuming a random sample of n observations from a population that has a proportion P whose members possess a particular attribute. If $P(1 - P) > 9$ and the sample proportion is $\hat{p}$, the following tests have significance level α:

1. To test either the hypothesis

   $$H_0 : P = P_0 \quad \text{or} \quad H_0 : P \leq P_0$$

   against the alternative

   $$H_1 : P > P_0$$

   the decision rule is

   $$\text{Reject } H_0 \text{ if } \quad \frac{\hat{p} - P_0}{\sqrt{P_0(1 - P_0)/n}} > z_\alpha \qquad (10.9)$$

2. To test either null hypothesis

   $$H_0 : P = P_0 \quad \text{or} \quad H_0 : P \geq P_0$$

   against the alternative

   $$H_1 : P < P_0$$

   the decision rule is

   $$\text{Reject } H_0 \text{ if } \quad \frac{\hat{p} - P_0}{\sqrt{P_0(1 - P_0)/n}} < -z_\alpha \qquad (10.10)$$

3. To test the null hypothesis

   $$H_0 : P = P_0$$

   against the two-sided alternative

   $$H_1 : P \neq P_0$$

   the decision rule is

   $$\text{Reject } H_0 \text{ if } \quad \frac{\hat{p} - P_0}{\sqrt{P_0(1 - P_0)/n}} > z_{\alpha/2} \quad \text{or} \quad \frac{\hat{p} - P_0}{\sqrt{P_0(1 - P_0)/n}} < -z_{\alpha/2} \qquad (10.11)$$

For all of these tests the p-value is the smallest significance level at which the null hypothesis can be rejected.

The tests presented here are summarized in Figure 10.11, located in the chapter summary.

Example 10.5 Supermarket Shoppers' Price Knowledge (Hypothesis Test Using Proportions)

Market Research Inc. wants to know if shoppers are sensitive to the prices of items sold in a supermarket. It obtained a random sample of 802 shoppers and found that 378 supermarket shoppers were able to state the correct price of an item immediately after putting it into their cart. Test at the 7% level the null hypothesis that at least one-half of all shoppers are able to state the correct price.

Solution We will let P denote the population proportion of supermarket shoppers able to state the correct price in these circumstances. Test the null hypothesis

$$H_0 : P \geq P_0 = 0.50$$

against the alternative

$$H_1 : P < 0.50$$

The decision rule is to reject the null hypothesis in favor of the alternative if

$$\frac{\hat{p} - P_0}{\sqrt{P_0(1 - P_0)/n}} < -z_\alpha$$

For this example $n = 802$ and $\hat{p} = 378/802 = 0.471$. For a 7% level test, $\alpha = 0.07$ and $z_\alpha = -1.474$ from the normal distribution table.

The test statistic is

$$\frac{\hat{p} - P_0}{\sqrt{P_0(1 - P_0)/n}} = \frac{0.471 - 0.50}{\sqrt{0.50(1 - 0.50)/802}} = -1.64$$

Since -1.64 is less than -1.474, we reject the null hypothesis and conclude that less than one-half of the shoppers can correctly state the price immediately after putting an item into their supermarket cart. Using the calculated test statistic value of -1.64, we also find that the p-value for the test is 0.051.

EXERCISES

Basic Exercises

10.28 A random sample of women is obtained, and each person in the sample is asked if she would purchase a new shoe model. To determine if the new shoe model would have sales at least 25% to meet corporate profit objectives, the following hypothesis test is performed at a level $\alpha = 0.03$ using the sample proportion of women who said yes $\hat{p}$.

$$H_0: P \leq 0.25$$
$$H_1: P > 0.25$$

What value of the sample proportion, $\hat{p}$, is required to reject the null hypothesis, given the following sample sizes?

a. $n = 400$
b. $n = 225$
c. $n = 625$
d. $n = 900$

10.29 A company is attempting to determine if it should retain a previously popular shoe model. A random sample of women is obtained, and each person in the sample is asked if she would purchase this existing shoe model. To determine if the old shoe model should be retained, the following hypothesis test is performed at a level $\alpha = 0.05$ using the sample proportion of women who said yes $\hat{p}$.

$$H_0: P \geq 0.25$$
$$H_1: P < 0.25$$

What value of the sample proportion, $\hat{p}$, is required to reject the null hypothesis, given the following sample sizes?

a. $n = 400$
b. $n = 225$
c. $n = 625$
d. $n = 900$

Application Exercises

10.30 In a random sample of 361 owners of small businesses that had gone into bankruptcy, 105 reported conducting no marketing studies prior to opening the business. Test the hypothesis that at most 25% of all members of this population conducted no marketing studies before opening the business. Use $\alpha = 0.05$.

10.31 In a random sample of 998 adults in the United States, 17.3% of the sample members indicated some measure of disagreement with this statement: "Globalization is more than an economic trade system—instead it includes institutions and culture." Test at the 5% level the hypothesis that at least 25% of all U.S. adults would disagree with this statement.

10.32 In a random sample of 160 business school students, 72 sample members indicated some measure of agreement with this statement: "Scores on a standardized entrance exam are less important for a student's chance to succeed academically than is the student's high school GPA." Test the null hypothesis that one-half of all business school graduates would agree with this statement against a two-sided alternative. Find and interpret the p-value of the test.

10.33 Of a random sample of 199 auditors, 104 indicated some measure of agreement with this statement: "Cash flow is an important indication of profitability." Test at the 10% significance level against a two-sided alternative the null hypothesis that one-half of the members of this population would agree with this statement. Also find and interpret the p-value of this test.

10.34 A random sample of 50 university admissions officers was asked about expectations in application interviews. Of these sample members, 28 agreed that the interviewer usually expects the interviewee to have volunteer experience doing community projects. Test the null hypothesis that one-half of all interviewers have this expectation against the alternative that the population proportion is bigger than one-half. Use $\alpha = 0.05$.

10.35 Of a random sample of 172 elementary school educators, 118 said that parental support was the most important source of a child's success. Test the hypothesis that parental support is the most important source of a child's success for at least 75% of elementary school educators against the alternative that the population percentage is less than 75%. Use $\alpha = 0.05$.

10.36 A random sample of 202 business faculty members was asked if there should be a required foreign language course for business majors. Of these sample members, 140 felt there was a need for a foreign language course. Test the hypothesis that at least 75% of all business faculty members hold this view. Use $\alpha = 0.05$.

10.5 Assessing the Power of a Test

In Sections 10.2 to 10.4 we have developed various hypothesis tests with significance level α. In all of these tests we developed decision rules for rejecting the null hypothesis in favor of an alternative hypothesis. In carrying out these various tests we know that the probability of committing a Type I error when we reject the null hypothesis is a small value α or less. In addition, we may also compute the p-value for the test, and, thus, we know the smallest significance level at which the null hypothesis can be rejected. When we reject the null hypothesis, we conclude that there is strong evidence to support our conclusion. But if we fail to reject the null hypothesis, we know that either the null hypothesis is true or we have committed a Type II error by failing to reject the null hypothesis when the alternative is true.

In this section we consider the characteristics of some of our tests when the null hypothesis is not true. We learn how to compute the probability of Type II error and also how to determine the power of the hypothesis test. Of course, a Type II error can occur only if the alternative hypothesis is true. Thus, we will consider Type II error and power for specific values of the population parameter that are included in the alternative hypothesis.

Tests of the Mean of a Normal Distribution: Population Variance Known

Following the procedures of Section 10.2, we want to test the null hypothesis that the mean of a normal population is equal to a specific value, μ_0.

Determining the Probability of Type II Error

Consider the test

$$H_0 : \mu = \mu_0$$

against the alternative

$$H_1 : \mu > \mu_0$$

Using the decision rule

$$\text{Reject } H_0 \text{ if } \quad \frac{\bar{x} - \mu_0}{\sigma / \sqrt{n}} > z_\alpha \quad \text{or} \quad \bar{x} > \bar{x}_c = \mu_0 + z_\alpha \sigma / \sqrt{n}$$

determine the values of the sample mean that result in failing to reject the null hypothesis. Now, for any value of the population mean defined by the alternative hypothesis, H_1, find the probability that the sample mean will be in the nonrejection region for the null hypothesis. This is the probability of Type II error. Thus, we consider a $\mu = \mu^*$ such that $\mu^* > \mu_0$. Then for μ^* the probability of Type II error is

$$\beta = P(\bar{x} < \bar{x}_c \mid \mu = \mu^*) = P\left(z < \frac{\bar{x}_c - \mu^*}{\sigma / \sqrt{n}}\right) \tag{10.12}$$

and

$$\text{Power} = 1 - \beta$$

The value of β and the power will be different for every μ^*.

Consider an example where we are testing the null hypothesis that the population mean weight of ball bearings from a production process is 5 ounces versus the alternative hypothesis that the population mean weight is greater than 5 ounces. We conduct the test with a random sample of 16 observations and a significance level of 0.05. The population distribution is assumed to be a normal distribution with a standard deviation of 0.1 ounce. Thus, the null hypothesis is

$$H_0 : \mu = 5$$

versus the alternative hypothesis

$$H_1 : \mu > 5$$

and the decision rule is

$$\text{Reject } H_0 \text{ if } \quad \frac{\bar{x} - 5}{0.1 / \sqrt{16}} > 1.645 \quad \text{or} \quad \bar{x} > 5 + 1.645(0.1 / \sqrt{16}) = 5.041$$

Now, if the sample mean is less than or equal to 5.041, then, using our rule, we will fail to reject the null hypothesis.

Suppose that we want to determine the probability that the null hypothesis will not be rejected if the true mean weight is 5.05 ounces. Clearly, the alternative hypothesis is correct, and we want to determine the probability that we will fail to reject the null hypothesis and thus have a Type II error. That is, we want to determine the probability that the sample mean is less than 5.041 if the population mean is actually 5.05. Using the 16 observations we compute the probability of Type II error as

$$\beta = P(\overline{X} \leq 5.041 \mid \mu = 5.05) = P\left(Z \leq \frac{5.041 - 5.05}{0.1/\sqrt{16}}\right)$$
$$= P(Z \leq -0.36)$$
$$= 1 - 0.6406 = 0.3594$$

Thus, using the preceding decision rule, we can show that the probability, β, of Type II error when the population mean is 5.05 ounces is 0.3594. Since the power of a test is 1 minus the probability of Type II error we have when the population mean is 5.05,

$$\text{Power} = 1 - \beta = 1 - 0.3594 = 0.6406$$

These power calculations are shown in Figure 10.5. In part (a), we see that, when the population mean is 5, the probability that the sample mean exceeds 5.041 is 0.05, the significance level of the test. Part (b) of the figure shows the density function of the sampling distribution of the sample mean when the population mean is 5.05. The shaded area in this figure shows the probability that the sample mean exceeds 5.041 when the population mean is 5.05—the power of the test. Similar calculations could be made to determine the power and probability of a Type II error for any value of μ greater than 5.0.

By computing the power of a test for all values of μ included in the null hypothesis, the power function can be generated, as shown in Figure 10.6. The power function has the following features:

1. The farther the true mean is from the hypothesized mean μ_0, the greater is the power of the test, everything else being equal. Figure 10.6 illustrates this result.
2. The smaller the significance level (α) of the test, the smaller the power, everything else being equal. Thus, reducing the probability of Type I error (α) increases the probability of Type II error (β), but reducing α by 0.01 does not generally increase β by 0.01—the changes are not linear.
3. The larger the population variance, the lower the power of the test, everything else being equal.
4. The larger the sample size, the greater the power of the test, everything else being equal. Note that larger sample sizes reduce the variance of the sample mean and thus provide a greater chance that we will reject H_0 when it is not

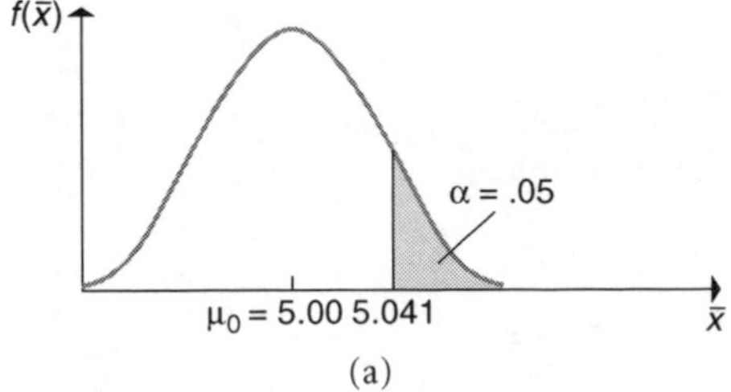

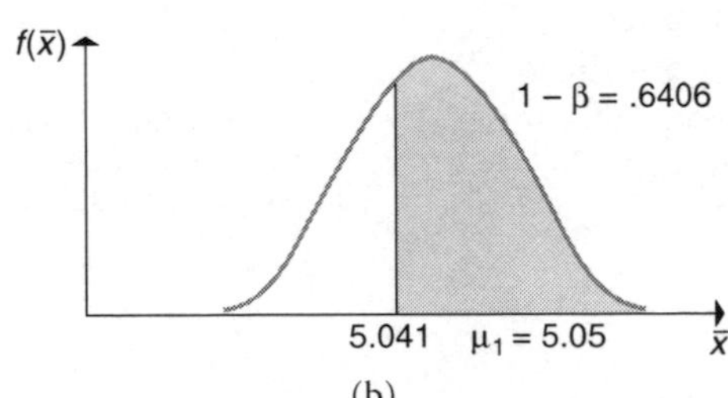

Figure 10.5 Sampling Distribution of Sample Mean for 16 Observations with $\sigma = 0.1$

Figure 10.6 Power Function for Test H_0: $\mu = 5$ Against H_1: $\mu > 5$ ($\alpha = 0.05$, $\sigma = 0.1$, $n = 16$)

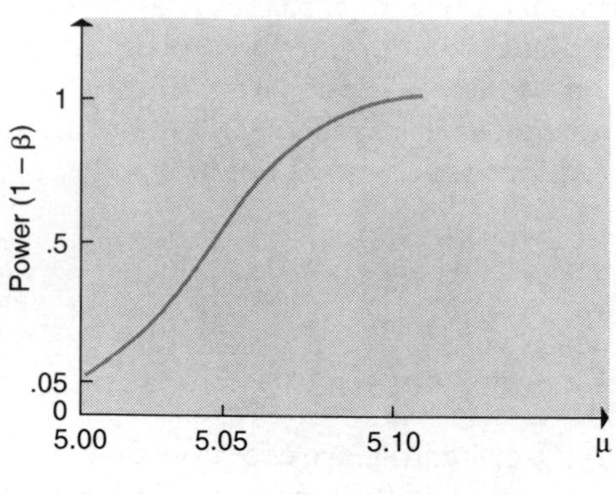

Figure 10.7 Power Functions for Test H_0: $\mu = 5$ Against H_1: $\mu > 5$ ($\alpha = 0.05$, $\sigma = 0.1$) for Sample Sizes 4, 9, and 16

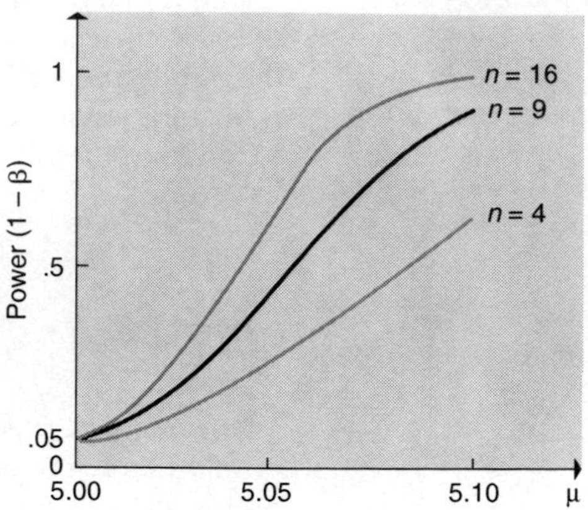

correct. Figure 10.7 presents a set of power curves at sample sizes of 4, 9, and 16 that illustrate the effect.

5. The power of the test at the critical value equals 0.5 because the probability that a sample mean is above ($\mu_0 = \bar{x}_c$) is, of course, 0.50.

Many statistical computer packages have computational routines to compute the power of a test. For example, Figure 10.8 presents the Minitab output for the discussion example. The small differences in the power values are the result of rounding error.

Power of Population Proportion Tests (Large Samples)

In Section 10.4 we developed hypothesis tests and decision rules for testing if the population proportion had certain values. Using methods similar to those in the previous section, we can also develop the probability of Type II error for proportion tests. The probability, β, of making a Type II error for any given population proportion P_1 included in H_1 is found as follows:

1. From the test decision rule, find the range of values of the sample proportion leading to failure to reject the null hypothesis.
2. Using the value P_1 for the population proportion—where P_1 is included in the alternative hypothesis—find the probability that the sample proportion will be in the nonrejection range determined in step (1) for samples of n observations when the population proportion is P_1.

We demonstrate this procedure in the following example.

Figure 10.8 Computer Computation of Power (Minitab Output)

Power and Sample Size

```
1-Sample Z test

Testing mean = null (versus > null)
Calculating power for mean = null + difference
Alpha = 0.05 Assumed standard deviation = 0.1


                Sample
Difference        Size       Power
0.05                16    0.638760
```

```
Minitab steps
1. stat
2. Power and Sample Size
3. 1 Sample Z
4. Enter Sample Size 16
5. Difference 0.05
6. Standard Deviation 0.1.
7. Options Greater than
```

Example 10.6 Forecasts of Corporate Earnings for Electronic Investors Inc. (Power and Type II Error)

The president of Electronic Investors Inc. has asked you to prepare an analysis of the forecasts of corporate earnings per share that were made by a group of financial analysts. These researchers were equally interested in the proportion of forecasts that exceeded the actual level of earnings and the proportion of forecasts that were less than the actual level of earnings.

Solution Begin your analysis by constructing a hypothesis test to determine if there was strong evidence to conclude that the proportion of forecasts that were above actual earnings was different from 50%. Using P to denote the proportion of forecasts that exceeded the actual level, the null hypothesis is

$$H_0 : P = P_0 = 0.50$$

and the alternative hypothesis is

$$H_1 : P \neq 0.50$$

The decision rule is

$$\text{Reject } H_0 \text{ if} \quad \frac{\hat{p}_x - P_0}{\sqrt{\dfrac{P_0(1 - P_0)}{n}}} > z_{\alpha/2} \quad \text{or} \quad \frac{\hat{p}_x - P_0}{\sqrt{\dfrac{P_0(1 - P_0)}{n}}} < -z_{\alpha/2}$$

A random sample of $n = 600$ forecasts was obtained, and it was determined that 382 exceeded actual earnings. Using a significance level of $\alpha = 0.05$, the decision rule is to reject the null hypothesis if

$$\frac{\hat{p}_x - 0.50}{\sqrt{\dfrac{(0.50)(0.50)}{600}}} > 1.96 \quad \text{or} \quad \frac{\hat{p}_x - 0.50}{\sqrt{\dfrac{(0.50)(0.50)}{600}}} < -1.96$$

Also, H_0 is rejected if

$$\hat{p}_x > 0.50 + 1.96\sqrt{\frac{(0.50)(0.50)}{600}} = 0.50 + 0.04 = 0.54$$

or

$$\hat{p}_x < 0.50 - 0.04 = 0.46$$

The observed sample proportion is

$$\hat{p}_x = \frac{382}{600} = 0.637$$

and, thus, the null hypothesis is rejected at the 5% level.

Now, we want to determine the probability of a Type II error when this decision rule is used. Suppose that the true population proportion was $P_1 = 0.55$. We want to determine the probability that the sample proportion is between 0.46 and 0.54 if the population proportion is 0.55. Thus, the probability of Type II error is

$$P(0.46 \le \hat{p}_x \le 0.54 \mid P = 0.55) = P\left[\frac{0.46 - P_1}{\sqrt{\frac{P_1(1-P_1)}{n}}} \le Z \le \frac{0.54 - P_1}{\sqrt{\frac{P_1(1-P_1)}{n}}}\right]$$

$$= P\left[\frac{0.46 - 0.55}{\sqrt{\frac{(0.55)(0.45)}{600}}} \le Z \le \frac{0.54 - 0.55}{\sqrt{\frac{0.55(0.45)}{600}}}\right]$$

$$= P(-4.43 \le Z \le -0.49) = 0.3121$$

Given the decision rule, the probability of a Type II error involved in failing to reject the null hypothesis when the true proportion is 0.55 is $\beta = 0.3121$. The power of the test for this value of the population proportion is

$$\text{Power} = 1 - \beta = 0.6879$$

This probability can be calculated for any proportion P_1. Figure 10.9 shows the power function for this example. Because the alternative hypothesis is two-sided, the power function differs in shape from that of Figure 10.6. Here, we are considering possible values of the population proportion on either side of the hypothesized value, 0.50. As we see, the probability of rejecting the null hypothesis when it is false increases the farther the true population proportion is from the hypothesized value.

Figure 10.9 Power Function for Test of $H_0: P = 0.50$ Versus $H_1: P \ne 0.50$ ($\alpha = 0.05$, $n = 600$)

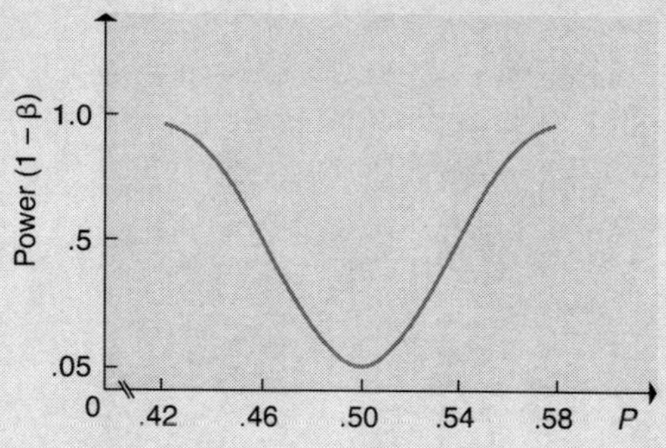

Exercises

Basic Exercises

10.37 Consider a problem with the hypothesis test

$$H_0: \mu = 5$$
$$H_1: \mu > 5$$

and the decision rule

$$\text{Reject } H_0 \text{ if } \frac{x - 5}{0.1/\sqrt{16}} > 1.645 \quad \text{or}$$
$$\bar{x} > 5 + 1.645(0.1/\sqrt{16}) = 5.041$$

Compute the probability of Type II error and the power for the following true population means.

a. $\mu = 5.10$
b. $\mu = 5.03$
c. $\mu = 5.15$
d. $\mu = 5.07$

10.38 Consider Example 10.6 with the null hypothesis

$$H_0: P = P_0 = 0.50$$

and the alternative hypothesis

$$H_0: P \ne 0.50$$

The decision rule is

$$\text{Reject } H_0 \text{ if } \frac{\hat{p}_x - 0.50}{\sqrt{\frac{(0.50)(0.50)}{600}}} > 1.96 \quad \text{or} \quad \frac{\hat{p}_x - 0.50}{\sqrt{\frac{(0.50)(0.50)}{600}}} < -1.96$$

with a sample size $n = 600$. What is the probability of Type II error if the actual population proportion is

a. $P = 0.52$?
b. $P = 0.58$?
c. $P = 0.53$?
d. $P = 0.48$?
e. $P = 0.43$?

Application Exercises

10.39 A company that receives shipments of batteries tests a random sample of nine of them before agreeing to take a shipment. The company is concerned that the true mean lifetime for all batteries in the shipment should be at least 50 hours. From past experience it is safe to conclude that the population distribution of lifetimes is normal with standard deviation 3 hours. For one particular shipment the mean lifetime for a sample of nine batteries was 48.2 hours.

a. Test at the 10% level the null hypothesis that the population mean lifetime is at least 50 hours.
b. Find the power of a 10%-level test when the true mean lifetime of batteries is 49 hours.

10.40 A pharmaceutical manufacturer is concerned that the impurity concentration in pills does not exceed 3%. It is known that from a particular production run impurity concentrations follow a normal distribution with standard deviation 0.4%. A random sample of 64 pills from a production run was checked, and the sample mean impurity concentration was found to be 3.07%.

a. Test at the 5% level the null hypothesis that the population mean impurity concentration is 3% against the alternative that it is more than 3%.
b. Find the probability of a 5%-level test rejecting the null hypothesis when the true mean impurity concentration is 3.10%.

10.41 A random sample of 1,562 undergraduates enrolled in management ethics courses was asked to respond on a scale from 1 (strongly disagree) to 7 (strongly agree) to this proposition: "Senior corporate executives are interested in social justice." The sample mean response was 4.27, and the sample standard deviation was 1.32.

a. Test at the 1% level against a two-sided alternative the null hypothesis that the population mean is 4.
b. Find the probability of a 1%-level test accepting the null hypothesis when the true mean response is 3.95.

10.42 A random sample of 802 supermarket shoppers had 378 shoppers that preferred generic brand items if the price was lower. Test at the 10% level the null hypothesis that at least one-half of all shoppers preferred generic brand items against the alternative that the population proportion is less than one-half. Find the power of a 10%-level test if, in fact, 45% of the supermarket shoppers are able to state the correct price of an item immediately after putting it into the cart.

10.43 In a random sample of 998 adults in the United States, 17.3% of the sample members indicated some measure of disagreement with this statement: "Globalization is more than an economic trade system—instead it includes institutions and culture."

a. Test at the 5% level the null hypothesis that at least 25% of all U.S. adults would disagree with this statement.
b. Find the probability of rejecting the null hypothesis with a 5%-level test if, in fact, 20% of all U.S. adults would disagree with the statement.

10.44 Of a random sample of 199 auditors, 104 indicated some measure of agreement with this statement: "Cash flow is an important indication of profitability."

a. Test at the 10% significance level against a two-sided alternative the null hypothesis that one-half of the members of this population would agree with this statement. Also find and interpret the p-value of this test.
b. Find the probability of accepting the null hypothesis with a 10%-level test if, in fact, 60% of all auditors agree that cash flow is an important indicator of profitability.

10.45 A fast-food chain tests each day that the average weight of its "two-pounders" is at least 32 ounces. The alternative hypothesis is that the average weight is less than 32 ounces, indicating that new processing procedures are needed. The weights of two-pounders can be assumed to be normally distributed, with a standard deviation of 3 ounces. The decision rule adopted is to reject the null hypothesis if the sample mean weight is less than 30.8 ounces.

a. If random samples of $n = 36$ two-pounders are selected, what is the probability of a Type I error, using this decision rule?
b. If random samples of $n = 9$ two-pounders are selected, what is the probability of a Type I

error, using this decision rule? Explain why your answer differs from that in part (a).

c. Suppose that the true mean weight is 31 ounces. If random samples of 36 two-pounders are selected, what is the probability of a Type II error, using this decision rule?

10.46 A wine producer claims that the proportion of its customers who cannot distinguish its product from frozen grape juice is at most 0.10. The producer decides to test this null hypothesis against the alternative that the true proportion is more than 0.10. The decision rule adopted is to reject the null hypothesis if the sample proportion who cannot distinguish between these two flavors exceeds 0.14.

a. If a random sample of 100 customers is chosen, what is the probability of a Type I error, using this decision rule?

b. If a random sample of 400 customers is selected, what is the probability of a Type I error, using this decision rule? Explain, in words and graphically, why your answer differs from that in part (a).

c. Suppose that the true proportion of customers who cannot distinguish between these flavors is 0.20. If a random sample of 100 customers is selected, what is the probability of a Type II error?

d. Suppose that, instead of the given decision rule, it is decided to reject the null hypothesis if the sample proportion of customers who cannot distinguish between the two flavors exceeds 0.16. A random sample of 100 customers is selected.

i. Without doing the calculations, state whether the probability of a Type I error will be higher than, lower than, or the same as in part (a).

ii. If the true proportion is 0.20, will the probability of a Type II error be higher than, lower than, or the same as in part (c)?

SUMMARY

In this chapter the methodology for classical hypothesis testing was developed, beginning with the rationale for making decisions in the face of uncertainty. Decisions are defined that involve the choice between two options. Decisions are made by rejecting a null hypothesis in the face of strong evidence in favor of the alternative hypothesis. There are two possible errors: Type I, rejecting the null hypothesis when it is true, and Type II, failing to reject the null hypothesis when it is not true. A variety of specific test procedures and decision rules were presented. These involve tests of the mean when the variances are both known and unknown and tests involving proportions. The procedures for determining the power and the probability of Type II error were developed for different assumptions concerning the actual population mean or proportion.

Decision rules are summarized in Figures 10.10 and 10.11. In Figure 10.10 decision rules are developed for testing hypotheses related to a population mean, μ. Note that tests are considered for the three different forms of hypotheses and for cases where the population variance is both known and unknown. In Figure 10.11 decision rules are developed for testing hypotheses related to a population proportion, P. Again, note that tests are considered for the three different forms of hypotheses.

KEY WORDS

- alternative hypothesis
- composite hypothesis
- counter factual argument
- critical value
- determining the probability of type II error
- hypothesis-testing terminology
- interpretation of the probability value or *p*-value
- null hypothesis
- power
- power function
- simple hypothesis
- states of nature and decisions on null hypothesis
- test of the mean of a normal distribution against two-sided alternative: population variance unknown
- tests of the mean of a normal distribution: population variance unknown
- test of the mean of a normal distribution (variance known): composite null and alternative hypotheses
- test of the mean of a normal distribution (variance known): composite or simple null and alternative hypotheses
- test of the mean of a normal population: population variance unknown
- tests of the population proportion (large sample sizes)
- Type I error
- Type II error

Figure 10.10 Guidelines for Choosing the Appropriate Decision Rule for a Population Mean

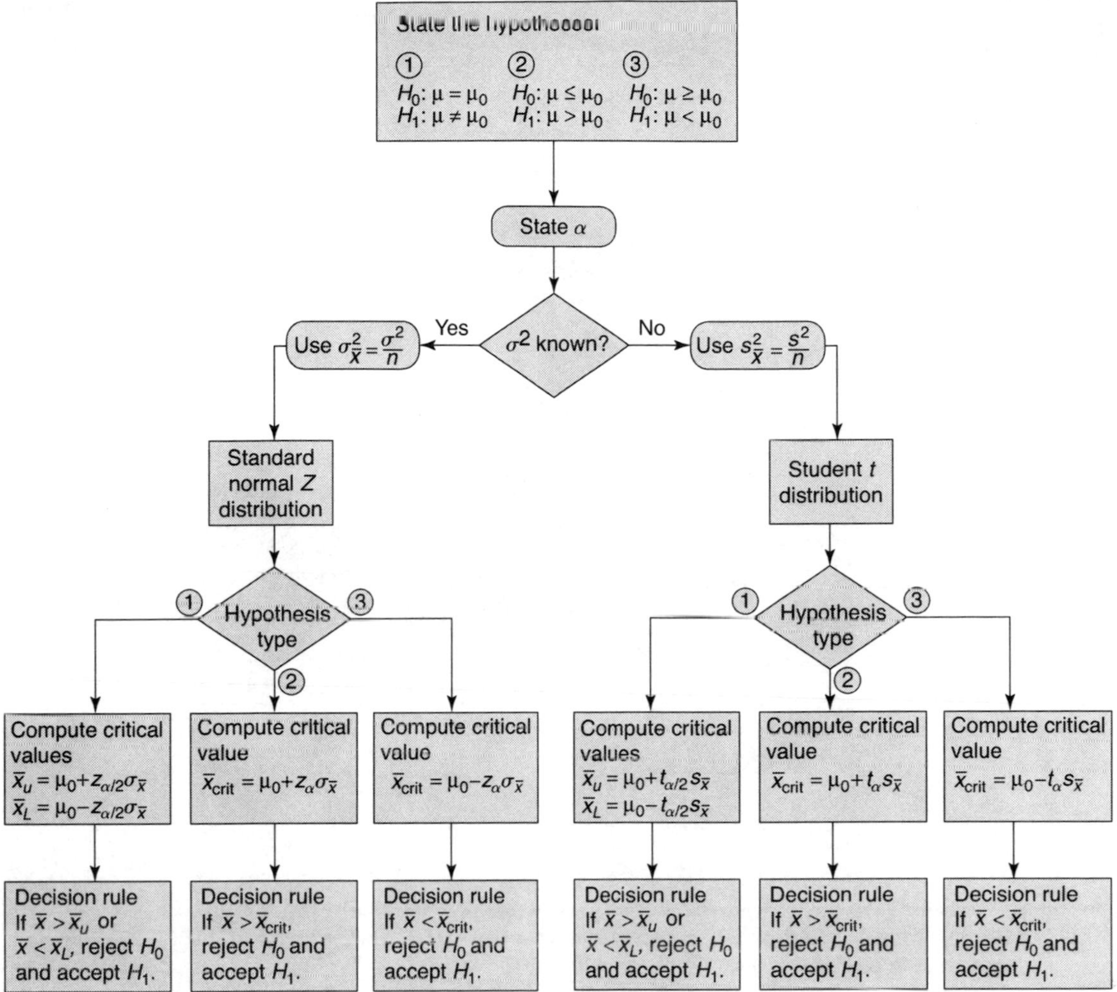

Figure 10.11 Guidelines for Choosing the Appropriate Decision Rule for a Population Proportion

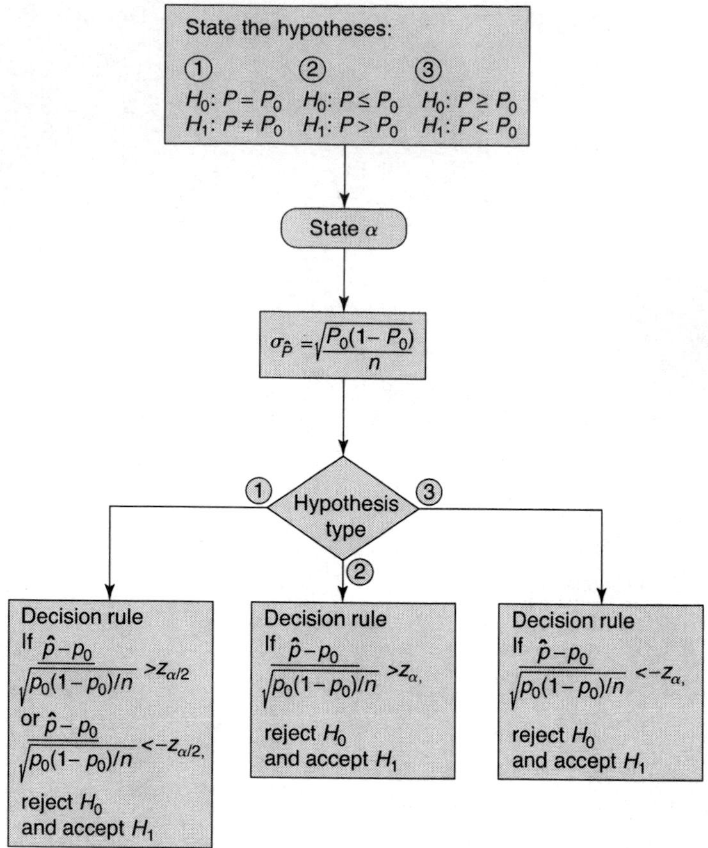

Chapter Exercises and Applications

10.47 Explain carefully the distinction between each of the following pairs of terms:

a. Null and alternative hypotheses
b. Simple and composite hypotheses
c. One-sided and two-sided alternatives
d. Type I and Type II errors
e. Significance level and power

10.48 Carefully explain what is meant by the *p*-value of a test, and discuss the use of this concept in hypothesis testing.

10.49 A random sample of 10 students contains the following observations, in hours, for time spent studying in the week before final exams.

28 57 42 35 61 39 55 46 49 38

Assume that the population distribution is normal.

a. Find the sample mean and standard deviation.
b. Test at the 5% significance level the null hypothesis that the population mean is 40 hours against the alternative that it is higher.

10.50 State whether each of the following is true or false.

a. The significance level of a test is the probability that the null hypothesis is false.
b. A Type I error occurs when a true null hypothesis is rejected.
c. A null hypothesis is rejected at the 0.025 level, but is not rejected at the 0.01 level. This means that the *p*-value of the test is between 0.01 and 0.025
d. The power of a test is the probability of accepting a null hypothesis that is true.
e. If a null hypothesis is rejected against an alternative at the 5% level, then using the same data, it must be rejected against that alternative at the 1% level.
f. If a null hypothesis is rejected against an alternative at the 1% level, then using the same data, it must be rejected against the alternative at the 5% level.
g. The *p*-value of a test is the probability that the null hypothesis is true.

10.51 An insurance company employs agents on a commission basis. It claims that in their first year agents will earn a mean commission of at least $40,000 and that the population standard deviation is no more than $6,000. A random sample of nine agents found, for commission in the first year,

$$\sum_{i=1}^{9} x_i = 333 \quad \text{and} \quad \sum_{i=1}^{9} (x_i - \bar{x})^2 = 312$$

where x_i is measured in thousands of dollars and the population distribution can be assumed to be normal. Test at the 5% level the null hypothesis that the population mean is at least $40,000.

10.52 Supporters claim that a new windmill can generate an average of at least 800 kilowatts of power per day. Daily power generation for the windmill is assumed to be normally distributed with a standard deviation of 120 kilowatts. A random sample of 100 days is taken to test this claim against the alternative hypothesis that the true mean is less than 800 kilowatts. The claim will not be rejected if the sample mean is 776 kilowatts or more and rejected otherwise.

a. What is the probability α of a Type I error using the decision rule if the population mean is, in fact, 800 kilowatts per day?
b. What is the probability β of a Type II error using this decision rule if the population mean is, in fact, 740 kilowatts per day?
c. Suppose that the same decision rule is used, but with a sample of 200 days rather than 100 days.

   i. Would the value of α be larger than, smaller than, or the same as that found in part (a)?
   ii. Would the value of β be larger than, smaller than, or the same as that found in part (b)?

d. Suppose that a sample of 100 observations was taken, but that the decision rule was changed so that the claim would not be rejected if the sample mean was at least 765 kilowatts.

   i. Would the value of α be larger than, smaller than, or the same as that found in part (a)?
   ii. Would the value of β be larger than, smaller than, or the same as that found in part (b)?

10.53 In a random sample of 545 accountants engaged in preparing county operating budgets for use in planning and control, 117 indicated that estimates of cash flow were the most difficult element of the budget to derive.

a. Test at the 5% level the null hypothesis that at least 25% of all accountants find cash flow estimates the most difficult estimates to derive.
b. Based on the procedure used in part (a), what is the probability that the null hypothesis would be rejected if the true percentage of those finding cash flow estimates most difficult was

   i. 20%?
   ii. 25%?
   iii. 30%?

10.54 A random sample of 104 marketing vice presidents from large Fortune 500 corporations was questioned on future developments in the business environment. Of those sample members, 50 indicated some measurement of agreement with this statement: "Firms will concentrate their efforts more on cash flow than on profits." What is the lowest level of significance at which the null hypothesis, which states that the true proportion of all such executives who would agree with this statement is one-half, can be rejected against a two-sided alternative?

10.55 In a random sample of 99 National Basketball Association games the home team won 57 games. Test the null hypothesis that the home team wins one-half of all games against the alternative that the home team wins a majority of games.

10.56 In a random sample of 150 business graduates 50 agreed or strongly agreed that businesses should focus their efforts on innovative e-commerce strategies. Test at the 5% level the null hypothesis that at most 25% of all business graduates would be in agreement with this assertion.

10.57 Of a random sample of 142 admissions counselors on college campuses 39 indicated that, on average, they spent 15 minutes or less studying each résumé. Test the null hypothesis that at most 20% of all admissions counselors spend this little time studying résumés.

10.58 Northeastern Franchisers Ltd. has a number of clients that use their process for producing exotic Norwegian dinners for customers throughout New England. The operating cost for the franchised process has a fixed cost of $1,000 per week plus $5 for every unit produced. Recently, a number of restaurant owners using the process have complained that the cost model is no longer valid and, in fact, the weekly costs are higher. Your job is to determine if there is strong evidence to support their claim. You obtain a random sample of $n = 25$ restaurants and determine their costs. You also know that the number of units produced in each restaurant is normally distributed with mean $\mu = 400$ and variance $\sigma^2 = 625$. The random sample mean ($n = 25$) for weekly costs was $3,050. Prepare and implement an analysis to determine if there is strong evidence to conclude that costs are greater than those predicted by the cost model.

10.59 Prairie Flower Cereal Inc. has asked you to study the variability of the weights of cereal bags produced in plant 2, located in rural Malaysia. The package weights are known to be normally distributed. Using a random sample of size $n = 71$, you find that the sample mean weight is 40 and the sample variance is 50.

The marketing vice president claims that there is a very small probability that the population mean weight is less than 39. Using an appropriate statistical analysis, comment on his claim.

It is recommend that a computer be used for computing analysis statistics for the following exercises.

10.60 Two financial analysts were asked to predict earnings per share for a random sample of 12 corporations over the coming year. The quality of their forecasts was evaluated in terms of absolute percentage forecast error, defined as

$$100 \cdot \left(\frac{|\text{Actual} - \text{Predicted}|}{\text{Actual}} \right)$$

The absolute percentage forecast errors made are shown in the data file **Analyst Prediction**. Stating any assumptions you make, test against a two-sided alternative the null hypothesis that the population mean absolute percentage forecast errors are the same for these two financial analysts.

10.61 BBW Ltd. does quality control work on the final loaves of bread produced. The data file named **BBWltd**, which is stored on your data disk or local computer system, contains data collected as part of its analysis of the market. The variables in the file are

1. "Dbread," which contains a random sample of weights, in grams, of their dark bread collected from supermarket shelves.
2. "Sbread," which contains a random sample of weights, in grams, of their specialty bread collected from supermarket shelves.
3. "Csbread," which contains a random sample of weights, in grams, of their competitor's specialty bread collected from supermarket shelves.

The company guarantees that its dark bread will have a weight of 100 grams or more. Based on the sample, does the company have strong evidence, $\alpha = 0.05$, that the guarantee is being met? Provide an appropriate hypothesis test result as evidence.

10.62 Big River Inc., a major Alaskan fish processor, is attempting to determine the weight of salmon in the Northwest Green River. A random sample of salmon was obtained and weighed. The data are stored in the file labeled **Bigfish**. Use a classical hypothesis test to determine if there is strong evidence to conclude that the population mean weight for the fish is greater than 40. Use a probability of Type I error equal to 0.05

Prepare a power curve for the test. *Hint*: Determine the population mean values for $\beta = 0.50$, $\beta = 0.25$, $\beta = 0.10$, and $\beta = 0.05$, and plot those means versus the power of the test.

Topic 22

Hypothesis Testing II

Chapter 11

Hypothesis Testing II

Chapter Outline

Introduction

In this chapter we develop procedures for testing the differences between two population means or proportions and for testing variances. This form of inference compares and complements the estimation procedures developed in Chapter 9. Our discussion in this chapter follows the development in Chapter 10, and we assume that the reader is familiar with the hypothesis testing procedure developed in Section 10.1. The process for comparing two populations begins with an investigator forming a hypothesis about the nature of the two populations and the difference between their means or proportions. The hypothesis is stated clearly as involving two options concerning the difference, and then a decision is made based on the results of a statistic computed from random samples of data from the two populations. Hypothesis tests involving variances are becoming more important as business firms work to reduce process variability in order to ensure high quality for every unit produced. Following are two examples of typical problems.

1. An instructor is interested in determining if assigning case studies increases students' test scores in her course. She could assign cases in one section and not in the other. Then, by collecting data from each class, she could determine if there is strong evidence that the use of case studies increases exam scores.

   Suppose that the instructor conjectures that completing assigned cases does not increase overall examination scores. Let μ_1 denote the mean final examination score in the class that used case studies, and let μ_2 denote the mean final examination score in the class that did not use case studies. The null hypothesis is the composite hypothesis

   $$H_0 : \mu_1 - \mu_2 \leq 0$$

   The alternative of interest is that the use of cases actually increases the average examination score, and, thus, the alternative hypothesis is

   $$H_1 : \mu_1 - \mu_2 > 0$$

   In this problem the instructor would decide to assign cases only if there is strong evidence that using cases increases the mean examination score. Strong evidence results from rejecting H_0 and accepting H_1.
2. A news reporter wants to know if a tax reform appeals equally to men and women. To test this, he obtains the opinions of randomly selected men and women. These data are used to provide an answer. The reporter might hold, as a working hypothesis, that a new tax proposal is equally appealing to men and women. Using P_1, the proportion of men favoring the proposal, minus P_2, the proportion of women favoring the proposal, the null hypothesis is

   $$H_0 : P_1 - P_2 = 0$$

   If the reporter has no good reason to suspect that the bulk of support comes from either men or women, then this null hypothesis would be tested against the two-sided composite alternative hypothesis

   $$H_1 : P_1 - P_2 \neq 0$$

   In this example rejection of H_0 would provide strong evidence that there is a difference between men and women in their response to the tax proposal.

Once we have specified the null and alternative hypotheses and collected sample data, a decision concerning the null hypothesis must be made. We can either reject the null hypothesis and accept the alternative hypothesis, or fail to reject the null hypothesis. When we fail to reject the null hypothesis, then either the null hypothesis is true or our test procedure was not strong enough to reject and an error has been committed. To reject the null hypothesis a decision rule based on sample evidence needs to be developed. Further on in this chapter we will present specific decision rules for various problems.

11.1 Tests of the Difference Between Two Population Means

There are a number of applications where we wish to draw conclusions about the differences between population means instead of conclusions about the absolute levels of the means. For example, we might want to compare the output of two different production processes for which neither population mean is known. Similarly, we might want to know if one marketing strategy results in higher sales than another without knowing the population mean sales for either. These questions can be handled effectively by various different hypothesis-testing procedures. As we saw in Section 9.1, several different assumptions can be made when confidence intervals are computed for the differences between two population means. These assumptions generally lead to specific methods for computing the population variance for the difference between sample means. There are parallel hypothesis tests that involve similar methods for obtaining the variance. We organize our discussion of the various hypothesis-testing procedures in parallel with the confidence interval estimates in Section 9.1.

Two Means, Matched Pairs

Here, we assume that a random sample of n matched pairs of observations is obtained from populations with means μ_x and μ_y. The observations will be denoted $(x_1, y_1), (x_2, y_2), \ldots, (x_n, y_n)$. When we have matched pairs and the pairs are positively correlated, the variance of the difference between the sample means

$$\bar{d} = \bar{x} - \bar{y}$$

will be reduced compared to using independent samples. This results because some of the characteristics of the pairs are similar, and, thus, that portion of the variability is removed from the total variability of the differences between the means. For example, when we consider measures of human behavior, differences between twins will usually be less than the differences between two randomly selected people. In general, the dimensions for two parts produced on the same specific machine will be closer than the dimensions for parts produced on two different randomly selected machines. Thus, whenever possible, we would prefer to use matched pairs of observations when comparing two populations because the variance of the difference will be smaller. With a smaller variance there is a greater probability that we will reject H_0 when the null hypothesis is not true. This principle was developed in Section 10.5 in the discussion of the power of a test. The specific decision rules for different forms of the hypothesis test are summarized in Equations 11.1, 11.2, and 11.3.

Tests of the Difference Between Population Means: Matched Pairs

Suppose that we have a random sample of n matched pairs of observations from distributions with means μ_x and μ_y. Let $\bar{d}$ and s_d denote the observed sample mean and standard deviation for the n differences $(x_i - y_i)$. If the population distribution of the differences is a normal distribution, then the following tests have significance level α.

1. To test either null hypothesis

$$H_0 : \mu_x - \mu_y = D_0 \quad \text{or} \quad H_0 : \mu_x - \mu_y \leq D_0$$

against the alternative

$$H_1 : \mu_x - \mu_y > D_0$$

the decision rule is

$$\text{Reject } H_0 \text{ if } \quad \frac{\bar{d} - D_0}{s_d / \sqrt{n}} > t_{n-1,\alpha} \tag{11.1}$$

2. To test either null hypothesis

$$H_0 : \mu_x - \mu_y = D_0 \quad \text{or} \quad H_0 : \mu_x - \mu_y \geq D_0$$

against the alternative

$$H_1 : \mu_x - \mu_y < D_0$$

the decision rule is

$$\text{Reject } H_0 \text{ if } \quad \frac{\bar{d} - D_0}{s_d / \sqrt{n}} < -t_{n-1,\alpha} \tag{11.2}$$

3. To test the null hypothesis

$$H_0 : \mu_x - \mu_y = D_0$$

against the two-sided alternative

$$H_1 : \mu_x - \mu_y \neq D_0$$

the decision rule is

$$\text{Reject } H_0 \text{ if } \quad \frac{\bar{d} - D_0}{s_d / \sqrt{n}} < -t_{n-1,\alpha/2} \quad \text{or} \quad \frac{\bar{d} - D_0}{s_d / \sqrt{n}} > t_{n-1,\alpha/2} \tag{11.3}$$

Here, $t_{n-1,\alpha}$ is the number for which

$$P(t_{n-1} > t_{n-1,\alpha}) = \alpha$$

where the random variable t_{n-1} follows a Student's t distribution with $(n - 1)$ degrees of freedom.

When we want to test the null hypothesis that the two population means are equal, we set $D_0 = 0$ in the formulas.

p-values for all of these tests are interpreted as the probability of getting a value at least as extreme as the one obtained, given the null hypothesis.

Example 11.1 Brain Activity and Recall of TV Advertising

Researchers conducted a study to estimate the relationship between a subject's brain activity while watching a television commercial and the subject's subsequent ability to recall the contents of the commercial. Subjects were shown two commercials for each of 10 products. For each commercial the ability to recall 24 hours later was measured. Each member of a pair of commercials viewed by a specific subject was then designated "high-recall" or "low-recall." Table 11.1 shows an index of the total amount of brain activity from the random sample of subjects while they were watching these commercials. Researchers wanted to know if brain wave activity was higher for high-recall ads compared to low-recall ads.

Solution Denote μ_x the population mean for high-recall commercials and μ_y the population mean for low-recall commercials. Then the differences d_i ($i = 1, \ldots, 10$) are a random sample of 10 observations from a population with mean $(\mu_x - \mu_y)$. Using these assumptions, we can define the null hypothesis as no difference in brain activity levels:

$$H_0 : \mu_x - \mu_y = 0$$

against the alternative that, on average, brain activity is greater for the high-recall commercials; that is,

$$H_1 : \mu_x - \mu_y > 0$$

Response to Commercials

In this test we compute the sample standard deviation of the differences, and, thus, we will use the Student's t distribution for the test.

The pattern of paired data is illustrated in Table 11.1 and contained in the data file **Response to Commercials.** Each subject was given a high-recall and a low-recall ad, and these are paired by observation number. The Minitab output for this problem is shown in Figure 11.1. The test is based on the statistic

$$t = \frac{\bar{d} - D_0}{s_d/\sqrt{n}} = \frac{23}{33.0/\sqrt{10}} = 2.21$$

Table 11.1 Brain Activities of Subjects Watching 10 Pairs of Television Commercials

Product Observation	High-Recall X	Low-Recall Y
1	141	55
2	139	116
3	87	83
4	129	88
5	51	36
6	50	68
7	118	91
8	161	115
9	61	90
10	148	113

Figure 11.1 Hypothesis Testing for Differences Between Brain Waves (Minitab Output)

Paired T-Test and CI: X, Y

```
Paired T for X - Y

              N        Mean      St Dev    SE Mean
X            10     108.500      42.506     13.441
Y            10      85.500      26.471      8.371
Difference   10     23.0000     32.9848    10.4307
95% lower bound for mean difference: 3.8793
T-Test of mean difference = 0 (vs > 0): T-Value = 2.21  P-Value = 0.027
```

Minitab Instructions
1. Stat
2. Basic statistics
3. Paired *t*

We found the value $t_{9,0.05} = 1.833$ in Appendix Table 8. Since 2.21 exceeds this value, we reject the null hypothesis and accept the alternative hypothesis. Thus, we conclude that there is substantial evidence to conclude that brain activity is higher for the high-recall compared to the low-recall group. We note that the *p*-value for this test is 0.027, as shown in the Minitab output.

Finally, we note that missing data are a problem that often occurs in applied statistical work. For example, suppose that the brain wave measurement was lost for one of the two ads for a particular subject. Standard procedure would argue that the entire observation should be removed and the analysis carried out with nine paired observations.

Two Means, Independent Samples, Known Population Variances

Now we will consider the case where we have independent random samples from two normally distributed populations. The first population has mean μ_x and variance σ_x^2, and we obtain a random sample of size n_x. The second population has mean μ_y and variance σ_y^2, and a random sample of size n_y is obtained.

In Section 9.1, we showed that, if the sample means are denoted $\bar{x}$ and $\bar{y}$, then the random variable

$$Z = \frac{(\bar{x} - \bar{y}) - (\mu_x - \mu_y)}{\sqrt{\dfrac{\sigma_x^2}{n_x} + \dfrac{\sigma_y^2}{n_y}}}$$

has a standard normal distribution. If the two population variances are known, tests of the difference between the population means can be based on this result, using the same arguments as before. Generally, we are comfortable using known population variances if the process being studied has been stable over some time and we have obtained similar variance measurements over this time. And because of the central limit theorem, the results presented here hold for large sample sizes even if the populations are not normal. For large sample sizes the approximation is quite satisfactory when sample variances are used for population variances. Of course, we can also perform a hypothesis test of the variance, as shown in Section 11.3. This allows the derivation of tests of wide applicability, as summarized in Equations 11.4, 11.5, and 11.6.

Tests of the Difference Between Population Means: Independent Samples (Known Variances)

Suppose that we have independent random samples of n_x and n_y observations from normal distributions with means μ_x and μ_y and variances σ_x^2 and σ_y^2, respectively. If the observed sample means are $\bar{x}$ and $\bar{y}$, then the following tests have significance level α.

1. To test either null hypothesis

$$H_0 : \mu_x - \mu_y = D_0 \quad \text{or} \quad H_0 : \mu_x - \mu_y \le D_0$$

against the alternative

$$H_1 : \mu_x - \mu_y > D_0$$

the decision rule is

$$\text{Reject } H_0 \text{ if } \quad \frac{\bar{x} - \bar{y} - D_0}{\sqrt{\dfrac{\sigma_x^2}{n_x} + \dfrac{\sigma_y^2}{n_y}}} > z_\alpha \tag{11.4}$$

2. To test either null hypothesis

$$H_0 : \mu_x - \mu_y = D_0 \quad \text{or} \quad H_0 : \mu_x - \mu_y \ge D_0$$

against the alternative

$$H_1 : \mu_x - \mu_y < D_0$$

the decision rule is

$$\text{Reject } H_0 \text{ if } \quad \frac{\bar{x} - \bar{y} - D_0}{\sqrt{\dfrac{\sigma_x^2}{n_x} + \dfrac{\sigma_y^2}{n_y}}} < -z_\alpha \tag{11.5}$$

3. To test the null hypothesis

$$H_0 : \mu_x - \mu_y = D_0$$

against the two-sided alternative

$$H_1 : \mu_x - \mu_y \ne D_0$$

the decision rule is

$$\text{Reject } H_0 \text{ if } \quad \frac{\bar{x} - \bar{y} - D_0}{\sqrt{\dfrac{\sigma_x^2}{n_x} + \dfrac{\sigma_y^2}{n_y}}} < -z_{\alpha/2} \quad \text{or} \quad \frac{\bar{x} - \bar{y} - D_0}{\sqrt{\dfrac{\sigma_x^2}{n_x} + \dfrac{\sigma_y^2}{n_y}}} > z_{\alpha/2} \tag{11.6}$$

If the sample sizes are large ($n > 100$), then a good approximation at significance level α can be made if we replace the population variances with the sample variances. In addition, the central limit theorem leads to good approximations even if the populations are not normally distributed.

p-values for all of these tests are interpreted as the probability of getting a value at least as extreme as the one obtained, given the null hypothesis.

Example 11.2 Comparison of Alternative Fertilizers (Hypothesis Test for Differences Between Means)

Shirley Brown, an agricultural economist, wants to compare cow manure and turkey dung as fertilizers. Historically, farmers had used cow manure on their cornfields. Recently, a major turkey farmer offered to sell composted turkey dung at a favorable price. The farmers decided that they would use this new fertilizer only if there was strong evidence that productivity increased over the productivity that occurred with cow manure. Shirley was asked to conduct the research and statistical analysis in order to develop a recommendation to the farmers.

Solution To begin the study, Shirley specified a hypothesis test with

$$H_0 : \mu_x - \mu_y \leq 0$$

versus the alternative that

$$H_1 : \mu_x - \mu_y > 0$$

where μ_x is the population mean productivity using turkey dung and μ_y is the population mean productivity using cow manure. H_1 indicates that turkey dung results in higher productivity. The farmers will not change their fertilizer unless there is strong evidence in favor of increased productivity. She decided before collecting the data that a significance level of $\alpha = 0.05$ would be used for this test.

Using this design, Shirley implemented an experiment to test the hypothesis. Cow manure was applied to one set of $n_y = 25$ randomly selected fields. The sample mean productivity was $\bar{y} = 100$. From past experience the variance in productivity for these fields was assumed to be $\sigma_y^2 = 400$. Turkey dung was applied to a second random sample of $n_x = 25$ fields, and the sample mean productivity was $\bar{x} = 115$. Based on published research reports, the variance for these fields was assumed to be $\sigma_x^2 = 625$. The two sets of random samples were independent. The decision rule is to reject H_0 in favor of H_1 if

$$\frac{\bar{x} - \bar{y}}{\sqrt{\dfrac{\sigma_x^2}{n_x} + \dfrac{\sigma_y^2}{n_y}}} > z_\alpha$$

The computed statistics for this problem are

$$n_x = 25 \qquad \bar{x} = 115 \qquad \sigma_x^2 = 625$$

$$n_y = 25 \qquad \bar{y} = 100 \qquad \sigma_y^2 = 400$$

$$z = \frac{115 - 100}{\sqrt{\dfrac{625}{25} + \dfrac{400}{25}}} = 2.34$$

Comparing the computed value of $z = 2.34$ with $z_{0.05} = 1.645$, Shirley concluded that the null hypothesis is clearly rejected. In fact, we found that the p-value for this test is 0.0096. As a result, there is overwhelming evidence that turkey dung results in higher productivity than cow manure.

Two Means, Independent Populations, Unknown Variances Assumed to Be Equal

In those cases where the population variances are not known and the sample sizes are under 100, we need to use the Student's t distribution. There are some theoretical problems when we use the Student's t distribution for differences between sample means. However, these problems can be solved using the procedure that follows if we can assume that the population variances are equal. This assumption is realistic in many cases where we are comparing groups. In Section 11.4 we present a procedure for testing the equality of variances from two normal populations.

The major difference is that this procedure uses a common pooled estimator of the equal population variance. This estimator is

$$s_p^2 = \frac{(n_x - 1)s_x^2 + (n_y - 1)s_y^2}{(n_x + n_y - 2)}$$

The hypothesis test is performed using the Student's t statistic for the difference between two means

$$t = \frac{(\bar{x} - \bar{y}) - (\mu_x - \mu_y)}{\sqrt{\frac{s_p^2}{n_x} + \frac{s_p^2}{n_y}}}$$

Note that the form for the test statistic is similar to that of the Z statistic, which is used when the population variances are known. The various tests using this procedure are summarized below.

Tests of the Difference Between Population Means: Population Variances Unknown and Equal

In these tests it is assumed that we have independent random samples of size n_x and n_y observations drawn from normally distributed populations with means μ_x and μ_y and a common variance. The sample variances s_x^2 and s_y^2 are used to compute a pooled variance estimator

$$s_p^2 = \frac{(n_x - 1)s_x^2 + (n_y - 1)s_y^2}{(n_x + n_y - 2)} \tag{11.7}$$

We emphasize here that s_p^2 is the weighted average of the two sample variances, s_x^2 and s_y^2.

Then, using the observed sample means $\bar{x}$ and $\bar{y}$, the following tests have significance level α.

1. To test either null hypothesis

$$H_0 : \mu_x - \mu_y = D_0 \quad \text{or} \quad H_0 : \mu_x - \mu_y \leq D_0$$

against the alternative

$$H_1 : \mu_x - \mu_y > D_0$$

the decision rule is

$$\text{Reject } H_0 \text{ if } \frac{\bar{x} - \bar{y} - D_0}{\sqrt{\frac{s_p^2}{n_x} + \frac{s_p^2}{n_y}}} > t_{n_x+n_y-2,\alpha} \tag{11.8}$$

2. To test either null hypothesis

$$H_0 : \mu_x - \mu_y = D_0 \quad \text{or} \quad H_0 : \mu_x - \mu_y \geq D_0$$

against the alternative

$$H_1 : \mu_x - \mu_y < D_0$$

the decision rule is

$$\text{Reject } H_0 \text{ if } \frac{\bar{x} - \bar{y} - D_0}{\sqrt{\frac{s_p^2}{n_x} + \frac{s_p^2}{n_y}}} < -t_{n_x+n_y-2,\alpha} \tag{11.9}$$

3. To test the null hypothesis

$$H_0 : \mu_x - \mu_y = D_0$$

against the two-sided alternative

$$H_1 : \mu_x - \mu_y \neq D_0$$

the decision rule is

$$\text{Reject } H_0 \text{ if } \frac{\bar{x} - \bar{y} - D_0}{\sqrt{\frac{s_p^2}{n_x} + \frac{s_p^2}{n_y}}} < -t_{n_x+n_y-2,\alpha/2} \quad \text{or} \quad \frac{\bar{x} - \bar{y} - D_0}{\sqrt{\frac{s_p^2}{n_x} + \frac{s_p^2}{n_y}}} > t_{n_x+n_y-2,\alpha} \tag{11.10}$$

Here, $t_{n_x+n_y-2,\alpha}$ is the number for which

$$P(t_{n_x+n_y-2} > t_{n_x+n_y-2,\alpha}) = \alpha$$

p-values for all of these tests are interpreted as the probability of getting a value as extreme as the one obtained, given the null hypothesis.

Example 11.3 Retail Sales Patterns (Hypothesis Test for Differences Between Means)

A sporting goods store operates in a medium-sized shopping mall. In order to plan staffing levels, the manager has asked for your assistance to determine if there is strong evidence that Monday sales are higher than Saturday sales.

Solution To answer the question, you decide to gather random samples of 25 Saturdays and 25 Mondays from a population of several years of data. The samples are drawn independently. You decide to test the null hypothesis

$$H_0 : \mu_M - \mu_S \leq 0$$

against the alternative hypothesis

$$H_1: \mu_M - \mu_S > 0$$

where the subscripts M and S refer to Monday and Saturday sales. The sample statistics are

$$\bar{x}_M = 1078 \quad s_M = 633 \quad n_M = 25$$
$$\bar{y}_S = 908.2 \quad s_S = 469.8 \quad n_S = 25$$

The pooled variance estimate is

$$s_p^2 = \frac{(25-1)(633)^2 + (25-1)(469.8)^2}{25+25-2} = 310{,}700$$

The test statistic is then computed as

$$t = \frac{\bar{x} - \bar{y}}{\sqrt{\dfrac{s_p^2}{n_x} + \dfrac{s_p^2}{n_y}}} = \frac{1078 - 908.2}{\sqrt{\dfrac{310{,}700}{25} + \dfrac{310{,}700}{25}}} = 1.08$$

Using a significance level of $\alpha = 0.05$ and 48 degrees of freedom, we find that the critical value of t is 1.677. Therefore, we conclude that there is not sufficient evidence to reject the null hypothesis, and, thus, there is no reason to conclude that mean sales on Mondays are higher.

Example 11.4 Brain Activity Study (Hypothesis Test for Differences Between Means)

Response to Commercials

In this example we examine the effect of using different assumptions for Student's t tests for differences between population means. Recall that in Example 11.1 we prepared the analysis assuming that the sample observations were paired. We found that there was evidence to reject the hypothesis that there was no difference between the population means and to accept the hypothesis that the high-recall ads had a higher population mean brain activity. Here, we will revisit Example 11.1 using other assumptions (use the data file **Response to Commercials**).

Solution First, we drop the assumption that the sample observations are matched pairs and correlated. We will, however, assume that the two population variances are equal. We are testing the same hypothesis that was tested in Example 11.1. The Minitab results are shown in Figure 11.2. The computed Student's t value is 1.45, the p-value is 0.082, and the degrees of freedom are 18. Thus, with a significance level of 0.05 we cannot reject the null hypothesis, and there is not strong evidence to support a difference in brain wave activity. Without the assumption of paired and positively correlated samples the variance of the difference is too large to conclude that the difference is significant.

Figure 11.2 Brain Wave Study: Independent Samples, Population Variances Equal (Minitab Output)

Two-Sample T-Test and CI: X,Y

```
Two-sample T for X vs Y

X        10      108.5      42.5       13
Y        10       85.5      26.5      8.4

Difference = mu (X) - mu (Y)
Estimate for difference:    23.0000
95% lower bound for difference:   -4.4587
T-Test of difference = 0 (vs >): T-Value = 1.45  P-Value = 0.082  DF = 18
Both use Pooled StDev = 35.4079
```

Minitab Instructions
1. Stat
2. Basic statistics
3. 2-sample t
4. Assume equal variances

Two Means, Independent Samples, Unknown Population Variances Assumed to Be Not Equal

Hypothesis tests of differences between population means when the individual variances are unknown and not equal require modification of the variance computation and the degrees of freedom. The computation of sample variance for the difference between sample means is changed. There are substantial complexities in the determination of degrees of freedom for the critical value of the Student's t statistic. The specific computational forms were presented in Section 9.1. Equations 11.11 through 11.14 below summarize the procedures.

Tests of the Difference Between Population Means: Population Variances Unknown and Not Equal

These tests assume that we have independent random samples of size n_x and n_y observations from normal populations with means μ_x and μ_y and unequal variances. The sample variances s_x^2 and s_y^2 are used. The degrees of freedom v for the Student's t statistic is given by

$$v = \frac{\left[\left(\frac{s_x^2}{n_x}\right) + \left(\frac{s_y^2}{n_y}\right)\right]^2}{\left(\frac{s_x^2}{n_x}\right)^2 / (n_x - 1) + \left(\frac{s_y^2}{n_y}\right)^2 / (n_y - 1)} \tag{11.11}$$

Then, using the observed sample means $\bar{x}$ and $\bar{y}$, the following tests have significance level α.

1. To test either null hypothesis

$$H_0 : \mu_x - \mu_y = D_0 \quad \text{or} \quad H_0 : \mu_x - \mu_y \leq D_0$$

against the alternative

$$H_1 : \mu_x - \mu_y > D_0$$

the decision rule is

$$\text{Reject } H_0 \text{ if } \frac{\bar{x} - \bar{y} - D_0}{\sqrt{\frac{s_x^2}{n_x} + \frac{s_y^2}{n_y}}} > t_{v,\alpha} \tag{11.12}$$

2. To test either null hypothesis

$$H_0 : \mu_x - \mu_y = D_0 \quad \text{or} \quad H_0 : \mu_x - \mu_y \geq D_0$$

against the alternative

$$H_1 : \mu_x - \mu_y < D_0$$

the decision rule is

$$\text{Reject } H_0 \text{ if } \frac{\bar{x} - \bar{y} - D_0}{\sqrt{\frac{s_x^2}{n_x} + \frac{s_y^2}{n_y}}} < -t_{v,\alpha} \tag{11.13}$$

3. To test the null hypothesis

$$H_0 : \mu_x - \mu_y = D_0$$

against the two-sided alternative

$$H_1 : \mu_x - \mu_y \neq D_0$$

the decision rule is

$$\text{Reject } H_0 \text{ if } \frac{\bar{x} - \bar{y} - D_0}{\sqrt{\frac{s_x^2}{n_x} + \frac{s_y^2}{n_y}}} < -t_{v,\alpha/2} \quad \text{or} \quad \frac{\bar{x} - \bar{y} - D_0}{\sqrt{\frac{s_x^2}{n_x} + \frac{s_y^2}{n_y}}} > t_{v,\alpha/2} \tag{11.14}$$

Here, $t_{r,\alpha}$ is the number for which

$$P(t_r > t_{r,\alpha}) = \alpha$$

The analysis for Example 11.4 will be run again without assuming equal population variances. The Excel results are shown in Figure 11.3. Here, the only important change is that the degrees of freedom are lower, resulting in a slightly higher p-value.

Figure 11.3 Brain Wave Study: Independent Samples (Excel Output)

t-Test: Two-Sample Assuming Unequal Variances

	Variable 1	*Variable* 2
Mean	108.5	85.5
Variance	1806.72222	700.7222222
Observations	10	10
Hypothesized Mean Difference	0	
df	15	
t Stat	1.45248674	
P(T<= t) one-tail	0.0834817	
t Critical one-tail	1.75305104	
P(T<= t) two tail	0.1669634	
t Critical two-tail	2.13145086	

Excel Instructions
1. Tools
2. Data analysis
3. t-Test: Two sample assuming unequal variances

EXERCISES

Basic Exercises

11.1 You have been asked to determine if two different production processes have different mean numbers of units produced per hour. Process 1 has a mean defined as μ_1 and process 2 has a mean defined as μ_2. The null and alternative hypotheses are

$$H_0 : \mu_1 - \mu_2 = 0$$
$$H_1 : \mu_1 - \mu_2 > 0$$

Using a random sample of 25 paired observations, the sample means are 50 and 60 for populations 1 and 2. Can you reject the null hypothesis using a probability of Type I error $\alpha = 0.05$ if

a. The sample standard deviation of the difference is 20?
b. The sample standard deviation of the difference is 30?
c. The sample standard deviation of the difference is 15?
d. The sample standard deviation of the difference is 40?

11.2 You have been asked to determine if two different production processes have different mean numbers of units produced per hour. Process 1 has a mean defined as μ_1 and process 2 has a mean defined as μ_2. The null and alternative hypotheses are

$$H_0 : \mu_1 - \mu_2 \geq 0$$
$$H_1 : \mu_1 - \mu_2 < 0$$

Using a random sample of 25 paired observations, the sample means are 56 and 50 for populations 1 and 2. Can you reject the null hypothesis using a probability of Type I error $\alpha = 0.05$ if

a. The sample standard deviation of the difference is 20?
b. The sample standard deviation of the difference is 30?
c. The sample standard deviation of the difference is 15?
d. The sample standard deviation of the difference is 40?

Application Exercises

11.3 In a study comparing banks in Germany and Great Britain, a sample of 145 matched pairs of banks was formed. Each pair contained one bank from Germany and one from Great Britain. The pairings were made in such a way that the two members were as similar as possible in regard to such factors as size and age. The ratio of total loans outstanding to total assets was calculated for each of the banks. For this ratio, the sample mean difference (German – Great Britain) was 0.0518, and the sample standard deviation of the differences was 0.3055. Test against a two-sided alternative the null hypothesis that the two population means are equal.

11.4 A screening procedure was designed to measure attitudes toward minorities as managers. High scores indicate negative attitudes and low scores indicate positive attitudes. Independent random samples were taken of 151 male financial analysts and 108 female financial analysts. For the former group the sample mean and standard deviation scores were 85.8 and 19.13, while the corresponding statistics for the latter group were 71.5 and 12.2. Test the null hypothesis that the two population means are equal against the alternative that the true mean score is higher for male than for female financial analysts.

11.5 For a random sample of 125 British entrepreneurs the mean number of job changes was 1.91 and the sample standard deviation was 1.32. For an independent random sample of 86 British corporate managers the mean number of job changes was 0.21 and the sample standard deviation was 0.53. Test the null hypothesis that the population means are equal against the alternative that the mean number of job changes is higher for British entrepreneurs than for British corporate managers.

11.6 A political science professor is interested in comparing the characteristics of students who do and do not vote in national elections. For a random sample of 114 students who claimed to have voted in the last presidential election, she found a mean grade point average of 2.71 and a standard deviation of 0.64. For an independent random sample of 123 students who did not vote, the mean grade point average was 2.79 and the standard deviation was 0.56. Test against a two-sided alternative the null hypothesis that the population means are equal.

11.7 In light of a recent large corporation bankruptcy, auditors are becoming increasingly concerned about the possibility of fraud. Auditors might be helped in determining the chances of fraud if they carefully measure cash flow. To evaluate this possibility, samples of midlevel auditors from CPA firms were presented with cash-flow information from a fraud case, and they were asked to indicate the chance of material fraud on a scale from 0 to 100. A random sample of 36 auditors used the cash-flow information. Their mean assessment was 36.21, and the sample standard deviation was

22.93. For an independent random sample of 36 auditors not using the cash-flow information, the sample mean and standard deviation were respectively 47.56 and 27.56. Assuming that the two population distributions are normal with equal variances, test against a two-sided alternative the null hypothesis that the population means are equal.

11.8 Initial public offerings' prospectuses were examined. In a random sample of 70 prospectuses in which sales forecasts were disclosed, the mean debt-to-equity ratio prior to the offering issue was 3.97, and the sample standard deviation was 6.14. For an independent random sample of 51 prospectuses in which sales earnings forecasts were not disclosed, the mean debt-to-equity ratio was 2.86, and the sample standard deviation was 4.29. Test against a two-sided alternative the null hypothesis that population mean debt-to-equity ratios are the same for disclosers and nondisclosers of earnings forecasts.

11.9 A publisher is interested in the effects on sales of college texts that include more than 100 data files. The publisher plans to produce 20 texts in the business area and randomly chooses 10 to have more than 100 data files. The remaining 10 are produced with at most 100 data files. For those with more than 100, first-year sales averaged 9,254, and the sample standard deviation was 2,107. For the books with at most 100, average first-year sales were 8,167, and the sample standard deviation was 1,681. Assuming that the two population distributions are normal with the same variance, test the null hypothesis that the population means are equal against the alternative that the true mean is higher for books with more than 100 data files.

It is recommend that a computer be used for the computations in the following exercises.

11.10 A college placement office wants to determine whether male and female economics graduates receive, on average, different salary offers for their first position after graduation. The placement officer randomly selected eight pairs of business graduates in such a way that the qualifications, interests, and backgrounds of the members of any pair were as similar as possible. The data file **Salary Pair** contains the highest salary offer received by each sample member at the end of the recruiting round. Assuming that the distributions are normal, test the null hypothesis that the population means are equal against the alternative that the true mean for males is higher than for females.

11.11 An agency offers students preparation courses for a graduate school admissions test. As part of an experiment to evaluate the merits of the course, 12 students were chosen and divided into six pairs in such a way that the members of any pair had similar academic records. Before taking the test, one member of each pair was assigned at random to take the preparation course, while the other member took no course. The achievement test scores are contained in the **Student Pair** data file. Assuming that the differences in scores follow a normal distribution, test at the 5% level the null hypothesis that the two population means are equal against the alternative that the true mean is higher for students taking the preparation course.

11.2 Tests of the Difference Between Two Population Proportions (Large Samples)

Next, we will develop procedures for comparing two population proportions. We will consider a standard model with a random sample of n_x observations from a population with a proportion P_x of "successes" and a second independent random sample of n_y observations from a population with a proportion P_y of "successes."

In Chapter 6 we saw that, for large samples, proportions can be approximated as normally distributed random variables, and, as a result,

$$Z = \frac{(\hat{p}_x - \hat{p}_y) - (P_x - P_y)}{\sqrt{\dfrac{P_x(1-P_x)}{n_x} + \dfrac{P_y(1-P_y)}{n_y}}}$$

has a standard normal distribution.

We want to test the hypothesis that the population proportions P_x and P_y are equal. Denote their common value by P_0. Then under this hypothesis

$$Z = \frac{(\hat{p}_x - \hat{p}_y)}{\sqrt{\frac{P_0(1-P_0)}{n_x} + \frac{P_0(1-P_0)}{n_y}}}$$

follows to a close approximation a standard normal distribution.

Finally, the unknown proportion P_0 can be estimated by a pooled estimator defined as

$$\hat{p}_0 = \frac{n_x\hat{p}_x + n_y\hat{p}_y}{n_x + n_y}$$

The null hypothesis in these tests assumes that the population proportions are equal. If the null hypothesis is true, then an unbiased and efficient estimator for P_0 can be obtained by combining the two random samples, and, as a result, $\hat{p}_0$ is computed using this equation. Then we can replace the unknown P_0 by $\hat{p}_0$ to obtain a random variable that has a distribution close to the standard normal, for large sample sizes.

The tests are summarized as follows.

Testing the Equality of Two Population Proportions (Large Samples)

We are given independent random samples of size n_x and n_y with proportion of successes $\hat{p}_x$ and $\hat{p}_y$. When we assume that the population proportions are equal, an estimate of the common proportion is

$$\hat{p}_0 = \frac{n_x\hat{p}_x + n_y\hat{p}_y}{n_x + n_y}$$

For large sample sizes—$nP_0(1-P_0) > 9$—the following tests have significance level α.

1. To test either null hypothesis

$$H_0 : P_x - P_y = 0 \quad \text{or} \quad H_0 : P_x - P_y \leq 0$$

against the alternative

$$H_1 : P_x - P_y > 0$$

the decision rule is

$$\text{Reject } H_0 \text{ if } \frac{(\hat{p}_x - \hat{p}_y)}{\sqrt{\frac{\hat{p}_0(1-\hat{p}_0)}{n_x} + \frac{\hat{p}_0(1-\hat{p}_0)}{n_y}}} > z_\alpha \qquad (11.15)$$

2. To test either null hypothesis

$$H_0 : P_x - P_y = 0 \quad \text{or} \quad H_0 : P_x - P_y \geq 0$$

against the alternative

$$H_1 : P_x - P_y < 0$$

the decision rule is

$$\text{Reject } H_0 \text{ if } \frac{(\hat{p}_x - \hat{p}_y)}{\sqrt{\frac{\hat{p}_0(1-\hat{p}_0)}{n_x} + \frac{\hat{p}_0(1-\hat{p}_0)}{n_y}}} < -z_\alpha \quad (11.16)$$

3. To test the null hypothesis

$$H_0 : P_x - P_y = 0$$

against the two-sided alternative

$$H_1 : P_x - P_y \neq 0$$

the decision rule is

$$\text{Reject } H_0 \text{ if } \frac{(\hat{p}_x - \hat{p}_y)}{\sqrt{\frac{\hat{p}_0(1-\hat{p}_0)}{n_x} + \frac{\hat{p}_0(1-\hat{p}_0)}{n_y}}} < -z_{\alpha/2} \quad \text{or}$$

$$\frac{(\hat{p}_x - \hat{p}_y)}{\sqrt{\frac{\hat{p}_0(1-\hat{p}_0)}{n_x} + \frac{\hat{p}_0(1-\hat{p}_0)}{n_y}}} > z_{\alpha/2} \quad (11.17)$$

It is also possible to compute and interpret *p*-values as the probability of getting a value at least as extreme as the one obtained, given the null hypothesis.

Example 11.5 Humor in British and American Trade Magazine Advertisements (Hypothesis Tests of Differences Between Proportions)

A study was conducted to determine if there was a difference in humor content in British and American trade magazine advertisements. In an independent random sample of 270 American trade magazine advertisements, 56 were humorous. An independent random sample of 203 British trade magazine advertisements contained 52 humorous ads. Do these data provide evidence that there is a difference in the proportion of humorous ads in British versus American trade magazines?

Solution Define P_x and P_y as the population proportions of humorous British and American advertisements, respectively. The null hypothesis is

$$H_0 : P_x - P_y = 0$$

and the alternative hypothesis is

$$H_1 : P_x - P_y \neq 0$$

The decision rule is to reject H_0 in favor of H_1 if

$$\frac{(\hat{p}_x - \hat{p}_y)}{\sqrt{\frac{P_0(1-P_0)}{n_x} + \frac{P_0(1-P_0)}{n_y}}} < -z_{\alpha/2} \quad \text{or} \quad > z_{\alpha/2}$$

The data for this problem are

$$n_x = 203 \quad \hat{p}_x = 52/203 = 0.256 \quad n_y = 270 \quad \hat{p}_y = 56/270 = 0.207$$

The estimate of the common variance P_0 under the null hypothesis is

$$\hat{p}_0 = \frac{n_x\hat{p}_x + n_y\hat{p}_y}{n_x + n_y} = \frac{(203)(0.256) + (270)(0.207)}{203 + 270} = 0.228$$

The test statistic is

$$\frac{(\hat{p}_x - \hat{p}_y)}{\sqrt{\frac{\hat{p}_0(1-\hat{p}_0)}{n_x} + \frac{\hat{p}_0(1-\hat{p}_0)}{n_y}}} = \frac{0.256 - 0.207}{\sqrt{\frac{(0.228)(1-0.228)}{203} + \frac{(0.228)(1-0.228)}{270}}} = 1.26$$

For a two-tailed test with $\alpha = 0.10$, the $z_{0.05}$ value is 1.645. Thus, it is not possible to reject the null hypothesis, and we have little evidence that there is a difference in humorous ads in the two countries' trade magazines.

EXERCISES

Basic Exercise

11.12 Test the hypotheses

$$H_0 : P_x - P_y = 0$$
$$H_1 : P_x - P_y > 0$$

using the following statistics from random samples:

a. $\hat{p}_x = 0.42,\ n_x = 500;\ \hat{p}_y = 0.50,\ n_y = 600$
b. $\hat{p}_x = 0.60,\ n_x = 500;\ \hat{p}_y = 0.64,\ n_y = 600$
c. $\hat{p}_x = 0.42,\ n_x = 500;\ \hat{p}_y = 0.49,\ n_y = 600$
d. $\hat{p}_x = 0.25,\ n_x = 500;\ \hat{p}_y = 0.34,\ n_y = 600$
e. $\hat{p}_x = 0.39,\ n_x = 500;\ \hat{p}_y = 0.42,\ n_y = 600$

Application Exercises

11.13 Random samples of 900 people in the United States and in Great Britain indicated that 60% of the people in the United States were positive about the future economy, while 66% of the people in Great Britain were positive about the future economy. Does this provide strong evidence that the people in Great Britain are more optimistic about the economy?

11.14 A random sample of 1,556 people in country A were asked to respond to this statement: "Increased world trade can increase our per capita prosperity." Of these sample members, 38.4% agreed with the statement. When the same statement was presented to a random sample of 1,108 people in country B, 52.0% agreed. Test the null hypothesis that the population proportions agreeing with this statement were the same in the two countries against the alternative that a higher proportion agreed in country B.

11.15 Small-business telephone users were surveyed 6 months after access to carriers other than AT&T became available for wide-area telephone service. Of a random sample of 368 users, 92 said they were attempting to learn more about their options, as did 37 of an independent random sample of 116 users of alternate carriers. Test at the 5% significance level, against a two-sided alternative, the null hypothesis that the two population proportions are the same.

11.16 Employees of a building materials chain, facing a shutdown, were surveyed on a prospective employee ownership plan. Some employees pledged $10,000 to this plan, putting up $800 immediately, while others indicated that they did not intend to pledge. Of a random sample of 175 pledgers, 78 had already been laid off, while 208 of a random sample of 604 nonpledgers had already been laid off. Test at the 5% level, against a two-sided alternative, the null hypothesis that the population proportions already laid off were the same for pledgers as for nonpledgers.

11.17 Of a random sample of 381 high-quality investment equity options, 191 had less than 30% debt. Of an independent random sample of 166 high-risk investment equity options, 145 had less than 30% debt. Test against a two-sided alternative the null hypothesis that the two population proportions are equal.

11.18 Independent random samples of consumers were asked about satisfaction with their computer system in two slightly different ways. The options available for answer were the same in the two cases. When asked how *satisfied* they were with their computer system, 138 of 240 sample members opted for "very satisfied." When asked how *dissatisfied* they were with their computer system, 128 of 240 sample members opted for "very satisfied." Test at the 5% significance level, against the obvious one-sided alternative, the null hypothesis that the two population proportions are equal.

11.19 Of a random sample of 1,200 people in Denmark, 480 had a positive attitude toward car salesmen. Of an independent random sample of 1,000 people in France, 790 had a positive attitude toward car salesmen. Test at the 1% level the null hypothesis that the population proportions are equal against the alternative that a higher proportion of French have a positive attitude toward car salesmen.

11.3 Tests of the Variance of a Normal Distribution

In addition to the need for tests based on the sample mean, there are a number of situations where we want to determine if the population variance is a particular value or set of values. In modern quality control work this need is particularly important because a process that, for example, has an excessively large variance can produce many defective items. Here, we will develop procedures for testing the population variance σ^2, based on the sample variance s_x^2, computed using a random sample of n observations from a normally distributed population. The basis for developing particular tests lies in the fact that the random variable

$$\chi^2_{n-1} = \frac{(n-1)s^2}{\sigma^2}$$

follows a chi-square distribution with $(n - 1)$ degrees of freedom. If the null hypothesis is that the population variance is equal to some specified value σ_0^2, that is,

$$H_0 : \sigma^2 = \sigma_0^2$$

then when this hypothesis is true, the random variable

$$\chi^2_{n-1} = \frac{(n-1)s^2}{\sigma^2}$$

obeys a chi-square distribution with $(n - 1)$ degrees of freedom. Hypothesis tests are based on computed values of this statistic. If the alternative hypothesis is that the population variance is larger than σ_0^2, we would be suspicious of the null hypothesis if the sample variance greatly exceeded σ_0^2. A high computed value of χ_{n-1}^2 would result in the rejection of the null hypothesis. Conversely, an alternative hypothesis that the population variance is less than σ_0^2 would be accepted and the null hypothesis rejected if the value of χ_{n-1}^2 was small. For a two-sided alternative that the population variance differs from σ_0^2, we would reject the null hypothesis if the value was either unusually high or unusually low. The chi-square distribution tests are more sensitive to the assumption of normality in the underlying distribution compared to the standard normal distribution tests. Thus, if the underlying population deviates considerably from the normal, the significance levels computed using the chi-square distribution may deviate from the correct significance levels based on the exact distribution.

The rationale for the development of appropriate tests follows the logic developed in Section 11.2 and uses the chi-square distribution notation developed in Section 9.3. We denote $\chi_{v,\alpha}^2$ as the number that is exceeded with probability α by a chi-square random variable with v degrees of freedom. That is,

$$P(\chi_v^2 > \chi_{v,\alpha}^2) = \alpha$$

and/or

$$P(\chi_v^2 < \chi_{v,1-\alpha}^2) = \alpha$$

and for two-tailed tests

$$P(\chi_v^2 > \chi_{v,\alpha/2}^2 \quad \text{or} \quad \chi_v^2 < \chi_{v,1-\alpha/2}^2) = \alpha$$

These probabilities are shown in Figure 9.5, and the various tests are summarized in Equations 11.18, 11.19, and 11.20.

It is also possible to determine p-values for the chi-square test for variances. From the general result just stated, the p-value for the chi-square test is the probability of getting a value at least as extreme as the one obtained, given the null hypothesis.

Tests of Variance of a Normal Population

We are given a random sample of n observations from a normally distributed population with variance σ^2. If we observe the sample variance s^2, then the following tests have significance level α.

1. To test either null hypothesis

$$H_0 : \sigma^2 = \sigma_0^2 \quad \text{or} \quad H_0 : \sigma^2 \le \sigma_0^2$$

against the alternative

$$H_1 : \sigma^2 > \sigma_0^2$$

the decision rule is

$$\text{Reject } H_0 \text{ if } \quad \frac{(n-1)s^2}{\sigma_0^2} > \chi_{n-1,\alpha}^2 \qquad (11.18)$$

2. To test either null hypothesis

$$H_0 : \sigma^2 = \sigma_0^2 \quad \text{or} \quad H_0 : \sigma^2 \geq \sigma_0^2$$

against the alternative

$$H_1 : \sigma^2 < \sigma_0^2$$

the decision rule is

$$\text{Reject } H_0 \text{ if } \quad \frac{(n-1)s^2}{\sigma_0^2} < \chi^2_{n-1,1-\alpha} \qquad (11.19)$$

3. To test the null hypothesis

$$H_0 : \sigma^2 = \sigma_0^2$$

against the two-sided alternative

$$H_1 : \sigma^2 \neq \sigma_0^2$$

the decision rule is

$$\text{Reject } H_0 \text{ if } \quad \frac{(n-1)s^2}{\sigma_0^2} > \chi^2_{n-1,\alpha/2} \quad \text{or} \quad \frac{(n-1)s^2}{\sigma_0^2} < \chi^2_{n-1,1-\alpha/2} \qquad (11.20)$$

where χ^2_{n-1} is a chi-square random variable and $P(\chi^2_{n-1} > \chi^2_{n-1,\alpha}) = \alpha$.

The *p*-value for these tests is the probability of getting a value at least as extreme as the one obtained, given the null hypothesis.

Example 11.6 Variance of Chemical Impurities (Hypothesis Tests of Population Variances)

The quality control manager of Stonehead Chemicals has asked you to determine if the variance of impurities in its shipments of fertilizer is within the established standard. This standard states that for 100-pound bags of fertilizer, the variance in the pounds of impurities cannot exceed 4.

Solution A random sample of 20 bags is obtained, and the pounds of impurities are measured for each bag. The sample variance is computed to be 6.62. In this problem we are testing the null hypothesis

$$H_0 : \sigma^2 \leq \sigma_0^2 = 4$$

against the alternative

$$H_1 : \sigma^2 > 4$$

Based on the assumption that the population has a normal distribution, the decision rule, for a test of significance level α, is to reject H_0 in favor of H_1 if

$$\frac{(n-1)s_x^2}{\sigma_0^2} > \chi^2_{n-1,\alpha}$$

For this test, with $\alpha = 0.05$ and 19 degrees of freedom, the critical value of the chi-square variable is 30.14, from the Chi-Square Table 7 in the Appendix. Then, using the test data, we find that

$$\frac{(n-1)s_x^2}{\sigma_0^2} = \frac{(20-1)(6.62)}{4} = 31.45 > \chi^2_{n-1,\alpha} = 30.14$$

Therefore, we reject the null hypothesis and conclude that the variability of the impurities exceeds the standard. As a result, we recommend that the production process should be studied and improvements made to reduce the variability of the product components.

The p-value for this test is the probability of obtaining a chi-square statistic with 19 degrees of freedom that is greater than the observed 31.45:

$$p\text{-Value} = P\left(\frac{(19)s_x^2}{\sigma_0^2} > \chi^2_{19} = 31.45\right) = 0.036$$

The p-value of 0.036 was computed using the Minitab probability distribution function for the chi-square distribution.

Exercises

Basic Exercise

11.20 Test the hypotheses

$$H_0: \sigma^2 \le 100$$
$$H_1: \sigma^2 > 100$$

using the following results from a random sample.

a. $s^2 = 165$; $n = 25$
b. $s^2 = 165$; $n = 29$
c. $s^2 = 159$; $n = 25$
d. $s^2 = 67$; $n = 38$

Application Exercises

11.21 At the insistence of a government inspector a new safety device is installed in an assembly-line operation. After the installation of this device a random sample of 8 days' output gave the following results for numbers of finished components produced:

618 660 638 625 571 598 639 582

Management is concerned about the variability of daily output and views as undesirable any variance above 500. Test at the 10% significance level the null hypothesis that the population variance for daily output does not exceed 500.

11.22 Plastic sheets produced by a machine are periodically monitored for possible fluctuations in thickness. If the true variance in thicknesses exceeds 2.25 square millimeters, there is cause for concern about product quality. Thickness measurements for a random sample of 10 sheets produced in a particular shift were taken, giving the following results (in millimeters):

226 226 232 227 225
228 225 228 229 230

a. Find the sample variance.
b. Test at the 5% significance level the null hypothesis that the population variance is at most 2.25.

11.23 One way to evaluate the effectiveness of a teaching assistant is to examine the scores achieved by his or her students on an examination at the end of the course. Obviously, the mean score is of interest. However, the variance also contains useful information—some teachers have a style that works very well with more able students but is unsuccessful with less able or poorly motivated students. A professor sets a standard examination at the end of each semester for all sections of a course. The variance of the scores on this test is typically very close to 300. A new teaching assistant has a class of 30 students, whose test scores had a variance of 480. Regarding these students' test scores as a random sample from a normal population, test against a two-sided alternative the null hypothesis that the population variance of their scores is 300.

11.24 A company produces electric devices operated by a thermostatic control. The standard deviation of the temperature at which these controls actually operate should not exceed 2.0 degrees Fahrenheit. For a random sample of 20 of these controls the sample standard deviation of operating temperatures was 2.36 degrees Fahrenheit. Stating any assumptions you need to make, test at the 5% level the null hypothesis that the population standard deviation is 2.0 against the alternative that it is bigger.

11.25 An instructor has decided to introduce a greater component of independent study into an intermediate microeconomics course as a way of motivating students to work independently and think more carefully about the course material. A colleague cautions that a possible consequence may be increased variability in student performance. However, the instructor responds that she would expect less variability. From her records she found that, in the past, student scores on the final exam for this course followed a normal distribution with standard deviation 18.2 points. For a class of 25 students using the new approach, the standard deviation of scores on the final exam was 15.3 points. Assuming that these 25 students can be viewed as a random sample of all those who might be subjected to the new approach, test the null hypothesis that the population standard deviation is at least 18.2 points against the alternative that it is lower.

11.4 Tests of the Equality of the Variances Between Two Normally Distributed Populations

There are a number of situations where we are interested in comparing the variances from two normally distributed populations. For example, the Student's t test in Section 11.1 assumed equal variances and used the two sample variances to compute a pooled estimator for the common variances. We will see that comparisons of variances are also important inferential procedures for regression analysis—see Chapters 12 and 13—and for analysis of variance—see Chapter 17. Quality control studies are often concerned with the question of which process has the smaller variance.

In this section we develop a procedure for testing the assumption that population variances from independent samples are equal. To perform such tests, we introduce the F probability distribution. We begin by letting s_x^2 be the sample variance for a random sample of n_x observations from a normally distributed population with population variance σ_x^2. A second independent random sample of size n_y provides a sample variance of s_y^2 from a normal population with population variance σ_y^2. Then the random variable

$$F = \frac{s_x^2/\sigma_x^2}{s_y^2/\sigma_y^2}$$

follows a distribution known as the F distribution. This family of distributions, which is widely used in statistical analysis, is identified by the degrees of freedom for the numerator and the degrees of freedom for the denominator. The degrees of freedom for the numerator are associated with the sample variance s_x^2 and equal to $(n_x - 1)$.

Similarly, the degrees of freedom for the denominator are associated with the sample variance s_y^2 and equal to $(n_y - 1)$.

The F distribution is constructed as the ratio of two chi-square random variables, each divided by its degrees of freedom. The chi-square distribution relates the sample and population variances for a normally distributed population. Hypothesis tests that use the F distribution depend on the assumption of a normal distribution. The characteristics of the F distribution are summarized below.

The *F* Distribution

We have two independent random samples with n_x and n_y observations from two normal populations with variances σ_x^2 and σ_y^2. If the sample variances are s_x^2 and s_y^2, then the random variable

$$F = \frac{s_x^2/\sigma_x^2}{s_y^2/\sigma_y^2} \tag{11.21}$$

has an F distribution with numerator degrees of freedom $(n_x - 1)$ and denominator degrees of freedom $(n_y - 1)$.

An F distribution with numerator degrees of freedom v_1 and denominator degrees of freedom v_2 will be denoted F_{v_1,v_2}. We denote as $F_{v_1,v_2,\alpha}$ the number for which

$$P(F_{v_1,v_2} > F_{v_1,v_2,\alpha}) = \alpha$$

We need to emphasize that this test is quite sensitive to the assumption of normality.

The cutoff points for $F_{v_1,v_2,\alpha}$, for α equal to 0.05 and 0.01, are provided in Table 9 of the Appendix. For example, for 10 numerator degrees of freedom and 20 denominator degrees of freedom, we see from the table that

$$F_{10,20,0.05} = 2.35 \quad \text{and} \quad F_{10,20,0.01} = 3.37$$

Hence,

$$P(F_{10,20} > 2.35) = 0.05 \quad \text{and} \quad P(F_{10,20} > 3.37) = 0.01$$

Figure 11.4 presents a schematic description of the F distribution for this example.

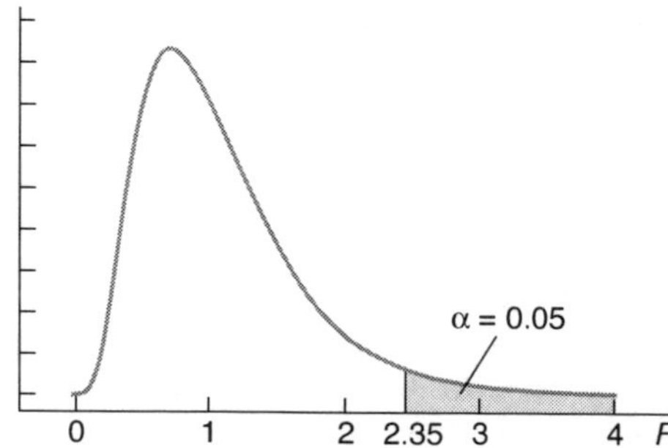

Figure 11.4 *F* Probability Density Function with 10 Numerator Degrees of Freedom and 20 Denominator Degrees of Freedom

In practical applications we usually arrange the F ratio so that the larger sample variance is in the numerator and the smaller is in the denominator. Thus, we only need to use the upper cutoff points to test the hypothesis of equality of variances. When the population variances are equal, the F random variable becomes

$$F = \frac{s_x^2}{s_y^2}$$

and this ratio of sample variances becomes the test statistic. The intuition for this test is quite simple: If one of the sample variances greatly exceeds the other, then we must conclude that the population variances are not equal. The hypothesis tests of equality of variances are summarized as follows.

Tests of Equality of Variances from Two Normal Populations

Let s_x^2 and s_y^2 be observed sample variances from independent random samples of size n_x and n_y from normally distributed populations with variances σ_X^2 and σ_Y^2. Use s_x^2 to denote the larger variance. Then the following tests have significance level α.

1. To test either null hypothesis

$$H_0 : \sigma_X^2 = \sigma_Y^2 \quad \text{or} \quad H_0 : \sigma_X^2 \leq \sigma_Y^2$$

against the alternative

$$H_1 : \sigma_X^2 > \sigma_Y^2$$

the decision rule is

$$\text{Reject } H_0 \text{ if } \quad \frac{s_x^2}{s_y^2} > F_{n_x-1,n_y-1,\alpha} \tag{11.22}$$

2. To test the null hypothesis

$$H_0 : \sigma_X^2 = \sigma_Y^2$$

against the two-sided alternative

$$H_1 : \sigma_X^2 \neq \sigma_Y^2$$

the decision rule is

$$\text{Reject } H_0 \text{ if } \quad \frac{s_x^2}{s_y^2} > F_{n_x-1,n_y-1,\alpha/2} \tag{11.23}$$

where s_x^2 is the larger of the two sample variances. Since either sample variance could be larger, this rule is actually based on a two-tailed test, and, hence, we use $\alpha/2$ as the upper tail probability.

Here, F_{n_x-1,n_y-1} is the number for which

$$P(F_{n_x-1,n_y-1} > F_{n_x-1,n_y-1,\alpha}) = \alpha$$

where F_{n_x-1, n_y-1} has an F distribution with $(n_x - 1)$ numerator degrees of freedom and $(n_y - 1)$ denominator degrees of freedom.

For all of these tests a *p*-value is the probability of getting a value at least as extreme as the one obtained, given the null hypothesis. Because of the complexity of the *F* distribution, critical values are computed for only a few special cases. Thus, *p*-values will be typically computed using a statistical package such as Minitab.

Example 11.7 Study of Maturity Variances by Investors Now (Hypothesis Tests of Two Variances)

The research staff of Investors Now, an on-line financial trading firm, were interested in determining if there is a difference in the variance of the maturities of AAA-rated industrial bonds compared to CCC-rated industrial bonds.

Solution This question requires that we design a study that compares the population variances of maturities for the two different bonds. We will test the null hypothesis

$$H_0 : \sigma_X^2 = \sigma_Y^2$$

against the alternative hypothesis

$$H_1 : \sigma_X^2 \neq \sigma_Y^2$$

where σ_X^2 is the variance in maturities for AAA-rated bonds and σ_Y^2 is the variance in maturities for CCC-rated bonds. The significance level of the test was chosen as $\alpha = 0.02$.

The decision rule is to reject H_0 in favor of H_1 if

$$\frac{s_x^2}{s_y^2} > F_{n_x-1, n_y-1, \alpha/2}$$

Note here that either sample variance could be larger and thus in the denominator. Hence, the probability for this upper tail is $\alpha/2$. A random sample of 17 AAA-rated bonds resulted in a sample variance $s_x^2 = 123.35$, and an independent random sample of 11 CCC-rated bonds resulted in a sample variance $s_y^2 = 8.02$. The test statistic is thus

$$\frac{s_x^2}{s_y^2} = \frac{123.35}{8.02} = 15.38$$

Given a significance level of $\alpha = 0.02$, we find that the critical value of F, from interpolation in Table 9 of the Appendix, is

$$F_{16,10,0.01} = 4.53$$

Clearly, the computed value of F (15.38) exceeds the critical value (4.53), and we reject H_0 in favor of H_1. Thus, there is strong evidence that variances in maturities are different for these two types of bonds.

Exercises

Basic Exercise

11.26 Test the hypothesis

$$H_0: \sigma_x^2 = \sigma_y^2$$
$$H_1: \sigma_x^2 > \sigma_y^2$$

using the following data:

a. $s_x^2 = 125, n_x = 45; s_y^2 = 51, n_y = 41$

b. $s_x^2 = 125, n_x = 45; s_y^2 = 235, n_y = 44$

c. $s_x^2 = 134, n_x = 48; s_y^2 = 51, n_y = 41$

d. $s_x^2 = 88, n_x = 39; s_y^2 = 167, n_y = 25$

Application Exercises

11.27 It is hypothesized that the more expert a group of people examining personal income tax filings, the more variable will be their judgments about the accuracy. Independent random samples, each of 30 individuals, were chosen from groups with different levels of expertise. The "low-expertise" group consisted of people who had just completed their first intermediate accounting course. Members of the "high-expertise" group had completed undergraduate studies and were employed by reputable CPA firms. The sample members were asked to judge the accuracy of personal income tax filings. For the low-expertise group the sample variance was 451.770, while for the high-expertise group it was 1,614.208. Test the null hypothesis that the two population variances are equal against the alternative that the true variance is higher for the high-expertise group.

11.28 It is hypothesized that the total sales of a corporation should vary more in an industry with active price competition than in one with duopoly and tacit collusion. In a study of the merchant ship production industry it was found that in four years of active price competition the variance of company A's total sales was 114.09. In the following seven years, during which there was duopoly and tacit collusion, this variance was 16.08. Assume that the data can be regarded as an independent random sample from two normal distributions. Test at the 5% level the null hypothesis that the two population variances are equal against the alternative that the variance of total sales is higher in years of active price competition.

11.29 In Exercise 11.7 it was assumed that population variances for assessments of the chance of material fraud were the same for auditors using cash-flow information as for auditors not using cash-flow information. Test this assumption against a two-sided alternative hypothesis.

11.30 In Exercise 11.9 it was assumed that population variances were equal for first-year sales of textbooks with more than 100 data files and those with at most 100 data files. Test this assumption against a two-sided alternative.

11.31 A university research team was studying the relationship between idea generation by groups with and without a moderator. For a random sample of four groups with a moderator the mean number of ideas generated per group was 78.0, and the standard deviation was 24.4. For a random sample of four groups without a moderator the mean number of ideas generated was 63.5, and the standard deviation was 20.2 Test the assumption that the two population variances were equal against the alternative that the population variance is higher for groups with a moderator.

11.5 Some Comments on Hypothesis Testing

In this chapter we have presented several important applications of hypothesis-testing methodology. In an important sense, this methodology is fundamental to decision making and analysis in the face of random variability. As a result, the procedures have great applicability to a number of research and management decisions.

The procedures are relatively easy to use, and various computer processes minimize the computational effort. Thus, we have a tool that is appealing and quite easy to use. However, there are some subtle problems and areas of concern that we need to consider in order to avoid serious mistakes.

The null hypothesis plays a crucial role in the hypothesis-testing framework. In a typical investigation we set the significance level, α, at a small probability value. Then we obtain a random sample and use the data to compute a test statistic. If the test statistic is outside of the acceptance region (depending on the direction of the test), the null hypothesis is rejected and the alternative hypothesis is accepted. When we do reject the null hypothesis, we have strong evidence—a small probability of error—in favor of the alternative hypothesis. In some cases we may fail to reject a drastically false null hypothesis simply because we have only limited sample information or because the test has low power. There may be important cases where this outcome is appropriate. For example, we would not change an existing process that is working effectively unless we had strong evidence that a new process clearly would be even better. In other cases, however, the special status of the null hypothesis is neither warranted nor appropriate. In those cases we might consider the costs of making both Type I and Type II errors in a decision process. We might also consider a different specification of the null hypothesis—noting that rejection of the null provides strong evidence in favor of the alternative. When we have two alternatives, we could initially choose either as the null hypothesis. In the cereal-package weight example at the beginning of Chapter 10 the null hypothesis could be either that

$$H_0 : \mu \geq 16$$

or that

$$H_0 : \mu \leq 16$$

In the first case rejection would provide strong evidence that the population mean weight is less than 16. In the latter case rejection would provide strong evidence that the population mean weight is greater than 16. As we have indicated, failure to reject either of these null hypotheses would not provide strong evidence. There are also procedures for controlling both Type I and Type II errors simultaneously (see, for example, Reference 1).

On some occasions very large amounts of sample information are available, and we reject the null hypothesis even when differences are not practically important. Thus, we need to contrast statistical significance with a broader definition of significance. Suppose that very large samples are used to compare annual mean family incomes in two cities. One result might be that the sample means differ by $2.67, and that difference might lead us to reject a null hypothesis and thus conclude that one city has a higher mean family income than the other. While that result might be statistically significant, it clearly has no practical significance with respect to consumption or quality of life.

INTERPRETATION

In specifying a null hypothesis and a testing rule, we are defining the test conditions before we look at the sample data that were generated by a process that includes a random component. Thus, if we look at the data before defining the null and alternative hypotheses, we no longer have the stated probability of error, and the concept of "strong evidence" resulting from rejecting the null hypothesis is not valid. For example, if we decide on the significance level of our test after we have seen the *p*-values, then we cannot interpret our results in probability terms. Suppose that an economist compares each of five different income-enhancing programs against a standard minimal level using a hypothesis test. After collecting the data and computing p-values, he determines that the null hypothesis—income not above the standard minimal level—can be rejected for one of the five programs with a significance level of $\alpha = 0.20$. Clearly, this result violates the proper use of hypothesis testing. But we have seen this done by supposedly professional economists.

As statistical computing tools have become more powerful, there are a number of new ways to violate the principle of specifying the null hypothesis before seeing the data. The recent popularity of data mining—using a computer program to search for relationships between variables in a very large data set—introduces new possibilities for abuse. Data mining can provide a description of subsets and differences in a particularly large sample of data. However, after seeing the results from a data mining operation, analysts may be tempted to define hypothesis tests that will use random samples from the same data set. This clearly violates the principle of defining the hypothesis test before seeing the data. A drug company may screen large numbers of medical treatment cases and discover that 5 out of 100 drugs have significant effects for the treatment of previously unintended diseases. Such a result might legitimately be used to identify potential research questions for a new research study with new random samples. However, if the original data are then used to test a hypothesis concerning the treatment benefits of the 5 drugs, we have a serious violation of the proper application of hypothesis testing, and none of the probabilities of error are correct.

Defining the null and alternative hypotheses requires careful consideration of the objectives of the analysis. For example, we might be faced with a proposal to introduce a specific new production process. In one case the present process might include considerable new equipment, well-trained workers, and a belief that the process performs very well. In that case we would define the productivity for the present process as the null hypothesis and the new process as the alternative. Then we would adopt the new process only if there is strong evidence—rejecting the null hypothesis with a small α—that the new process has higher productivity. Alternatively, the present process might be old and include equipment that needs to be replaced and a number of workers that require supplementary training. In that case we might choose to define the new process productivity as the null hypothesis. Thus, we would continue with the old process only if there is strong evidence that the old process's productivity is higher.

When we establish control charts for monitoring process quality, as we will see in Chapter 20, we set the desired process level as the null hypothesis and also set a very small significance level $\alpha < 0.01$. Thus, we reject only when there is very strong evidence that the process is no longer performing properly. However, these control chart hypothesis tests are established only after there has been considerable work to bring the process under control and minimize its variability. Therefore, we are quite confident that the process is working properly, and we do not wish to change in response to small variations in the sample data. But if we do find a test statistic from sample data outside the acceptance interval and hence reject the null hypothesis, we can be quite confident that something has gone wrong and we need to fix the process immediately.

The tests developed in this chapter are based on the assumption that the underlying distribution is normal or that the central limit theorem applies for the distribution of sample means or proportions. When the normality assumption no longer holds, those probabilities of error may not be valid. Since we cannot be sure that most populations are precisely normal, we might have some serious concerns for the validity of our tests. Considerable research has shown that tests involving means do not strongly depend on the normality assumption. These tests are said to be "robust" with respect to normality. However, tests involving variances are not robust. Thus, greater caution is required when using hypothesis tests based on variances.

Figure 11.5 Flow Chart for Selecting the Appropriate Hypothesis Test When Comparing Two Population Means

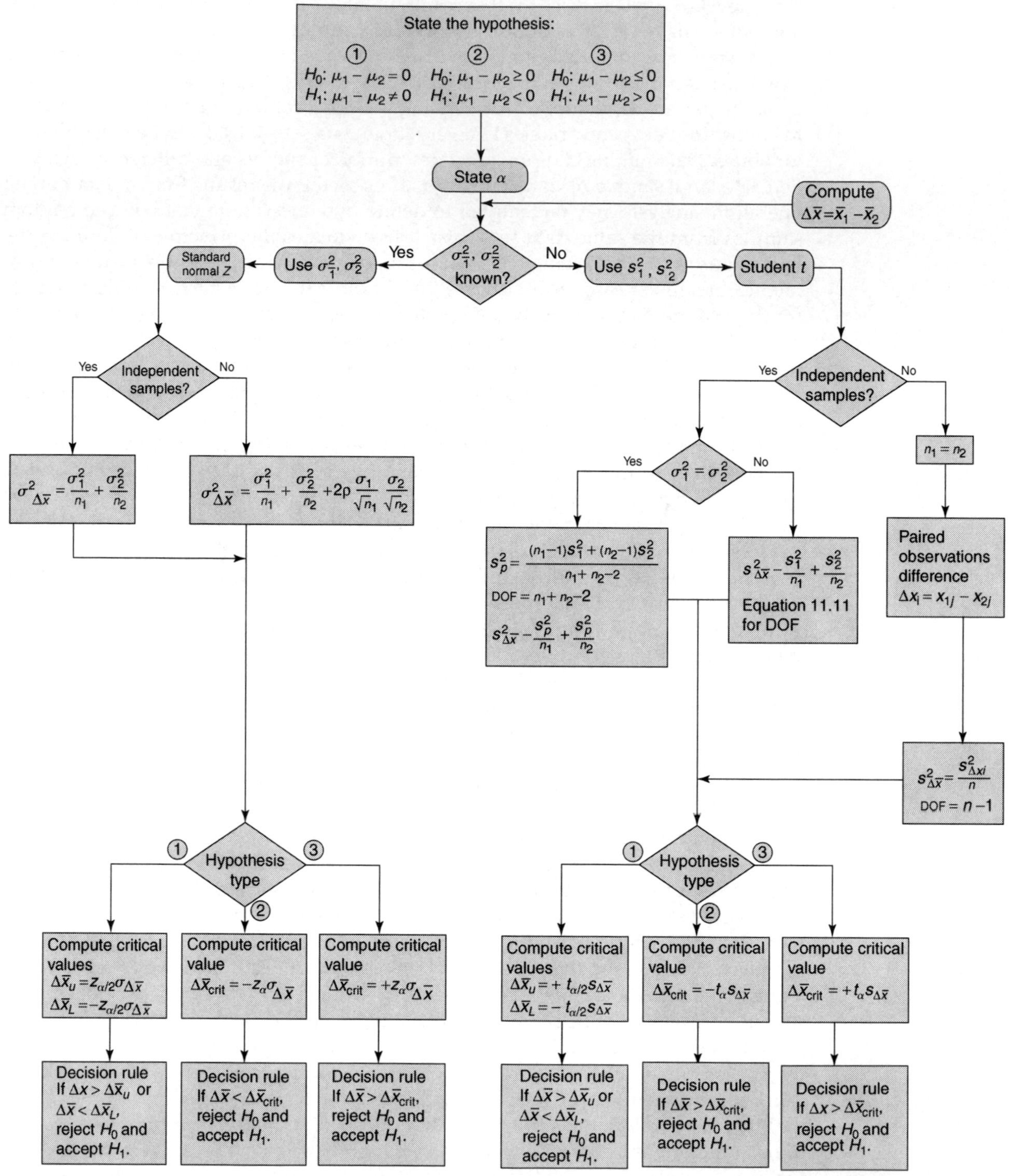

SUMMARY

In this chapter we have continued our development of the methodology for classical hypothesis testing. Building on the work in Chapter 10 we developed procedures for comparing population means and proportions. Hypothesis tests of the differences between population means and between population proportions were developed. In addition, we developed procedures for testing population variances by using sample variances. Finally, we developed procedures for comparing population variances from two different populations. In addition, we considered characteristics of the problem-solving environment and noted appropriate and inappropriate applications of hypothesis testing.

Figure 11.5 presents a flow chart for selecting the appropriate hypothesis test when comparing two population means. Similarly, Figure 11.6 presents a flow chart for selecting an appropriate hypothesis test when comparing two population proportions. Both of these flow charts provide a good summary of the various hypothesis test options and could be helpful in your future work.

Figure 11.6 Flow Chart for Selecting the Appropriate Hypothesis Test When Comparing Two Population Proportions

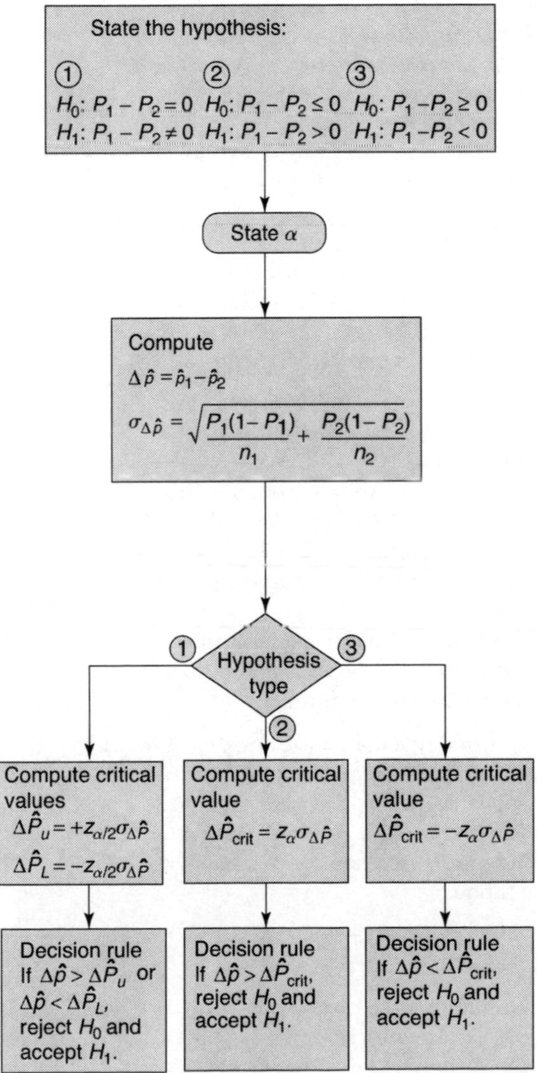

KEY WORDS

- alternative hypothesis
- *F* distribution
- null hypothesis
- test of the equality of two population proportions
- tests of equality of variances from two normal populations
- tests of the difference between population means: independent samples (known variances)
- tests of the difference between population means: matched pairs
- tests of the difference between population means: population variances unknown and equal
- tests of the difference between population means: population variances unknown and not equal
- tests of the difference between population proportions (large samples)
- tests of variance of a normal population

CHAPTER EXERCISES AND APPLICATIONS

Note: If the probability of Type I error is not indicated, select a level that is appropriate for the situation described.

11.32 A statistician tests the null hypothesis that the proportion of men favoring a tax reform proposal is the same as the proportion of women. Based on sample data, the null hypothesis is rejected at the 5% significance level. Does this imply that the probability is at least 0.95 that the null hypothesis is false? If not, provide a valid probability statement.

11.33 A process produces cable for the local telephone company. When the process is operating correctly, cable diameter follows a normal distribution with mean 1.6 inches and standard deviation 0.05 inch. A random sample of 16 pieces of cable found diameters with sample mean 1.615 inches and sample standard deviation 0.086 inch.

a. Assuming that the population standard deviation is 0.05 inch, test at the 10% level against a two-sided alternative the null hypothesis that the population mean is 1.6 inches. Find also the lowest level of significance at which this null hypothesis can be rejected against the two-sided alternative.
b. Test at the 10% level the null hypothesis that the population standard deviation is 0.05 inch against the alternative that it is bigger.

11.34 When operating normally, a manufacturing process produces tablets for which the mean weight of the active ingredient is 5 grams, and the standard deviation is 0.025 gram. For a random sample of 12 tablets the following weights of active ingredient (in grams) were found:

5.01	4.69	5.03	4.98	4.98	4.95
5.00	5.00	5.03	5.01	5.04	4.95

a. Without assuming that the population variance is known, test the null hypothesis that the population mean weight of active ingredient per tablet is 5 grams. Use a two-sided alternative and a 5% significance level. State any assumptions that you make.
b. Stating any assumptions that you make, test the null hypothesis that the population standard deviation is 0.025 gram against the alternative hypothesis that the population standard deviation exceeds 0.025 gram. Use a 5% significance level.

11.35 An insurance company employs agents on a commission basis. It claims that, in their first year, agents will earn a mean commission of at least \$40,000 and that the population standard deviation is no more than \$6,000. A random sample of nine agents found, for commission in the first year,

$$\sum_{i=1}^{9} x_i = 333 \quad \text{and} \quad \sum_{i=1}^{9} (x_i - \bar{x})^2 = 312$$

measured in thousands of dollars. The population distribution can be assumed to be normal.

a. Test at the 5% level the null hypothesis that the population mean is at least \$40,000.
b. Test at the 10% level the null hypothesis that the population standard deviation is at most \$6,000.

11.36 In a study of performance ratings of ex-smokers a random sample of 34 ex-smokers had a mean rating of 2.21 and a sample standard deviation of 2.21. For an independent random sample of 86 long-term ex-smokers the mean rating was 1.47 and the sample standard deviation was 1.69. Find the lowest level of significance at which the null hypothesis of equality of the two population means can be rejected against a two-sided alternative.

11.37 Independent random samples of business managers and college economics faculty were asked to respond on a scale from 1 (strongly disagree) to

7 (strongly agree) to this statement: "Grades in advanced economics are good indicators of students' analytical skills." For a sample of 70 business managers the mean response was 4.4 and the sample standard deviation was 1.3. For a sample of 106 economics faculty the mean response was 5.3 and the sample standard deviation was 1.4.

a. Test at the 5% level the null hypothesis that the population mean response for business managers would be at most 4.0.
b. Test at the 5% level the null hypothesis that the population means are equal against the alternative that the population mean response is higher for economics faculty than for business managers.

11.38 Independent random samples of bachelor's and master's degree holders in statistics, whose initial job was with a major actuarial firm and who subsequently moved to an insurance company, were questioned. For a sample of 44 bachelor's degree holders the mean number of months before the first job change was 35.02 and the sample standard deviation was 18.20. For a sample of 68 master's degree holders the mean number of months before the first job change was 36.34 and the sample standard deviation was 18.94. Test at the 10% level, against a two-sided alternative, the null hypothesis that the population mean numbers of months before the first job change are the same for the two groups.

11.39 A study was aimed at assessing the effects of group size and group characteristics on the generation of advertising concepts. To assess the influence of group size, groups of four and eight members were compared. For a random sample of four 4-member groups the mean number of advertising concepts generated per group was 78.0 and the sample standard deviation was 24.4. For an independent random sample of four 8-member groups, the mean number of advertising concepts generated per group was 114.7 and the sample standard deviation was 14.6. (In each case, the groups had a moderator.) Stating any assumptions that you need to make, test at the 1% level the null hypothesis that the population means are the same against the alternative that the mean is higher for 8-member groups.

11.40 An index of reading difficulty of a written text is calculated through the following steps:

i. Find the average number of words per sentence.
ii. Find the percentage of words with four or more syllables.
iii. The index is 40% of the sum of (i) and (ii).

A random sample of six advertisements taken from magazine A had the following indices:

15.75 11.55 11.16 9.92 9.23 8.20

An independent random sample of six advertisements from magazine B had the following indices:

9.17 8.44 6.10 5.78 5.58 5.36

Stating any assumptions you need to make, test at the 5% level the null hypothesis that the population mean indices are the same against the alternative that the true mean is higher for magazine A than for magazine B.

11.41 From Exercise 11.40 the indices for a random sample of six advertisements in magazine C were as follows:

9.50 8.60 8.59 6.50 4.79 4.29

For an independent random sample of six advertisements in magazine D, the indices were as follows:

10.21 9.66 7.67 5.12 4.88 3.12

Stating any assumptions you need to make, test against a two-sided alternative the null hypothesis that the two population mean indices are the same.

11.42 Independent random samples of business and economics faculty were asked to respond on a scale from 1 (strongly disagree) to 4 (strongly agree) to this statement: "The threat and actuality of takeovers of publicly held companies provide discipline for boards and managers to maximize the value of the company to shareholders." For a sample of 202 business faculty the mean response was 2.83 and the sample standard deviation was 0.89. For a sample of 291 economics faculty the mean response was 3.00 and the sample standard deviation was 0.67. Test the null hypothesis that the population means are equal against the alternative that the mean is higher for economics faculty.

11.43 Independent random samples of patients who had received knee and hip replacement were asked to assess the quality of service on a scale from 1 (low) to 7 (high). For a sample of 83 knee patients the mean rating was 6.543 and the sample standard deviation was 0.649. For a sample of 54 hip patients the mean rating was 6.733 and the sample standard deviation was 0.425. Test against a two-sided alternative the null hypothesis that the population mean ratings for these two types of patients are the same.

11.44 Of a random sample of 148 accounting majors 75 rated a sense of humor as a very important trait to their career performance. This same view was held by 81 of an independent random sample of 178 finance majors.

a. Test at the 5% level the null hypothesis that at least one-half of all finance majors rate a sense of humor as very important.
b. Test at the 5% level against a two-sided alternative the null hypothesis that the population proportions of accounting and finance majors who rate a sense of humor as very important are the same.

11.45 Aimed at finding substantial earnings decreases, a random sample of 23 firms with substantial earnings decreases showed that the mean return on assets three years previously was 0.058 and the sample standard deviation was 0.055. An independent random sample of 23 firms without substantial earnings decreases showed a mean return of 0.146 and a standard deviation 0.058 for the same period. Assume that the two population distributions are normal with equal standard deviations. Test at the 5% level the null hypothesis that the population mean returns on assets are the same against the alternative that the true mean is higher for firms without substantial earnings decrease.

11.46 Random samples of employees in fast-food restaurants where the employer provides a training program were drawn. Of a sample of 67 employees who had not completed high school 11 had participated in a training program provided by their current employer. Of an independent random sample of 113 employees who had completed high school but had not attended college, 27 had participated. Test at the 1% level the null hypothesis that the participation rates are the same for the two groups against the alternative that the rate is lower for those who have not completed high school.

11.47 Of a random sample of 69 health insurance firms 47 did public relations in-house, as did 40 of an independent random sample of 69 casualty insurance firms. Find and interpret the p-value of a test of equality of the population proportions against a two-sided alternative.

11.48 Independent random samples were taken of male and female clients of University Entrepreneurship Centers. These clients were considering starting a business. Of 94 male clients 53 actually started a business venture, as did 47 of 68 female clients. Find and interpret the p-value of a test of equality of the population proportions against the alternative that the proportion of female clients actually starting a business is higher than the proportion of male clients.

11.49 An index of reading difficulty of a written text is calculated through the following steps:

i. Find the average number of words per sentence.
ii. Find the percentage of words with four or more syllables.
iii. The index is 40% of the sum of (i) and (ii).

A random sample of six advertisements taken from magazine A had the following indices:

15.75	11.55	11.16	9.92	9.23	8.20

An independent random sample of six advertisements from magazine B had the following indices:

9.17	8.44	6.10	5.78	5.58	5.36

Test against a two-sided alternative the null hypothesis that the population standard deviation of the index of advertisements in magazine A is the same as the population standard deviation of the index of advertisements in magazine B.

11.50 Two financial analysts were asked to predict earnings per share for a random sample of 12 corporations over the coming year. The quality of their forecasts was evaluated in terms of absolute percentage forecast error, defined as

$$100 \times \frac{|\text{Actual} - \text{Predicted}|}{\text{Actual}}$$

The absolute percentage forecast errors made are shown in the data file **Analyst Prediction**.

Test the null hypothesis of equality of population variances for absolute percentage forecast errors for the two analysts.

11.51 You are in charge of rural economic development in a rapidly developing country that is using its new-found oil wealth to develop the entire country. As part of your responsibility you have been asked to determine if there is evidence that the new rice-growing procedures have increased output per hectare. A random sample of 27 fields was planted using the old procedure, and the sample mean output was 60 per hectare with a sample variance of 100. During the second year the new procedure was applied to the same fields and the sample mean output was 64 per hectare, with a sample variance of 150. The sample correlation between the two fields was 0.38. The population variances are assumed to be equal, and that assumption should be used for the problem analysis.

a. Use a hypothesis test with a probability of Type I error = 0.05 to determine if there is strong evidence to support the conclusion that the new process leads to higher output per hectare, and interpret the results.
b. Under the assumption that the population variances are equal, construct a 95%

acceptance interval for the ratio of the sample variances. Do the observed sample variances lead us to conclude that the population variances are the same? Please explain.

11.52 The president of Amalgamated Retailers International, Samiha Peterson, has asked for your assistance in studying the market penetration for the company's new cell phone. You are asked to study two markets and determine if the difference in market share remains the same. Historically, in market 1, in western Poland, Amalgamated has had a 30% market share. Similarly, in market 2, in southern Austria, Amalgamated has had a 35% market share. You obtain a random sample of potential customers from each area. From market 1, 258 out of a total sample of 800 indicate they will purchase from Amalgamated. From market 2, 260 out of 700 indicate they will purchase from Amalgamated.

a. Using a probability of error $\alpha = 0.03$, test the hypothesis that the market shares are equal versus the hypothesis that they are not equal (market 2 – market 1).
b. Using a probability of error $\alpha = 0.03$, test the hypothesis that the market shares are equal versus the hypothesis that the share in market 2 is larger.

11.53 In an agricultural experiment two expensive, high-yield varieties of corn are to be tested and the yield improvements measured. The experiment is arranged so that each variety is planted in 10 pairs of similar plots. The data contained in data file **Corn Yield** are the percentage yield increases obtained for these two varieties. Stating any assumptions you make, test at the 10% level the null hypothesis that the two population mean percentage yield increases are the same. Use a two-sided alternative hypothesis.

11.54 You are the product manager for brand 4 in a large food company. The company president has complained that a competing brand, called brand 2, has higher average sales. The data services group has stored the latest product sales ("saleb2" and "saleb4") and price data ("apriceb2" and "apriceb4") in a file named **Storet**, which is contained on your data disk or local computer system.

a. Based on a statistical hypothesis test, does the president have strong evidence to support his complaint? Show all statistical work and reasoning.
b. After analyzing the data, you note that a large outlier of value 971 is contained in the sample for brand 2. Repeat part (a) with this extreme observation removed. What do you now conclude about the president's complaint?

11.55 Joe Ortega is the product manager for Ole ice cream. You have been asked to determine if Ole ice cream has greater sales than Carl's ice cream, which is a strong competitor. The data file **Ole** contains weekly sales and price data for the competing brands over the year in three different supermarket chains. These sample data represent a random sample of all ice cream sales for the two brands.

a. Design and implement an analysis to determine if there is strong evidence to conclude that Ole ice cream has higher mean sales than Carl's ice cream ($\alpha = 0.05$). Explain your procedure and show all computations. You may include Minitab output if appropriate to support your analysis. Explain your conclusions.
b. Design and implement an analysis to determine if the prices charged for the two brands are different ($\alpha = 0.05$). Carefully explain your analysis, show all computations, and interpret your results.

11.56 Mary Peterson is in charge of preparing blended flour for exotic bread making. The process is to take two different types of flour and mix them together in order to achieve high-quality breads. For one of the products flour A and flour B are mixed together. The package of flour A comes from a packing process that has a population mean weight of 8 ounces with a population variance of 0.04. The package of flour B has a population mean weight of 8 ounces and a population variance of 0.06. The package weights have a correlation of 0.40. The A and B packages are mixed together to obtain a 16-ounce package of special exotic flour. Every 60 minutes a random sample of four packages of exotic flour are selected from the process, and the mean weight for the four packages is computed. Prepare a 99% acceptance interval for a quality control chart for the sample means from the sample of four packages. Show all of your work and explain your reasoning. Explain how this acceptance chart would be used to ensure that the package weights continue to meet the standard.

REFERENCE

1. Carlson, W. L., and B. Thorne. *Applied Statistical Methods*. Upper Saddle River, NJ: Prentice Hall, 1997. pp. 539–53.

Topic 23

Time Series and Forecasting

CHAPTER 4

Time series and forecasting

Objectives

By the end of this chapter you should be able to:

- use time series data to find both trend and seasonal variation as a basis for forecasting;
- apply the technique of moving averages to help in the calculation of trend lines and seasonal factors;
- combine time series and regression analysis for purposes of forecasting;
- apply exponential smoothing as a forecasting technique;
- be aware of the use of other approaches to forecasting in contemporary business practice.

Introduction

Data can be collected for purposes of analysis in a number of ways. For example data for household expenditure on food can be collected in different locations (nation, region, city, etc.) at a *single point of time*. These are called **cross-sectional data**. Alternatively data for household expenditure on food can be collected for a given location (nation, region, city, etc.) at *different points in time*. This is called **time series data**.

In this chapter we consider the use of such **time series** data as a basis for estimating both trend and seasonal variation. As we shall see, such estimates can then be used as a basis for **forecasting**.

In fact we have already touched on forecasting in Chapter 3 when we used the least squares line to predict values of the dependent variable (Y) for as yet unobtained values of the independent variable (X). We take this aspect of forecasting using regression analysis a little further in this chapter. Indeed we see how we can usefully *combine* regression analysis with the results of our time series analysis to forecast future outcomes.

The chapter concludes with a more general review of forecasting techniques, including **exponential smoothing** and other widely used techniques in current business practice.

Answers to the 'Self-check questions', responses to each 'Pause for thought' and answers to the 'Review questions' can be found at the end of the book.

4.1 Time series analysis

Many types of data have been recorded through time, such as monthly, quarterly or annual data for output, sales revenue, profit, employment, unemployment, prices, etc.

Components of time series

Typically such **time series** data exhibit one or more of the following components.

- A **trend component (*T*)**, whereby the variable appears to broadly rise or fall (or remain unchanged) through time.
- A **seasonal component (*S*)**, whereby the variable moves in regular cycles *within a year* around that trend line. For example within a broadly rising value of sales through time (trend), an ice cream manufacturer may regularly experience peaks for sales in summer months and troughs for sales in winter months (seasonal).

Note that although the term 'seasonal' has been applied to such short-term cycles, these may involve any units of time within a year; for example days within a week (e.g. high sales on Fridays and low sales on Mondays), weeks within a month, months or quarters or 'seasons' within a year.

PAUSE FOR THOUGHT 4.1 *Can you list six products (goods or services) other than the ice cream already mentioned, the demand for which you might expect to experience seasonal variation within a year?*

- A **cyclical component** (C), whereby the variable moves in a rather less regular cycle over the medium to longer term around the trend line. For example some have claimed to observe a *business cycle* of some eight to ten years between periods of 'boom' and 'bust' in modern industrialised economies. Others have claimed to observe still longer cycles over 50 years, with the peaks of such cycles related to new technological breakthroughs, such as water power, steam, electricity, microelectronics, etc. These have sometimes been referred to as *Kondratief cycles*, after a Russian economist of that name.

Note that the **period** of a cycle is often referred to as the time between successive peaks or successive troughs.

- An **irregular component** (I), which is entirely unpredictable. The stock market crash of 1987 was, for example, a dramatic and unexpected departure from trend in terms of share prices.

PAUSE FOR THOUGHT 4.2 *Can you name three other irregular components which have influenced a wide range of UK producers in the past ten years?*

Figure 4.1 presents two possible time series profiles for the value of a dependent variable (*Y*).

figure 4.1
Some time series profiles

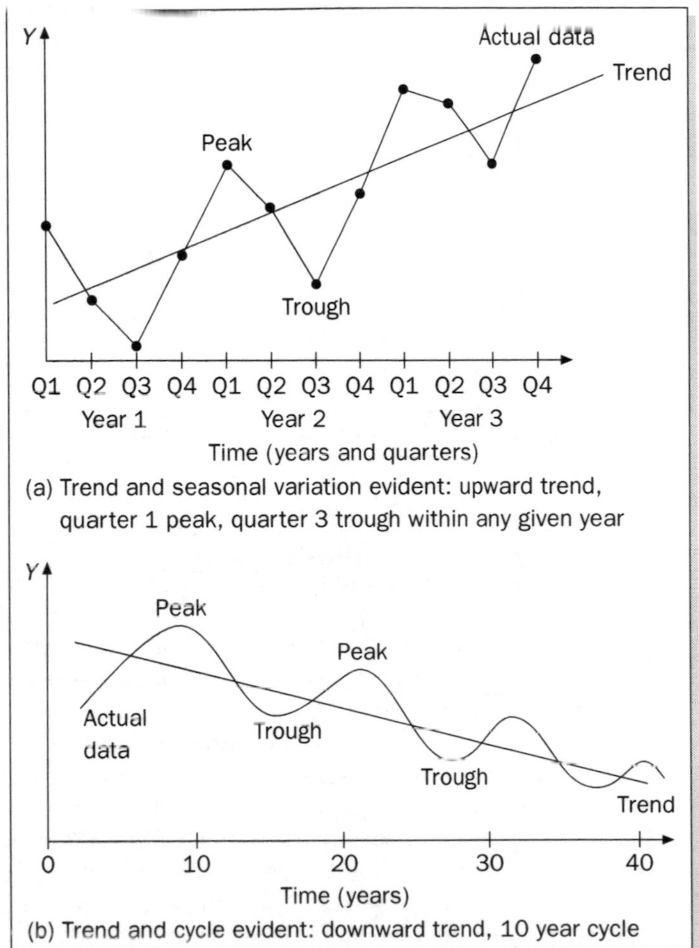

(a) Trend and seasonal variation evident: upward trend, quarter 1 peak, quarter 3 trough within any given year

(b) Trend and cycle evident: downward trend, 10 year cycle

In Figure 4.1(a) a clear upward trend is evident, around which there is *seasonal variation*, with quarter 1 representing successive peaks and quarter 3 successive troughs within each year. In Figure 4.1(b) a clear downward trend is evident, around which there is a *cyclical component* with a period of around ten years between successive peaks or successive troughs.

Of course many variants are possible for such profiles. We may, for example, have a shorter-term seasonal variation (e.g. quarterly or monthly) superimposed on a time series showing both a cycle and trend using longer-term (e.g. annual) data.

> ***DID YOU KNOW?***
> *The construction industry is widely regarded as a barometer for economic prospects throughout the economy. Traditionally it is one of the earliest sectors to be affected by economic recession and one of the earliest sectors to experience higher demand when economic recovery occurs.*

Additive or multiplicative model

We can represent or 'model' our time series using the four components already identified. We can do this in one of two ways; either *adding* or *multiplying* the respective components.

figure 4.2
Choosing an appropriate time series model

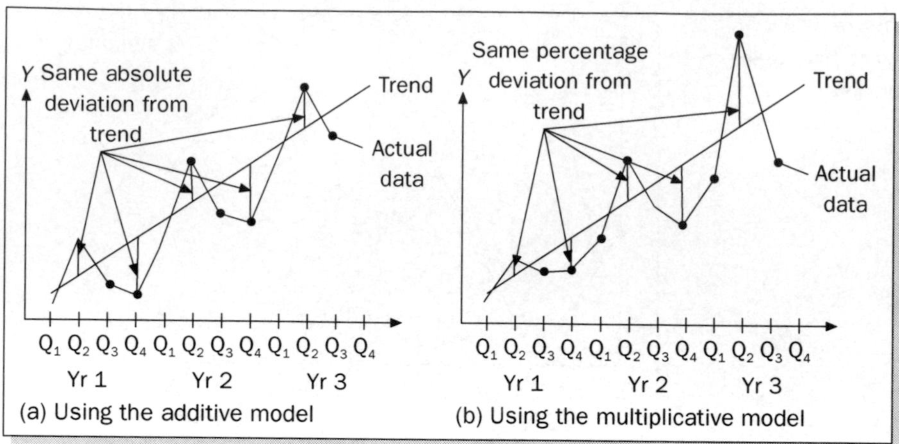

(a) Using the additive model (b) Using the multiplicative model

- $Y = T + S + C + I$ **Additive model**
- $Y = T \times S \times C \times I$ **Multiplicative model**

As we shall see, we can use either of these models to calculate any trend line or seasonal variation. However there may be circumstances where one approach is more appropriate than another!

As we see in Figure 4.2(a), the **additive model** is the most appropriate where deviations from the trend line are of a similar *absolute magnitude* from one peak (or trough) to another. This is shown in Figure 4.2(a) as occurring for short-term cycles (e.g. seasonal variations, with Q2 providing peaks and Q4 troughs). The same principle would equally apply if we were using annual data and comparing successive peaks or troughs in a business cycle over, say, an eight to ten year period.

However as we see in Figure 4.2(b), the **multiplicative model** is the most appropriate where deviations from the trend line are of a similar *percentage* from one peak (or trough) to another. We can see that the absolute magnitude of the deviations from the trend line grows over time as the dependent variable (Y) rises, but that the percentage deviations remain roughly constant.

4.2 Moving average

As we shall see in the next section, we can use the idea of a **moving average** to find the **trend** of the data. To find the moving average we initially find the simple average (arithmetic mean) for a specified number of items of data. We then recalculate that average having dropped the initial item of data and added a subsequent item of data.

In the worked example below involving quarterly data for sales value, we initially find the simple average for four items of data, and then *move* that average along.

WORKED EXAMPLE 4.1

Find a four quarter centred moving average for the following data on sales value (£000):

Solution

(1) Year and	Quarter	*(2)* Sales value (£000)	*(3)* 4 quarter moving total	*(4)* 4 quarter moving average	*(5)* Centred 4 quarter moving average
1998	1	87.5			
	2	73.2			
			314.0	78.5	
	3	64.8			78.9
			316.8	79.2	
	4	88.5			79.6
			319.6	79.9	
1999	1	90.3			80.5
			324.0	81.0	
	2	76.0			81.8
			330.2	82.6	
	3	69.2			83.1
			333.8	83.5	
	4	94.7			83.8
			336.2	84.1	
2000	1	93.9			84.5
			339.0	84.8	
	2	78.4			85.5
			344.6	86.2	
	3	72.0			
	4	100.3			

It is often helpful to find the four quarter centred moving average in stages.

- **Four quarter moving total (column 3).** Here we simply sum the data for the initial four quarters in column (2) to find the four quarter *moving total*. Notice that the moving totals fall in between the actual quarterly data in column (2). For example the first moving total falls in between quarters 2 and 3 for 1998.
- **Four quarter moving average (column 4).** We then divide the respective four quarter *moving totals* in column (3) by 4 to find the four quarter *moving average*.
- **Four quarter centred moving average (column 5).** It will help to *align* the moving averages with the specific quarterly data in column (2). For this reason we *centre* the data in column (4) by summing respective pairs of data and dividing by 2.

DID YOU KNOW?
Survey evidence suggests that the technique of moving averages is used by around 25 per cent of UK businesses in an attempt to forecast future demand.

4.3 Finding the trend

In practice we are often presented with monthly or quarterly data over a number of years for which no obvious business cycle (C) of eight to ten years is present. We can therefore regard the *actual data*, Y, as having only three of the four components previously mentioned

i.e. $Y = T + S + I$ (Additive)

or $Y = T \times S \times I$ (Multiplicative)

If we calculate an appropriate *moving average* for the monthly or quarterly data, then we can *eliminate* both the seasonal variation component (S) and the irregular component (I) from the actual data. This will leave us with T, the required trend line.

- Using a four quarter moving average in column (4) of the worked example above means that we can *eliminate any seasonal variation* (S) as regards high or low quarters. For example in column (3) after our initial calculation of 314 we drop the first quarter of 1998 but add the first quarter of 1999 to get 316.8. Our four quarter moving total which is the basis for the subsequent centred four quarter moving average in column (5) therefore continually takes in *all* quarters, both high (as for quarter 1) and low (as for quarter 3). In this way column (5) continually eliminates S, the seasonal variation component.
- In calculating columns (4) and (5) we are *averaging*, and any averaging helps eliminate any irregular component. In this way column (5) helps eliminate I, the irregular component.

  If $Y = T + S + I$

  or $Y = T \times S \times I$

then column (5), having eliminated S and I, leaves us with T, the trend line.

Figure 4.3 plots the original quarterly data (Y) of column (2) and the trend line (T) of column (5) for the worked example.

Notice how we use the four quarter centred moving average for the trend line and use straight lines to connect successive points. An alternative approach would, of course, be to draw a single least squares line (see p. 52) which 'best fits' the points which correspond to the trend. We consider this alternative approach below (p. 87).

PAUSE FOR THOUGHT 4.3 *Can you name three products (goods or services) for which an upward sales trend is well established, and three products for which a downward sales trend is well established?*

The nature of the data will define the *type* of moving average required to eliminate S and I and therefore leave only the trend line, T.

Using moving averages to find trend (T)

- **Quarterly data**: use four quarter centred moving average to eliminate S and I, and leave T.
- **Monthly data**: use 12 month centred moving average to eliminate S and I, and leave T.

figure 4.3
Plotting the trend line

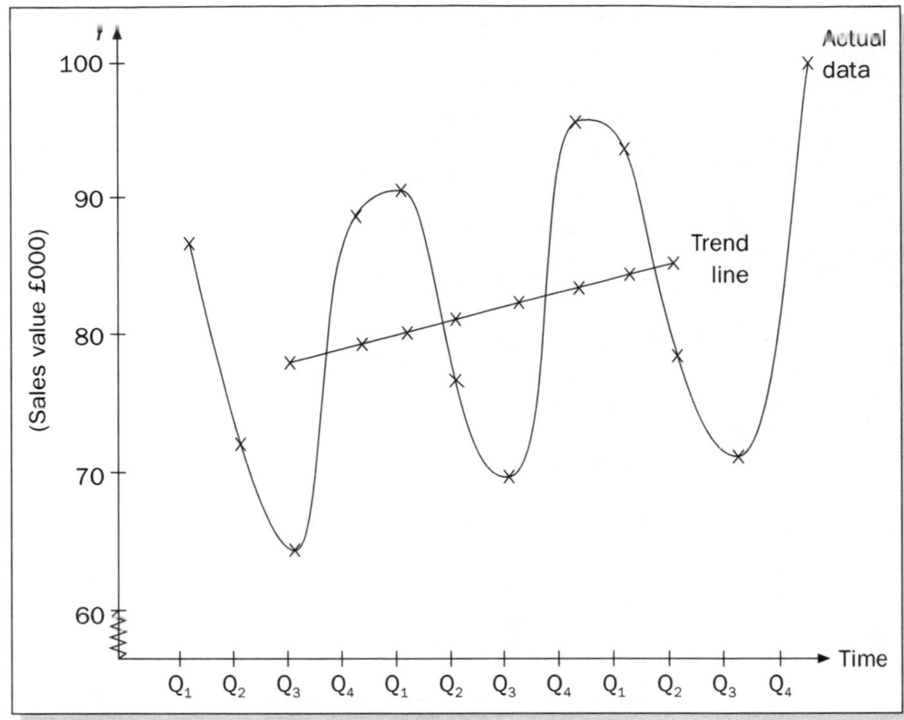

SELF-CHECK QUESTION

4.1 UK passenger movements by air are shown in the table below (data in 100,000 passengers):

Year	*Q1*	*Q2*	*Q3*	*Q4*
1998	**44**	**80**	**120**	**60**
1999	**52**	**88**	**126**	**62**
2000	**60**	**98**	**140**	**68**

Use an appropriate moving average to find the trend of the data. Plot the original data and your trend line on a graph.

Note: **An answer can be found on p. 334.**

4.4 Finding and eliminating the seasonal variation

When the original data (Y) has no obvious longer-term business cycle in evidence, we have already noted that it can be represented as either:

$$Y = T + S + I \quad \text{(additive model)}$$

or $$Y = T \times S \times I \quad \text{(multiplicative model)}$$

Finding the seasonal variation (S)

We can easily extend our work in using moving averages to find T, the trend component, so that we can find S, the seasonal variation component. Essentially we need only add an extra column to the calculations already undertaken to find T. This extra column which gives us S (and I) will be $(Y - T)$ in the case of the *additive model* or $\left(\frac{Y}{T}\right)$ in the case of the multiplicative model, for the following reasons:

$$Y = T + S + I \text{ (additive model)}$$

$$MA = T$$

$$\underline{Y - MA = S + I}$$

or $Y = T \times S \times I$ (multiplicative model)

$$MA = T$$

$$\frac{Y}{MA} = S \times I$$

As we shall see, a further simple averaging process will remove I, leaving S, the seasonal variation which we require.

WORKED EXAMPLE **4.2**

We can demonstrate this approach by using the earlier calculations (p. 81) for sales value in Worked Example 4.1. Here we shall use the *additive* model.

Solution

table 4.1
Time series of quarterly sales value (£000)

		Y (original data)	T Four quarter centred moving average	S + I (Y − T)
1998	Q1	87.5		
	Q2	73.2		
	Q3	64.8	78.9	−14.1
	Q4	88.5	79.6	8.9
1999	Q1	90.3	80.5	9.8
	Q2	76.0	81.8	−5.8
	Q3	69.2	83.1	−13.9
	Q4	94.7	83.8	10.9
2000	Q1	93.9	84.5	9.4
	Q2	78.4	85.5	−7.1
	Q3	72.0		
	Q4	100.3		

Subtracting our trend values (T) from the corresponding quarterly sales values (Y) gives us $S + I$ over successive quarters. The averaging process will then tend to remove I, leaving us with S as required.

A simple table can usefully illustrate this process.

table 4.2
Finding the seasonal variation factors (£000)

	Q1	Q2	Q3	Q4
1998			–14.1	8.9
1999	9.8	–5.8	–13.9	10.9
2000	9.4	–7.1		
Total	19.2	–12.9	–28.0	19.8
average (S)	9.6	–6.45	–14	9.9

The averaging process for each quarter leaves us with S, the seasonal variation for that quarter. Clearly quarters 1 and 4 are high sales quarters for this product, whereas quarter 2 and especially quarter 3 are low sales quarters.

Adjusted S

The data shown in the 'average' row for S are actually *unadjusted*. If we sum the plus values we have +19.5 (9.6 + 9.9) but if we sum the negative values we have –20.45 (–6.45 + –14.0). In other words there is a *net value* for S of –0.95.

Strictly speaking the plus and minus values should cancel out. We can compensate for the –0.95 by adding +0.95/4 (i.e. +0.24) to *each* of the four quarterly values for S. These values would then be the **adjusted values** for S.

table 4.3
Finding the adjusted seasonal variation factors (£000)

	Q1	Q2	Q3	Q4
Unadjusted S (0.95 net)	+9.6	–6.45	–14.0	+9.9
Adjusted *S (zero net)	+9.84	–6.21	–13.76	+10.14

$* + \left(\frac{0.95}{4}\right)$ i.e. +0.24 added to each quarter

It is these adjusted values for S that we usually refer to as the seasonal variation components. Here we can see that sales are normally +9.84 above trend for Q1, but –6.21 below trend for Q2, and so on (all values in £000).

Eliminating the seasonal variations (S)

Having found S, the seasonal variation component, our next step is to *eliminate* S from the original data, Y. We will then have an estimate of Y without any 'distortion' resulting from seasonal influences on Y. Such data with the seasonal variation removed is sometimes called **deseasonalised data**.

table 4.4
Eliminating the seasonal variation from the original data (i.e. deseasonalising the data)

		Y (original data)	S (adjusted seasonal variation)	Y – S (deseasonalised data)
1998	Q1	87.5	+9.84	77.66
	Q2	73.2	–6.21	79.41
	Q3	64.8	–13.76	78.56
	Q4	88.5	+10.14	78.36
1999	Q1	90.3	+ 9.84	80.46
	Q2	76.0	–6.21	82.21
	Q3	69.2	–13.76	82.96
	Q4	94.7	+10.14	84.56
2000	Q1	93.9	+9.84	84.06
	Q2	78.4	–6.21	84.61
	Q3	72.0	–13.76	85.76
	Q4	100.3	+10.14	90.16

Notice that in eliminating S by subtracting S from Y, we sometimes have – – = +, as in Q2 of 1998 when 73.2 – – 6.21 = 79.41.

Using the adjusted seasonal variation component, *S*, calculated above we can easily eliminate *S* from the original data, *Y*. Here we use the *additive* model for illustration purposes and therefore *subtract S* from *Y* for each quarter (in the multiplicative model we would *divide S* into *Y* for each quarter).

ACTIVITY **4**

It can be an involved process calculating the components of time series data. The spreadsheet (p. 467) provides a template for such calculations with the values of the respective quarterly data entered in column D and the calculations and results carried out automatically. Although the layout is for quarterly data, the concept can be adapted for any time series data. The values 2 and two in cells **I1** and **J1** determine the number of decimal places in selected columns.

The layout and formulae for the spreadsheet are shown in Figure A4.2 (p. 467).

As you will see, you are using the technique of a four quarter centred moving average to estimate the trend of the data (had the data been monthly, you would have used a twelve month centred moving average to estimate trend). You are also finding the (adjusted) seasonal factors. If you are using your trend values for *forecasting* you will need to subtract the seasonal factors from each quarterly trend estimate to get a more accurate forecast for that quarter.

Set up your spreadsheet and then enter the quarterly data values shown below.

Year	Q1	Q2	Q3	Q4
Year 1	196.9	295.5	349.4	389.3
Year 2	324.1	418.0	447.5	456.4
Year 3	415.2	528.6	550.6	615.3
Year 4	513.6	650.8	670.6	754.4

- Comment on your results
- Check your solution with the response on p. 466
- Repeat the procedure using the quarterly data values in the various Self-check and Review questions involving moving averages.

4.5 Forecasting: time series

We have already looked at prediction (forecasting) using the simple regression analysis of Chapter 3 (p. 52). Here we *combine* the idea of finding a least squares line (line of 'best fit') with our analysis of time series components. We can then *extrapolate* (take forward) the regression line which best fits the trend estimates to derive a forecast of future sales, etc.

Forecasting: trend value only

For example we can fit a single *least squares line* to the trend estimates on the earlier scatter diagrams (e.g. Figure 4.3, p. 83), instead of merely linking successive trend estimates by a sequence of straight lines. This regression line, once calculated, can then be used for prediction (forecasting) of future trend values.

We must initially calculate the regression line for the eight trend estimates shown in Figure 4.3 and Table 4.1. We can use *either* of the two approaches considered in Chapter 3 for calculating a regression line. Here we use the 'original data' formula (p. 53), with the dependent variable Y standing for the trend value and the independent variable X standing for time (quarters). With trend estimates available for eight successive quarters, we let $X = 1$ for the first available quarter for a trend estimate (Q2, 1998), rising to $X = 8$ for the eighth available quarter for a trend estimate (Q3, 2000).

From Table 4.1 above (p. 84) we can then construct a new table allowing the application of our regression formula:

X (*quarter of data*)	Y (*trend value*)	XY	X^2	Y^2
1	78.9	78.9	1	6,225.2
2	79.6	159.2	4	6,336.2
3	80.5	241.5	9	6,480.3
4	81.8	327.2	16	6,691.2
5	83.1	415.5	25	6,905.6
6	83.8	502.8	36	7,022.4
7	84.5	591.5	49	7,140.3
8	85.5	684.0	64	7,310.3
$\Sigma X = 36$	$\Sigma Y = 657.7$	$\Sigma XY = 3{,}000.6$	$\Sigma X^2 = 204$	$\Sigma Y^2 = 54{,}111.5$

$$\bar{X} = \frac{36}{8} = 4.5 \quad \bar{Y} = \frac{657.7}{8} = 82.2$$

We noted (p. 53) that, using original data, the formula for the regression (least squares) line is:

$$\hat{Y} = mX + c$$

where $m = \dfrac{n\sum XY - \sum X \sum Y}{n\sum X^2 - \left(\sum X\right)^2}$

and $c = \bar{Y} - m\bar{X}$

where n = the number of observations

i.e. $m = \dfrac{8(3{,}000.6) - (36)(657.7)}{8(204) - (36)^2}$

$$m = \frac{24{,}004.8 - 23{,}677.2}{1{,}632 - 1{,}296}$$

$$m = \frac{327.6}{336}$$

$$\underline{m = +0.975}$$

$$c = \bar{Y} - m\bar{X}$$

i.e. $c = 82.2 - 0.975(4.5)$

$$\underline{c = 77.8}$$

$$\underline{\hat{Y}_T = 0.975X + 77.8}$$

where $\hat{Y}_T$ = trend sales value (£000)

X = quarterly time period (Q2, 1998 = 0)

We can now use this regression line to **predict** or **forecast** future trend values should this past relationship hold into the future.

Figure 4.4 plots this regression line for the trend and extrapolates the trend line into the future.

The dashed part of the trend line indicates where the extrapolation occurs, i.e. where the line is extended beyond that for which data are currently available.

We can use the regression line for forecasting. For example we can see from Figure 4.4 that:

when $X = 12$ (i.e. Q2, 2001)

$$\hat{Y}_T = 0.975(12) + 77.8$$

$$\hat{Y}_T = 11.7 + 77.8$$

i.e. $\underline{\hat{Y}_T = 89.5 \text{ (to 1 d.p.)}}$

Similarly, when $X = 20$ (i.e. Q2, 2003)

$\hat{Y}_T = 0.975(20) + 77.8$

$\hat{Y}_T = 19.5 + 77.8$

$\underline{\hat{Y}_T = 97.3 \text{ (to 1 d.p.)}}$

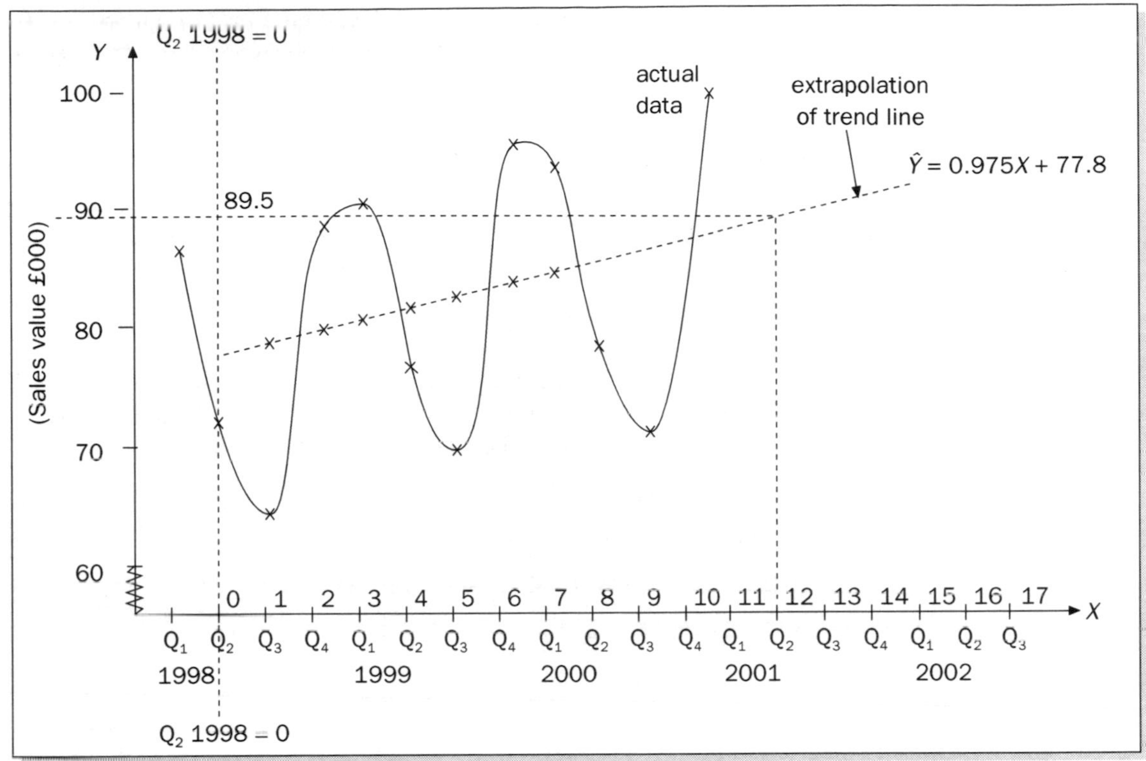

figure 4.4
Using the regression analysis to find the trend line and using that line for forecasting

Of course, the better the fit of our regression line to the existing trend data, the more confident we can be in extrapolating the line to make forecasts in the future.

This brings us back to the coefficients of determination and correlation (Chapter 3, pp. 58–68). In this particular case there is an extremely good fit for our trend regression line.

Using original data

$$R^2 = \left[\frac{n\sum XY - \sum X \sum Y}{\sqrt{\left[n\sum X^2 - \left(\sum X\right)^2\right] \times \left[n\sum Y^2 - \left(\sum Y\right)^2\right]}} \right]^2$$

$$\text{i.e. } R^2 = \left[\frac{8(3{,}000.6) - (36)(657.7)}{\sqrt{\left[8(204) - (36)^2\right] \times \left[8(54{,}111.5) - (657.7)^2\right]}} \right]^2$$

$$\text{i.e. } R^2 = \left[\frac{24{,}004.8 - 23{,}677.2}{\sqrt{\left[1{,}632 - 1{,}296\right] \times \left[432{,}892.0 - 432{,}569.3\right]}} \right]^2$$

$$R^2 = \left[\frac{327.6}{\sqrt{336 \times 322.7}} \right]^2 = \left[\frac{327.6}{329.3} \right]^2 = [0.995]$$

$\underline{R^2 = \text{coefficient of determination} = 0.995}$

$\underline{R\ = \text{coefficient of correlation} = 0.997}$

With over 99 per cent of the total variation 'explained' or 'accounted for' by our regression line (see p. 60), we can have considerable confidence in forecasting into the future by extrapolating from our regression line.

Forecasting: trend and seasonal factors

Of course any forecast for the sales in a particular quarter will be more accurate if it takes into account the *seasonal variation, S,* components already identified as well as the trend. The adjusted values for S were as follows (£000):

Q1 (+9.84) Q2 (−6.21) Q3 (−13.76) Q4 (+10.14)

We must add or subtract these seasonal variation values to our trend forecast if we are to be more realistic about the likely future sales in a particular quarter.

For example, we can forecast the trend using the equation

$$\hat{Y}_T = 0.975X + 77.8$$

where $X = 0$ for Q2, 1998.

This gives the *trend* forecast for Q2, 2001 as follows:

- when $X = 12$ (i.e. Q2, 2001)

$$\hat{Y}_T = 0.975\ (12) + 77.8$$

$$\underline{\hat{Y}_T = 89.5}$$

However Q2 also has a *seasonal* component

$\underline{S = -6.21}$

So our forecast for $\hat{Y}_{T+S}$ with *both* T and S included is:

$\hat{Y}_{T+S} = 89.5 - 6.21$

$\underline{\hat{Y}_{T+S} = 83.29\ (£000)}$

Table 4.5 shows the forecast ($\hat{Y}$) for sales value (£000) over the period 2001–2003 inclusive.

table 4.5
Forecasts of $\hat{Y}_{T+S}$ including trend (T) and seasonal variation (S) components. Additive model with least squares line $\hat{Y}_T = 0.975X + 77.8$ for trend forecast (Q2, 1998 = 0).

Year and quarter		*X**	*($\hat{Y}_T$) Trend forecast*	*(S) Seasonal variation*	*$\hat{Y}_{T+S}$ Total forecast*
2001	Q1	11	88.5	+9.84	98.34
	Q2	12	89.5	−6.21	83.29
	Q3	13	90.5	−13.76	76.74
	Q4	14	91.5	+10.14	101.64
2002	Q1	15	92.4	+9.84	102.24
	Q2	16	93.4	−6.21	87.19
	Q3	17	94.4	−13.76	80.64
	Q4	18	95.4	+10.14	105.54
2003	Q1	19	96.4	+9.84	106.24
	Q2	20	97.3	−6.21	91.09
	Q3	21	98.3	−13.76	84.54
	Q4	22	99.3	+10.14	109.44
	etc.				

Note: * Quarter 2 1998 = 0

SELF CHECK QUESTION

4.2 The data below show UK sales of a particular model of car over three years (figures in 100,000 units).

Quarter	1	2	3	4
1998	66	106	140	82
1999	73	119	165	91
2000	85	130	205	100

(a) Use the technique of moving averages to find values for the trend component (*T*).
(b) Plot the original data and your trend values on a scatter diagram.
(c) Find a 'least squares line' to best fit your trend values.
(d) Estimate the season variation component (*S*).
(e) Forecast future sales, taking both trend and seasonal variation into account in:
(i) Quarter 1, year 2003
(ii) Quarter 3, year 2003
(f) How confident can you be in these forecasts?

Note: **An answer can be found on p. 335.**

4.6 Forecasting: exponential smoothing

A widely used technique in business forecasting is that of **exponential smoothing**. The idea here is that the forecast at time t for the next time period $(t + 1)$ should take into account the *observed error* in the forecast made for t in the previous time period $(t - 1)$.

Clearly such 'exponential smoothing' implies a learning process, whereby future forecasts are continually revised (smoothed) in the light of previous experience. Strictly speaking, this approach is most appropriate when there is little or no trend (T) in the data and little or no seasonal variation (S). It is best used for short-term forecasting, for example forecasting the outcome of the next time period.

We can express this approach as follows:

Next forecast = Previous forecast + Some proportion of the previous forecasting error

$$\hat{Y}_{t+1} = \hat{Y}_t + \alpha(Y_t - \hat{Y}_t)$$

where Y_t = actual data (observed outcome) in time period t.
$\hat{Y}_t, \hat{Y}_{t+1}$ = forecast data for next time period (t or $t + 1$) made in previous time period (t – 1 or t respectively)
α = smoothing constant

Put another way

$\hat{Y}_{t+1} = \hat{Y}_t + \alpha(E_t)$

where E_t = error term = $Y_t - \hat{Y}_t$

The value assigned to α, the **smoothing constant**, can vary between zero and one

i.e. $0 \le \alpha \le 1$

We can usefully consider the extreme values of α by way of illustration.

- When $\alpha = 0$, no adjustment is made for the previous forecasting error. The next forecast is then assumed to be the same as the previous forecast.
- When $\alpha = 1$, full adjustment is made for the previous forecasting error. The next forecast is then the previous forecast ± the entire amount of any previous forecasting error.

In practice α can be derived *experimentally*, based on the average size of the error term in previous forecasts. Values of between 0.1 and 0.3 are typically assigned to α.

In the Table 4.6 below we continue this exponential forecast into other quarters, based on the actual values of Y (quarterly sales) shown (000 units)

table 4.6
Exponential forecast of future demand (000 units), $\alpha = 0.2$

Quarter	Y_t *(actual sales)*	$\hat{Y}_t$ *(forecast sales)*	E_t $(Y_t - \hat{Y}_t)$
1	96		
2	102	84	18
3	104	87.6	16.4
4	100	90.9	9.1
5	88	92.7	−4.7
6	92	91.8	0.2
7	96	91.8	4.2
8	94	92.6	1.4
9	90	92.9	−2.9
10	96	92.3	3.7

WORKED EXAMPLE **4.3**

A firm is at the end of quarter 2. At the end of quarter 1 it had forecast that demand for its product in quarter 2 would be 84,000 units, only to find that actual demand turned out to be higher at 102,000 units. Provide an exponential forecast for demand in quarter 3, using $\alpha = 0.2$.

Solution

Y_2 = 102,000 (actual demand Q2)

$\hat{Y}_2$ = 84,000 (forecast demand Q2)

Here t, the current time period, is quarter 2 and α is 0.2.

$$\hat{Y}_{t+1} = \hat{Y}_t + \alpha(Y_t - \hat{Y}_t)$$

i.e. $\hat{Y}_{2+1} = \hat{Y}_2 + 0.2(Y_2 - \hat{Y}_2)$

$\hat{Y}_3 = 84{,}000 + 0.2\ (102{,}000 - 84{,}000)$

$\hat{Y}_3 = 84{,}000 + 0.2\ (18{,}000)$

$\hat{Y}_3 = 84{,}000 + 3{,}600$

$\underline{\hat{Y}_3 = 87{,}600}$

The impact of this exponential smoothing with $\alpha = 0.2$ on forecast sales is shown in Figure 4.5.

figure 4.5
Forecasting future sales using exponential smoothing and different values for α

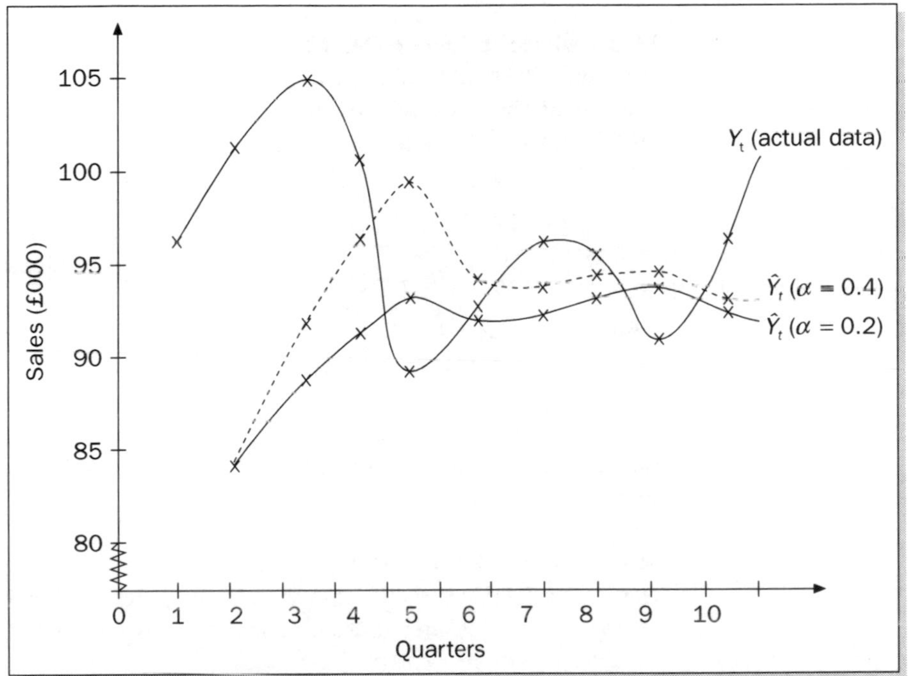

Different values of α

In Table 4.6 we assumed the 'smoothing constant', α, to be 0.2. We have already looked at the impact of extreme values ($\alpha = 0$, $\alpha = 1$) of α on exponential smoothing. In general we can say the following.

- When α is close to 0, only a small proportion of the latest error (E_t) will be included in the next forecast ($\hat{Y}_{t+1}$). Clearly that next forecast will not differ greatly from the previous forecast.
- When α is close to 1, a large proportion of the latest error (E_t) will be included in the next forecast ($\hat{Y}_{t+1}$). Clearly that next forecast will differ greatly from the previous forecast.

As we can see from Figure 4.5, using $\alpha = 0.2$ gives a smoother sequence of forecasts than would occur using $\alpha = 0.4$. This is because the $\alpha = 0.2$ sequence of forecasts for $\hat{Y}_{t+1}$ is less influenced by any actual observation (Y_t) and its divergence from its forecast value ($\hat{Y}_t$).

Choosing a value for α

It would seem reasonable to choose a value of α which, on previous experience, would have produced the 'best' forecast using exponential smoothing. 'Best' in this context would arguably be the value of α which gave a smaller sequence of errors (E_t), where $E_t = Y_t - \hat{Y}_t$.

Two possible ways of evaluating previous forecasts suggest themselves.

Mean absolute error (MAE)

Here we select that value of α which, on previous experience, minimises the average of the *absolute errors* (ignoring sign) of deviations between actual (Y_t) and forecast ($\hat{Y}_t$) values:

$$\text{MAE} = \frac{\sum_{i=1}^{n} |E_t|}{n}$$

where | | is modulus, i.e. ignore signs
n is number of error terms ($Y_t - \hat{Y}_t$)

Notice that n, the number of error terms, will be one less than the number of items of data since we do not have a forecast and therefore error term for the first item of data.

Mean squared error (MSE)

Here we select that value of α which, on previous experience, minimises the average of the *squares* of the errors. We have no sign problem here, as all squared values are positive:

$$\text{MSE} = \frac{\sum_{i=1}^{n} E_t^2}{n}$$

where n is number of error terms ($Y_t - \hat{Y}_t$)

WORKED EXAMPLE 4.4

Use the data of Table 4.6 to provide forecasts using $\alpha = 0.2$, 0.3 and 0.4 respectively. Which value of α would you select for future forecasts?

Solution

We have already plotted the data for $\alpha = 0.2$ and 0.4 on Figure 4.5. Here we formally work out MAE and MSE for the nine error terms (E_t) based on these ten items of data.

		$\alpha = 0.2$		$\alpha = 0.3$		$\alpha = 0.4$	
Quarter	Y_t	E_t	E_t^2	E_t	E_t^2	E_t	E_t^2
1	96						
2	102	18.0	324.0	18.0	324.0	18.0	324.0
3	104	16.4	269.0	14.6	213.2	12.8	163.8
4	100	9.1	82.8	6.2	38.4	3.7	13.7
5	88	−4.7	22.1	−7.6	57.8	−9.8	96.0
6	92	0.2	0.0	−1.4	2.0	−1.9	3.6
7	96	4.2	17.6	3.1	9.6	2.9	8.4
8	94	1.4	2.0	0.1	0.0	−0.3	0.1
9	90	−2.9	8.4	−3.9	15.2	−4.2	17.6
10	96	3.7	13.7	3.3	10.9	3.5	12.3
		$\Sigma\lvert E_t\rvert = 60.6$	$\Sigma E_t^2 = 739.6$	$\Sigma\lvert E_t\rvert = 58.2$	$\Sigma E_t^2 = 671.1$	$\Sigma\lvert E_t\rvert = 57.1$	$\Sigma E_t^2 = 639.5$

Note: Although there are ten items of data there are only nine error terms, hence $n = 9$.

$$\text{MAE} = \frac{\sum |E|_t}{n}$$

(a) $\alpha = 0.2 = \dfrac{60.6}{9} = 6.73$

(b) $\alpha = 0.3 = \dfrac{58.2}{9} = 6.47$

(c) $\alpha = 0.4 = \dfrac{57.1}{9} = 6.34$

$$\text{MSE} = \frac{\sum E_t^2}{n}$$

(a) $\alpha = 0.2 = \dfrac{739.6}{9} = 82.18$

(b) $\alpha = 0.3 = \dfrac{671.1}{9} = 74.57$

(c) $\alpha = 0.4 = \dfrac{639.5}{9} = 71.06$

In this particular example the value $\alpha = 0.4$ will give the minimum value for *both* mean absolute error (MAE) and mean square error (MSE). It follows that our previous experiences of forecasting would arguably lead to the choice of $\alpha = 0.4$ for future forecasts when choosing between the possible values of $\alpha = 0.2$, 0.3 or 0.4.

REVIEW QUESTIONS

4.1 As a result of local government cutbacks some branch libraries are threatened with closure. A newly appointed chief librarian claims that a certain branch library has a declining patronage, based on his observations of the last three months. The head librarian of the branch disagrees with the analysis and quotes quarterly data recorded over the past three years for book issues to support his case. That data are as follows:

Year	Q1	Q2	Q3	Q4
1998	2,542	2,826	2,991	2,644
1999	2,766	2,905	3,048	3,137
2000	2,944	3,140	3,333	3,125

(a) Calculate the trend line using the moving average method.
(b) Plot the original data and the trend values on a scatter diagram.
(c) Calculate the seasonal variation factors.

4.2 The manufacturer of snow chains is considering building a new production plant to cope with growing demand. A tyre firm is interested in investing in the company and has been provided with the following quarterly sales figures:

Unit sales 1997–2000 (000s)

Year	Q1	Q2	Q3	Q4
1	441.1	397.7	396.1	472.8
2	476.4	454.4	450.8	553.5
3	580.7	573.2	571.6	703.6
4	692.0	676.5	659.9	752.8

(a) Calculate the trend line using the moving average method.
(b) Plot the original data and the trend values on a scatter diagram.
(c) Estimate and then eliminate the season variation component. In other words find the deseasonalised data.

4.3 A company producing torches is negotiating with a company for the supply of torch bulbs. The bulb company therefore needs to plan its production to meet the needs of the torch company and thus uses that company's quarterly sales figures over the past three years to forecast future demand. The sales figures are as follows:

Quarterly sales figures 1998–2000 (000s)

Year	Q1	Q2	Q3	Q4
1	349.4	295.5	196.9	389.3
2	447.5	418	324.1	456.4
3	550.6	528.6	415.2	615.3

Using the moving average technique find the trend observations and the seasonal variation factors. Fit a least squares regression line to the trend observations. Use this trend regression line and your estimates of the seasonal variation factors to forecast future demand for the four quarters of year 4 for torches.

4.4 The area sales manager of a company is responsible for providing a forecast for the value of sales. However, she has been taken ill and the deputy has now to make the forecast for the next month. The exponential smoothing method, favoured by the company, uses an α of 0.2. However, the deputy believes that an α of 0.3 is a more realistic smoothing constant. Using the data provided, forecast for the next month using each smoothing constant.

t	Y
1	3.85
2	3.22
3	3.18
4	3.61
5	3.62
6	3.48
7	3.53
8	3.62
9	3.36
10	3.58
11	3.62
12	3.24

Calculate the mean absolute error and the mean square error for each smoothing constant (assume an initial forecast for t=1 of 3.49). Which smoothing constant should be recommended based on the criterion of minimising the mean square error?

Note: Answers can be found on pp. 402–415.

Further study and data

Texts

Bancroft, G. and O'Sullivan, G. (1993), *Quantitative methods for accounting and business studies*, 3rd edn, McGraw Hill, chapter 10.

Curwin, J. and Slater, R. (1996), *Quantitative methods for business decisions*, 4th edn, International Thompson Business Press, chapter 20.

Lawson, M., Hubbard, S. and Pugh, P. (1995), *Maths and statistics for business*, Addison Wesley Longman, chapter 11.

Morris, C. (1999), *Quantitative approaches in business studies*, 5th edn, Pitman, chapter 16.

Oakshott, L. (1996), *Essential elements of quantitative methods*, BPP, chapter 3.

Swift, L. (2001), *Quantitative methods for business, management and finance*, Palgrave Publishers, part S.

Thomas, R. (1997), *Quantitative methods for business studies*, Prentice Hall, chapter 6.

Waters, D. (1997), *Quantitative methods for business*, 2nd edn, Addison Wesley Longman, chapter 9.

Wisniewski, M. with Stead, R. (1996), *Foundation quantitative methods for business*, Pitman, chapter 13.

Sources of information and data

See the list at the end of Chapter 1 (p. 25).

On-line exercises

Check the web site *www.booksites.net/burton* to find extra questions, Spreadsheet and on-line exercises for this chapter.

Appendices

Appendix 1

Solutions to Selected Odd-Numbered Problems from Taylor

Solutions to Selected Odd-Numbered Problems

Chapter 1

1. (a) $TC = \$27,500$; $TR = \$54,000$; $Z = \$26,500$; (b) $v = 69.56$ tables
3. (a) $TC = \$29,100$; $TR = \$23,400$; $Z = -\$5,700$; (b) $v = 24,705.88$ yd./month
7. (a) $v = 1,250$ dolls
9. 98.8%
11. reduces v to 2,727.3 tires
13. increases v to 65,789.47 lb.
15. do not raise price
17. yes, v will be reduced
19. (a) executive plan; (b) 937.5 min. per month
21. (a) $v = 26.9$ pupils; (b) $v = 106.3$ pupils; (c) $p = \$123.67$
23. $v = 209.2$ teams
25. $x = 30, y = 10, Z = \$1,400$
27. 34,500 visits

Chapter 2

1. $x_1 = 4, x_2 = 0, Z = 40$
3. (a) min. $Z = .05x_1 + .03x_2$; s.t. $8x_1 + 6x_2 \geq 48, x_1 + 2x_2 \geq 12, x_i \geq 0$; (b) $x_1 = 0, x_2 = 8, Z = 0.24$
5. (a) min. $Z = 3x_1 + 5x_2$; s.t. $10x_1 + 2x_2 \geq 20, 6x_1 + 6x_2 \geq 36, x_2 \geq 2, x_i \geq 0$; (b) $x_1 = 4, x_2 = 2, Z = 22$
7. No labor, 4.8 lb. wood
9. (a) max. $Z = x_1 + 5x_2$; s.t. $5x_1 + 5x_2 \leq 25, 2x_1 + 4x_2 \leq 16, x_1 \leq 5, x_1, x_2 \geq 0$; (b) $x_1 = 0, x_2 = 4, Z = 20$
11. $x_1 = 0, x_2 = 9, Z = 54$
13. (a) max. $Z = 300x_1 + 400x_2$; s.t. $3x_1 + 2x_2 \leq 18, 2x_1 + 4x_2 \leq 20, x_2 \leq 4, x_1, x_2 \geq 0$; (b) $x_1 = 4, x_2 = 3, Z = 2,400$
15. (a) maximum demand is not achieved by one bracelet; (b) \$600
17. $x_1 = 15.8, x_2 = 20.5, Z = 1,610$
19. A: $s_1 = 4, s_2 = 1, s_3 = 0$; B: $s_1 = 0, s_2 = 5, s_3 = 0$; C: $s_1 = 0, s_2 = 6, s_3 = 1$
21. A: $s_1 = 0, s_2 = 0, s_3 = 8, s_4 = 0$; B: $s_1 = 0, s_2 = 3.2, s_3 = 0, s_4 = 4.8$; C: $s_1 = 26, s_2 = 24, s_3 = 0, s_4 = 10$
23. changes the optimal solution
25. $x_1 = 28.125, x_2 = 0, Z = \$1,671.95$; no effect
27. infeasible solution
29. $x_1 = 4, x_2 = 1, Z = 18$
31. $x_1 = 4.8, x_2 = 2.4, Z = 26.4$
33. $x_1 = 3.2, x_2 = 6, Z = 37.6$
35. no additional profit
37. (a) max. $Z = 800x_1 + 900x_2$; s.t. $2x_1 + 4x_2 \leq 30, 4x_1 + 2x_2 \leq 30, x_1 + x_2 \geq 9, x_i \geq 0$; (b) $x_1 = 5, x_2 = 5, Z = 8,500$
39. $x_1 = 5.3, x_2 = 4.7, Z = 806$
41. (a) 12 hr.; (b) new solution: $x_1 = 5.09, x_2 = 5.45, Z = 111.27$
43. $x_1 = 38.4, x_2 = 57.6, Z = 19.78$; profit reduced
45. (a) min. $Z = .09x_1 + .18x_2$, s.t. $.46x_1 + .35x_2 \leq 2,000, x_1 \geq 1,000, x_2 \geq 1,000, .91x_1 - .82x_2 = 3,500, x_1 \geq 0, x_2 \geq 0$; (b) 32 fewer defects
47. $x_1 = 160, x_2 = 106.67, Z = 568$
49. $x_1 = 25.71, x_2 = 14.29, Z = 14,571$
51. (a) max. $Z = .18x_1 + .06x_2$, s.t. $x_1 + x_2 \leq 720,000, x_1/(x_1 + x_2) \leq .65, .22x_1 + .05x_2 \leq 100,000, x_1, x_2 \geq 0$ (b) $x_1 = 376,470.59, x_2 = 343,526.41, Z = 88,376.47$
53. one more hour for Sarah would reduce the regraded exams from 10 to 9.8; another hour for Brad has no effect
55. only more Columbian would affect the solution; 1 lb of Columbian would increase sales to \$463.20; increasing the brewing capacity has no effect; extra advertising increases sales
57. infeasible

Chapter 3

3. Cells: B10:B12; Constraints: B10:B12 $\geq$ 0, G6 $\leq$ F6, G7 $\leq$ F7; Profit: = B10*C4+B11*D4+B12*E4; Target cell = B13.
5. (a and b) max. $Z = 12x_1 + 16x_2 + 0s_1 + 0s_2$; s.t. $3x_1 + 2x_2 + s_1 = 500, 4x_1 + 5x_2 + s_2 = 800, x_i \geq 0, s_i \geq 0$
7. (a and b) $\infty \leq c_1, \leq 12.8, 15 \leq c_2 \leq \infty, 320 \leq q_1 \leq \infty, 0 \leq q_2 \leq 1,250$; (c) \$0, \$3.20
9. (a) $x_1 = 4, x_2 = 3, Z = 57$, A: $s_1 = 40, s_2 = 0$, B: $s_1 = 0, s_2 = 0$, C: $s_1 = 0, s_2 = 20$; (b) $x_1 = 2, x_2 = 4$; (c) solution point same for profit = \$15, new solution $x_1 = 0, x_2 = 5, Z = 100$ for profit = \$20
11. (a and b) max. $Z = 2.25x_1 + 3.10x_2 + 0s_1 + 0s_2 + 0s_3$; s.t. $5.0x_1 + 7.5x_2 + s_1 = 6,500, 3.0x_1 + 3.2x_2 + s_2 = 3,000, x_2 + s_3 = 510, x_i \geq 0, s_j \geq 0$
13. (a) Additional processing time, \$0.75/hr.; (b) $0 \leq c_1 \leq 2.906, 2.4 \leq c_2 \leq \infty, 6,015 \leq q_1 \leq \infty, 1,632 \leq q_2 \leq 3,237, 0 \leq q_3 \leq 692.308$
15. (a) $x_1 = 4, x_2 = 0, s_1 = 12, s_2 = 0, s_3 = 11, Z = 24,000$; (b) $x_1 = 1, x_2 = 3, Z = 28,500$; (c) C still optimal
17. (a and b) max. $Z = 300x_1 + 520x_2$; s.t. $x_1 + x_2 = 410, 105x_1 + 210x_2 = 52,500, x_2 = 100, x_i \geq 0$
19. (a) no, max. price = \$80; (b) \$2.095

21. (a) $x_1 = 300, x_2 = 100, s_1 = 0$ lb., $s_2 = 15$ lb., $s_4 = 0.6$ hr., $Z = 230$; (b) $c_1 = \$0.60, x_1 = 257, x_2 = 143, Z = 240$; (c) $x_1 = 300, x_2 = 125, Z = 242.50$

23. (a and b) min. $Z = 50x_1 + 70x_2$; s.t. $80x_1 + 40x_2 = 3{,}000$, $80x_1 = 1{,}000$, $40x_2 = 800$, x_i

25. (a) personal interviews, \$0.625/interview; (b) $25 \le c_2 \le \infty$, $1{,}800 \le q_1 \le \infty$

27. (a) $x_1 = 333.3, x_2 = 166.7, s_1 = 100$ gal., $s_2 = 133.3$ gal., $s_3 = 83.3$ gal., $s_4 = 100$ gal., $Z = 1{,}666$; (b) any values of c

29. max. $Z = 1.20x_1 + 1.30x_2$; s.t. $x_1 + x_2 \le 95{,}000$, $.18x_1 + .30x_2 \le 20{,}000$, $x_i \ge 0$

31. (a) 5%, \$16,111.11; (b) $x_1 = 0, x_2 = 66{,}666.7, Z = 86{,}666.67$

33. (a and b) min. $Z = 400x_1 + 180x_2 + 90x_3$ s.t. $x_1 \ge 200, x_2 \ge 300, x_3 \ge 100$, $4x_3 - x_1 - x_2 \le 0$, $x_1 + x_2 + x_3 = 1{,}000$, $x_i \ge 0$; (c) $x_1 = 200, x_2 = 600, x_3 = 200, Z = 206{,}000$

35. max. $Z = 0.50x_1 + 0.75x_2$; s.t. $0.17x_1 + 0.25x_2 \le 4{,}000$, $x_1 + x_2 \le 18{,}000$, $x_1 \ge 8{,}000$, $x_2 \ge 8{,}000$, $x_1, x_2 \ge 0$; (b) max. $Z = 0.50x_1 + 0.75x_2$; $0.17x_1 + 0.25x_2 = 4{,}000$, $x_1 + x_2 = 18{,}000$, $x_1 = 8{,}000$, $x_2 = 8{,}000$, $x_i \ge 0$

37. $x_1 = 8{,}000, x_2 = 10{,}000, Z = 11{,}500$; (a) \$375; increase, $x_1 = 8{,}000$, $x_2 = 10{,}500$, $Z = \$11{,}875$; $x_1 = 8{,}000, x_2 = 10{,}560, Z = \$11{,}920$

39. (a) purchase land; (b) not purchase land

41. (a) \$0.78, 360 cartons; (b) \$0; (c) $x_1 = 108, x_2 = 54, x_3 = 162$, $Z = 249.48$, no discount

43. $x_1 = 3, x_3 = 6, Z = 3{,}600$; (a) more assembly hr.; (b) additional profit = \$600; (c) no effect

45. $x_1 = 1{,}000, x_2 = 800, x_3 = 200, Z = 760$; (a) increase by 100, \$38 in additional profit; (b) $x_1 = 1{,}000, x_2 = 1{,}000, Z = 770$; (c) $Z = 810$; $x_1 = 1{,}600, x_2 = 200, x_3 = 200$

47. $x_1 = 20, x_2 = 33.33, x_3 = 26.67, Z = \$703{,}333.4$

49. $x_{13} = 350, x_{21} = 158.33, x_{22} = 296.67, x_{23} = 75, x_{31} = 610, x_{42} = 240$, $Z = \$77{,}910$

51. max $Z = 12x_1 + 8x_2 + 10x_3 + 6x_4$; s.t. $2x_1 + 9x_2 + 1.3x_3 + 2.5x_4 \le 74$; $2x_1 + .25x_2 + x_3 + x_4 \le 24$; $2x_1 + 5x_3 + 2x_4 \le 36$; $45x_1 + 35x_2 + 50x_3 + 16x_4 \le 480$, $x_i \ge 0$.

Chapter 4

1. Model must be resolved; $Z = 43{,}310$, do not implement; no; $x_1 = x_2 = x_3 = x_4 = 112.5$

3. No effect; \$740; $x_1 = 22{,}363.636, x_3 = 43{,}636.364, x_4 = 14{,}000$

5. Add slack variables for 3 warehouses $\le$ constraints; coefficients in objective function—\$9 for s_1, \$6 for s_2, \$7 for s_3, solution does not change

7. (a) max. $Z = 190x_1 + 170x_2 + 155x_3$; s.t. $3.5x_1 + 5.2x_2 + 2.8x_3 \le 500$, $1.2x_1 + 0.8x_2 + 1.5x_3 \le 240$, $40x_1 + 55x_2 + 20x_3 \le 6{,}500$, $x_i \ge 0$; (b) $x_1 = 41.27, x_2 = 0, x_3 = 126.98, Z = 27{,}523.81$

9. (a) min. $Z = 4x_1 + 3x_2 + 2x_3$; s.t. $2x_1 + 4x_2 + x_3 \ge 16$, $3x_1 + 2x_2 + x_3 \ge 12$, $x_i \ge 0$; (b) $x_1 = 2, x_2 = 3, Z = \$0.17$

11. (a) max. $Z = 8x_1 + 10x_2 + 7x_3$; s.t. $7x_1 + 10x_2 + 5x_3 \le 2{,}000$, $2x_1 + 3x_2 + 2x_3 \le 660$, $x_1 \le 200, x_2 \le 300, x_3 \le 150, x_1 \ge 0, x_2 \ge 0, x_3 \ge 0$; (b) $x_1 = 178.57, x_3 = 150, Z = 2{,}478.57$

13. (a) max. $Z = 7x_1 + 5x_2 + 5x_3 + 4x_4$; s.t. $2x_1 + 4x_2 + 2x_3 + 3x_4 \le 45{,}000$, $x_1 + x_2 \le 6{,}000$, $x_3 + x_4 \le 7{,}000$, $x_1 + x_3 \le 5{,}000$, $x_2 + x_4 \le 6{,}000$, $x_1 \ge 0$, $x_2 \ge 0, x_3 \ge 0, x_4 \ge 0$; (b) $x_1 = 5{,}000, x_2 = 1{,}000, x_4 = 5{,}000, Z = 60{,}000$

15. (a) max. $Z = 1{,}800x_{1a} + 2{,}100x_{1b} + 1{,}600x_{1c} + 1{,}000x_{2a} + 700x_{2b} + 900x_{2c} + 1{,}400x_{3a} + 800x_{3b} + 2{,}200x_{3c}$; s.t. $x_{1a} + x_{1b} + x_{1c} = 30$, $x_{2a} + x_{2b} + x_{2c} = 30$, $x_{3a} + x_{3b} + x_{3c} = 30$, $x_{1a} + x_{2a} + x_{3a} \le 40$, $x_{1b} + x_{2b} + x_{3b} \le 60$, $x_{1c} + x_{2c} + x_{3c} \le 50$, $x_{ij} \ge 0$; (b) $x_{1b} = 30, x_{2a} = 30$, $x_{3c} = 30, Z = 159{,}000$

17. (a) min. $Z = 1.7(x_{t1} + x_{t2} + x_{t3}) + 2.8(x_{m1} + x_{m2} + x_{m3}) + 3.25(x_{b1} + x_{b2} + x_{b3})$; s.t. $.50x_{t1} - .50x_{m1} - .50x_{b1} \le 0$; $-.20x_{t1} + .80x_{m1} - .20x_{b1} \ge 0$, $-.30x_{t2} - .30x_{m2} + .70x_{b2} \ge 0$, $-.30x_{t2} + .70x_{m2} - .30x_{b2} \ge 0$, $.80x_{t2} - .20x_{m2} - .20x_{b2} \le 0$, $.50x_{t3} - .50x_{m3} - .50x_{b3} \ge 0$, $.30x_{t3} - .70x_{m3} - .70x_{b3} \le 0$, $-.10x_{t3} - .10x_{m3} + .90x_{b3} \ge 0$, $x_{t1} + x_{m1} + x_{b1} \ge 1{,}200$, $x_{t2} + x_{m2} + x_{b2} \ge 900$, $x_{t3} + x_{m3} + x_{b3} \ge 2{,}400$; $x_{ij} \ge 0$ (b) $x_{t1} = 600, x_{t2} = 180, x_{t3} = 1{,}680, x_{m1} = 600, x_{m2} = 450$, $x_{m3} = 480, x_{b1} = 0, x_{b2} = 270, x_{b3} = 240, Z = 10{,}123.50$

19. (a) max. $Z = .02x_1 + .09x_2 + .06x_3 + .04x_4$; s.t. $x_1 + x_2 + x_3 + x_4 = 4{,}000{,}000$, $x_1 \le 1{,}600{,}000$, $x_2 \le 1{,}600{,}000$, $x_3 \le 1{,}600{,}000$, $x_4 \le 1{,}600{,}000$, $x_2 - x_3 - x_4 \le 0$, $x_1 - x_3 \ge 0$, $x_1 \ge 0, x_2 \ge 0, x_3 \ge 0$, $x_4 \ge 0$; (b) $x_1 = 800{,}000, x_2 = 1{,}600{,}000, x_3 = 800{,}000, x_4 = 800{,}000$, $Z = 240{,}000$

21. (a) max. $Z = 7.8x_{11} + 7.8x_{12} + 8.2x_{13} + 7.9x_{14} + 6.7x_{21} + 8.9x_{22} + 9.2x_{23} + 6.3x_{24} + 8.4x_{31} + 8.1x_{32} + 9.0x_{33} + 5.8x_{34}$; s.t. $35x_{11} + 40x_{21} + 38x_{31} \le 9{,}000$, $41x_{12} + 36x_{22} + 37x_{32} \le 14{,}400$, $34x_{13} + 32x_{23} + 33x_{33} \le 12{,}000$, $39x_{14} + 43x_{24} + 40x_{34} \le 15{,}000$, $x_{11} + x_{12} + x_{13} + x_{14} = 400$, $x_{21} + x_{22} + x_{23} + x_{24} = 570$, $x_{31} + x_{32} + x_{33} + x_{34} = 320$, $x_{ij} \ge 0$; (b) $x_{11} = 15.385, x_{14} = 384.615, x_{22} = 400, x_{23} = 170, x_{31} = 121.212$, $x_{33} = 198.788, Z = 11{,}089.73$

23. (a) min. $Z = 1.7x_{11} + 1.4x_{12} + 1.2x_{13} + 1.1x_{14} + 1.05x_{15} + 1.0x_{16} + 1.7x_{21} + 1.4x_{22} + 1.2x_{23} + 1.1x_{24} + 1.05x_{25} + 1.7x_{31} + 1.4x_{32} + 1.2x_{33} + 1.1x_{34} + 1.7x_{41} + 1.4x_{42} + 1.2x_{43} + 1.7x_{51} + 1.4x_{52} + 1.7x_{61}$; s.t. $x_{11} + x_{12} + x_{13} + x_{14} + x_{15} + x_{16} = 47{,}000$, $x_{12} + x_{13} + x_{14} + x_{15} + x_{16} + x_{21} + x_{22} + x_{23} + x_{24} + x_{25} = 35{,}000$, $x_{13} + x_{14} + x_{15} + x_{16} + x_{22} + x_{23} + x_{24} + x_{25} + x_{31} + x_{32} + x_{33} + x_{34} = 52{,}000$, $x_{14} + x_{15} + x_{16} + x_{23} + x_{24} + x_{25} + x_{32} + x_{33} + x_{34} + x_{41} + x_{42} + x_{43} = 27{,}000$, $x_{15} + x_{16} + x_{24} + x_{25} + x_{33} + x_{34} + x_{42} + x_{43} + x_{51} + x_{52} = 19{,}000$, $x_{16} + x_{25} + x_{34} + x_{43} + x_{52} + x_{61} = 15{,}000$, (b) $x_{11} = 12{,}000, x_{13} = 25{,}000, x_{14} = 8{,}000$, $x_{15} = 2{,}000, x_{33} = 2{,}000, x_{34} = 15{,}000, Z = \$80{,}200$; (c) $x_{16} = 52{,}000$, $Z = \$52{,}000$

25. (a) add $x_{ss} \le 150, x_{ww} \le 300, x_{cc} \le 250$; $x_{nc} = 700, x_{nw} = 0, x_{sw} = 150$, $x_{ss} = 150, x_{es} = 900, x_{wc} = 250, x_{ww} = 300, x_{cc} = 250, x_{cw} = 250$, $x_{ws} = 50, Z = 20{,}400$; (b) changes demand constraints from $\le 1{,}200$ to $= 1{,}000$; $x_{nc} = 400, x_{nw} = 300, x_{sw} = 150, x_{ss} = 150, x_{ec} = 50$, $x_{es} = 850, x_{wc} = 300, x_{ww} = 300, x_{cc} = 250, x_{cw} = 250, Z = 21{,}200$

27. (a) max. $Z = 2x_1 + 4x_2 + 3x_3 + 7x_4$; s.t. $x_2 + x_4 \le 300$, $6x_1 + 15x_2 \le 1{,}200$, $5x_3 + 12x_4 \le 2{,}400$, $x_i \ge 0$; (b) $x_1 = 200, x_3 = 480$, $Z = 1{,}840$

29. (a) max. $Z = 35x_1 + 20x_2 + 58x_3$; s.t. $14x_1 + 12x_2 + 35x_3 \le 35{,}000$, $6x_1 + 3x_2 + 12x_3 \le 20{,}000$, $x_1 \ge 0, x_2 \ge 0, x_3 \ge 0$; (b) $x_1 = 2{,}500, Z = 87{,}500$

31. (a) min. $Z = 15{,}000x_1 + 4{,}000x_2 + 6{,}000x_3$; s.t. $x_3/x_2 \ge 2/1$, $25{,}000x_1 + 10{,}000x_2 + 15{,}000x_3 \ge 100{,}000$, $(15{,}000x_1 + 3{,}000x_2 + 12{,}000x_3)/(10{,}000x_1 + 7{,}000x_2 + 3{,}000x_3) \ge 2/1$, $(15{,}000x_1 + 4{,}000x_2 + 9{,}000x_3)/(25{,}000x_1 + 10{,}000x_2 + 15{,}000)\ x_3 \ge .30$, $x_2 \le 7$, $x_1 \ge 0$, $x_2 \ge 0, x_3 \ge 0$; (b) $x_2 = 2.5, x_3 = 5.0, Z = 40{,}000$; (c) x_4, no effect

33. (a) min. $Z = .11x_1 + .05\sum_{1}^{6} y_i$; s.t. $x_1 + y_1 + 20{,}000 - c_1 = 60{,}000$, $c_1 + y_2 + 30{,}000 - c_2 = 60{,}000 + y_1$, $c_2 + y_3 + 40{,}000 - c_3 = 80{,}000 + y_2$, $c_3 + y_4 + 50{,}000 - c_4 = 30{,}000 + y_3$, $c_4 + y_5 + 80{,}000 - c_5 = 30{,}000 + y_4$, $c_5 + y_6 + 100{,}000 - c_6 = 20{,}000 + y_5$, $x_1 + y_6 \le c_6$, $x_1, y_i, c_i \ge 0$; (b) $x_1 = 70{,}000, y_3 = 40{,}000, y_4 = 20{,}000, y_1 = y_2 = y_5 = y_6 = 0$, $c_1 = 30{,}000, c_5 = 30{,}000, c_6 = 110{,}000, Z = \$10{,}700$; (c) $x_1 = 90{,}000, y_3 = 20{,}000, c_1 = 50{,}000, c_2 = 20{,}000, c_5 = 50{,}000, c_6 = 130{,}000, Z = \$9{,}100$

35. (a) max. $Z = .7x_{cr} + .6x_{br} + .4x_{pr} + .85x_{ar} + 1.05x_{cb} + .95x_{bb} + .75x_{pb} + 1.20x_{ab} + 1.55x_{cm} + 1.45x_{bm} + 1.25x_{pm} + 1.70x_{am}$; s.t. $x_{cr} + x_{cb} +$

$x_{cm} \leq 200, x_{br} + x_{bb} + x_{bm} \leq 300, x_{pr} + x_{pb} + x_{pm} \leq 150, x_{ar} + x_{ab} + x_{am} \leq 400, .90x_{br} + .90x_{pr} - .10x_{cr} - .10x_{ar} \leq 0, .80x_{cb} - .20x_{bb} - .20x_{pr} - .20x_{ar} \geq 0, .25x_{bb} + .75x_{cb} - .75x_{pb} - .75x_{ab} \geq 0, x_{am} = 0, .5x_{bm} + .5x_{pm} - .5x_{cm} - .5x_{am} \leq 0, x_{ij} \geq 0$; (b) $x_{cm} = 125, x_{ar} = 300, x_{cr} = 75, x_{bb} = 300, x_{pm} = 125, x_{ab} = 100, Z = 1{,}602.50$

37. (a) min. $Z = 40x_1 + 65x_2 + 70x_3 + 30x_4$; s.t. $x_1 + x_2 = 250, x_3 + x_4 = 400, x_1 + x_3 = 300, x_2 + x_4 = 350, x_1 \geq 0, x_2 \geq 0, x_3 \geq 0, x_4 \geq 0$; (b) $x_1 = 250, x_3 = 50, x_4 = 350, Z = 24{,}000$

39. (a) max. $Z = 175\,(7x_1)$; s.t. $8x_1 + 5x_2 + 6.5x_3 \leq 3{,}000, x_1 + x_2 + x_3 \leq 120, 90(7x_1) \leq 10{,}000, 7x_1 - 12x_2 = 0, 12x_2 - 10x_3 = 0, 7x_1 - 10x_3 = 0, x_1 \geq 0, x_2 \geq 0, x_3 \geq 0$; (b) $x_1 = 15.9, x_2 = 9.3, x_3 = 11.1, Z = 19{,}444.44$

41. (a) min. $Z = 3x_{13} + 4x_{14} + 5x_{12} + 2x_{34} + 7x_{45} + 8x_{25}$; s.t. $x_{13} + x_{14} + x_{12} = 5, x_{45} + x_{25} = 5, x_{13} = x_{34}, x_{14} + x_{34} = x_{45}, x_{12} = x_{25}, x_{ij} \geq 0$; (b) $x_{14} = 5, x_{45} = 5, Z = 55{,}000$

43. (a) min. $Z = x_1 + x_2 + x_3 + x_4 + x_5 + x_6$; s.t. $3x_1 + 2x_2 + 2x_3 + x_4 = 700, x_3 + 2x_4 + x_5 = 1{,}200, x_2 + x_5 + 2x_6 = 300, x_i \geq 0$; (b) $x_2 = 50, x_4 = 600, x_6 = 125, Z = 775$; (c) min. $Z = 4x_1 + x_2 + 2x_3 + 0x_4 + 6x_5 + 5x_6$; s.t. $3x_1 + 2x_2 + 2x_3 + x_4 \geq 700, x_3 + 2x_4 + x_5 \geq 1{,}200, x_2 + x_5 + 2x_6 \geq 300, x_i \geq 0; x_2 = 300, x_4 = 600, Z = 300$

45. (a) max. $Z = 4x_1 + 8x_2 + 6x_3 + 7x_4 - 5y_1 - 6y_2 - 7y_3$; s.t. $s_0 = 2{,}000, x_1 \leq s_0, s_1 = s_0 - x_1 + y_1, s_1 \leq 10{,}000, x_2 \leq s_1, s_2 = s_1 - x_2 + y_2, s_2 \leq 10{,}000, x_3 \leq s_2, s_3 = s_2 - x_3 + y_3, s_3 \leq 10{,}000, x_4 \leq s_3, x_i \geq 0, y_i \geq 0, s_i \geq 0$; (b) $x_1 = 0, x_2 = 10{,}000, x_4 = 10{,}000, y_1 = 8{,}000, y_2 = 10{,}000, s_0 = 2{,}000, s_1 = s_2 = s_3 = 10{,}000, Z = 50{,}000$

47. (a) max. $Z = 130x_{1a} + 150x_{1b} + 90x_{1c} + 275x_{2a} + 300x_{2b} + 100x_{2c} + 180x_{3a} + 225x_{3b} + 140x_{3c} + 200x_{4a} + 120x_{4b} + 160x_{4c}$; s.t. $x_{1a} + x_{1b} + x_{1c} = 1, x_{2a} + x_{2b} + x_{2c} = 1, x_{3a} + x_{3b} + x_{3c} = 1, x_{4a} + x_{4b} + x_{4c} = 1, 1 \leq x_{1a} + x_{2a} + x_{3a} + x_{4a} \leq 2, 1 \leq x_{1b} + x_{2b} + x_{3b} + x_{4b} \leq 2, 1 \leq x_{1c} + x_{2c} + x_{3c} + x_{4c} \leq 2, x_{ij} \geq 0$; (b) $x_{1a} = 1, x_{2b} = 1, x_{3b} = 1, x_{4c} = 1, Z = 815$; (c) max. $Z = 130x_{1a} + 150x_{1b} + 90x_{1c} + 275x_{2a} + 300x_{2b} + 100x_{2c} + 180x_{3a} + 225x_{3b} + 140x_{3c} + 200x_{4a} + 120x_{4b} + 160x_{4c}$; s.t. $x_{1a} + x_{1b} + x_{1c} \leq 1, x_{2a} + x_{2b} + x_{2c} \leq 1, x_{3a} + x_{3b} + x_{3c} \leq 1, x_{4a} + x_{4b} + x_{4c} \leq 1, x_{1a} + x_{2a} + x_{3a} + x_{4a} = 1, x_{1b} + x_{2b} + x_{3b} + x_{4b} = 1, x_{1c} + x_{2c} + x_{3c} + x_{4c} = 1, x_{ij} \geq 0; x_{2a} = 1, x_{3b} = 1, x_{4c} = 1, Z = 660$

49. Z values: A = 1.000, B = 1.000, C = 1.000; all 3 efficient

51. (a) min. $Z = x$; s.t. $150x = 650 + y_1, 150x + y_1 = 450 + y_2, 150x + y_2 = 600 + y_3, 150x + y_3 = 500 + y_4, 150x + y_4 = 700 + y_5, 150x + y_5 = 650 + y_6, 150x + y_6 = 750 + y_7, 150x + y_7 = 900 + y_8, 150x + y_8 = 800 + y_9, 150x + y_9 = 650 + y_{10}, 150x + y_{10} = 700 + y_{11}, 150x + y_{11} \geq 500$; (b) $Z = x = 4.45, y_1 = 18.18, y_2 = 236.36, y_3 = 304.54, y_4 = 472.72, y_5 = 440.91, y_6 = 459.09, y_7 = 377.27, y_8 = 145.45, y_9 = 13.63, y_{10} = 31.81, y_{11} = 0$

53. (a) max. $Z = y$; s.t. $y - x_1 = 0, y - x_2 = 0, y - x_3 = 0, 10x_1 + 8x_2 + 6x_3 \leq 960, 9x_1 + 21x_2 + 15x_3 \leq 1{,}440, 2x_1 - 3x_2 - 2x_3 \leq 60, -2x_1 + 3x_2 + 2x_3 \leq 60, x_i \geq 0, y \geq 0$; (b) $x_1 = x_2 = x_3 = y = 20$; (c) remove balancing requirement, $x_1 = x_2 = x_3 = y = 32$

55. max. $Z = 850x_1 + 600x_n + 750x_s + 1{,}000x_w$; s.t. $x_1 + x_n + x_s + x_w = 18, x_1 + x_n + x_s + x_w + y_1 + y_n + y_s + y_w = 60, 400y_1 + 100y_n + 175y_s + 90y_w \leq 9{,}000, 10 \leq y_1 \leq 25, 5 \leq y_n \leq 10, 5 \leq y_s \leq 10, 5 \leq y_w \leq 10, x_1 \leq 6, x_n \leq 6, x_s \leq 6, x_w \leq 6, x_i \geq 0, y_i \geq 0; x_1 = 6, x_n = 0, x_s = 6, x_w = 6, y_1 = 14.44, y_n = 10, y_s = 7.56, y_w = 10, Z = 15{,}600$ (multiple optimal)

57. (a) max. $Z = .85x_1 + .90x_2 - y_1 - y_2$; s.t. $x_1 \leq 5{,}000 + 3y_1, x_2 \leq 4{,}000 + 5y_2, .60x_1 + .85x_2 + y_1 + y_2 \leq 16{,}000, x_1 \geq .3(x_1 + x_2), x_1 \leq .6(x_1 + x_2), x_1 \geq 0, x_2 \geq 0, y_1 \geq 0, y_2 \geq 0$; (b) $x_1 = 5{,}458.128, x_2 = 12{,}735.63, y_1 = 152.709, y_2 = 1{,}747.126, Z = 14{,}201.64$

59. (a) min. $Z = \Sigma\Sigma$ (ranking)$\cdot x_{ij}$, s.t. $\Sigma x_{ij} \leq$ hr., $\Sigma x_{ij} =$ project hr., Σ (hourly rate)$\cdot x_{ij} \leq$ budget; (b) $x_{A3} = 400, x_{A4} = 50, x_{B4} = 250, x_{B5} = 350, x_{C4} = 175, x_{C7} = 274.1, x_{C8} = 50.93, x_{D2} = 131.7, x_{D7} = 15.93, x_{E1} = 208.33, x_{E8} = 149.07, x_{F1} = 291.67, x_{F2} = 108.3, x_{F6} = 460, Z = \$12{,}853.33$

61. $x_1 = 0, x_2 = 4, x_3 = 18.4, x_4 = 6.4, x_5 = 24.8, y_1 = 72.22, y_2 = 72.44, y_3 = 64.95, y_4 = 62.34, y_5 = 52.24, y_6 = 38.9, y_7 = 28.53, y_8 = 43.35, Z = \$360{,}196$

63. min. $Z = \Sigma x_{ij}$ (priority ij) s.t. $\sum_{j=1}^{12} x_{ij} = 1, \sum_{i=1}^{16} x_{ij} \leq$ available slots j, U11B: 3-5M, U11G: 3-5T, U12B: 3-5T, U12G: 3-5M, U13B: 3-5T, U13G: 3-5M, U14B: 5-7M, U14G: 3-5M, U15B: 5-7T, U15G: 3-5M, U16B: 5-7T, U16G: 5-7T, U17B: 5-7M, U17G: 5-7T, U18B: 3-5T, U18G: 5-7M, $Z = 27$

65. 1-D (1 hr.), 2-E (1 hr.), 3-F (2 hr.), 3-H (6 hr.), 4-I (1 hr.), 5-J (1 hr.), A-5 (8 hr.), B-4 (5 hr.), C-6 (8 hr.), G-7 (2 hr.), $Z = 35$ hr.; 6 crews originate in Pittsburgh, 4 in Orlando

67. min. $Z = .41x_{14} + .57x_{15} + .37x_{24} + .48x_{25} + .51x_{34} + .60x_{35} + .22x_{46} + .10x_{47} + .20x_{48} + .15x_{56} + .16x_{57} + .18x_{58}$; s.t. $x_{14} + x_{15} \leq 24{,}000, x_{24} + x_{25} \leq 18{,}000, x_{34} + x_{35} \leq 32{,}000, x_{14} + x_{24} + x_{34} \leq 48{,}000, x_{15} + x_{25} + x_{35} \leq 35{,}000\ (x_{14} + x_{24} + x_{34})/2 = x_{46} + x_{47} + x_{48}, (x_{15} + x_{25} + x_{35})/2 = x_{56} + x_{57} + x_{58}, x_{46} + x_{56} = 9{,}000, x_{47} + x_{57} = 12{,}000, x_{47} + x_{58} = 15{,}000, x_{ij} \geq 0; x_{14} = 24{,}000, x_{24} = 18{,}000, x_{34} = 6{,}000, x_{35} = 24{,}000, x_{47} = 12{,}000, x_{48} = 12{,}000, x_{56} = 9{,}000, x_{58} = 3{,}000, Z = \$39{,}450$

Chapter 14

1. (a and b) $\mu \approx 3.48$, $EV = 3.65$, the results differ because not enough simulations were done in part a; (c) approximately 21 calls; no; repeat simulations to get enough observations
3. (a and b) $\mu \approx 2.95$
5. sun visors
7. (a) $\mu = \$256$
9. (a) average time between arrivals ≈ 4.3 days, average waiting time ≈ 6.25 days, average number of tankers waiting ≈ 1.16; (b) system has not reached steady state
11. total yardage ≈ 155 yd.; the sportswriter will predict Tech will win
13. [*Tribune Daily News*] = [.50 .50]; too few iterations to approach a steady state
15. expansion is probably warranted
17. two of five trials (depended on random number stream)
19. system inadequate
21. avg. Salem dates = 2.92
23. P(capacity > demand) = .75
25. avg. maintenance cost = $3,594.73; P(cost ≤ $3,000) = .435
27. avg. rating = 2.91; $P(x \geq 3.0) = .531$
29. (a) $P(1,2) = .974$, $P(1,3) = .959$, $P(1,4) = .981$, $P(2,3) = .911$, $P(2,4) = .980$, $P(3,4) = .653$; (b) (1,4) and (2,4).
31. (a) 700 rooms; (b) 690 rooms

Chapter 16

1. (a) $Q = 79.7$; (b) $13,550; (c) 15.05 orders; (d) 24.18 days
3. (a) $Q = 240$; (b) $4,800; (c) 80 orders; (d) 4 days
5. (a) $Q = 190{,}918.8$ yd.; (b) $15,273.51; (c) 6.36 orders; (d) 57.4 days
7. $Q = 67.13$, $S = 15.49$, $TC = \$3{,}872.98$
9. (a) $Q = 774.6$ boxes, $TC = \$619.68$, $R = 43.84$ boxes
11. $Q = 23{,}862$, $TC = \$298{,}276$
13. (a) $Q = 2{,}529.8$ logs; (b) $TC = \$12{,}649.11$; (c) $T_b = 63.3$ days; (d) 42.16 days
15. $Q = 17{,}544.2$; $S = 4{,}616.84$; $TC = \$3{,}231.84$
17. $Q = 569.32$, $S = 32.79$, $TC = \$1{,}475.45$
19. (a) $Q = 11{,}062.62$, $TC = \$5{,}532.14$, runs = 1.63, max. level = 4,425.7; (b) $Q = 6{,}250$, $TC = \$6{,}458.50$
21. (a) $Q = 4{,}912.03$, $TC = \$18{,}420.11$; (b) $Q = 3{,}833.19$, $TC = \$17{,}249.36$; select new location
23. $C_c = \$950$
25. take discount, $Q = 300$
27. $Q = 500$, $TC = \$64{,}424$
29. $Q = 6{,}000$, $TC = \$85{,}230.33$
31. $Q = 30{,}000$, $TC = \$14{,}140$
33. $Q = 20{,}000$, $TC = \$893{,}368$
35. 91%
37. R (90%) = 74.61 gal; increase safety stock to 26.37 gal.
39. 254.4 gal.
41. $R = 24.38$
43. 120 pizzas
45. (a) 15.15%; (b) $R = 6.977$ pizzas

Appendix 2

Answers to Selected Even-Numbered Exercises from Newbold

Chapter 9

9.2 a. .79772 b. -2.59766 to -1.00234 c. 2.07737

9.4 $27.0649 < \mu_x - \mu_y < 47.5351$

9.6 5.4831 up to 14.5169

9.8 a. 33.25 b. 33.2727 c. 21.2105

9.10 a. 2.3204 b. 3.5026
c. Doubling the size of both samples will reduce the margin of error; however, it does not reduce it in half.

9.12 5.0579 up to 9.3421

9.14 $-.00591$ up to .061907

9.16 a. .083367 b. .063062 c. .056126

9.18 .0971 up to .3625

9.20 -0.3001 to -0.0627

9.22 $-.0314$ up to .0816

9.24 a. $9.8332 < \sigma^2 < 35.036$ b. $34.9218 < \sigma^2 < 153.3546$ c. $126.9138 < \sigma^2 < 533.446$

9.26 No evidence of non-normality

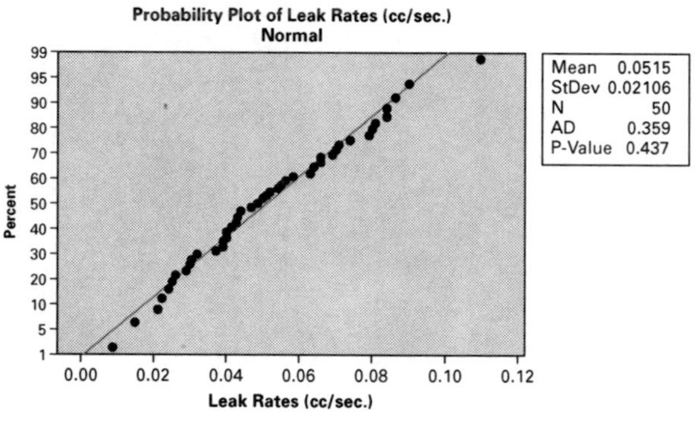

$3.279E-4 < \sigma^2 < 7.238E-4$

9.28 3.8289 up to 14.1167. Assume the population is normally distributed.

9.30 a. 2.9852 up to 13.8498 b. wider

9.32 a. 427 b. 107
c. In order to cut the ME in half, the sample size must be quadrupled.

9.34 a. 666 b. 271
c. In order to increase the confidence level for a given margin of error, the sample size must be increased.

9.36 666

9.38 25.4893 to 54.5107

9.40 a. −60.21056 to −19.7894 b. −60.669 to −19.331

9.42 −6.2971 to 2.8971

9.44 −0.04136 to 0.14295

9.46 6.055 up to 13.945. Assume both populations are distributed normally with equal variances and a 90% confidence level. Since both endpoints of the confidence interval are positive, this provides evidence that the new machine provides a larger mean filling weight than the old.

9.48 −1.18066 to 10.18066

9.50 .23915 up to .36085

Chapter 10

10.2 H_0: No change in interest rates is warranted.
H_1: Reduce interest rates to stimulate the economy.

10.4 a. European perspective:
H_0: Genetically modified food stuffs are not safe.
H_1: They are safe.
b. U.S. farmer perspective:
H_0: Genetically modified food stuffs are safe.
H_1: They are not safe.

10.6 a. Reject H_0 if $\bar{x} > \bar{x}_c = \mu_0 + z_\alpha \sigma/\sqrt{n} = 108.225$
b. Reject H_0 if $\bar{x} > \bar{x}_c = \mu_0 + z_\alpha \sigma/\sqrt{n} = 110.28125$
c. Reject H_0 if $\bar{x} > \bar{x}_c = \mu_0 + z_\alpha \sigma/\sqrt{n} = 106.1998$
d. Reject H_0 if $\bar{x} > \bar{x}_c = \mu_0 + z_\alpha \sigma/\sqrt{n} = 107.26994$

10.8 The critical value $\bar{x}_c$ is farther away from the hypothesized value the smaller the sample size n. This is due to the increase in the standard error with a smaller sample size.
The critical value $\bar{x}_c$ is farther away from the hypothesized value the larger the population variance. This is due to the increased standard error with a larger population variance.

10.10 a. .0004 b. .0475 c. .0062 d. .020

10.12 $H_0 : \mu \geq 50$; $H_1 : \mu < 50$; reject H_0 if $Z_{.10} < -1.28$
$Z = \dfrac{48.2 - 50}{3/\sqrt{9}} = -1.8$, therefore, reject H_0 at the 10% level.

10.14 a. Reject if $t = \dfrac{\bar{x} - \mu_0}{s/\sqrt{n}} > t_{n-1,\alpha/2}$, $t = 2.00$. Since 2.00 is greater than the critical value of 1.711, there is sufficient evidence to reject the null hypothesis.

b. Reject if $t = \dfrac{\bar{x} - \mu_0}{s/\sqrt{n}} > t_{n-1,\alpha/2}$, $t = 2.00$. Since 2.00 is greater than the critical value of 1.711, there is sufficient evidence to reject the null hypothesis.
c. Reject if $t = \dfrac{\bar{x} - \mu_0}{s/\sqrt{n}} < -t_{n-1,\alpha/2}$, $t = -2.50$. Since -2.50 is less than the critical value of -1.711, there is sufficient evidence to reject the null hypothesis.
d. Reject if $t = \dfrac{\bar{x} - \mu_0}{s/\sqrt{n}} < -t_{n-1,\alpha/2}$, $t = -2.22$. Since -2.22 is less than the critical value of -1.711, there is sufficient evidence to reject the null hypothesis.

10.16 $H_0 : \mu \geq 3; H_1 : \mu < 3;$
$Z = \dfrac{2.4 - 3}{1.8/\sqrt{100}} = -3.33$, p-value = .0004, therefore, reject H_0 at significance levels less than .04%; $\alpha = .04$

10.18 $H_0 : \mu = 0; H_1 : \mu \neq 0;$
$Z = \dfrac{.078 - 0}{.201/\sqrt{76}} = 3.38$, p-value = .0008, therefore, reject H_0 at significance levels less than .08%; $\alpha = .08$

10.20 $H_0 : \mu = 0; H_1 : \mu < 0;$
$Z = \dfrac{-2.91 - 0}{11.33/\sqrt{170}} = -3.35$, p-value = .0004, therefore, reject H_0 at any common level of alpha.

10.22 a. No, the 95% confidence level provides for 2.5% of the area in either tail. This does not correspond to a one-tailed hypothesis test with an alpha of 5% which has 5% of the area in one of the tails.
b. Yes.

10.24 $H_0 : \mu = 20; H_1 : \mu \neq 20$; reject H_0 if $|t_{8, .05/2}| > 2.306$
$t = \dfrac{20.3556 - 20}{.6126/\sqrt{9}} = 1.741$, therefore, do not reject H_0 at the 5% level.

10.26 The population values must be assumed to be normally distributed.
$H_0 : \mu \geq 50; H_1 : \mu < 50$; reject H_0 if $t_{19, .05} < -1.729$
$t = \dfrac{41.3 - 50}{12.2/\sqrt{20}} = -3.189$, therefore, reject H_0 at the 5% level.

10.28 a. .2907 b. .30427 c. .28256 d. .2771

10.30 $H_0 : p \leq .25; H_1 : p > .25;$
$z = 1.79$, p-value = .0367, therefore, reject H_0 at alpha greater than 3.67%.

10.32 $H_0 : p = .5; H_1 : p \neq 5;$
$z = -1.26$, p-value = .2076. The probability of finding a random sample with a sample proportion this far or further from .5 if the null hypothesis is really true is .2076

10.34 $H_0 : p = .5; H_1 : p > .5;$
$z = .85$, p-value = .1977, therefore, reject H_0 at alpha levels in excess of 19.77%.

10.36 $H_0 : p \geq .75; H_1 : p < 75;$
$z = -1.87$, p-value = .0307, therefore, reject H_0 at alpha levels in excess of 3.07%.

10.38 a. .8349 b. .0233 c. .6876 d. .8349 e. .0694

10.40 a. H_0 is rejected when $\dfrac{\bar{X} - 3}{4/\sqrt{64}} > 1.645$ or when $\bar{X} > 3.082$. Since the sample mean is 3.07% which is less than the critical value, the decision is to not reject the null hypothesis.
b. $\beta = .3594$. The power of the test $= 1 - \beta = .6406$

10.42 H_0 is rejected when $\frac{p - .5}{\sqrt{.25/802}} < -1.28$ or when p < .477

The power of the test = 1 − β = .9382

10.44 a. H_0 is rejected when $-1.645 > \frac{p - .5}{\sqrt{.25/199}} > 1.645$ or when .442 > p > .558. Since the sample proportion is .5226 which is within the critical values, the decision is do not reject the null hypothesis.

b. β = .1131

10.46 a. α = P(Z > 1.33) = .0918

b. α = P(Z > 2.67) = .0038. Note that the larger sample size results in a smaller standard error of the mean.

c. β = .0668

d. i) lower, ii) higher

10.48 The p-value indicates the likelihood of getting the sample result at least as far away from the hypothesized value as the one that was found, assuming that the distribution is really centered on the null hypothesis. The smaller the p-value, the stronger the evidence against the null hypothesis.

10.50 a. False b. True c. True d. False
e. False f. True g. False

10.52 a. α = P(Z < −2) = .0228 b. β = P(Z > 3) = .0014
c. i) smaller ii) smaller d. i) smaller ii) larger

10.54 $H_0 : p = .5; H_1 : p \neq .5;$
$z = -.39$, p-value =.6966, therefore, reject H_0 at levels in excess of 69.66%.

10.56 $H_0 : p \leq .25; H_1 : p > .25;$ reject H_0 if $z_{.05} > 1.645$
$z = 2.356$, therefore, reject H_0 at the 5% level.

10.58 Cost Model where W = Total Cost: W = 1,000 + 5X
$\mu_W = 1{,}000 + 5(400) = 3{,}000$
$\sigma_W^2 = (5)^2(625) = 15{,}625, \sigma_W = 125, \sigma_{\overline{W}} = \frac{125}{\sqrt{25}} = 25$
$H_0 : W \leq 3000; H_1 : W > 3000;$

Using the test statistic criteria: (3050 − 3000)/25 = 2.00 which yields a p-value of .0228, therefore, reject H_0 at the .05 level.

Using the sample statistic criteria: $\overline{X}_{crit} = 3{,}000 + (25)(1.645) = 3041.1$, $\overline{X}_{calc} = 3{,}050$, since $\overline{X}_{crit} = 3{,}050 > \overline{X}_{crit} = 3041.1$, therefore, reject H_0 at the .05 level.

10.60 Assume that the population of matched differences are normally distributed
$H_0 : \mu_x - \mu_y = 0;\ H_1 : \mu_x - \mu_y \neq 0;$
$t = 1.961$, therefore, reject H_0 at the 10% level since $1.96 > 1.796 = t_{(11, .05)}$

10.62 $H_0 : \mu \leq 40, H_1 : \mu > 40; \overline{X} = 49.73 > 42.86$ reject H_0

One-Sample T: Salmon Weight

```
Test of mu = 40 vs mu > 40

Variable        N      Mean     StDev   SE Mean
Salmon Weigh   39     49.73     10.60      1.70

Variable      95.0% Lower Bound       T        P
Salmon Weigh              46.86    5.73    0.000
```

Reject the null and accept the alternative that the mean weight is significantly greater than 40
$\overline{X}_{crit} = H_0 + t_{crit}(S_{\overline{x}}) = 42.8662$
Population mean for β = .50 (power = .50): $t_{crit} = 0.0$: 42.8662
Population mean for β = .25 (power = .75): $t_{crit} = .681$: 44.0239

Population mean for $\beta = .10$ (power = .90): $t_{crit} = 1.28$: 45.0422
Population mean for $\beta = .05$ (power = .95): $t_{crit} = 1.645$: 45.6627

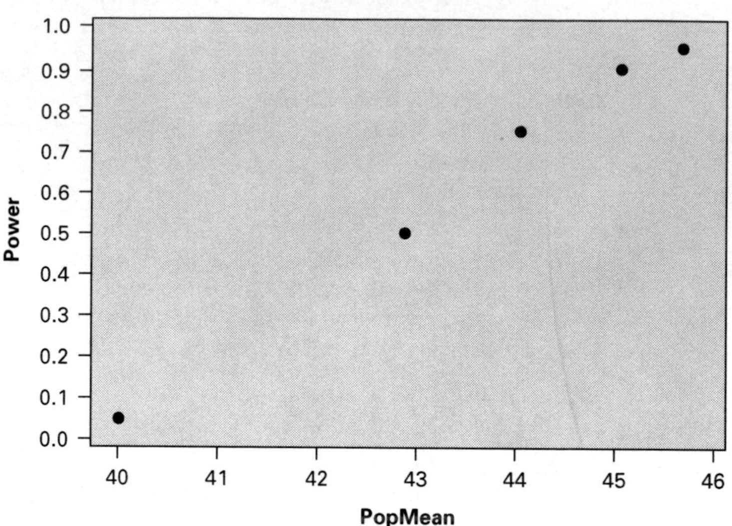

Chapter 11

11.2 a. $t = -1.50$, p-value = .073, do not reject H_0 at alpha of .05
b. $t = -1.00$, p-value = .164, do not reject H_0 at alpha of .05
c. $t = -2.00$, p-value = .028
d. $t = -.75$, p-value = .230

11.4 $z = 7.334$, reject H_0 at all common levels of alpha.

11.6 $z = -1.0207$, p-value = .3078, reject H_0 at levels of alpha in excess of 30.78%.

11.8 $t = 1.108$, do not reject H_0 at the 10% alpha level since $1.108 < 1.645 = t_{(119,.05)}$

11.10 $t = 2.239$, p-value = .0301, reject H_0 at levels in excess of 3%.

11.12 a. $z = -2.65$, p-value = .004, reject H_0 at all common levels of alpha.
b. $z = -1.36$, p-value = .0869, reject H_0 at .10 level, but do not reject at the .05 level of alpha.
c. $z = -2.32$, p-value = .0102, reject H_0 at the .05 level, but do not reject at the .01 level of alpha.
d. $z = -3.25$, p-value = .0006, reject H_0 at all common levels of alpha.
e. $z = -1.01$, p-value = .1562, do not reject H_0 at any common level of alpha.

11.14 $z = -6.97$, reject H_0 at all common levels of alpha.

11.16 $z = 2.465$, reject H_0 at the 5% level.

11.18 $z = .926$, do not reject H_0 at the 5% level.

11.20 a. $\chi^2 = 39.6$, $\chi^2_{(24,.025)} = 39.36$, $\chi^2_{(24,.010)} = 42.98$, reject H_0 at the 2.5% level but not at the 1% level of significance.
b. $\chi^2 = 46.2 = 46.2$, $\chi^2_{(28,.025)} = 44.46$, $\chi^2_{(28,.010)} = 48.28$, reject H_0 at the 2.5% level but not at the 1% level of significance.

c. $\chi^2 = 38.16$, $\chi^2_{(24,.050)} = 36.42$, $\chi^2_{(24,.025)} = 39.36$, reject H_0 at the 5% level but not at the 2.5% level of significance.
d. $\chi^2 = 24.79 = 24.79$, $\chi^2_{(30,.100)} = 40.26$, $\chi^2_{(40,.100)} = 51.81$, do not reject H_0 at any common level of significance.

11.22 a. $s^2 = 5.1556$
b. $\chi^2 = 20.6224$, reject H_0 if $\chi^2_{(9,.05)} > 16.92$, reject H_0 at the 5% level.

11.24 The hypothesis test assumes that the population values are normally distributed Reject H_0 if $\chi^2_{(19,.05)} > 30.14$. $\chi^2 = 26.4556$, do not reject H_0 at the 5% level.

11.26 a. $F = 2.451$, reject H_0 at the 1% level since $2.451 > 2.11 \approx F_{(44,40,.01)}$
b. $F = 1.88$, reject H_0 at the 5% level since $1.88 > 1.69 \approx F_{(43,44,.05)}$
c. $F = 2.627$, reject H_0 at the 1% level since $2.627 > 2.11 \approx F_{(47,40,.01)}$
d. $F = 1.90$, reject H_0 at the 5% level since $1.90 > 1.79 \approx F_{(24,38,.05)}$

11.28 Reject H_0 if $F_{(3,6,.05)} > 4.76$, $F = 7.095$, reject H_0 at the 5% level.

11.30 $F = 1.57$, do not reject H_0 at the 10% level since $1.57 < 3.18 \approx F_{(9,9,.05)}$

11.32 No. The probability of rejecting the null hypothesis given that it is true is 5%.

11.34 a. Assume that the population is normally distributed. Reject H_0 if $|t_{(11,\ .025)}| > 2.201$ $t = -1.018$, do not reject H_0 at the 5% level.
b. Assume that the population is normally distributed.
Reject H_0 if $\chi^2_{(11,.05)} > 19.68$, $\chi^2 = 154.19$, reject H_0 at the 5% level.

11.36 Assuming equal population variances, $t = 1.974$, reject at the 5% level but not at the 1% level.

11.38 Assuming equal population variances, $t = -.2099$, do not reject at the 10% level or at any common level of alpha.

11.40 Assume the populations are normally distributed with equal variances and independent random samples. Reject H_0 if $t_{(10,.05)} > 1.812$. $t = 3.33$, reject H_0 at the 5% level.

11.42 $z = -2.30$, p-value = .0107, reject H_0 at levels of alpha in excess of 1.07%.

11.44 a. Reject H_0 if $z_{.05} < -1.645$, $z = -1.2$, do not reject H_0 at the 5% level.
b. Reject H_0 if $|z_{.025}| > 1.96$, $z = .932$, do not reject H_0 at the 5% level.

11.46 Reject H_0 if $|z_{.01}| < -2.33$, $z = -1.19$, do not reject H_0 at the 1% level.

11.48 $z = -1.653$, p-value = .0495, reject H_0 at levels of alpha 4.95%.

11.50 Reject H_0 if $F_{11,11,.05} > 2.85$, $F = 1.05$, therefore, do not reject H_0

11.52 a. Reject H_0 if $|z_{.015}| > 2.17$, $z = 1.987$, do not reject at the 3% level.
b. Reject H_0 if $|z_{.03}| > 1.88$, $z = 1.987$, reject at the 3% level.

11.54 a. $t = 1.74$, p-value = .044. The matched pairs t-test on the original data shows a significant difference between the weekly sales with brand 2 found to be significantly larger than brand 4 at the .05 level.
b. $t = 1.42$, p-value = .081. With the largest outlier removed from the data of brand 2, the difference between the two brands becomes insignificant at the .05 level.

11.56 The control limits will be at 16.48 and 15.52.

Appendix 3

Answers to 'Self-Check' Questions from Burton

Chapter 4: Time series and forecasting

4.1

Year and quarter	*Y*	*4 quarter moving total*	*4 quarter moving average*	*Centred 4 quarter moving average*
1998 Q1	44			
Q2	80			
		304	76.0	
Q3	120			77.00
		312	78.0	
Q4	60			79.00
		320	80.0	
1999 Q1	52			80.75
		326	81.5	
Q2	88			81.75
		328	82.0	
Q3	126			83.00
		336	84.0	
Q4	62			85.25
		346	86.5	
2000 Q1	60			88.25
		360	90.0	
Q2	98			90.75
		366	91.5	
Q3	140			
Q4	68			

The centred 4 quarter moving average gives you the trend points, which can then be plotted on a scatter diagram containing the original data (all values 100,000 passengers).

4.2

Year and quarter	*Y*	*4 quarter moving total*	*4 quarter moving average*	*Centred 4 quarter moving average (T)*	*(Y – T)*
1998 Q1	66				
Q2	106				
		394	98.50		
Q3	140			99.38	40.62
		401	100.25		
Q4	82			101.88	–19.88
		414	103.50		
1999 Q1	73			106.63	–33.63
		439	109.75		
Q2	119			110.88	8.12
		448	112.00		
Q3	165			113.50	51.50
		460	115.00		
Q4	91			116.38	–25.38
		471	117.75		
2000 Q1	85			122.75	–37.75
		511	127.75		
Q2	130			128.88	1.12
		520	130.00		
Q3	205				
Q4	100				

(a) The centred 4 quarter moving average provides the values (100,000 units) for the trend component.

(b) The trend values and the original *Y* values can be plotted on a scatter diagram.

(c) We can use either of the approaches in Chapter 3 to find the least squares line. Let the first trend estimate for the independent variable (time) equal 1, i.e. let Q3 of 1998 equal 1.

Year and quarter	*Y (centred 4 qr moving average)*	*X (Time)*	*XY*	X^2	Y^2
1998 Q3	99.38	1	99.38	1	9,876.4
Q4	101.88	2	203.76	4	10,379.5
1999 Q1	106.63	3	319.89	9	11,370.0
Q2	110.88	4	443.52	16	12,294.4
Q3	113.50	5	567.50	25	12,882.3
Q4	116.38	6	698.28	36	13,544.3
2000 Q1	122.75	7	859.25	49	15,067.6
Q2	128.88	8	1,031.04	64	16,610.1
	900.28	36	4,222.62	204	102,024.6

Using Approach 1, original data

$$m = \frac{n\sum XY - \sum X \sum Y}{n\sum X^2 - \left(\sum X\right)^2}$$

$$m = \frac{8(4{,}222.62) - (36)(900.28)}{8(204) - (36)^2}$$

$$m = \frac{33{,}780.96 - 32{,}410.08}{1{,}632 - 1{,}296}$$

$$m = \frac{1{,}370.88}{336} = 4.08$$

$$m = 4.08$$

$$c = \overline{Y} - m\overline{X}$$

$$\overline{Y} = \frac{900.28}{8} = 112.5$$

$$\overline{X} = \frac{36}{8} = 4.5$$

$$c = 112.5 - 4.08(4.5)$$

$$c = 112.5 - 18.4$$

$$\underline{c = 94.1}$$

(d) We can estimate $S + I$ by subtracting T, the centred 4 quarter moving average, from Y and then averaging to remove I.

$Y - T = T + S + I - T = S + I$ (ignoring the cycle, C)

	Q1	*Q2*	*Q3*	*Q4*
1998			+40.62	−19.88
1999	−33.63	+8.12	+51.50	−25.38
2000	−37.75	+1.12		
Average	−35.69	+4.62	+46.06	−22.63

If we sum the averages for S for each quarter we get

−35.69 + 4.62 + 46.06 + (−22.63) = −7.64

So to *adjust* the S factors we add $+\frac{7.64}{4} = 1.91$ to each quarter.

This gives the adjusted S factors as:

[Q1] −33.78 [Q2] 6.53 [Q3] 47.97 [Q4] 20.72

(e) $\hat{Y}_{T+S}$ is the trend forecast

($\hat{Y}_T$) + the adjusted seasonal variation factor for that quarter

(i) Q1, year 2003 gives $X = 19$ (Q2, 1998 = 0)

So $\hat{Y}_T = 4.08(19) + 94.1$

i.e. $\underline{\hat{Y}_T = 77.5 + 94.1 = 171.6}$

$\underline{S \text{ for Q1} = -33.78}$

So $\hat{Y}_{T+S} = 171.6 + (-33.78)$

$\underline{\hat{Y}_{T+S} = 137.82}$

Forecast for Q1, year 2003 is 137.82.
Since units are 100,000, this gives 13,782,000 units.

(ii) Q3, Year 2003 gives $X = 21$ (Q2, 1998 = 0)

$\hat{Y}_T = 4.08(21) + 94.1$

$\underline{\hat{Y}_T = 85.7 + 94.1 = 179.8}$

$\underline{S \text{ for Q3} = +47.97}$

So $\hat{Y}_{T+S} = 179.8 + 47.97$

$\underline{\hat{Y}_{T+S} = 227.77}$

Forecast for Q3, year 2003 is 227.77
Since units are 100,000, this gives 22,777,000 units.

(f) Finding R^2, the coefficient of determination will help us decide how confident we can be in our forecast for the trend value.

Again, using Approach 1, original data.

$$R^2 = \left[\frac{n\sum XY - \sum X \sum Y}{\sqrt{\left[n\sum X^2 - \left(\sum X\right)^2\right] \times \left[n\sum Y^2 - \left(\sum Y\right)^2\right]}}\right]^2$$

$$R^2 = \left[\frac{8(4{,}222.62) - (36)(900.28)}{\sqrt{\left[8(204) - (36)^2\right] \times \left[8(102{,}024.6) - (900.28)^2\right]}}\right]^2$$

$$R^2 = \left[\frac{33{,}780.96 - 32{,}410.08}{\sqrt{[336] \times [5{,}692.7]}}\right]^2$$

$$R^2 = \left[\frac{1{,}370.88}{1{,}383.02}\right]^2$$

$R^2 = [0.99]^2$

$\underline{R^2 = 0.98}$

We can have considerable confidence in using the least squares regression line of forecasting future trend values since 98 per cent of total variation is 'explained' or accounted for by the trend regression line. Of course the overall forecast also includes our adjusted seasonal variation factors. Nevertheless this is an encouraging background for such forecasts.

Appendix 4

Responses to ‘Pause for Thought’ from Burton

Chapter 4: Time series and forecasting

Pause for thought 4.1

Many possibilities here. For example chocolate (Easter and Christmas peaks), Sun lotion (Summer), gloves (Autumn and Winter), Hotels (Summer and festivals), swimwear (Spring and Summer), freelance gardeners (Spring and Summer), etc.

Pause for thought 4.2

Many possibilities here. For example the exit of sterling from the exchange rate mechanism (ERM) in 1992 (helped UK exporters, harmed UK importers), the financial problems in many of the Pacific Rim countries in 1997 (harmed UK exporters and reduced inward investment from that region into the UK), the impacts of global warming on weather patterns (less rain creating problems for water companies), etc.

Pause for thought 4.3

Many possibilities here. For example three products with a well-established upward sales trend might include mobile telephones, designer clothes and cinema attendance. On the other hand three products with a well-established downward sales trend might include coal, anoraks, cassette tapes, etc.

Appendix 5

Tables

APPENDIX TABLES

Table 1 Cumulative Distribution Function of the Standard Normal Distribution

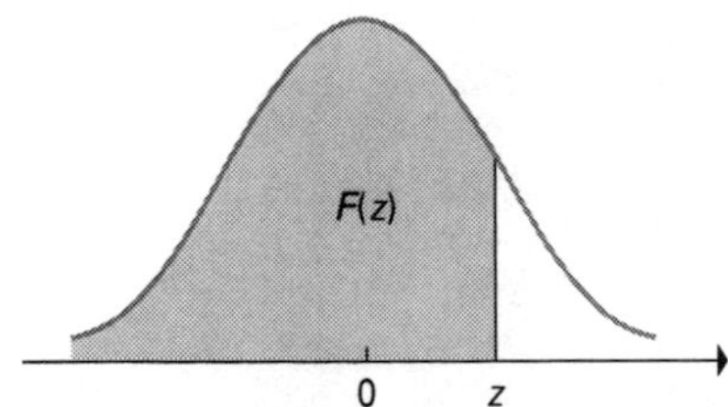

z	F(z)	z	F(z)	z	F(z)	z	F(z)	z	F(z)	z	F(z)
.00	.5000										
.01	.5040	.31	.6217	.61	.7291	.91	.8186	1.21	.8869	1.51	.9345
.02	.5080	.32	.6255	.62	.7324	.92	.8212	1.22	.8888	1.52	.9357
.03	.5120	.33	.6293	.63	.7357	.93	.8238	1.23	.8907	1.53	.9370
.04	.5160	.34	.6331	.64	.7389	.94	.8264	1.24	.8925	1.54	.9382
.05	.5199	.35	.6368	.65	.7422	.95	.8289	1.25	.8944	1.55	.9394
.06	.5239	.36	.6406	.66	.7454	.96	.8315	1.26	.8962	1.56	.9406
.07	.5279	.37	.6443	.67	.7486	.97	.8340	1.27	.8980	1.57	.9418
.08	.5319	.38	.6480	.68	.7517	.98	.8365	1.28	.8997	1.58	.9429
.09	.5359	.39	.6517	.69	.7549	.99	.8389	1.29	.9015	1.59	.9441
.10	.5398	.40	.6554	.70	.7580	1.00	.8413	1.30	.9032	1.60	.9452
.11	.5438	.41	.6591	.71	.7611	1.01	.8438	1.31	.9049	1.61	.9463
.12	.5478	.42	.6628	.72	.7642	1.02	.8461	1.32	.9066	1.62	.9474
.13	.5517	.43	.6664	.73	.7673	1.03	.8485	1.33	.9082	1.63	.9484
.14	.5557	.44	.6700	.74	.7704	1.04	.8508	1.34	.9099	1.64	.9495
.15	.5596	.45	.6736	.75	.7734	1.05	.8531	1.35	.9115	1.65	.9505
.16	.5636	.46	.6772	.76	.7764	1.06	.8554	1.36	.9131	1.66	.9515
.17	.5675	.47	.6803	.77	.7794	1.07	.8577	1.37	.9147	1.67	.9525
.18	.5714	.48	.6844	.78	.7823	1.08	.8599	1.38	.9162	1.68	.9535
.19	.5753	.49	.6879	.79	.7852	1.09	.8621	1.39	.9177	1.69	.9545
.20	.5793	.50	.6915	.80	.7881	1.10	.8643	1.40	.9192	1.70	.9554
.21	.5832	.51	.6950	.81	.7910	1.11	.8665	1.41	.9207	1.71	.9564
.22	.5871	.52	.6985	.82	.7939	1.12	.8686	1.42	.9222	1.72	.9573
.23	.5910	.53	.7019	.83	.7967	1.13	.8708	1.43	.9236	1.73	.9582
.24	.5948	.54	.7054	.84	.7995	1.14	.8729	1.44	.9251	1.74	.9591
.25	.5987	.55	.7088	.85	.8023	1.15	.8749	1.45	.9265	1.75	.9599
.26	.6026	.56	.7123	.86	.8051	1.16	.8770	1.46	.9279	1.76	.9608
.27	.6064	.57	.7157	.87	.8078	1.17	.8790	1.47	.9292	1.77	.9616
.28	.6103	.58	.7190	.88	.8106	1.18	.8810	1.48	.9306	1.78	.9625
.29	.6141	.59	.7224	.89	.8133	1.19	.8830	1.49	.9319	1.79	.9633
.30	.6179	.60	.7257	.90	.8159	1.20	.8849	1.50	.9332	1.80	.9641

Table 1 Cumulative Distribution Function of the Standard Normal Distribution Continued

z	F(z)	z	F(z)	z	F(z)	z	F(z)	z	F(z)	z	F(z)
1.81	.9649	2.21	.9864	2.61	.9955	3.01	.9987	3.41	.9997	3.81	.9999
1.82	.9656	2.22	.9868	2.62	.9956	3.02	.9987	3.42	.9997	3.82	.9999
1.83	.9664	2.23	.9871	2.63	.9957	3.03	.9988	3.43	.9997	3.83	.9999
1.84	.9671	2.24	.9875	2.64	.9959	3.04	.9988	3.44	.9997	3.84	.9999
1.85	.9678	2.25	.9878	2.65	.9960	3.05	.9989	3.45	.9997	3.85	.9999
1.86	.9686	2.26	.9881	2.66	.9961	3.06	.9989	3.46	.9997	3.86	.9999
1.87	.9693	2.27	.9884	2.67	.9962	3.07	.9989	3.47	.9997	3.87	.9999
1.88	.9699	2.28	.9887	2.68	.9963	3.08	.9990	3.48	.9997	3.88	.9999
1.89	.9706	2.29	.9890	2.69	.9964	3.09	.9990	3.49	.9998	3.89	1.0000
1.90	.9713	2.30	.9893	2.70	.9965	3.10	.9990	3.50	.9998	3.90	1.0000
1.91	.9719	2.31	.9896	2.71	.9966	3.11	.9991	3.51	.9998	3.91	1.0000
1.92	.9726	2.32	.9898	2.72	.9967	3.12	.9991	3.52	.9998	3.92	1.0000
1.93	.9732	2.33	.9901	2.73	.9968	3.13	.9991	3.53	.9998	3.93	1.0000
1.94	.9738	2.34	.9904	2.74	.9969	3.14	.9992	3.54	.9998	3.94	1.0000
1.95	.9744	2.35	.9906	2.75	.9970	3.15	.9992	3.55	.9998	3.95	1.0000
1.96	.9750	2.36	.9909	2.76	.9971	3.16	.9992	3.56	.9998	3.96	1.0000
1.97	.9756	2.37	.9911	2.77	.9972	3.17	.9992	3.57	.9998	3.97	1.0000
1.98	.9761	2.38	.9913	2.78	.9973	3.18	.9993	3.58	.9998	3.98	1.0000
1.99	.9767	2.39	.9916	2.79	.9974	3.19	.9993	3.59	.9998	3.99	1.0000
2.00	.9772	2.40	.9918	2.80	.9974	3.20	.9993	3.60	.9998		
2.01	.9778	2.41	.9920	2.81	.9975	3.21	.9993	3.61	.9998		
2.02	.9783	2.42	.9922	2.82	.9976	3.22	.9994	3.62	.9999		
2.03	.9788	2.43	.9925	2.83	.9977	3.23	.9994	3.63	.9999		
2.04	.9793	2.44	.9927	2.84	.9977	3.24	.9994	3.64	.9999		
2.05	.9798	2.45	.9929	2.85	.9978	3.25	.9994	3.65	.9999		
2.06	.9803	2.46	.9931	2.86	.9979	3.26	.9994	3.66	.9999		
2.07	.9808	2.47	.9932	2.87	.9979	3.27	.9995	3.67	.9999		
2.08	.9812	2.48	.9934	2.88	.9980	3.28	.9995	3.68	.9999		
2.09	.9817	2.49	.9936	2.89	.9981	3.29	.9995	3.69	.9999		
2.10	.9821	2.50	.9938	2.90	.9981	3.30	.9995	3.70	.9999		
2.11	.9826	2.51	.9940	2.91	.9982	3.31	.9995	3.71	.9999		
2.12	.9830	2.52	.9941	2.92	.9982	3.32	.9996	3.72	.9999		
2.13	.9834	2.53	.9943	2.93	.9983	3.33	.9996	3.73	.9999		
2.14	.9838	2.54	.9945	2.94	.9984	3.34	.9996	3.74	.9999		
2.15	.9842	2.55	.9946	2.95	.9984	3.35	.9996	3.75	.9999		
2.16	.9846	2.56	.9948	2.96	.9985	3.36	.9996	3.76	.9999		
2.17	.9850	2.57	.9949	2.97	.9985	3.37	.9996	3.77	.9999		
2.18	.9854	2.58	.9951	2.98	.9986	3.38	.9996	3.78	.9999		
2.19	.9857	2.59	.9952	2.99	.9986	3.39	.9997	3.79	.9999		
2.20	.9861	2.60	.9953	3.00	.9986	3.40	.9997	3.80	.9999		

Reproduced with permission of the trustees of Biometrika, from *Biometrika Tables for Statisticians*, vol. 1 (1966).

Table 2 Probability Function of the Binomial Distribution

The table shows the probability of x successes in n independent trials, each with probability of success P. For example, the probability of four successes in eight independent trials, each with probability of success .35, is .1875.

n	x	P .05	.10	.15	.20	.25	.30	.35	.40	.45	.50
1	0	.9500	.9000	.8500	.8000	.7500	.7000	.6500	.6000	.5500	.5000
	1	.0500	.1000	.1500	.2000	.2500	.3000	.3500	.4000	.4500	.5000
2	0	.9025	.8100	.7225	.6400	.5625	.4900	.4225	.3600	.3025	.2500
	1	.0950	.1800	.2550	.3200	.3750	.4200	.4550	.4800	.4950	.5000
	2	.0025	.0100	.0225	.0400	.0625	.0900	.1225	.1600	.2025	.2500
3	0	.8574	.7290	.6141	.5120	.4219	.3430	.2746	.2160	.1664	.1250
	1	.1354	.2430	.3251	.3840	.4219	.4410	.4436	.4320	.4084	.3750
	2	.0071	.0270	.0574	.0960	.1406	.1890	.2389	.2880	.3341	.3750
	3	.0001	.0010	.0034	.0080	.0156	.0270	.0429	.0640	.0911	.1250
4	0	.8145	.6561	.5220	.4096	.3164	.2401	.1785	.1296	.0915	.0625
	1	.1715	.2916	.3685	.4096	.4219	.4116	.3845	.3456	.2995	.2500
	2	.0135	.0486	.0975	.1536	.2109	.2646	.3105	.3456	.3675	.3750
	3	.0005	.0036	.0115	.0256	.0469	.0756	.1115	.1536	.2005	.2500
	4	.0000	.0001	.0005	.0016	.0039	.0081	.0150	.0256	.0410	.0625
5	0	.7738	.5905	.4437	.3277	.2373	.1681	.1160	.0778	.0503	.0312
	1	.2036	.3280	.3915	.4096	.3955	.3602	.3124	.2592	.2059	.1562
	2	.0214	.0729	.1382	.2048	.2637	.3087	.3364	.3456	.3369	.3125
	3	.0011	.0081	.0244	.0512	.0879	.1323	.1811	.2304	.2757	.3125
	4	.0000	.0004	.0022	.0064	.0146	.0284	.0488	.0768	.1128	.1562
	5	.0000	.0000	.0001	.0003	.0010	.0024	.0053	.0102	.0185	.0312
6	0	.7351	.5314	.3771	.2621	.1780	.1176	.0754	.0467	.0277	.0156
	1	.2321	.3543	.3993	.3932	.3560	.3025	.2437	.1866	.1359	.0938
	2	.0305	.0984	.1762	.2458	.2966	.3241	.3280	.3110	.2780	.2344
	3	.0021	.0146	.0415	.0819	.1318	.1852	.2355	.2765	.3032	.3125
	4	.0001	.0012	.0055	.0154	.0330	.0595	.0951	.1382	.1861	.2344
	5	.0000	.0001	.0004	.0015	.0044	.0102	.0205	.0369	.0609	.0938
	6	.0000	.0000	.0000	.0001	.0002	.0007	.0018	.0041	.0083	.0156
7	0	.6983	.4783	.3206	.2097	.1335	.0824	.0490	.0280	.0152	.0078
	1	.2573	.3720	.3960	.3670	.3115	.2471	.1848	.1306	.0872	.0547
	2	.0406	.1240	.2097	.2753	.3115	.3177	.2985	.2613	.2140	.1641
	3	.0036	.0230	.0617	.1147	.1730	.2269	.2679	.2903	.2918	.2734
	4	.0002	.0026	.0109	.0287	.0577	.0972	.1442	.1935	.2388	.2734
	5	.0000	.0002	.0012	.0043	.0115	.0250	.0466	.0774	.1172	.1641
	6	.0000	.0000	.0001	.0004	.0013	.0036	.0084	.0172	.0320	.0547
	7	.0000	.0000	.0000	.0000	.0001	.0002	.0006	.0016	.0037	.0078
8	0	.6634	.4305	.2725	.1678	.1001	.0576	.0319	.0168	.0084	.0039
	1	.2793	.3826	.3847	.3355	.2670	.1977	.1373	.0896	.0548	.0312
	2	.0515	.1488	.2376	.2936	.3115	.2965	.2587	.2090	.1569	.1094
	3	.0054	.0331	.0839	.1468	.2076	.2541	.2786	.2787	.2568	.2188
	4	.0004	.0046	.0185	.0459	.0865	.1361	.1875	.2322	.2627	.2734
	5	.0000	.0004	.0026	.0092	.0231	.0467	.0808	.1239	.1719	.2188
	6	.0000	.0000	.0002	.0011	.0038	.0100	.0217	.0413	.0703	.1094
	7	.0000	.0000	.0000	.0001	.0004	.0012	.0033	.0079	.0164	.0312
	8	.0000	.0000	.0000	.0000	.0000	.0001	.0002	.0007	.0017	.0039
9	0	.6302	.3874	.2316	.1342	.0751	.0404	.0207	.0101	.0046	.0020
	1	.2985	.3874	.3679	.3020	.2253	.1556	.1004	.0605	.0339	.0176
	2	.0629	.1722	.2597	.3020	.3003	.2668	.2162	.1612	.1110	.0703
	3	.0077	.0446	.1069	.1762	.2336	.2668	.2716	.2508	.2119	.1641
	4	.0006	.0074	.0283	.0661	.1168	.1715	.2194	.2508	.2600	.2461
	5	.0000	.0008	.0050	.0165	.0389	.0735	.1181	.1672	.2128	.2461
	6	.0000	.0001	.0006	.0028	.0087	.0210	.0424	.0743	.1160	.1641
	7	.0000	.0000	.0000	.0003	.0012	.0039	.0098	.0212	.0407	.0703

Table 2 Probability Function of the Binomial Distribution Continued

n	x	P									
		.05	.10	.15	.20	.25	.30	.35	.40	.45	.50
	8	.0000	.0000	.0000	.0000	.0001	.0004	.0013	.0035	.0083	.0176
	9	.0000	.0000	.0000	.0000	.0000	.0000	.0001	.0003	.0008	.0020
10	0	.5987	.3487	.1969	.1074	.0563	.0282	.0135	.0060	.0025	.0010
	1	.3151	.3874	.3474	.2684	.1877	.1211	.0725	.0403	.0207	.0098
	2	.0746	.1937	.2759	.3020	.2816	.2335	.1757	.1209	.0763	.0439
	3	.0105	.0574	.1298	.2013	.2503	.2668	.2522	.2150	.1665	.1172
	4	.0010	.0112	.0401	.0881	.1460	.2001	.2377	.2508	.2384	.2051
	5	.0001	.0015	.0085	.0264	.0584	.1029	.1536	.2007	.2340	.2461
	6	.0000	.0001	.0012	.0055	.0162	.0368	.0689	.1115	.1596	.2051
	7	.0000	.0000	.0001	.0008	.0031	.0090	.0212	.0425	.0746	.1172
	8	.0000	.0000	.0000	.0001	.0004	.0014	.0043	.0106	.0226	.0439
	9	.0000	.0000	.0000	.0000	.0000	.0001	.0004	.0016	.0042	.0098
	10	.0000	.0000	.0000	.0000	.0000	.0000	.0000	.0001	.0003	.0010
11	0	.5688	.3138	.1673	.0859	.0422	.0198	.0088	.0036	.0014	.0005
	1	.3293	.3835	.3248	.2362	.1549	.0932	.0518	.0266	.0125	.0054
	2	.0867	.2131	.2866	.2953	.2581	.1998	.1395	.0887	.0513	.0269
	3	.0137	.0710	.1517	.2215	.2581	.2568	.2254	.1774	.1259	.0806
	4	.0014	.0158	.0536	.1107	.1721	.2201	.2428	.2365	.2060	.1611
	5	.0001	.0025	.0132	.0388	.0803	.1321	.1830	.2207	.2360	.2256
	6	.0000	.0003	.0023	.0097	.0268	.0566	.0985	.1471	.1931	.2256
	7	.0000	.0000	.0003	.0017	.0064	.0173	.0379	.0701	.1128	.1611
	8	.0000	.0000	.0000	.0002	.0011	.0037	.0102	.0234	.0462	.0806
	9	.0000	.0000	.0000	.0000	.0001	.0005	.0018	.0052	.0126	.0269
	10	.0000	.0000	.0000	.0000	.0000	.0000	.0002	.0007	.0021	.0054
	11	.0000	.0000	.0000	.0000	.0000	.0000	.0000	.0000	.0002	.0005
12	0	.5404	.2824	.1422	.0687	.0317	.0138	.0057	.0022	.0008	.0002
	1	.3413	.3766	.3012	.2062	.1267	.0712	.0368	.0174	.0075	.0029
	2	.0988	.2301	.2924	.2835	.2323	.1678	.1088	.0639	.0339	.0161
	3	.0173	.0852	.1720	.2362	.2581	.2397	.1954	.1419	.0923	.0537
	4	.0021	.0213	.0683	.1329	.1936	.2311	.2367	.2128	.1700	.1208
	5	.0002	.0038	.0193	.0532	.1032	.1585	.2039	.2270	.2225	.1934
	6	.0000	.0005	.0040	.0155	.0401	.0792	.1281	.1766	.2124	.2256
	7	.0000	.0000	.0006	.0033	.0015	.0291	.0591	.1009	.1489	.1934
	8	.0000	.0000	.0001	.0005	.0024	.0078	.0199	.0420	.0762	.1208
	9	.0000	.0000	.0000	.0001	.0004	.0015	.0048	.0125	.0277	.0537
	10	.0000	.0000	.0000	.0000	.0000	.0002	.0008	.0025	.0068	.0161
	11	.0000	.0000	.0000	.0000	.0000	.0000	.0001	.0003	.0010	.0029
	12	.0000	.0000	.0000	.0000	.0000	.0000	.0000	.0000	.0001	.0002
13	0	.5133	.2542	.1209	.0550	.0238	.0097	.0037	.0013	.0004	.0001
	1	.3512	.3672	.2774	.1787	.1029	.0540	.0259	.0113	.0045	.0016
	2	.1109	.2448	.2937	.2680	.2059	.1388	.0836	.0453	.0220	.0095
	3	.0214	.0997	.1900	.2457	.2517	.2181	.1651	.1107	.0660	.0349
	4	.0028	.0277	.0838	.1535	.2097	.2337	.2222	.1845	.1350	.0873
	5	.0003	.0055	.0266	.0691	.1258	.1803	.2154	.2214	.1989	.1571
	6	.0000	.0008	.0063	.0230	.0559	.1030	.1546	.1968	.2169	.2095
	7	.0000	.0001	.0011	.0058	.0186	.0442	.0833	.1312	.1775	.2095
	8	.0000	.0000	.0001	.0011	.0047	.0142	.0336	.0656	.1089	.1571
	9	.0000	.0000	.0000	.0001	.0009	.0034	.0101	.0243	.0495	.0873
	10	.0000	.0000	.0000	.0000	.0001	.0006	.0022	.0065	.0162	.0349
	11	.0000	.0000	.0000	.0000	.0000	.0001	.0003	.0012	.0036	.0095
	12	.0000	.0000	.0000	.0000	.0000	.0000	.0000	.0001	.0005	.0016
	13	.0000	.0000	.0000	.0000	.0000	.0000	.0000	.0000	.0000	.0001
14	0	.4877	.2288	.1028	.0440	.0178	.0068	.0024	.0008	.0002	.0001
	1	.3593	.3559	.2539	.1539	.0832	.0407	.0181	.0073	.0027	.0009
	2	.1229	.2570	.2912	.2501	.1802	.1134	.0634	.0317	.0141	.0056

Table 2 Probability Function of the Binomial Distribution Continued

n	x	P									
		.05	.10	.15	.20	.25	.30	.35	.40	.45	.50
	3	.0259	.1142	.2056	.2501	.2402	.1943	.1366	.0845	.0462	.0222
	4	.0037	.0348	.0998	.1720	.2202	.2290	.2022	.1549	.1040	.0611
	5	.0004	.0078	.0352	.0860	.1468	.1963	.2178	.2066	.1701	.1222
	6	.0000	.0013	.0093	.0322	.0734	.1262	.1759	.2066	.2088	.1833
	7	.0000	.0002	.0019	.0092	.0280	.0618	.1082	.1574	.1952	.2095
	8	.0000	.0000	.0003	.0020	.0082	.0232	.0510	.0918	.1398	.1833
	9	.0000	.0000	.0000	.0003	.0018	.0066	.0183	.0408	.0762	.1222
	10	.0000	.0000	.0000	.0000	.0003	.0014	.0049	.0136	.0312	.0611
	11	.0000	.0000	.0000	.0000	.0000	.0002	.0010	.0033	.0093	.0222
	12	.0000	.0000	.0000	.0000	.0000	.0000	.0001	.0005	.0019	.0056
	13	.0000	.0000	.0000	.0000	.0000	.0000	.0000	.0001	.0002	.0009
	14	.0000	.0000	.0000	.0000	.0000	.0000	.0000	.0000	.0000	.0001
15	0	.4633	.2059	.0874	.0352	.0134	.0047	.0016	.0005	.0001	.0000
	1	.3658	.3432	.2312	.1319	.0668	.0305	.0126	.0047	.0016	.0005
	2	.1348	.2669	.2856	.2309	.1559	.0916	.0476	.0219	.0090	.0032
	3	.0307	.1285	.2184	.2501	.2252	.1700	.1110	.0634	.0318	.0139
	4	.0049	.0428	.1156	.1876	.2252	.2186	.1792	.1268	.0780	.0417
	5	.0006	.0105	.0449	.1032	.1651	.2061	.2123	.1859	.1404	.0916
	6	.0000	.0019	.0132	.0430	.0917	.1472	.1906	.2066	.1914	.1527
	7	.0000	.0003	.0030	.0138	.0393	.0811	.1319	.1771	.2013	.1964
	8	.0000	.0000	.0005	.0035	.0131	.0348	.0710	.1181	.1647	.1964
	9	.0000	.0000	.0001	.0007	.0034	.0116	.0298	.0612	.1048	.1527
	10	.0000	.0000	.0000	.0001	.0007	.0030	.0096	.0245	.0515	.0916
	11	.0000	.0000	.0000	.0000	.0001	.0006	.0024	.0074	.0191	.0417
	12	.0000	.0000	.0000	.0000	.0000	.0001	.0004	.0016	.0052	.0139
	13	.0000	.0000	.0000	.0000	.0000	.0000	.0001	.0003	.0010	.0032
	14	.0000	.0000	.0000	.0000	.0000	.0000	.0000	.0000	.0001	.0005
	15	.0000	.0000	.0000	.0000	.0000	.0000	.0000	.0000	.0000	.0000
16	0	.4401	.1853	.0743	.0281	.0100	.0033	.0010	.0003	.0001	.0000
	1	.3706	.3294	.2097	.1126	.0535	.0228	.0087	.0030	.0009	.0002
	2	.1463	.2745	.2775	.2111	.1336	.0732	.0353	.0150	.0056	.0018
	3	.0359	.1423	.2285	.2463	.2079	.1465	.0888	.0468	.0215	.0085
	4	.0061	.0514	.1311	.2001	.2552	.2040	.1553	.1014	.0572	.0278
	5	.0008	.0137	.0555	.1201	.1802	.2099	.2008	.1623	.1123	.0667
	6	.0001	.0028	.0180	.0550	.1101	.1649	.1982	.1983	.1684	.1222
	7	.0000	.0004	.0045	.0197	.0524	.1010	.1524	.1889	.1969	.1746
	8	.0000	.0001	.0009	.0055	.0197	.0487	.0923	.1417	.1812	.1964
	9	.0000	.0000	.0001	.0012	.0058	.0185	.0442	.0840	.1318	.1746
	10	.0000	.0000	.0000	.0002	.0014	.0056	.0167	.0392	.0755	.1222
	11	.0000	.0000	.0000	.0000	.0002	.0013	.0049	.0142	.0337	.0667
	12	.0000	.0000	.0000	.0000	.0000	.0002	.0011	.0040	.0115	.0278
	13	.0000	.0000	.0000	.0000	.0000	.0000	.0002	.0008	.0029	.0085
	14	.0000	.0000	.0000	.0000	.0000	.0000	.0000	.0001	.0005	.0018
	15	.0000	.0000	.0000	.0000	.0000	.0000	.0000	.0000	.0001	.0002
	16	.0000	.0000	.0000	.0000	.0000	.0000	.0000	.0000	.0000	.0000
17	0	.4181	.1668	.0631	.0225	.0075	.0023	.0007	.0002	.0000	.0000
	1	.3741	.3150	.1893	.0957	.0426	.0169	.0060	.0019	.0005	.0001
	2	.1575	.2800	.2673	.1914	.1136	.0581	.0260	.0102	.0035	.0010
	3	.0415	.1556	.2359	.2393	.1893	.1245	.0701	.0341	.0144	.0052
	4	.0076	.0605	.1457	.2093	.2209	.1868	.1320	.0796	.0411	.0182
	5	.0010	.0175	.0068	.1361	.1914	.2081	.1849	.1379	.0875	.0472
	6	.0001	.0039	.0236	.0680	.1276	.1784	.1991	.1839	.1432	.0944
	7	.0000	.0007	.0065	.0267	.0668	.1201	.1685	.1927	.1841	.1484
	8	.0000	.0001	.0014	.0084	.0279	.0644	.1134	.1606	.1883	.1855
	9	.0000	.0000	.0003	.0021	.0093	.0276	.0611	.1070	.1540	.1855

Table 2 Probability Function of the Binomial Distribution Continued

n	x	P									
		.05	.10	.15	.20	.25	.30	.35	.40	.45	.50
	10	.0000	.0000	.0000	.0004	.0025	.0095	.0263	.0571	.1008	.1484
	11	.0000	.0000	.0000	.0001	.0005	.0026	.0090	.0242	.0525	.0944
	12	.0000	.0000	.0000	.0000	.0001	.0006	.0024	.0081	.0215	.0472
	13	.0000	.0000	.0000	.0000	.0000	.0001	.0005	.0021	.0068	.0182
	14	.0000	.0000	.0000	.0000	.0000	.0000	.0001	.0004	.0016	.0052
	15	.0000	.0000	.0000	.0000	.0000	.0000	.0000	.0001	.0003	.0010
	16	.0000	.0000	.0000	.0000	.0000	.0000	.0000	.0000	.0000	.0001
	17	.0000	.0000	.0000	.0000	.0000	.0000	.0000	.0000	.0000	.0000
18	0	.3972	.1501	.0536	.0180	.0056	.0016	.0004	.0001	.0000	.0000
	1	.3763	.3002	.1704	.0811	.0338	.0126	.0042	.0012	.0003	.0001
	2	.1683	.2835	.2556	.1723	.0958	.0458	.0190	.0069	.0022	.0006
	3	.0473	.1680	.2406	.2297	.1704	.1046	.0547	.0246	.0095	.0031
	4	.0093	.0700	.1592	.2153	.2130	.1681	.1104	.0614	.0291	.0117
	5	.0014	.0218	.0787	.1507	.1988	.2017	.1664	.1146	.0666	.0327
	6	.0002	.0052	.0301	.0816	.1436	.1873	.1941	.1655	.1181	.0708
	7	.0000	.0010	.0091	.0350	.0820	.1376	.1792	.1892	.1657	.1214
	8	.0000	.0002	.0022	.0120	.0376	.0811	.1327	.1734	.1864	.1669
	9	.0000	.0000	.0004	.0033	.0139	.0386	.0794	.1284	.1694	.1855
	10	.0000	.0000	.0001	.0008	.0042	.0149	.0385	.0771	.1248	.1669
	11	.0000	.0000	.0000	.0001	.0010	.0046	.0151	.0374	.0742	.1214
	12	.0000	.0000	.0000	.0000	.0002	.0012	.0047	.0145	.0354	.0708
	13	.0000	.0000	.0000	.0000	.0000	.0002	.0012	.0044	.0134	.0327
	14	.0000	.0000	.0000	.0000	.0000	.0000	.0002	.0011	.0039	.0117
	15	.0000	.0000	.0000	.0000	.0000	.0000	.0000	.0002	.0009	.0031
	16	.0000	.0000	.0000	.0000	.0000	.0000	.0000	.0000	.0001	.0006
	17	.0000	.0000	.0000	.0000	.0000	.0000	.0000	.0000	.0000	.0001
	18	.0000	.0000	.0000	.0000	.0000	.0000	.0000	.0000	.0000	.0000
19	0	.3774	.1351	.0456	.0144	.0042	.0011	.0003	.0001	.0000	.0000
	1	.3774	.2852	.1529	.0685	.0268	.0093	.0029	.0008	.0002	.0000
	2	.1787	.2852	.2428	.1540	.0803	.0358	.0138	.0046	.0013	.0003
	3	.0533	.1796	.2428	.2182	.1517	.0869	.0422	.0175	.0062	.0018
	4	.0112	.0798	.1714	.2182	.2023	.1419	.0909	.0467	.0203	.0074
	5	.0018	.0266	.0907	.1636	.2023	.1916	.1468	.0933	.0497	.0222
	6	.0002	.0069	.0374	.0955	.1574	.1916	.1844	.1451	.0949	.0518
	7	.0000	.0014	.0122	.0443	.0974	.1525	.1844	.1797	.1443	.0961
	8	.0000	.0002	.0032	.0166	.0487	.0981	.1489	.1797	.1771	.1442
	9	.0000	.0000	.0007	.0051	.0198	.0514	.0980	.1464	.1771	.1762
	10	.0000	.0000	.0001	.0013	.0066	.0220	.0528	.0976	.1449	.1762
	11	.0000	.0000	.0000	.0003	.0018	.0077	.0233	.0532	.0970	.1442
	12	.0000	.0000	.0000	.0000	.0004	.0022	.0083	.0237	.0529	.0961
	13	.0000	.0000	.0000	.0000	.0001	.0005	.0024	.0085	.0233	.0518
	14	.0000	.0000	.0000	.0000	.0000	.0001	.0006	.0024	.0082	.0222
	15	.0000	.0000	.0000	.0000	.0000	.0000	.0001	.0005	.0022	.0074
	16	.0000	.0000	.0000	.0000	.0000	.0000	.0000	.0001	.0005	.0018
	17	.0000	.0000	.0000	.0000	.0000	.0000	.0000	.0000	.0001	.0003
	18	.0000	.0000	.0000	.0000	.0000	.0000	.0000	.0000	.0000	.0000
	19	.0000	.0000	.0000	.0000	.0000	.0000	.0000	.0000	.0000	.0000
20	0	.3585	.1216	.0388	.0115	.0032	.0008	.0002	.0000	.0000	.0000
	1	.3774	.2702	.1368	.0576	.0211	.0068	.0020	.0005	.0001	.0000
	2	.1887	.2852	.2293	.1369	.0669	.0278	.0100	.0031	.0008	.0002
	3	.0596	.1901	.2428	.2054	.1339	.0716	.0323	.0123	.0040	.0011
	4	.0133	.0898	.1821	.2182	.1897	.1304	.0738	.0350	.0139	.0046
	5	.0022	.0319	.1028	.1746	.2023	.1789	.1272	.0746	.0365	.0148
	6	.0003	.0089	.0454	.1091	.1686	.1916	.1712	.1244	.0746	.0370
	7	.0000	.0020	.0160	.0545	.1124	.1643	.1844	.1659	.1221	.0739
	8	.0000	.0004	.0046	.0222	.0609	.1144	.1614	.1797	.1623	.1201

Table 2 Probability Function of the Binomial Distribution Continued

n	x	P									
		.05	.10	.15	.20	.25	.30	.35	.40	.45	.50
	9	.0000	.0001	.0011	.0074	.0271	.0654	.1158	.1597	.1771	.1602
	10	.0000	.0000	.0002	.0020	.0099	.0308	.0686	.1171	.1593	.1762
	11	.0000	.0000	.0000	.0005	.0030	.0120	.0336	.0710	.1185	.1602
	12	.0000	.0000	.0000	.0001	.0008	.0039	.0136	.0355	.0727	.1201
	13	.0000	.0000	.0000	.0000	.0002	.0010	.0045	.0146	.0366	.0739
	14	.0000	.0000	.0000	.0000	.0000	.0002	.0012	.0049	.0150	.0370
	15	.0000	.0000	.0000	.0000	.0000	.0000	.0003	.0013	.0049	.0148
	16	.0000	.0000	.0000	.0000	.0000	.0000	.0000	.0003	.0013	.0046
	17	.0000	.0000	.0000	.0000	.0000	.0000	.0000	.0000	.0002	.0011
	18	.0000	.0000	.0000	.0000	.0000	.0000	.0000	.0000	.0000	.0002
	19	.0000	.0000	.0000	.0000	.0000	.0000	.0000	.0000	.0000	.0000
	20	.0000	.0000	.0000	.0000	.0000	.0000	.0000	.0000	.0000	.0000

Reproduced with permission from National Bureau of Standards, *Tables of the Binomial Probability Distribution*, United States Department of Commerce (1950).

Table 3 Cumulative Binomial Probabilities

The table shows the probability of x or fewer successes in n independent trials each with probability of success P. For example, the probability of two or less successes in four independent trials, each with probability of success, 0.35 is 0.874.

n	x	P									
		.05	.10	.15	.20	.25	.30	.35	.40	.45	.500
2	0	.902	.81	.722	.64	.562	.49	.422	.36	.302	.25
	1	.998	.99	.978	.96	.937	.91	.877	.84	.797	.75
	2	1.00	1.00	1.00	1.00	1.00	1.00	1.00	1.00	1.00	1.00
3	0	.857	.729	.614	.512	.422	.343	.275	.216	.166	.125
	1	.993	.972	.939	.896	.844	.784	.718	.648	.575	.500
	2	1.00	.999	.997	.992	.984	.973	.957	.936	.909	.875
	3	1.00	1.00	1.00	1.00	1.00	1.00	1.00	1.00	1.00	1.000
4	0	.815	.656	.522	.41	.316	.24	.179	.13	.092	.062
	1	.986	.948	.89	.819	.738	.652	.563	.475	.391	.312
	2	1.00	.996	.988	.973	.949	.916	.874	.821	.759	.687
	3	1.00	1.00	.999	.998	.996	.992	.985	.974	.959	.937
	4	1.00	1.00	1.00	1.00	1.00	1.00	1.00	1.00	1.00	1.000
5	0	.774	.59	.444	.328	.237	.168	.116	.078	.05	.031
	1	.977	.919	.835	.737	.633	.528	.428	.337	.256	.187
	2	.999	.991	.973	.942	.896	.837	.765	.683	.593	.500
	3	1.00	1.00	.998	.993	.984	.969	.946	.913	.869	.812
	4	1.00	1.00	1.00	1.00	.999	.998	.995	.99	.982	.969
	5	1.00	1.00	1.00	1.00	1.00	1.00	1.00	1.00	1.00	1.000
6	0	.735	.531	.377	.262	.178	.118	.075	.047	.028	.016
	1	.967	.886	.776	.655	.534	.42	.319	.233	.164	.109
	2	.998	.984	.953	.901	.831	.744	.647	.544	.442	.344
	3	1.00	.999	.994	.983	.962	.93	.883	.821	.745	.656
	4	1.00	1.00	1.00	.998	.995	.989	.978	.959	.931	.891
	5	1.00	1.00	1.00	1.00	1.00	.999	.998	.996	.992	.984
	6	1.00	1.00	1.00	1.00	1.00	1.00	1.00	1.00	1.00	1.000
7	0	.698	.478	.321	.21	.133	.082	.049	.028	.015	.008
	1	.956	.85	.717	.577	.445	.329	.234	.159	.102	.062
	2	.996	.974	.926	.852	.756	.647	.532	.42	.316	.227
	3	1.00	.997	.988	.967	.929	.874	.80	.71	.608	.500
	4	1.00	1.00	.999	.995	.987	.971	.944	.904	.847	.773
	5	1.00	1.00	1.00	1.00	.999	.996	.991	.981	.964	.937
	6	1.00	1.00	1.00	1.00	1.00	1.00	.999	.998	.996	.992
	7	1.00	1.00	1.00	1.00	1.00	1.00	1.00	1.00	1.00	1.000
8	0	.663	.43	.272	.168	.10	.058	.032	.017	.008	.004
	1	.943	.813	.657	.503	.367	.255	.169	.106	.063	.035
	2	.994	.962	.895	.797	.679	.552	.428	.315	.22	.145
	3	1.00	.995	.979	.944	.886	.806	.706	.594	.477	.363
	4	1.00	1.00	.997	.99	.973	.942	.894	.826	.74	.637
	5	1.00	1.00	1.00	.999	.996	.989	.975	.95	.912	.855
	6	1.00	1.00	1.00	1.00	1.00	.999	.996	.991	.982	.965
	7	1.00	1.00	1.00	1.00	1.00	1.00	1.00	.999	.998	.996
	8	1.00	1.00	1.00	1.00	1.00	1.00	1.00	1.00	1.00	1.000
9	0	.63	.387	.232	.134	.075	.04	.021	.01	.005	.002
	1	.929	.775	.599	.436	.30	.196	.121	.071	.039	.020
	2	.992	.947	.859	.738	.601	.463	.337	.232	.15	.090
	3	.999	.992	.966	.914	.834	.73	.609	.483	.361	.254
	4	1.00	.999	.994	.98	.951	.901	.828	.733	.621	.500
	5	1.00	1.00	.999	.997	.99	.975	.946	.901	.834	.746
	6	1.00	1.00	1.00	1.00	.999	.996	.989	.975	.95	.910
	7	1.00	1.00	1.00	1.00	1.00	1.00	.999	.996	.991	.980
	8	1.00	1.00	1.00	1.00	1.00	1.00	1.00	1.00	.999	.998
	9	1.00	1.00	1.00	1.00	1.00	1.00	1.00	1.00	1.00	1.000

Table 3 Cumulative Binomial Probabilities Continued

n	x	P									
		.05	.10	.15	.20	.25	.30	.35	.40	.45	.500
10	0	.599	.349	.197	.107	.056	.028	.013	.006	.003	.001
	1	.914	.736	.544	.376	.244	.149	.086	.046	.023	.011
	2	.988	.93	.82	.678	.526	.383	.262	.167	.10	.055
	3	.999	.987	.95	.879	.776	.65	.514	.382	.266	.172
	4	1.00	.998	.99	.967	.922	.85	.751	.633	.504	.377
	5	1.00	1.00	.999	.994	.98	.953	.905	.834	.738	.623
	6	1.00	1.00	1.00	.999	.996	.989	.974	.945	.898	.828
	7	1.00	1.00	1.00	1.00	1.00	.998	.995	.988	.973	.945
	8	1.00	1.00	1.00	1.00	1.00	1.00	.999	.998	.995	.989
	9	1.00	1.00	1.00	1.00	1.00	1.00	1.00	1.00	1.00	.999
	10	1.00	1.00	1.00	1.00	1.00	1.00	1.00	1.00	1.00	1.000
11	0	.569	.314	.167	.086	.042	.02	.009	.004	.001	.000
	1	.898	.697	.492	.322	.197	.113	.061	.03	.014	.006
	2	.985	.91	.779	.617	.455	.313	.20	.119	.065	.033
	3	.998	.981	.931	.839	.713	.57	.426	.296	.191	.113
	4	1.00	.997	.984	.95	.885	.79	.668	.533	.397	.274
	5	1.00	1.00	.997	.988	.966	.922	.851	.753	.633	.500
	6	1.00	1.00	1.00	.998	.992	.978	.95	.901	.826	.726
	7	1.00	1.00	1.00	1.00	.999	.996	.988	.971	.939	.887
	8	1.00	1.00	1.00	1.00	1.00	.999	.998	.994	.985	.967
	9	1.00	1.00	1.00	1.00	1.00	1.00	1.00	.999	.998	.994
	10	1.00	1.00	1.00	1.00	1.00	1.00	1.00	1.00	1.00	1.000
	11	1.00	1.00	1.00	1.00	1.00	1.00	1.00	1.00	1.00	1.000
12	0	.54	.282	.142	.069	.032	.014	.006	.002	.001	.000
	1	.882	.659	.443	.275	.158	.085	.042	.02	.008	.003
	2	.98	.889	.736	.558	.391	.253	.151	.083	.042	.019
	3	.998	.974	.908	.795	.649	.493	.347	.225	.134	.073
	4	1.00	.996	.976	.927	.842	.724	.583	.438	.304	.194
	5	1.00	.999	.995	.981	.946	.882	.787	.665	.527	.387
	6	1.00	1.00	.999	.996	.986	.961	.915	.842	.739	.613
	7	1.00	1.00	1.00	.999	.997	.991	.974	.943	.888	.806
	8	1.00	1.00	1.00	1.00	1.00	.998	.994	.985	.964	.927
	9	1.00	1.00	1.00	1.00	1.00	1.00	.999	.997	.992	.981
	10	1.00	1.00	1.00	1.00	1.00	1.00	1.00	1.00	.999	.997
	11	1.00	1.00	1.00	1.00	1.00	1.00	1.00	1.00	1.00	1.000
	12	1.00	1.00	1.00	1.00	1.00	1.00	1.00	1.00	1.00	1.000
13	0	.513	.254	.121	.055	.024	.01	.004	.001	.00	.000
	1	.865	.621	.398	.234	.127	.064	.03	.013	.005	.002
	2	.975	.866	.692	.502	.333	.202	.113	.058	.027	.011
	3	.997	.966	.882	.747	.584	.421	.278	.169	.093	.046
	4	1.00	.994	.966	.901	.794	.654	.501	.353	.228	.133
	5	1.00	.999	.992	.97	.92	.835	.716	.574	.427	.291
	6	1.00	1.00	.999	.993	.976	.938	.871	.771	.644	.50
	7	1.00	1.00	1.00	.999	.994	.982	.954	.902	.821	.709
	8	1.00	1.00	1.00	1.00	.999	.996	.987	.968	.93	.867
	9	1.00	1.00	1.00	1.00	1.00	.999	.997	.992	.98	.954
	10	1.00	1.00	1.00	1.00	1.00	1.00	1.00	.999	.996	.989
	11	1.00	1.00	1.00	1.00	1.00	1.00	1.00	1.00	.999	.998
	12	1.00	1.00	1.00	1.00	1.00	1.00	1.00	1.00	1.00	1.000
14	0	.488	.229	.103	.044	.018	.007	.002	.001	.00	.000
	1	.847	.585	.357	.198	.101	.047	.021	.008	.003	.001
	2	.97	.842	.648	.448	.281	.161	.084	.04	.017	.006
	3	.996	.956	.853	.698	.521	.355	.22	.124	.063	.029
	4	1.00	.991	.953	.87	.742	.584	.423	.279	.167	.090
	5	1.00	.999	.988	.956	.888	.781	.641	.486	.337	.212

Table 3 Cumulative Binomial Probabilities Continued

n	x	P .05	.10	.15	.20	.25	.30	.35	.40	.45	.500
	6	1.00	1.00	.998	.988	.962	.907	.816	.692	.546	.395
	7	1.00	1.00	1.00	.998	.99	.969	.925	.85	.741	.605
	8	1.00	1.00	1.00	1.00	.998	.992	.976	.942	.881	.788
	9	1.00	1.00	1.00	1.00	1.00	.998	.994	.982	.957	.910
	10	1.00	1.00	1.00	1.00	1.00	1.00	.999	.996	.989	.971
	11	1.00	1.00	1.00	1.00	1.00	1.00	1.00	.999	.998	.994
	12	1.00	1.00	1.00	1.00	1.00	1.00	1.00	1.00	1.00	.999
	13	1.00	1.00	1.00	1.00	1.00	1.00	1.00	1.00	1.00	1.000
15	0	.463	.206	.087	.035	.013	.005	.002	.00	.00	.000
	1	.829	.549	.319	.167	.08	.035	.014	.005	.002	.000
	2	.964	.816	.604	.398	.236	.127	.062	.027	.011	.004
	3	.995	.944	.823	.648	.461	.297	.173	.091	.042	.018
	4	.999	.987	.938	.836	.686	.515	.352	.217	.12	.059
	5	1.00	.998	.983	.939	.852	.722	.564	.403	.261	.151
	6	1.00	1.00	.996	.982	.943	.869	.755	.61	.452	.304
	7	1.00	1.00	.999	.996	.983	.95	.887	.787	.654	.500
	8	1.00	1.00	1.00	.999	.996	.985	.958	.905	.818	.696
	9	1.00	1.00	1.00	1.00	.999	.996	.988	.966	.923	.849
	10	1.00	1.00	1.00	1.00	1.00	.999	.997	.991	.975	.941
	11	1.00	1.00	1.00	1.00	1.00	1.00	1.00	.998	.994	.982
	12	1.00	1.00	1.00	1.00	1.00	1.00	1.00	1.00	.999	.996
	13	1.00	1.00	1.00	1.00	1.00	1.00	1.00	1.00	1.00	1.000
16	0	.44	.185	.074	.028	.01	.003	.001	.00	.00	.000
	1	.811	.515	.284	.141	.063	.026	.01	.003	.001	.000
	2	.957	.789	.561	.352	.197	.099	.045	.018	.007	.002
	3	.993	.932	.79	.598	.405	.246	.134	.065	.028	.011
	4	.999	.983	.921	.798	.63	.45	.289	.167	.085	.038
	5	1.00	.997	.976	.918	.81	.66	.49	.329	.198	.105
	6	1.00	.999	.994	.973	.92	.825	.688	.527	.366	.227
	7	1.00	1.00	.999	.993	.973	.926	.841	.716	.563	.402
	8	1.00	1.00	1.00	.999	.993	.974	.933	.858	.744	.598
	9	1.00	1.00	1.00	1.00	.998	.993	.977	.942	.876	.773
	10	1.00	1.00	1.00	1.00	1.00	.998	.994	.981	.951	.895
	11	1.00	1.00	1.00	1.00	1.00	1.00	.999	.995	.985	.962
	12	1.00	1.00	1.00	1.00	1.00	1.00	1.00	.999	.997	.989
	13	1.00	1.00	1.00	1.00	1.00	1.00	1.00	1.00	.999	.998
	14	1.00	1.00	1.00	1.00	1.00	1.00	1.00	1.00	1.00	1.000
17	0	.418	.167	.063	.023	.008	.002	.001	.00	.00	.000
	1	.792	.482	.252	.118	.05	.019	.007	.002	.001	.000
	2	.95	.762	.52	.31	.164	.077	.033	.012	.004	.001
	3	.991	.917	.756	.549	.353	.202	.103	.046	.018	.006
	4	.999	.978	.901	.758	.574	.389	.235	.126	.06	.025
	5	1.00	.995	.968	.894	.765	.597	.42	.264	.147	.072
	6	1.00	.999	.992	.962	.893	.775	.619	.448	.29	.166
	7	1.00	1.00	.998	.989	.96	.895	.787	.641	.474	.315
	8	1.00	1.00	1.00	.997	.988	.96	.901	.801	.663	.500
	9	1.00	1.00	1.00	1.00	.997	.987	.962	.908	.817	.685
	10	1.00	1.00	1.00	1.00	.999	.997	.988	.965	.917	.834
	11	1.00	1.00	1.00	1.00	1.00	.999	.997	.989	.97	.928
	12	1.00	1.00	1.00	1.00	1.00	1.00	.999	.997	.991	.975
	13	1.00	1.00	1.00	1.00	1.00	1.00	1.00	1.00	.998	.994
	14	1.00	1.00	1.00	1.00	1.00	1.00	1.00	1.00	1.00	.999
	15	1.00	1.00	1.00	1.00	1.00	1.00	1.00	1.00	1.00	1.00
18	0	.397	.15	.054	.018	.006	.002	.00	.00	.00	.000
	1	.774	.45	.224	.099	.039	.014	.005	.001	.00	.000

Table 3 Cumulative Binomial Probabilities Continued

n	x	P									
		.05	.10	.15	.20	.25	.30	.35	.40	.45	.500
	2	.942	.734	.48	.271	.135	.06	.024	.008	.003	.001
	3	.989	.902	.72	.501	.306	.165	.078	.033	.012	.004
	4	.998	.972	.879	.716	.519	.333	.189	.094	.041	.015
	5	1.00	.994	.958	.867	.717	.534	.355	.209	.108	.048
	6	1.00	.999	.988	.949	.861	.722	.549	.374	.226	.119
	7	1.00	1.00	.997	.984	.943	.859	.728	.563	.391	.240
	8	1.00	1.00	.999	.996	.981	.94	.861	.737	.578	.407
	9	1.00	1.00	1.00	.999	.995	.979	.94	.865	.747	.593
	10	1.00	1.00	1.00	1.00	.999	.994	.979	.942	.872	.760
	11	1.00	1.00	1.00	1.00	1.00	.999	.994	.98	.946	.881
	12	1.00	1.00	1.00	1.00	1.00	1.00	.999	.994	.982	.952
	13	1.00	1.00	1.00	1.00	1.00	1.00	1.00	.999	.995	.985
	14	1.00	1.00	1.00	1.00	1.00	1.00	1.00	1.00	.999	.996
	15	1.00	1.00	1.00	1.00	1.00	1.00	1.00	1.00	1.00	.999
	16	1.00	1.00	1.00	1.00	1.00	1.00	1.00	1.00	1.00	1.000
19	0	.377	.135	.046	.014	.004	.001	.00	.00	.00	.000
	1	.755	.42	.198	.083	.031	.01	.003	.001	.00	.000
	2	.933	.705	.441	.237	.111	.046	.017	.005	.002	.000
	3	.987	.885	.684	.455	.263	.133	.059	.023	.008	.002
	4	.998	.965	.856	.673	.465	.282	.15	.07	.028	.010
	5	1.00	.991	.946	.837	.668	.474	.297	.163	.078	.032
	6	1.00	.998	.984	.932	.825	.666	.481	.308	.173	.084
	7	1.00	1.00	.996	.977	.923	.818	.666	.488	.317	.180
	8	1.00	1.00	.999	.993	.971	.916	.815	.667	.494	.324
	9	1.00	1.00	1.00	.998	.991	.967	.913	.814	.671	.500
	10	1.00	1.00	1.00	1.00	.998	.989	.965	.912	.816	.676
	11	1.00	1.00	1.00	1.00	1.00	.997	.989	.965	.913	.820
	12	1.00	1.00	1.00	1.00	1.00	.999	.997	.988	.966	.916
	13	1.00	1.00	1.00	1.00	1.00	1.00	.999	.997	.989	.968
	14	1.00	1.00	1.00	1.00	1.00	1.00	1.00	.999	.997	.990
	15	1.00	1.00	1.00	1.00	1.00	1.00	1.00	1.00	.999	.998
	16	1.00	1.00	1.00	1.00	1.00	1.00	1.00	1.00	1.00	1.000
20	0	.358	.122	.039	.012	.003	.001	.00	.00	.00	.000
	1	.736	.392	.176	.069	.024	.008	.002	.001	.00	.000
	2	.925	.677	.405	.206	.091	.035	.012	.004	.001	.000
	3	.984	.867	.648	.411	.225	.107	.044	.016	.005	.001
	4	.997	.957	.83	.63	.415	.238	.118	.051	.019	.006
	5	1.00	.989	.933	.804	.617	.416	.245	.126	.055	.021
	6	1.00	.998	.978	.913	.786	.608	.417	.25	.13	.058
	7	1.00	1.00	.994	.968	.898	.772	.601	.416	.252	.132
	8	1.00	1.00	.999	.99	.959	.887	.762	.596	.414	.252
	9	1.00	1.00	1.00	.997	.986	.952	.878	.755	.591	.412
	10	1.00	1.00	1.00	.999	.996	.983	.947	.872	.751	.588
	11	1.00	1.00	1.00	1.00	.999	.995	.98	.943	.869	.748
	12	1.00	1.00	1.00	1.00	1.00	.999	.994	.979	.942	.868
	13	1.00	1.00	1.00	1.00	1.00	1.00	.998	.994	.979	.942
	14	1.00	1.00	1.00	1.00	1.00	1.00	1.00	.998	.994	.979
	15	1.00	1.00	1.00	1.00	1.00	1.00	1.00	1.00	.998	.994
	16	1.00	1.00	1.00	1.00	1.00	1.00	1.00	1.00	1.00	.999
	17	1.00	1.00	1.00	1.00	1.00	1.00	1.00	1.00	1.00	1.000

Table 4 Values of $e^{-\lambda}$

λ	$e^{-\lambda}$	λ	$e^{-\lambda}$	λ	$e^{-\lambda}$	λ	$e^{-\lambda}$
0.00	1.000000	2.60	.074274	5.10	.006097	7.60	.000501
0.10	.904837	2.70	.067206	5.20	.005517	7.70	.000453
0.20	.818731	2.80	.060810	5.30	.004992	7.80	.000410
0.30	.740818	2.90	.055023	5.40	.004517	7.90	.000371
0.40	.670320	3.00	.049787	5.50	.004087	8.00	.000336
0.50	.606531	3.10	.045049	5.60	.003698	8.10	.000304
0.60	.548812	3.20	.040762	5.70	.003346	8.20	.000275
0.70	.496585	3.30	.036883	5.80	.003028	8.30	.000249
0.80	.449329	3.40	.033373	5.90	.002739	8.40	.000225
0.90	.406570	3.50	.030197	6.00	.002479	8.50	.000204
1.00	.367879	3.60	.027324	6.10	.002243	8.60	.000184
1.10	.332871	3.70	.024724	6.20	.002029	8.70	.000167
1.20	.301194	3.80	.022371	6.30	.001836	8.80	.000151
1.30	.272532	3.90	.020242	6.40	.001661	8.90	.000136
1.40	.246597	4.00	.018316	6.50	.001503	9.00	.000123
1.50	.223130	4.10	.016573	6.60	.001360	9.10	.000112
1.60	.201897	4.20	.014996	6.70	.001231	9.20	.000101
1.70	.182684	4.30	.013569	6.80	.001114	9.30	.000091
1.80	.165299	4.40	.012277	6.90	.001008	9.40	.000083
1.90	.149569	4.50	.011109	7.00	.000912	9.50	.000075
2.00	.135335	4.60	.010052	7.10	.000825	9.60	.000068
2.10	.122456	4.70	.009095	7.20	.000747	9.70	.000061
2.20	.110803	4.80	.008230	7.30	.000676	9.80	.000056
2.30	.100259	4.90	.007447	7.40	.000611	9.90	.000050
2.40	.090718	5.00	.006738	7.50	.000553	10.00	.000045
2.50	.082085						

Table 5 Individual Poisson Probabilities

	Mean Arrival Rate λ									
	0.1	0.2	0.3	0.4	0.5	0.6	0.7	0.8	0.9	1.0
0	.9048	.8187	.7408	.6703	.6065	.5488	.4966	.4493	.4066	.3679
1	.0905	.1637	.2222	.2681	.3033	.3293	.3476	.3595	.3659	.3679
2	.0045	.0164	.0333	.0536	.0758	.0988	.1217	.1438	.1647	.1839
3	.0002	.0011	.0033	.0072	.0126	.0198	.0284	.0383	.0494	.0613
4	.0	.0001	.0003	.0007	.0016	.0030	.0050	.0077	.0111	.0153
5	.0	.0	.0	.0001	.0002	.0004	.0007	.0012	.0020	.0031
6	.0	.0	.0	.0	.0	.0	.0001	.0002	.0003	.0005
7	.0	.0	.0	.0	.0	.0	.0	.0	.0	.0001

	Mean Arrival Rate λ									
	1.1	1.2	1.3	1.4	1.5	1.6	1.7	1.8	1.9	2.0
0	.3329	.3012	.2725	.2466	.2231	.2019	.1827	.1653	.1496	.1353
1	.3662	.3614	.3543	.3452	.3347	.3230	.3106	.2975	.2842	.2707
2	.2014	.2169	.2303	.2417	.2510	.2584	.2640	.2678	.2700	.2707
3	.0738	.0867	.0998	.1128	.1255	.1378	.1496	.1607	.1710	.1804
4	.0203	.0260	.0324	.0395	.0471	.0551	.0636	.0723	.0812	.0902
5	.0045	.0062	.0084	.0111	.0141	.0176	.0216	.0260	.0309	.0361
6	.0008	.0012	.0018	.0026	.0035	.0047	.0061	.0078	.0098	.0120
7	.0001	.0002	.0003	.0005	.0008	.0011	.0015	.0020	.0027	.0034
8	.0	.0	.0001	.0001	.0001	.0002	.0003	.0005	.0006	.0009
9	.0	.0	.0	.0	.0	.0	.0001	.0001	.0001	.0002

	Mean Arrival Rate λ									
	2.1	2.2	2.3	2.4	2.5	2.6	2.7	2.8	2.9	3.0
0	.1225	.1108	.1003	.0907	.0821	.0743	.0672	.0608	.0550	.0498
1	.2572	.2438	.2306	.2177	.2052	.1931	.1815	.1703	.1596	.1494
2	.2700	.2681	.2652	.2613	.2565	.2510	.2450	.2384	.2314	.2240
3	.1890	.1966	.2033	.2090	.2138	.2176	.2205	.2225	.2237	.2240
4	.0992	.1082	.1169	.1254	.1336	.1414	.1488	.1557	.1622	.1680
5	.0417	.0476	.0538	.0602	.0668	.0735	.0804	.0872	.0940	.1008
6	.0146	.0174	.0206	.0241	.0278	.0319	.0362	.0407	.0455	.0504
7	.0044	.0055	.0068	.0083	.0099	.0118	.0139	.0163	.0188	.0216
8	.0011	.0015	.0019	.0025	.0031	.0038	.0047	.0057	.0068	.0081
9	.0003	.0004	.0005	.0007	.0009	.0011	.0014	.0018	.0022	.0027
10	.0001	.0001	.0001	.0002	.0002	.0003	.0004	.0005	.0006	.0008
11	.0	.0	.0	.0	.0	.0001	.0001	.0001	.0002	.0002
12	.0	.0	.0	.0	.0	.0	.0	.0	.0	.0001

	Mean Arrival Rate λ									
	3.1	3.2	3.3	3.4	3.5	3.6	3.7	3.8	3.9	4.0
0	.0450	.0408	.0369	.0334	.0302	.0273	.0247	.0224	.0202	.0183
1	.1397	.1304	.1217	.1135	.1057	.0984	.0915	.0850	.0789	.0733
2	.2165	.2087	.2008	.1929	.1850	.1771	.1692	.1615	.1539	.1465
3	.2237	.2226	.2209	.2186	.2158	.2125	.2087	.2046	.2001	.1954
4	.1733	.1781	.1823	.1858	.1888	.1912	.1931	.1944	.1951	.1954
5	.1075	.1140	.1203	.1264	.1322	.1377	.1429	.1477	.1522	.1563
6	.0555	.0608	.0662	.0716	.0771	.0826	.0881	.0936	.0989	.1042
7	.0246	.0278	.0312	.0348	.0385	.0425	.0466	.0508	.0551	.0595
8	.0095	.0111	.0129	.0148	.0169	.0191	.0215	.0241	.0269	.0298
9	.0033	.0040	.0047	.0056	.0066	.0076	.0089	.0102	.0116	.0132
10	.0010	.0013	.0016	.0019	.0023	.0028	.0033	.0039	.0045	.0053
11	.0003	.0004	.0005	.0006	.0007	.0009	.0011	.0013	.0016	.0019
12	.0001	.0001	.0001	.0002	.0002	.0003	.0003	.0004	.0005	.0006
13	.0	.0	.0	.0	.0001	.0001	.0001	.0001	.0002	.0002
14	.0	.0	.0	.0	.0	.0	.0	.0	.0	.0001

Table 5 Individual Poisson Probabilities Continued

	Mean Arrival Rate λ									
	4.1	4.2	4.3	4.4	4.5	4.6	4.7	4.8	4.9	5.0
0	.0166	.0150	.0136	.0123	.0111	.0101	.0091	.0082	.0074	.0067
1	.0679	.0630	.0583	.0540	.0500	.0462	.0427	.0395	.0365	.0337
2	.1393	.1323	.1254	.1188	.1125	.1063	.1005	.0948	.0894	.0842
3	.1904	.1852	.1798	.1743	.1687	.1631	.1574	.1517	.1460	.1404
4	.1951	.1944	.1933	.1917	.1898	.1875	.1849	.1820	.1789	.1755
5	.1600	.1633	.1662	.1687	.1708	.1725	.1738	.1747	.1753	.1755
6	.1093	.1143	.1191	.1237	.1281	.1323	.1362	.1398	.1432	.1462
7	.0640	.0686	.0732	.0778	.0824	.0869	.0914	.0959	.1002	.1044
8	.0328	.0360	.0393	.0428	.0463	.0500	.0537	.0575	.0614	.0653
9	.0150	.0168	.0188	.0209	.0232	.0255	.0281	.0307	.0334	.0363
10	.0061	.0071	.0081	.0092	.0104	.0118	.0132	.0147	.0164	.0181
11	.0023	.0027	.0032	.0037	.0043	.0049	.0056	.0064	.0073	.0082
12	.0008	.0009	.0011	.0013	.0016	.0019	.0022	.0026	.0030	.0034
13	.0002	.0003	.0004	.0005	.0006	.0007	.0008	.0009	.0011	.0013
14	.0001	.0001	.0001	.0001	.0002	.0002	.0003	.0003	.0004	.0005

	Mean Arrival Rate λ									
	5.1	5.2	5.3	5.4	5.5	5.6	5.7	5.8	5.9	6.0
0	.0061	.0055	.0050	.0045	.0041	.0037	.0033	.0030	.0027	.0025
1	.0311	.0287	.0265	.0244	.0225	.0207	.0191	.0176	.0162	.0149
2	.0793	.0746	.0701	.0659	.0618	.0580	.0544	.0509	.0477	.0446
3	.1348	.1293	.1239	.1185	.1133	.1082	.1033	.0985	.0938	.0892
4	.1719	.1681	.1641	.1600	.1558	.1515	.1472	.1428	.1383	.1339
5	.1753	.1748	.1740	.1728	.1714	.1697	.1678	.1656	.1632	.1606
6	.1490	.1515	.1537	.1555	.1571	.1584	.1594	.1601	.1605	.1606
7	.1086	.1125	.1163	.1200	.1234	.1267	.1298	.1326	.1353	.1377
8	.0692	.0731	.0771	.0810	.0849	.0887	.0925	.0962	.0998	.1033
9	.0392	.0423	.0454	.0486	.0519	.0552	.0586	.0620	.0654	.0688
10	.0200	.0220	.0241	.0262	.0285	.0309	.0334	.0359	.0386	.0413
11	.0093	.0104	.0116	.0129	.0143	.0157	.0173	.0190	.0207	.0225
12	.0039	.0045	.0051	.0058	.0065	.0073	.0082	.0092	.0102	.0113
13	.0015	.0018	.0021	.0024	.0028	.0032	.0036	.0041	.0046	.0052
14	.0006	.0007	.0008	.0009	.0011	.0013	.0015	.0017	.0019	.0022

	Mean Arrival Rate λ									
	6.1	6.2	6.3	6.4	6.5	6.6	6.7	6.8	6.9	7.0
0	.0022	.0020	.0018	.0017	.0015	.0014	.0012	.0011	.0010	.0009
1	.0137	.0126	.0116	.0106	.0098	.0090	.0082	.0076	.0070	.0064
2	.0417	.0390	.0364	.0340	.0318	.0296	.0276	.0258	.0240	.0223
3	.0848	.0806	.0765	.0726	.0688	.0652	.0617	.0584	.0552	.0521
4	.1294	.1249	.1205	.1162	.1118	.1076	.1034	.0992	.0952	.0912
5	.1579	.1549	.1519	.1487	.1454	.1420	.1385	.1349	.1314	.1277
6	.1605	.1601	.1595	.1586	.1575	.1562	.1546	.1529	.1511	.1490
7	.1399	.1418	.1435	.1450	.1462	.1472	.1480	.1486	.1489	.1490
8	.1066	.1099	.1130	.1160	.1188	.1215	.1240	.1263	.1284	.1304
9	.0723	.0757	.0791	.0825	.0858	.0891	.0923	.0954	.0985	.1014
10	.0441	.0469	.0498	.0528	.0558	.0588	.0618	.0649	.0679	.0710
11	.0244	.0265	.0285	.0307	.0330	.0353	.0377	.0401	.0426	.0452
12	.0124	.0137	.0150	.0164	.0179	.0194	.0210	.0227	.0245	.0263
13	.0058	.0065	.0073	.0081	.0089	.0099	.0108	.0119	.0130	.0142
14	.0025	.0029	.0033	.0037	.0041	.0046	.0052	.0058	.0064	.0071

Table 5 Individual Poisson Probabilities Continued

	Mean Arrival Rate λ									
	7.1	7.2	7.3	7.4	7.5	7.6	7.7	7.8	7.9	8.0
0	.0008	.0007	.0007	.0006	.0006	.0005	.0005	.0004	.0004	.0003
1	.0059	.0054	.0049	.0045	.0041	.0038	.0035	.0032	.0029	.0027
2	.0208	.0194	.0180	.0167	.0156	.0145	.0134	.0125	.0116	.0107
3	.0492	.0464	.0438	.0413	.0389	.0366	.0345	.0324	.0305	.0286
4	.0874	.0836	.0799	.0764	.0729	.0696	.0663	.0632	.0602	.0573
5	.1241	.1204	.1167	.1130	.1094	.1057	.1021	.0986	.0951	.0916
6	.1468	.1445	.1420	.1394	.1367	.1339	.1311	.1282	.1252	.1221
7	.1489	.1486	.1481	.1474	.1465	.1454	.1442	.1428	.1413	.1396
8	.1321	.1337	.1351	.1363	.1373	.1381	.1388	.1392	.1395	.1396
9	.1042	.1070	.1096	.1121	.1144	.1167	.1187	.1207	.1224	.1241
10	.0740	.0770	.08	.0829	.0858	.0887	.0914	.0941	.0967	.0993
11	.0478	.0504	.0531	.0558	.0585	.0613	.0640	.0667	.0695	.0722
12	.0283	.0303	.0323	.0344	.0366	.0388	.0411	.0434	.0457	.0481
13	.0154	.0168	.0181	.0196	.0211	.0227	.0243	.0260	.0278	.0296
14	.0078	.0086	.0095	.0104	.0113	.0123	.0134	.0145	.0157	.0169
15	.0037	.0041	.0046	.0051	.0057	.0062	.0069	.0075	.0083	.0090
16	.0016	.0019	.0021	.0024	.0026	.0030	.0033	.0037	.0041	.0045
17	.0007	.0008	.0009	.0010	.0012	.0013	.0015	.0017	.0019	.0021
18	.0003	.0003	.0004	.0004	.0005	.0006	.0006	.0007	.0008	.0009
19	.0001	.0001	.0001	.0002	.0002	.0002	.0003	.0003	.0003	.0004

	Mean Arrival Rate λ									
	8.1	8.2	8.3	8.4	8.5	8.6	8.7	8.8	8.9	9.0
0	.0003	.0003	.0002	.0002	.0002	.0002	.0002	.0002	.0001	.0001
1	.0025	.0023	.0021	.0019	.0017	.0016	.0014	.0013	.0012	.0011
2	.01	.0092	.0086	.0079	.0074	.0068	.0063	.0058	.0054	.0050
3	.0269	.0252	.0237	.0222	.0208	.0195	.0183	.0171	.0160	.0150
4	.0544	.0517	.0491	.0466	.0443	.0420	.0398	.0377	.0357	.0337
5	.0882	.0849	.0816	.0784	.0752	.0722	.0692	.0663	.0635	.0607
6	.1191	.1160	.1128	.1097	.1066	.1034	.1003	.0972	.0941	.0911
7	.1378	.1358	.1338	.1317	.1294	.1271	.1247	.1222	.1197	.1171
8	.1395	.1392	.1388	.1382	.1375	.1366	.1356	.1344	.1332	.1318
9	.1256	.1269	.1280	.1290	.1299	.1306	.1311	.1315	.1317	.1318
10	.1017	.1040	.1063	.1084	.1104	.1123	.1140	.1157	.1172	.1186
11	.0749	.0776	.0802	.0828	.0853	.0878	.0902	.0925	.0948	.0970
12	.0505	.0530	.0555	.0579	.0604	.0629	.0654	.0679	.0703	.0728
13	.0315	.0334	.0354	.0374	.0395	.0416	.0438	.0459	.0481	.0504
14	.0182	.0196	.0210	.0225	.0240	.0256	.0272	.0289	.0306	.0324
15	.0098	.0107	.0116	.0126	.0136	.0147	.0158	.0169	.0182	.0194
16	.0050	.0055	.0060	.0066	.0072	.0079	.0086	.0093	.0101	.0109
17	.0024	.0026	.0029	.0033	.0036	.0040	.0044	.0048	.0053	.0058
18	.0011	.0012	.0014	.0015	.0017	.0019	.0021	.0024	.0026	.0029
19	.0005	.0005	.0006	.0007	.0008	.0009	.0010	.0011	.0012	.0014

	Mean Arrival Rate λ									
	9.1	9.2	9.3	9.4	9.5	9.6	9.7	9.8	9.9	10.0
0	.0001	.0001	.0001	.0001	.0001	.0001	.0001	.0001	.0001	.0000
1	.0010	.0009	.0009	.0008	.0007	.0007	.0006	.0005	.0005	.0005
2	.0046	.0043	.0040	.0037	.0034	.0031	.0029	.0027	.0025	.0023
3	.0140	.0131	.0123	.0115	.0107	.01	.0093	.0087	.0081	.0076
4	.0319	.0302	.0285	.0269	.0254	.0240	.0226	.0213	.0201	.0189
5	.0581	.0555	.0530	.0506	.0483	.0460	.0439	.0418	.0398	.0378
6	.0881	.0851	.0822	.0793	.0764	.0736	.0709	.0682	.0656	.0631
7	.1145	.1118	.1091	.1064	.1037	.1010	.0982	.0955	.0928	.0901
8	.1302	.1286	.1269	.1251	.1232	.1212	.1191	.1170	.1148	.1126

Table 5 Individual Poisson Probabilities Continued

	Mean Arrival Rate λ									
	9.1	9.2	9.3	9.4	9.5	9.6	9.7	9.8	9.9	10.0
9	.1317	.1315	.1311	.1306	.13	.1293	.1284	.1274	.1263	.1251
10	.1198	.1210	.1219	.1228	.1235	.1241	.1245	.1249	.1250	.1251
11	.0991	.1012	.1031	.1049	.1067	.1083	.1098	.1112	.1125	.1137
12	.0752	.0776	.0799	.0822	.0844	.0866	.0888	.0908	.0928	.0948
13	.0526	.0549	.0572	.0594	.0617	.0640	.0662	.0685	.0707	.0729
14	.0342	.0361	.0380	.0399	.0419	.0439	.0459	.0479	.05	.0521
15	.0208	.0221	.0235	.0250	.0265	.0281	.0297	.0313	.0330	.0347
16	.0118	.0127	.0137	.0147	.0157	.0168	.0180	.0192	.0204	.0217
17	.0063	.0069	.0075	.0081	.0088	.0095	.0103	.0111	.0119	.0128
18	.0032	.0035	.0039	.0042	.0046	.0051	.0055	.0060	.0065	.0071
19	.0015	.0017	.0019	.0021	.0023	.0026	.0028	.0031	.0034	.0037

	Mean Arrival Rate λ									
	10.1	10.2	10.3	10.4	10.5	10.6	10.7	10.8	10.9	11.0
0	.00	.00	.00	.00	.00	.00	.00	.00	.00	.0000
1	.0004	.0004	.0003	.0003	.0003	.0003	.0002	.0002	.0002	.0002
2	.0021	.0019	.0018	.0016	.0015	.0014	.0013	.0012	.0011	.0010
3	.0071	.0066	.0061	.0057	.0053	.0049	.0046	.0043	.0040	.0037
4	.0178	.0168	.0158	.0148	.0139	.0131	.0123	.0116	.0109	.0102
5	.0360	.0342	.0325	.0309	.0293	.0278	.0264	.0250	.0237	.0224
6	.0606	.0581	.0558	.0535	.0513	.0491	.0470	.0450	.0430	.0411
7	.0874	.0847	.0821	.0795	.0769	.0743	.0718	.0694	.0669	.0646
8	.1103	.1080	.1057	.1033	.1009	.0985	.0961	.0936	.0912	.0888
9	.1238	.1224	.1209	.1194	.1177	.1160	.1142	.1124	.1105	.1085
10	.1250	.1249	.1246	.1241	.1236	.1230	.1222	.1214	.1204	.1194
11	.1148	.1158	.1166	.1174	.1180	.1185	.1189	.1192	.1193	.1194
12	.0966	.0984	.1001	.1017	.1032	.1047	.1060	.1072	.1084	.1094
13	.0751	.0772	.0793	.0814	.0834	.0853	.0872	.0891	.0909	.0926
14	.0542	.0563	.0584	.0604	.0625	.0646	.0667	.0687	.0708	.0728
15	.0365	.0383	.0401	.0419	.0438	.0457	.0476	.0495	.0514	.0534
16	.0230	.0244	.0258	.0272	.0287	.0303	.0318	.0334	.0350	.0367
17	.0137	.0146	.0156	.0167	.0177	.0189	.0200	.0212	.0225	.0237
18	.0077	.0083	.0089	.0096	.0104	.0111	.0119	.0127	.0136	.0145
19	.0041	.0045	.0048	.0053	.0057	.0062	.0067	.0072	.0078	.0084
20	.0021	.0023	.0025	.0027	.0030	.0033	.0036	.0039	.0043	.0046

	Mean Arrival Rate λ									
	11.1	11.2	11.3	11.4	11.5	11.6	11.7	11.8	11.9	12.0
0	.0000	.0000	.0000	.0000	.0000	.0000	.0000	.0000	.0000	.0000
1	.0002	.0002	.0001	.0001	.0001	.0001	.0001	.0001	.0001	.0001
2	.0009	.0009	.0008	.0007	.0007	.0006	.0006	.0005	.0005	.0004
3	.0034	.0032	.0030	.0028	.0026	.0024	.0022	.0021	.0019	.0018
4	.0096	.0090	.0084	.0079	.0074	.0069	.0065	.0061	.0057	.0053
5	.0212	.0201	.0190	.0180	.0170	.0160	.0152	.0143	.0135	.0127
6	.0393	.0375	.0358	.0341	.0325	.0310	.0295	.0281	.0268	.0255
7	.0623	.0600	.0578	.0556	.0535	.0514	.0494	.0474	.0455	.0437
8	.0864	.0840	.0816	.0792	.0769	.0745	.0722	.0700	.0677	.0655
9	.1065	.1045	.1024	.1003	.0982	.0961	.0939	.0917	.0895	.0874
10	.1182	.1170	.1157	.1144	.1129	.1114	.1099	.1082	.1066	.1048
11	.1193	.1192	.1189	.1185	.1181	.1175	.1169	.1161	.1153	.1144
12	.1104	.1112	.1120	.1126	.1131	.1136	.1139	.1142	.1143	.1144
13	.0942	.0958	.0973	.0987	.1001	.1014	.1025	.1036	.1046	.1056
14	.0747	.0767	.0786	.0804	.0822	.0840	.0857	.0874	.0889	.0905

Table 5 Individual Poisson Probabilities Continued

	Mean Arrival Rate λ									
	11.1	11.2	11.3	11.4	11.5	11.6	11.7	11.8	11.9	12.0
15	.0553	.0572	.0592	.0611	.0630	.0649	.0668	.0687	.0706	.0724
16	.0384	.0401	.0418	.0435	.0453	.0471	.0489	.0507	.0525	.0543
17	.0250	.0264	.0278	.0292	.0306	.0321	.0336	.0352	.0367	.0383
18	.0154	.0164	.0174	.0185	.0196	.0207	.0219	.0231	.0243	.0255
19	.0090	.0097	.0104	.0111	.0119	.0126	.0135	.0143	.0152	.0161
20	.0050	.0054	.0059	.0063	.0068	.0073	.0079	.0084	.0091	.0097

	Mean Arrival Rate λ									
	12.1	12.2	12.3	12.4	12.5	12.6	12.7	12.8	12.9	13.0
4	.0050	.0046	.0043	.0041	.0038	.0035	.0033	.0031	.0029	.0027
5	.0120	.0113	.0107	.0101	.0095	.0089	.0084	.0079	.0074	.0070
6	.0242	.0230	.0219	.0208	.0197	.0187	.0178	.0169	.0160	.0152
7	.0419	.0402	.0385	.0368	.0353	.0337	.0323	.0308	.0295	.0281
8	.0634	.0612	.0591	.0571	.0551	.0531	.0512	.0493	.0475	.0457
9	.0852	.0830	.0808	.0787	.0765	.0744	.0723	.0702	.0681	.0661
10	.1031	.1013	.0994	.0975	.0956	.0937	.0918	.0898	.0878	.0859
11	.1134	.1123	.1112	.1100	.1087	.1074	.1060	.1045	.1030	.1015
12	.1143	.1142	.1139	.1136	.1132	.1127	.1121	.1115	.1107	.1099
13	.1064	.1072	.1078	.1084	.1089	.1093	.1096	.1098	.1099	.1099
14	.0920	.0934	.0947	.0960	.0972	.0983	.0994	.1004	.1013	.1021
15	.0742	.0759	.0777	.0794	.0810	.0826	.0841	.0856	.0871	.0885
16	.0561	.0579	.0597	.0615	.0633	.0650	.0668	.0685	.0702	.0719
17	.0399	.0416	.0432	.0449	.0465	.0482	.0499	.0516	.0533	.0550
18	.0268	.0282	.0295	.0309	.0323	.0337	.0352	.0367	.0382	.0397
19	.0171	.0181	.0191	.0202	.0213	.0224	.0235	.0247	.0259	.0272
20	.0103	.0110	.0118	.0125	.0133	.0141	.0149	.0158	.0167	.0177

	Mean Arrival Rate λ									
	13.1	13.2	13.3	13.4	13.5	13.6	13.7	13.8	13.9	14.0
5	.0066	.0062	.0058	.0055	.0051	.0048	.0045	.0042	.0040	.0037
6	.0144	.0136	.0129	.0122	.0115	.0109	.0103	.0097	.0092	.0087
7	.0269	.0256	.0245	.0233	.0222	.0212	.0202	.0192	.0183	.0174
8	.0440	.0423	.0407	.0391	.0375	.0360	.0345	.0331	.0318	.0304
9	.0640	.0620	.0601	.0582	.0563	.0544	.0526	.0508	.0491	.0473
10	.0839	.0819	.0799	.0779	.0760	.0740	.0720	.0701	.0682	.0663
11	.0999	.0983	.0966	.0949	.0932	.0915	.0897	.0880	.0862	.0844
12	.1091	.1081	.1071	.1060	.1049	.1037	.1024	.1011	.0998	.0984
13	.1099	.1098	.1096	.1093	.1089	.1085	.1080	.1074	.1067	.1060
14	.1028	.1035	.1041	.1046	.1050	.1054	.1056	.1058	.1060	.1060
15	.0898	.0911	.0923	.0934	.0945	.0955	.0965	.0974	.0982	.0989
16	.0735	.0751	.0767	.0783	.0798	.0812	.0826	.0840	.0853	.0866
17	.0567	.0583	.0600	.0617	.0633	.0650	.0666	.0682	.0697	.0713
18	.0412	.0428	.0443	.0459	.0475	.0491	.0507	.0523	.0539	.0554
19	.0284	.0297	.0310	.0324	.0337	.0351	.0365	.0380	.0394	.0409
20	.0186	.0196	.0206	.0217	.0228	.0239	.0250	.0262	.0274	.0286

	Mean Arrival Rate λ									
	14.1	14.2	14.3	14.4	14.5	14.6	14.7	14.8	14.9	15.0
6	.0082	.0078	.0073	.0069	.0065	.0061	.0058	.0055	.0051	.0048
7	.0165	.0157	.0149	.0142	.0135	.0128	.0122	.0115	.0109	.0104
8	.0292	.0279	.0267	.0256	.0244	.0234	.0223	.0213	.0204	.0194
9	.0457	.0440	.0424	.0409	.0394	.0379	.0365	.0351	.0337	.0324
10	.0644	.0625	.0607	.0589	.0571	.0553	.0536	.0519	.0502	.0486
11	.0825	.0807	.0789	.0771	.0753	.0735	.0716	.0698	.0681	.0663

Table 5 Individual Poisson Probabilities Continued

	Mean Arrival Rate λ									
	14.1	14.2	14.3	14.4	14.5	14.6	14.7	14.8	14.9	15.0
12	.0970	.0955	.0940	.0925	.0910	.0894	.0878	.0861	.0845	.0829
13	.1052	.1043	.1034	.1025	.1014	.1004	.0992	.0981	.0969	.0956
14	.1060	.1058	.1057	.1054	.1051	.1047	.1042	.1037	.1031	.1024
15	.0996	.1002	.1007	.1012	.1016	.1019	.1021	.1023	.1024	.1024
16	.0878	.0889	.0900	.0911	.0920	.0930	.0938	.0946	.0954	.0960
17	.0728	.0743	.0757	.0771	.0785	.0798	.0811	.0824	.0836	.0847
18	.0570	.0586	.0602	.0617	.0632	.0648	.0663	.0677	.0692	.0706
19	.0423	.0438	.0453	.0468	.0483	.0498	.0513	.0528	.0543	.0557
20	.0298	.0311	.0324	.0337	.0350	.0363	.0377	.0390	.0404	.0418
21	.0200	.0210	.0220	.0231	.0242	.0253	.0264	.0275	.0287	.0299
22	.0128	.0136	.0143	.0151	.0159	.0168	.0176	.0185	.0194	.0204
23	.0079	.0084	.0089	.0095	.0100	.0106	.0113	.0119	.0126	.0133
24	.0046	.0050	.0053	.0057	.0061	.0065	.0069	.0073	.0078	.0083

	Mean Arrival Rate λ									
	15.1	15.2	15.3	15.4	15.5	15.6	15.7	15.8	15.9	16.0
7	.0098	.0093	.0088	.0084	.0079	.0075	.0071	.0067	.0063	.0060
8	.0186	.0177	.0169	.0161	.0153	.0146	.0139	.0132	.0126	.0120
9	.0311	.0299	.0287	.0275	.0264	.0253	.0243	.0232	.0223	.0213
10	.0470	.0454	.0439	.0424	.0409	.0395	.0381	.0367	.0354	.0341
11	.0645	.0628	.0611	.0594	.0577	.0560	.0544	.0527	.0512	.0496
12	.0812	.0795	.0778	.0762	.0745	.0728	.0711	.0695	.0678	.0661
13	.0943	.0930	.0916	.0902	.0888	.0874	.0859	.0844	.0829	.0814
14	.1017	.1010	.1001	.0993	.0983	.0974	.0963	.0953	.0942	.0930
15	.1024	.1023	.1021	.1019	.1016	.1012	.1008	.1003	.0998	.0992
16	.0966	.0972	.0977	.0981	.0984	.0987	.0989	.0991	.0992	.0992
17	.0858	.0869	.0879	.0888	.0897	.0906	.0914	.0921	.0928	.0934
18	.0720	.0734	.0747	.0760	.0773	.0785	.0797	.0808	.0819	.0830
19	.0572	.0587	.0602	.0616	.0630	.0645	.0659	.0672	.0686	.0699
20	.0432	.0446	.0460	.0474	.0489	.0503	.0517	.0531	.0545	.0559
21	.0311	.0323	.0335	.0348	.0361	.0373	.0386	.0400	.0413	.0426
22	.0213	.0223	.0233	.0244	.0254	.0265	.0276	.0287	.0298	.0310
23	.0140	.0147	.0155	.0163	.0171	.0180	.0188	.0197	.0206	.0216
24	.0088	.0093	.0099	.0105	.0111	.0117	.0123	.0130	.0137	.0144
25	.0053	.0057	.0061	.0064	.0069	.0073	.0077	.0082	.0087	.0092

	Mean Arrival Rate λ									
	16.1	16.2	16.3	16.4	16.5	16.6	16.7	16.8	16.9	17.0
7	.0057	.0054	.0051	.0048	.0045	.0043	.0040	.0038	.0036	.0034
8	.0114	.0108	.0103	.0098	.0093	.0088	.0084	.0080	.0076	.0072
9	.0204	.0195	.0187	.0178	.0171	.0163	.0156	.0149	.0142	.0135
10	.0328	.0316	.0304	.0293	.0281	.0270	.0260	.0250	.0240	.0230
11	.0481	.0466	.0451	.0436	.0422	.0408	.0394	.0381	.0368	.0355
12	.0645	.0628	.0612	.0596	.0580	.0565	.0549	.0534	.0518	.0504
13	.0799	.0783	.0768	.0752	.0736	.0721	.0705	.0690	.0674	.0658
14	.0918	.0906	.0894	.0881	.0868	.0855	.0841	.0828	.0814	.0800
15	.0986	.0979	.0971	.0963	.0955	.0946	.0937	.0927	.0917	.0906
16	.0992	.0991	.0989	.0987	.0985	.0981	.0978	.0973	.0968	.0963
17	.0939	.0944	.0949	.0952	.0956	.0958	.0960	.0962	.0963	.0963
18	.0840	.0850	.0859	.0868	.0876	.0884	.0891	.0898	.0904	.0909
19	.0712	.0725	.0737	.0749	.0761	.0772	.0783	.0794	.0804	.0814
20	.0573	.0587	.0601	.0614	.0628	.0641	.0654	.0667	.0679	.0692
21	.0439	.0453	.0466	.0480	.0493	.0507	.0520	.0533	.0547	.0560

Table 5 Individual Poisson Probabilities Continued

	Mean Arrival Rate λ									
	16.1	16.2	16.3	16.4	16.5	16.6	16.7	16.8	16.9	17.0
22	.0322	.0333	.0345	.0358	.0370	.0382	.0395	.0407	.0420	.0433
23	.0225	.0235	.0245	.0255	.0265	.0276	.0287	.0297	.0309	.0320
24	.0151	.0159	.0166	.0174	.0182	.0191	.0199	.0208	.0217	.0226
25	.0097	.0103	.0108	.0114	.0120	.0127	.0133	.0140	.0147	.0154

	Mean Arrival Rate λ									
	17.1	17.2	17.3	17.4	17.5	17.6	17.7	17.8	17.9	18.0
8	.0068	.0064	.0061	.0058	.0055	.0052	.0049	.0046	.0044	.0042
9	.0129	.0123	.0117	.0112	.0107	.0101	.0097	.0092	.0088	.0083
10	.0221	.0212	.0203	.0195	.0186	.0179	.0171	.0164	.0157	.0150
11	.0343	.0331	.0319	.0308	.0297	.0286	.0275	.0265	.0255	.0245
12	.0489	.0474	.0460	.0446	.0432	.0419	.0406	.0393	.0380	.0368
13	.0643	.0628	.0612	.0597	.0582	.0567	.0553	.0538	.0524	.0509
14	.0785	.0771	.0757	.0742	.0728	.0713	.0699	.0684	.0669	.0655
15	.0895	.0884	.0873	.0861	.0849	.0837	.0824	.0812	.0799	.0786
16	.0957	.0951	.0944	.0936	.0929	.0920	.0912	.0903	.0894	.0884
17	.0963	.0962	.0960	.0958	.0956	.0953	.0949	.0945	.0941	.0936
18	.0914	.0919	.0923	.0926	.0929	.0932	.0934	.0935	.0936	.0936
19	.0823	.0832	.0840	.0848	.0856	.0863	.0870	.0876	.0882	.0887
20	.0704	.0715	.0727	.0738	.0749	.0760	.0770	.0780	.0789	.0798
21	.0573	.0586	.0599	.0612	.0624	.0637	.0649	.0661	.0673	.0684
22	.0445	.0458	.0471	.0484	.0496	.0509	.0522	.0535	.0547	.0560
23	.0331	.0343	.0354	.0366	.0378	.0390	.0402	.0414	.0426	.0438
24	.0236	.0246	.0255	.0265	.0275	.0286	.0296	.0307	.0318	.0328
25	.0161	.0169	.0177	.0185	.0193	.0201	.0210	.0218	.0227	.0237

	Mean Arrival Rate λ									
	18.1	18.2	18.3	18.4	18.5	18.6	18.7	18.8	18.9	19.0
9	.0079	.0075	.0072	.0068	.0065	.0061	.0058	.0055	.0053	.0050
10	.0143	.0137	.0131	.0125	.0120	.0114	.0109	.0104	.0099	.0095
11	.0236	.0227	.0218	.0209	.0201	.0193	.0185	.0178	.0171	.0164
12	.0356	.0344	.0332	.0321	.0310	.0299	.0289	.0278	.0269	.0259
13	.0495	.0481	.0468	.0454	.0441	.0428	.0415	.0403	.0390	.0378
14	.0640	.0626	.0611	.0597	.0583	.0569	.0555	.0541	.0527	.0514
15	.0773	.0759	.0746	.0732	.0719	.0705	.0692	.0678	.0664	.0650
16	.0874	.0864	.0853	.0842	.0831	.0820	.0808	.0796	.0785	.0772
17	.0931	.0925	.0918	.0912	.0904	.0897	.0889	.0881	.0872	.0863
18	.0936	.0935	.0934	.0932	.0930	.0927	.0924	.0920	.0916	.0911
19	.0891	.0896	.0899	.0902	.0905	.0907	.0909	.0910	.0911	.0911
20	.0807	.0815	.0823	.0830	.0837	.0844	.0850	.0856	.0861	.0866
21	.0695	.0706	.0717	.0727	.0738	.0747	.0757	.0766	.0775	.0783
22	.0572	.0584	.0596	.0608	.0620	.0632	.0643	.0655	.0666	.0676
23	.0450	.0462	.0475	.0487	.0499	.0511	.0523	.0535	.0547	.0559
24	.0340	.0351	.0362	.0373	.0385	.0396	.0408	.0419	.0431	.0442
25	.0246	.0255	.0265	.0275	.0285	.0295	.0305	.0315	.0326	.0336

	Mean Arrival Rate λ									
	19.1	19.2	19.3	19.4	19.5	19.6	19.7	19.8	19.9	20.0
10	.0090	.0086	.0082	.0078	.0074	.0071	.0067	.0064	.0061	.0058
11	.0157	.0150	.0144	.0138	.0132	.0126	.0121	.0116	.0111	.0106
12	.0249	.0240	.0231	.0223	.0214	.0206	.0198	.0191	.0183	.0176
13	.0367	.0355	.0344	.0333	.0322	.0311	.0301	.0291	.0281	.0271
14	.0500	.0487	.0474	.0461	.0448	.0436	.0423	.0411	.0399	.0387
15	.0637	.0623	.0610	.0596	.0582	.0569	.0556	.0543	.0529	.0516
16	.0760	.0748	.0735	.0723	.0710	.0697	.0684	.0671	.0659	.0646

Table 5 Individual Poisson Probabilities Continued

	Mean Arrival Rate λ									
	19.1	19.2	19.3	19.4	19.5	19.6	19.7	19.8	19.9	20.0
17	.0854	.0844	.0835	.0825	.0814	.0804	.0793	.0782	.0771	.0760
18	.0906	.0901	.0895	.0889	.0882	.0875	.0868	.0860	.0852	.0844
19	.0911	.0910	.0909	.0907	.0905	.0903	.0900	.0896	.0893	.0888
20	.0870	.0874	.0877	.0880	.0883	.0885	.0886	.0887	.0888	.0888
21	.0791	.0799	.0806	.0813	.0820	.0826	.0831	.0837	.0842	.0846
22	.0687	.0697	.0707	.0717	.0727	.0736	.0745	.0753	.0761	.0769
23	.0570	.0582	.0594	.0605	.0616	.0627	.0638	.0648	.0659	.0669
24	.0454	.0466	.0477	.0489	.0500	.0512	.0523	.0535	.0546	.0557
25	.0347	.0358	.0368	.0379	.0390	.0401	.0412	.0424	.0435	.0446

	Mean Arrival Rate λ									
	20.1	20.2	20.3	20.4	20.5	20.6	20.7	20.8	20.9	21.0
10	.0055	.0053	.0050	.0048	.0045	.0043	.0041	.0039	.0037	.0035
11	.0101	.0097	.0092	.0088	.0084	.0080	.0077	.0073	.0070	.0067
12	.0169	.0163	.0156	.0150	.0144	.0138	.0132	.0127	.0122	.0116
13	.0262	.0253	.0244	.0235	.0227	.0219	.0211	.0203	.0195	.0188
14	.0376	.0365	.0353	.0343	.0332	.0322	.0311	.0301	.0292	.0282
15	.0504	.0491	.0478	.0466	.0454	.0442	.0430	.0418	.0406	.0395
16	.0633	.0620	.0607	.0594	.0581	.0569	.0556	.0543	.0531	.0518
17	.0748	.0736	.0725	.0713	.0701	.0689	.0677	.0665	.0653	.0640
18	.0835	.0826	.0817	.0808	.0798	.0789	.0778	.0768	.0758	.0747
19	.0884	.0879	.0873	.0868	.0861	.0855	.0848	.0841	.0834	.0826
20	.0888	.0887	.0886	.0885	.0883	.0881	.0878	.0875	.0871	.0867
21	.0850	.0854	.0857	.0860	.0862	.0864	.0865	.0866	.0867	.0867
22	.0777	.0784	.0791	.0797	.0803	.0809	.0814	.0819	.0824	.0828
23	.0679	.0688	.0698	.0707	.0716	.0724	.0733	.0741	.0748	.0756
24	.0568	.0579	.0590	.0601	.0611	.0622	.0632	.0642	.0652	.0661
25	.0457	.0468	.0479	.0490	.0501	.0512	.0523	.0534	.0545	.0555

Table 6 Cumulative Poisson Probabilities

	Mean Arrival Rate λ									
	0.1	0.2	0.3	0.4	0.5	0.6	0.7	0.8	0.9	1.0
0	.9048	.8187	.7408	.6703	.6065	.5488	.4966	.4493	.4066	.3679
1	.9953	.9825	.9631	.9384	.9098	.8781	.8442	.8088	.7725	.7358
2	.9998	.9989	.9964	.9921	.9856	.9769	.9659	.9526	.9371	.9197
3	1.0000	.9999	.9997	.9992	.9982	.9966	.9942	.9909	.9865	.9810
4	1.0000	1.0000	1.0000	.9999	.9998	.9996	.9992	.9986	.9977	.9963
5	1.0000	1.0000	1.0000	1.0000	1.0000	1.0000	.9999	.9998	.9997	.9994
6	1.0000	1.0000	1.0000	1.0000	1.0000	1.0000	1.0000	1.0000	1.0000	.9999
7	1.0000	1.0000	1.0000	1.0000	1.0000	1.0000	1.0000	1.0000	1.0000	1.0000

	Mean Arrival Rate λ									
	1.1	1.2	1.3	1.4	1.5	1.6	1.7	1.8	1.9	2.0
0	.3329	.3012	.2725	.2466	.2231	.2019	.1827	.1653	.1496	.1353
1	.6990	.6626	.6268	.5918	.5578	.5249	.4932	.4628	.4337	.4060
2	.9004	.8795	.8571	.8335	.8088	.7834	.7572	.7306	.7037	.6767
3	.9743	.9662	.9569	.9463	.9344	.9212	.9068	.8913	.8747	.8571
4	.9946	.9923	.9893	.9857	.9814	.9763	.9704	.9636	.9559	.9473
5	.9990	.9985	.9978	.9968	.9955	.9940	.9920	.9896	.9868	.9834
6	.9999	.9997	.9996	.9994	.9991	.9987	.9981	.9974	.9966	.9955
7	1.0000	1.0000	.9999	.9999	.9998	.9997	.9996	.9994	.9992	.9989
8	1.0000	1.0000	1.0000	1.0000	1.0000	1.0000	.9999	.9999	.9998	.9998
9	1.0000	1.0000	1.0000	1.0000	1.0000	1.0000	1.0000	1.0000	1.0000	1.0000

	Mean Arrival Rate λ									
	2.1	2.2	2.3	2.4	2.5	2.6	2.7	2.8	2.9	3.0
0	.1225	.1108	.1003	.0907	.0821	.0743	.0672	.0608	.0550	.0498
1	.3796	.3546	.3309	.3084	.2873	.2674	.2487	.2311	.2146	.1991
2	.6496	.6227	.5960	.5697	.5438	.5184	.4936	.4695	.4460	.4232
3	.8386	.8194	.7993	.7787	.7576	.7360	.7141	.6919	.6696	.6472
4	.9379	.9275	.9162	.9041	.8912	.8774	.8629	.8477	.8318	.8153
5	.9796	.9751	.9700	.9643	.9580	.9510	.9433	.9349	.9258	.9161
6	.9941	.9925	.9906	.9884	.9858	.9828	.9794	.9756	.9713	.9665
7	.9985	.9980	.9974	.9967	.9958	.9947	.9934	.9919	.9901	.9881
8	.9997	.9995	.9994	.9991	.9989	.9985	.9981	.9976	.9969	.9962
9	.9999	.9999	.9999	.9998	.9997	.9996	.9995	.9993	.9991	.9989
10	1.0000	1.0000	1.0000	1.0000	.9999	.9999	.9999	.9998	.9998	.9997
11	1.0000	1.0000	1.0000	1.0000	1.0000	1.0000	1.0000	1.0000	.9999	.9999
12	1.0000	1.0000	1.0000	1.0000	1.0000	1.0000	1.0000	1.0000	1.0000	1.0000

	Mean Arrival Rate λ									
	3.1	3.2	3.3	3.4	3.5	3.6	3.7	3.8	3.9	4.0
0	.0450	.0408	.0369	.0334	.0302	.0273	.0247	.0224	.0202	.0183
1	.1847	.1712	.1586	.1468	.1359	.1257	.1162	.1074	.0992	.0916
2	.4012	.3799	.3594	.3397	.3208	.3027	.2854	.2689	.2531	.2381
3	.6248	.6025	.5803	.5584	.5366	.5152	.4942	.4735	.4532	.4335
4	.7982	.7806	.7626	.7442	.7254	.7064	.6872	.6678	.6484	.6288
5	.9057	.8946	.8829	.8705	.8576	.8441	.8301	.8156	.8006	.7851
6	.9612	.9554	.9490	.9421	.9347	.9267	.9182	.9091	.8995	.8893
7	.9858	.9832	.9802	.9769	.9733	.9692	.9648	.9599	.9546	.9489
8	.9953	.9943	.9931	.9917	.9901	.9883	.9863	.9840	.9815	.9786
9	.9986	.9982	.9978	.9973	.9967	.9960	.9952	.9942	.9931	.9919
10	.9996	.9995	.9994	.9992	.9990	.9987	.9984	.9981	.9977	.9972
11	.9999	.9999	.9998	.9998	.9997	.9996	.9995	.9994	.9993	.9991
12	1.0000	1.0000	1.0000	.9999	.9999	.9999	.9999	.9998	.9998	.9997
13	1.0000	1.0000	1.0000	1.0000	1.0000	1.0000	1.0000	1.0000	.9999	.9999
14	1.0000	1.0000	1.0000	1.0000	1.0000	1.0000	1.0000	1.0000	1.0000	1.0000

Table 6 Cumulative Poisson Probabilities Continued

	Mean Arrival Rate λ									
	4.1	4.2	4.3	4.4	4.5	4.6	4.7	4.8	4.9	5.0
0	.0166	.0150	.0136	.0123	.0111	.0101	.0091	.0082	.0074	.0067
1	.0845	.0780	.0719	.0663	.0611	.0563	.0518	.0477	.0439	.0404
2	.2238	.2102	.1974	.1851	.1736	.1626	.1523	.1425	.1333	.1247
3	.4142	.3954	.3772	.3594	.3423	.3257	.3097	.2942	.2793	.2650
4	.6093	.5898	.5704	.5512	.5321	.5132	.4946	.4763	.4582	.4405
5	.7693	.7531	.7367	.7199	.7029	.6858	.6684	.6510	.6335	.6160
6	.8786	.8675	.8558	.8436	.8311	.8180	.8046	.7908	.7767	.7622
7	.9427	.9361	.9290	.9214	.9134	.9049	.8960	.8867	.8769	.8666
8	.9755	.9721	.9683	.9642	.9597	.9549	.9497	.9442	.9382	.9319
9	.9905	.9889	.9871	.9851	.9829	.9805	.9778	.9749	.9717	.9682
10	.9966	.9959	.9952	.9943	.9933	.9922	.9910	.9896	.9880	.9863
11	.9989	.9986	.9983	.9980	.9976	.9971	.9966	.9960	.9953	.9945
12	.9997	.9996	.9995	.9993	.9992	.9990	.9988	.9986	.9983	.9980
13	.9999	.9999	.9998	.9998	.9997	.9997	.9996	.9995	.9994	.9993
14	1.0000	1.0000	1.0000	.9999	.9999	.9999	.9999	.9999	.9998	.9998

	Mean Arrival Rate λ									
	5.1	5.2	5.3	5.4	5.5	5.6	5.7	5.8	5.9	6.0
0	.0061	.0055	.0050	.0045	.0041	.0037	.0033	.0030	.0027	.0025
1	.0372	.0342	.0314	.0289	.0266	.0244	.0224	.0206	.0189	.0174
2	.1165	.1088	.1016	.0948	.0884	.0824	.0768	.0715	.0666	.0620
3	.2513	.2381	.2254	.2133	.2017	.1906	.1800	.1700	.1604	.1512
4	.4231	.4061	.3895	.3733	.3575	.3422	.3272	.3127	.2987	.2851
5	.5984	.5809	.5635	.5461	.5289	.5119	.4950	.4783	.4619	.4457
6	.7474	.7324	.7171	.7017	.6860	.6703	.6544	.6384	.6224	.6063
7	.8560	.8449	.8335	.8217	.8095	.7970	.7841	.7710	.7576	.7440
8	.9252	.9181	.9106	.9027	.8944	.8857	.8766	.8672	.8574	.8472
9	.9644	.9603	.9559	.9512	.9462	.9409	.9352	.9292	.9228	.9161
10	.9844	.9823	.9800	.9775	.9747	.9718	.9686	.9651	.9614	.9574
11	.9937	.9927	.9916	.9904	.9890	.9875	.9859	.9841	.9821	.9799
12	.9976	.9972	.9967	.9962	.9955	.9949	.9941	.9932	.9922	.9912
13	.9992	.9990	.9988	.9986	.9983	.9980	.9977	.9973	.9969	.9964
14	.9997	.9997	.9996	.9995	.9994	.9993	.9991	.9990	.9988	.9986

	Mean Arrival Rate λ									
	6.1	6.2	6.3	6.4	6.5	6.6	6.7	6.8	6.9	7.0
0	.0022	.0020	.0018	.0017	.0015	.0014	.0012	.0011	.0010	.0009
1	.0159	.0146	.0134	.0123	.0113	.0103	.0095	.0087	.0080	.0073
2	.0577	.0536	.0498	.0463	.0430	.0400	.0371	.0344	.0320	.0296
3	.1425	.1342	.1264	.1189	.1118	.1052	.0988	.0928	.0871	.0818
4	.2719	.2592	.2469	.2351	.2237	.2127	.2022	.1920	.1823	.1730
5	.4298	.4141	.3988	.3837	.3690	.3547	.3406	.3270	.3137	.3007
6	.5902	.5742	.5582	.5423	.5265	.5108	.4953	.4799	.4647	.4497
7	.7301	.7160	.7017	.6873	.6728	.6581	.6433	.6285	.6136	.5987
8	.8367	.8259	.8148	.8033	.7916	.7796	.7673	.7548	.7420	.7291
9	.9090	.9016	.8939	.8858	.8774	.8686	.8596	.8502	.8405	.8305
10	.9531	.9486	.9437	.9386	.9332	.9274	.9214	.9151	.9084	.9015
11	.9776	.9750	.9723	.9693	.9661	.9627	.9591	.9552	.9510	.9467
12	.9900	.9887	.9873	.9857	.9840	.9821	.9801	.9779	.9755	.9730
13	.9958	.9952	.9945	.9937	.9929	.9920	.9909	.9898	.9885	.9872
14	.9984	.9981	.9978	.9974	.9970	.9966	.9961	.9956	.9950	.9943

Table 6 Cumulative Poisson Probabilities Continued

	Mean Arrival Rate λ									
	7.1	7.2	7.3	7.4	7.5	7.6	7.7	7.8	7.9	8.0
0	.0008	.0007	.0007	.0006	.0006	.0005	.0005	.0004	.0004	.0003
1	.0067	.0061	.0056	.0051	.0047	.0043	.0039	.0036	.0033	.0030
2	.0275	.0255	.0236	.0219	.0203	.0188	.0174	.0161	.0149	.0138
3	.0767	.0719	.0674	.0632	.0591	.0554	.0518	.0485	.0453	.0424
4	.1641	.1555	.1473	.1395	.1321	.1249	.1181	.1117	.1055	.0996
5	.2881	.2759	.2640	.2526	.2414	.2307	.2203	.2103	.2006	.1912
6	.4349	.4204	.4060	.3920	.3782	.3646	.3514	.3384	.3257	.3134
7	.5838	.5689	.5541	.5393	.5246	.5100	.4956	.4812	.4670	.4530
8	.7160	.7027	.6892	.6757	.6620	.6482	.6343	.6204	.6065	.5925
9	.8202	.8096	.7988	.7877	.7764	.7649	.7531	.7411	.7290	.7166
10	.8942	.8867	.8788	.8707	.8622	.8535	.8445	.8352	.8257	.8159
11	.9420	.9371	.9319	.9265	.9208	.9148	.9085	.9020	.8952	.8881
12	.9703	.9673	.9642	.9609	.9573	.9536	.9496	.9454	.9409	.9362
13	.9857	.9841	.9824	.9805	.9784	.9762	.9739	.9714	.9687	.9658
14	.9935	.9927	.9918	.9908	.9897	.9886	.9873	.9859	.9844	.9827
15	.9972	.9969	.9964	.9959	.9954	.9948	.9941	.9934	.9926	.9918
16	.9989	.9987	.9985	.9983	.9980	.9978	.9974	.9971	.9967	.9963
17	.9996	.9995	.9994	.9993	.9992	.9991	.9989	.9988	.9986	.9984
18	.9998	.9998	.9998	.9997	.9997	.9996	.9996	.9995	.9994	.9993
19	.9999	.9999	.9999	.9999	.9999	.9999	.9998	.9998	.9998	.9997
20	1.0000	1.0000	1.0000	1.0000	1.0000	1.0000	.9999	.9999	.9999	.9999

	Mean Arrival Rate λ									
	8.1	8.2	8.3	8.4	8.5	8.6	8.7	8.8	8.9	9.0
0	.0003	.0003	.0002	.0002	.0002	.0002	.0002	.0002	.0001	.0001
1	.0028	.0025	.0023	.0021	.0019	.0018	.0016	.0015	.0014	.0012
2	.0127	.0118	.0109	.0100	.0093	.0086	.0079	.0073	.0068	.0062
3	.0396	.0370	.0346	.0323	.0301	.0281	.0262	.0244	.0228	.0212
4	.0940	.0887	.0837	.0789	.0744	.0701	.0660	.0621	.0584	.0550
5	.1822	.1736	.1653	.1573	.1496	.1422	.1352	.1284	.1219	.1157
6	.3013	.2896	.2781	.2670	.2562	.2457	.2355	.2256	.2160	.2068
7	.4391	.4254	.4119	.3987	.3856	.3728	.3602	.3478	.3357	.3239
8	.5786	.5647	.5507	.5369	.5231	.5094	.4958	.4823	.4689	.4557
9	.7041	.6915	.6788	.6659	.6530	.6400	.6269	.6137	.6006	.5874
10	.8058	.7955	.7850	.7743	.7634	.7522	.7409	.7294	.7170	.7060
11	.8807	.8731	.8652	.8571	.8487	.8400	.8311	.8220	.8126	.8030
12	.9313	.9261	.9207	.9150	.9091	.9029	.8965	.8898	.8829	.8758
13	.9628	.9595	.9561	.9524	.9486	.9445	.9403	.9358	.9311	.9261
14	.9810	.9791	.9771	.9749	.9726	.9701	.9675	.9647	.9617	.9585
15	.9908	.9898	.9887	.9875	.9862	.9848	.9832	.9816	.9798	.9780
16	.9958	.9953	.9947	.9941	.9934	.9926	.9918	.9909	.9899	.9889
17	.9982	.9979	.9977	.9973	.9970	.9966	.9962	.9957	.9952	.9947
18	.9992	.9991	.9990	.9989	.9987	.9985	.9983	.9981	.9978	.9976
19	.9997	.9997	.9996	.9995	.9995	.9994	.9993	.9992	.9991	.9989
20	.9999	.9999	.9998	.9998	.9998	.9998	.9997	.9997	.9996	.9996

	Mean Arrival Rate λ									
	9.1	9.2	9.3	9.4	9.5	9.6	9.7	9.8	9.9	10.0
0	.0001	.0001	.0001	.0001	.0001	.0001	.0001	.0001	.0001	.0000
1	.0011	.0010	.0009	.0009	.0008	.0007	.0007	.0006	.0005	.0005
2	.0058	.0053	.0049	.0045	.0042	.0038	.0035	.0033	.0030	.0028
3	.0198	.0184	.0172	.0160	.0149	.0138	.0129	.0120	.0111	.0103
4	.0517	.0486	.0456	.0429	.0403	.0378	.0355	.0333	.0312	.0293
5	.1098	.1041	.0986	.0935	.0885	.0838	.0793	.0750	.0710	.0671
6	.1978	.1892	.1808	.1727	.1649	.1574	.1502	.1433	.1366	.1301

Table 6 Cumulative Poisson Probabilities Continued

	Mean Arrival Rate λ									
	9.1	9.2	9.3	9.4	9.5	9.6	9.7	9.8	9.9	10.0
7	.3123	.3010	.2900	.2792	.2687	.2584	.2485	.2388	.2294	.2202
8	.4426	.4296	.4168	.4042	.3918	.3796	.3676	.3558	.3442	.3328
9	.5742	.5611	.5479	.5349	.5218	.5089	.4960	.4832	.4705	.4579
10	.6941	.6820	.6699	.6576	.6453	.6329	.6205	.6080	.5955	.5830
11	.7932	.7832	.7730	.7626	.7520	.7412	.7303	.7193	.7081	.6968
12	.8684	.8607	.8529	.8448	.8364	.8279	.8191	.8101	.8009	.7916
13	.9210	.9156	.9100	.9042	.8981	.8919	.8853	.8786	.8716	.8645
14	.9552	.9517	.9480	.9441	.9400	.9357	.9312	.9265	.9216	.9165
15	.9760	.9738	.9715	.9691	.9665	.9638	.9609	.9579	.9546	.9513
16	.9878	.9865	.9852	.9838	.9823	.9806	.9789	.9770	.9751	.9730
17	.9941	.9934	.9927	.9919	.9911	.9902	.9892	.9881	.9870	.9857
18	.9973	.9969	.9966	.9962	.9957	.9952	.9947	.9941	.9935	.9928
19	.9988	.9986	.9985	.9983	.9980	.9978	.9975	.9972	.9969	.9965
20	.9995	.9994	.9993	.9992	.9991	.9990	.9989	.9987	.9986	.9984

	Mean Arrival Rate λ									
	10.1	10.2	10.3	10.4	10.5	10.6	10.7	10.8	10.9	11.0
0	.0000	.0000	.0000	.0000	.0000	.0000	.0000	.0000	.0000	.0000
1	.0005	.0004	.0004	.0003	.0003	.0003	.0003	.0002	.0002	.0002
2	.0026	.0023	.0022	.0020	.0018	.0017	.0016	.0014	.0013	.0012
3	.0096	.0089	.0083	.0077	.0071	.0066	.0062	.0057	.0053	.0049
4	.0274	.0257	.0241	.0225	.0211	.0197	.0185	.0173	.0162	.0151
5	.0634	.0599	.0566	.0534	.0504	.0475	.0448	.0423	.0398	.0375
6	.1240	.1180	.1123	.1069	.1016	.0966	.0918	.0872	.0828	.0786
7	.2113	.2027	.1944	.1863	.1785	.1710	.1636	.1566	.1498	.1432
8	.3217	.3108	.3001	.2896	.2794	.2694	.2597	.2502	.2410	.2320
9	.4455	.4332	.4210	.4090	.3971	.3854	.3739	.3626	.3515	.3405
10	.5705	.5580	.5456	.5331	.5207	.5084	.4961	.4840	.4719	.4599
11	.6853	.6738	.6622	.6505	.6387	.6269	.6150	.6031	.5912	.5793
12	.7820	.7722	.7623	.7522	.7420	.7316	.7210	.7104	.6996	.6887
13	.8571	.8494	.8416	.8336	.8253	.8169	.8083	.7995	.7905	.7813
14	.9112	.9057	.9	.8940	.8879	.8815	.8750	.8682	.8612	.8540
15	.9477	.9440	.9400	.9359	.9317	.9272	.9225	.9177	.9126	.9074
16	.9707	.9684	.9658	.9632	.9604	.9574	.9543	.9511	.9477	.9441
17	.9844	.9830	.9815	.9799	.9781	.9763	.9744	.9723	.9701	.9678
18	.9921	.9913	.9904	.9895	.9885	.9874	.9863	.9850	.9837	.9823
19	.9962	.9957	.9953	.9948	.9942	.9936	.9930	.9923	.9915	.9907
20	.9982	.9980	.9978	.9975	.9972	.9969	.9966	.9962	.9958	.9953

	Mean Arrival Rate λ									
	11.1	11.2	11.3	11.4	11.5	11.6	11.7	11.8	11.9	12.0
0	.0000	.0000	.0000	.0000	.0000	.0000	.0000	.0000	.0000	.0000
1	.0002	.0002	.0002	.0001	.0001	.0001	.0001	.0001	.0001	.0001
2	.0011	.0010	.0009	.0009	.0008	.0007	.0007	.0006	.0006	.0005
3	.0046	.0042	.0039	.0036	.0034	.0031	.0029	.0027	.0025	.0023
4	.0141	.0132	.0123	.0115	.0107	.0100	.0094	.0087	.0081	.0076
5	.0353	.0333	.0313	.0295	.0277	.0261	.0245	.0230	.0217	.0203
6	.0746	.0708	.0671	.0636	.0603	.0571	.0541	.0512	.0484	.0458
7	.1369	.1307	.1249	.1192	.1137	.1085	.1035	.0986	.0940	.0895
8	.2232	.2147	.2064	.1984	.1906	.1830	.1757	.1686	.1617	.1550
9	.3298	.3192	.3089	.2987	.2888	.2791	.2696	.2603	.2512	.2424
10	.4480	.4362	.4246	.4131	.4017	.3905	.3794	.3685	.3578	.3472
11	.5673	.5554	.5435	.5316	.5198	.5080	.4963	.4847	.4731	.4616
12	.6777	.6666	.6555	.6442	.6329	.6216	.6102	.5988	.5874	.5760
13	.7719	.7624	.7528	.7430	.7330	.7230	.7128	.7025	.6920	.6815
14	.8467	.8391	.8313	.8234	.8153	.8069	.7985	.7898	.7810	.7720

Table 6 Cumulative Poisson Probabilities Continued

	Mean Arrival Rate λ									
	11.1	11.2	11.3	11.4	11.5	11.6	11.7	11.8	11.9	12.0
15	.9020	.8963	.8905	.8845	.8783	.8719	.8653	.8585	.8510	.8444
16	.9403	.9364	.9323	.9280	.9236	.9190	.9142	.9092	.9040	.8987
17	.9654	.9628	.9601	.9572	.9542	.9511	.9478	.9444	.9408	.9370
18	.9808	.9792	.9775	.9757	.9738	.9718	.9697	.9674	.9651	.9626
19	.9898	.9889	.9879	.9868	.9857	.9845	.9832	.9818	.9803	.9787
20	.9948	.9943	.9938	.9932	.9925	.9918	.9910	.9902	.9893	.9884

	Mean Arrival Rate λ									
	12.1	12.2	12.3	12.4	12.5	12.6	12.7	12.8	12.9	13.0
5	.0191	.0179	.0168	.0158	.0148	.0139	.0130	.0122	.0115	.0107
6	.0433	.0410	.0387	.0366	.0346	.0326	.0308	.0291	.0274	.0259
7	.0852	.0811	.0772	.0734	.0698	.0664	.0631	.0599	.0569	.0540
8	.1486	.1424	.1363	.1305	.1249	.1195	.1143	.1093	.1044	.0998
9	.2338	.2254	.2172	.2092	.2014	.1939	.1866	.1794	.1725	.1658
10	.3368	.3266	.3166	.3067	.2971	.2876	.2783	.2693	.2604	.2517
11	.4502	.4389	.4278	.4167	.4058	.3950	.3843	.3738	.3634	.3532
12	.5645	.5531	.5417	.5303	.5190	.5077	.4964	.4853	.4741	.4631
13	.6709	.6603	.6495	.6387	.6278	.6169	.6060	.5950	.5840	.5730
14	.7629	.7536	.7442	.7347	.7250	.7153	.7054	.6954	.6853	.6751
15	.8371	.8296	.8219	.8140	.8060	.7978	.7895	.7810	.7724	.7636
16	.8932	.8875	.8816	.8755	.8693	.8629	.8563	.8495	.8426	.8355
17	.9331	.9290	.9248	.9204	.9158	.9111	.9062	.9011	.8959	.8905
18	.9600	.9572	.9543	.9513	.9481	.9448	.9414	.9378	.9341	.9302
19	.9771	.9753	.9734	.9715	.9694	.9672	.9649	.9625	.9600	.9573
20	.9874	.9863	.9852	.9840	.9827	.9813	.9799	.9783	.9767	.9750
21	.9934	.9927	.9921	.9914	.9906	.9898	.9889	.9880	.9870	.9859
22	.9966	.9963	.9959	.9955	.9951	.9946	.9941	.9936	.9930	.9924
23	.9984	.9982	.9980	.9978	.9975	.9973	.9970	.9967	.9964	.9960

	Mean Arrival Rate λ									
	13.1	13.2	13.3	13.4	13.5	13.6	13.7	13.8	13.9	14.0
5	.0101	.0094	.0088	.0083	.0077	.0072	.0068	.0063	.0059	.0055
6	.0244	.0230	.0217	.0204	.0193	.0181	.0171	.0161	.0151	.0142
7	.0513	.0487	.0461	.0438	.0415	.0393	.0372	.0353	.0334	.0316
8	.0953	.0910	.0868	.0828	.0790	.0753	.0718	.0684	.0652	.0621
9	.1593	.1530	.1469	.1410	.1353	.1297	.1244	.1192	.1142	.1094
10	.2432	.2349	.2268	.2189	.2117	.2037	.1964	.1893	.1824	.1757
11	.3431	.3332	.3234	.3139	.3045	.2952	.2862	.2773	.2686	.2600
12	.4522	.4413	.4305	.4199	.4093	.3989	.3886	.3784	.3684	.3586
13	.5621	.5511	.5401	.5292	.5182	.5074	.4966	.4858	.4751	.4644
14	.6649	.6546	.6442	.6338	.6233	.6128	.6022	.5916	.5810	.5704
15	.7547	.7456	.7365	.7272	.7178	.7083	.6987	.6890	.6792	.6694
16	.8282	.8208	.8132	.8054	.7975	.7895	.7813	.7730	.7645	.7559
17	.8849	.8791	.8732	.8671	.8609	.8545	.8479	.8411	.8343	.8272
18	.9261	.9219	.9176	.9130	.9084	.9035	.8986	.8934	.8881	.8826
19	.9546	.9516	.9486	.9454	.9421	.9387	.9351	.9314	.9275	.9235
20	.9732	.9713	.9692	.9671	.9649	.9626	.9601	.9576	.9549	.9521
21	.9848	.9836	.9823	.9810	.9796	.9780	.9765	.9748	.9730	.9712
22	.9917	.9910	.9902	.9894	.9885	.9876	.9866	.9856	.9845	.9833
23	.9956	.9952	.9948	.9943	.9938	.9933	.9927	.9921	.9914	.9907

	Mean Arrival Rate λ									
	14.1	14.2	14.3	14.4	14.5	14.6	14.7	14.8	14.9	15.0
6	.0134	.0126	.0118	.0111	.0105	.0098	.0092	.0087	.0081	.0076
7	.0299	.0283	.0268	.0253	.0239	.0226	.0214	.0202	.0191	.0180
8	.0591	.0562	.0535	.0509	.0484	.0460	.0437	.0415	.0394	.0374

Table 6 Cumulative Poisson Probabilities Continued

	Mean Arrival Rate λ									
	14.1	14.2	14.3	14.4	14.5	14.6	14.7	14.8	14.9	15.0
9	.1047	.1003	.0959	.0918	.0878	.0839	.0802	.0766	.0732	.0699
10	.1691	.1628	.1566	.1507	.1449	.1392	.1338	.1285	.1234	.1185
11	.2517	.2435	.2355	.2277	.2201	.2127	.2054	.1984	.1915	.1848
12	.3487	.3391	.3296	.3203	.3111	.3021	.2932	.2845	.2760	.2676
13	.4539	.4434	.4330	.4227	.4125	.4024	.3925	.3826	.3728	.3632
14	.5598	.5492	.5387	.5281	.5176	.5071	.4967	.4863	.4759	.4657
15	.6594	.6494	.6394	.6293	.6192	.6090	.5988	.5886	.5783	.5681
16	.7472	.7384	.7294	.7204	.7112	.7020	.6926	.6832	.6737	.6641
17	.8200	.8126	.8051	.7975	.7897	.7818	.7737	.7656	.7573	.7489
18	.8770	.8712	.8653	.8592	.8530	.8466	.8400	.8333	.8265	.8195
19	.9193	.9150	.9106	.9060	.9012	.8963	.8913	.8861	.8807	.8752
20	.9492	.9461	.9430	.9396	.9362	.9326	.9289	.9251	.9211	.9170
21	.9692	.9671	.9650	.9627	.9604	.9579	.9553	.9526	.9498	.9469
22	.9820	.9807	.9793	.9779	.9763	.9747	.9729	.9711	.9692	.9673
23	.9899	.9891	.9882	.9873	.9863	.9853	.9842	.9831	.9818	.9805
24	.9945	.9941	.9935	.9930	.9924	.9918	.9911	.9904	.9896	.9888
25	.9971	.9969	.9966	.9963	.9959	.9956	.9952	.9947	.9943	.9938

	Mean Arrival Rate λ									
	15.1	15.2	15.3	15.4	15.5	15.6	15.7	15.8	15.9	16.0
7	.0170	.0160	.0151	.0143	.0135	.0127	.0120	.0113	.0106	.0100
8	.0355	.0337	.0320	.0304	.0288	.0273	.0259	.0245	.0232	.0220
9	.0667	.0636	.0607	.0579	.0552	.0526	.0501	.0478	.0455	.0433
10	.1137	.1091	.1046	.1003	.0961	.0921	.0882	.0845	.0809	.0774
11	.1782	.1718	.1657	.1596	.1538	.1481	.1426	.1372	.1320	.1270
12	.2594	.2514	.2435	.2358	.2283	.2209	.2137	.2067	.1998	.1931
13	.3537	.3444	.3351	.3260	.3171	.3083	.2996	.2911	.2827	.2745
14	.4554	.4453	.4353	.4253	.4154	.4056	.3959	.3864	.3769	.3675
15	.5578	.5476	.5374	.5272	.5170	.5069	.4968	.4867	.4767	.4667
16	.6545	.6448	.6351	.6253	.6154	.6056	.5957	.5858	.5759	.5660
17	.7403	.7317	.7230	.7141	.7052	.6962	.6871	.6779	.6687	.6593
18	.8123	.8051	.7977	.7901	.7825	.7747	.7668	.7587	.7506	.7423
19	.8696	.8638	.8578	.8517	.8455	.8391	.8326	.8260	.8192	.8122
20	.9128	.9084	.9039	.8992	.8944	.8894	.8843	.8791	.8737	.8682
21	.9438	.9407	.9374	.9340	.9304	.9268	.9230	.9190	.9150	.9108
22	.9652	.9630	.9607	.9583	.9558	.9532	.9505	.9477	.9448	.9418
23	.9792	.9777	.9762	.9746	.9730	.9712	.9694	.9674	.9654	.9633
24	.9880	.9871	.9861	.9851	.9840	.9829	.9817	.9804	.9791	.9777
25	.9933	.9928	.9922	.9915	.9909	.9902	.9894	.9886	.9878	.9869

	Mean Arrival Rate λ									
	16.1	16.2	16.3	16.4	16.5	16.6	16.7	16.8	16.9	17.0
8	.0208	.0197	.0186	.0176	.0167	.0158	.0149	.0141	.0133	.0126
9	.0412	.0392	.0373	.0355	.0337	.0321	.0305	.0290	.0275	.0261
10	.0740	.0708	.0677	.0647	.0619	.0591	.0565	.0539	.0515	.0491
11	.1221	.1174	.1128	.1084	.1041	.0999	.0959	.0920	.0883	.0847
12	.1866	.1802	.1740	.1680	.1621	.1564	.1508	.1454	.1401	.1350
13	.2664	.2585	.2508	.2432	.2357	.2285	.2213	.2144	.2075	.2009
14	.3583	.3492	.3402	.3313	.3225	.3139	.3054	.2971	.2889	.2808
15	.4569	.4470	.4373	.4276	.4180	.4085	.3991	.3898	.3806	.3715
16	.5560	.5461	.5362	.5263	.5165	.5067	.4969	.4871	.4774	.4677
17	.6500	.6406	.6311	.6216	.6120	.6025	.5929	.5833	.5737	.5640
18	.7340	.7255	.7170	.7084	.6996	.6908	.6820	.6730	.6640	.6550
19	.8052	.7980	.7907	.7833	.7757	.7681	.7603	.7524	.7444	.7363
20	.8625	.8567	.8508	.8447	.8385	.8321	.8257	.8191	.8123	.8055
21	.9064	.9020	.8974	.8927	.8878	.8828	.8777	.8724	.8670	.8615
22	.9386	.9353	.9319	.9284	.9248	.9210	.9171	.9131	.9090	.9047

Table 6 Cumulative Poisson Probabilities Continued

	Mean Arrival Rate λ									
	16.1	16.2	16.3	16.4	16.5	16.6	16.7	16.8	16.9	17.0
23	.9611	.9588	.9564	.9539	.9513	.9486	.9458	.9429	.9398	.9367
24	.9762	.9747	.9730	.9713	.9696	.9677	.9657	.9637	.9616	.9594
25	.9859	.9849	.9839	.9828	.9816	.9804	.9791	.9777	.9763	.9748
26	.9920	.9913	.9907	.9900	.9892	.9884	.9876	.9867	.9858	.9848

	Mean Arrival Rate λ									
	17.1	17.2	17.3	17.4	17.5	17.6	17.7	17.8	17.9	18.0
8	.0119	.0112	.0106	.0100	.0095	.0089	.0084	.0079	.0075	.0071
9	.0248	.0235	.0223	.0212	.0201	.0191	.0181	.0171	.0162	.0154
10	.0469	.0447	.0426	.0406	.0387	.0369	.0352	.0335	.0319	.0304
11	.0812	.0778	.0746	.0714	.0684	.0655	.0627	.0600	.0574	.0549
12	.1301	.1252	.1206	.1160	.1116	.1074	.1033	.0993	.0954	.0917
13	.1944	.1880	.1818	.1758	.1699	.1641	.1585	.1531	.1478	.1426
14	.2729	.2651	.2575	.2500	.2426	.2354	.2284	.2215	.2147	.2081
15	.3624	.3535	.3448	.3361	.3275	.3191	.3108	.3026	.2946	.2867
16	.4581	.4486	.4391	.4297	.4204	.4112	.4020	.3929	.3839	.3751
17	.5544	.5448	.5352	.5256	.5160	.5065	.4969	.4875	.4780	.4686
18	.6458	.6367	.6275	.6182	.6089	.5996	.5903	.5810	.5716	.5622
19	.7281	.7199	.7115	.7031	.6945	.6859	.6773	.6685	.6598	.6509
20	.7985	.7914	.7842	.7769	.7694	.7619	.7542	.7465	.7387	.7307
21	.8558	.8500	.8441	.8380	.8319	.8255	.8191	.8126	.8059	.7991
22	.9003	.8958	.8912	.8864	.8815	.8765	.8713	.8660	.8606	.8551
23	.9334	.9301	.9266	.9230	.9193	.9154	.9115	.9074	.9032	.8989
24	.9570	.9546	.9521	.9495	.9468	.9440	.9411	.9381	.9350	.9317
25	.9732	.9715	.9698	.9680	.9661	.9641	.9621	.9599	.9577	.9554
26	.9838	.9827	.9816	.9804	.9791	.9778	.9764	.9749	.9734	.9718
27	.9905	.9898	.9891	.9883	.9875	.9866	.9857	.9848	.9837	.9827

	Mean Arrival Rate λ									
	18.1	18.2	18.3	18.4	18.5	18.6	18.7	18.8	18.9	19.0
9	.0146	.0138	.0131	.0124	.0117	.0111	.0105	.0099	.0094	.0089
10	.0289	.0275	.0262	.0249	.0237	.0225	.0214	.0203	.0193	.0183
11	.0525	.0502	.0479	.0458	.0438	.0418	.0399	.0381	.0363	.0347
12	.0881	.0846	.0812	.0779	.0748	.0717	.0688	.0659	.0632	.0606
13	.1376	.1327	.1279	.1233	.1189	.1145	.1103	.1062	.1022	.0984
14	.2016	.1953	.1891	.1830	.1771	.1714	.1658	.1603	.1550	.1497
15	.2789	.2712	.2637	.2563	.2490	.2419	.2349	.2281	.2214	.2148
16	.3663	.3576	.3490	.3405	.3321	.3239	.3157	.3077	.2998	.2920
17	.4593	.4500	.4408	.4317	.4226	.4136	.4047	.3958	.3870	.3784
18	.5529	.5435	.5342	.5249	.5156	.5063	.4970	.4878	.4786	.4695
19	.6420	.6331	.6241	.6151	.6061	.5970	.5879	.5788	.5697	.5606
20	.7227	.7146	.7064	.6981	.6898	.6814	.6729	.6644	.6558	.6472
21	.7922	.7852	.7781	.7709	.7636	.7561	.7486	.7410	.7333	.7255
22	.8494	.8436	.8377	.8317	.8256	.8193	.8129	.8065	.7998	.7931
23	.8944	.8899	.8852	.8804	.8755	.8704	.8652	.8600	.8545	.8490
24	.9284	.9249	.9214	.9177	.9139	.9100	.9060	.9019	.8976	.8933
25	.9530	.9505	.9479	.9452	.9424	.9395	.9365	.9334	.9302	.9269
26	.9701	.9683	.9665	.9646	.9626	.9606	.9584	.9562	.9539	.9514
27	.9816	.9804	.9792	.9779	.9765	.9751	.9736	.9720	.9704	.9687

	Mean Arrival Rate λ									
	19.1	19.2	19.3	19.4	19.5	19.6	19.7	19.8	19.9	20.0
10	.0174	.0165	.0157	.0149	.0141	.0134	.0127	.0120	.0114	.0108
11	.0331	.0315	.0301	.0287	.0273	.0260	.0248	.0236	.0225	.0214
12	.0580	.0556	.0532	.0509	.0488	.0467	.0446	.0427	.0408	.0390
13	.0947	.0911	.0876	.0842	.0809	.0778	.0747	.0717	.0689	.0661

Table 6 Cumulative Poisson Probabilities Continued

	Mean Arrival Rate λ									
	19.1	19.2	19.3	19.4	19.5	19.6	19.7	19.8	19.9	20.0
14	.1447	.1397	.1349	.1303	.1257	.1213	.1170	.1128	.1088	.1049
15	.2084	.2021	.1959	.1899	.1840	.1782	.1726	.1671	.1617	.1565
16	.2844	.2768	.2694	.2621	.2550	.2479	.2410	.2342	.2276	.2211
17	.3698	.3613	.3529	.3446	.3364	.3283	.3203	.3124	.3047	.2970
18	.4604	.4514	.4424	.4335	.4246	.4158	.4071	.3985	.3899	.3814
19	.5515	.5424	.5333	.5242	.5151	.5061	.4971	.4881	.4792	.4703
20	.6385	.6298	.6210	.6122	.6034	.5946	.5857	.5769	.5680	.5591
21	.7176	.7097	.7016	.6935	.6854	.6772	.6689	.6605	.6521	.6437
22	.7863	.7794	.7724	.7653	.7580	.7507	.7433	.7358	.7283	.7206
23	.8434	.8376	.8317	.8257	.8196	.8134	.8071	.8007	.7941	.7875
24	.8888	.8842	.8795	.8746	.8697	.8646	.8594	.8541	.8487	.8432
25	.9235	.9199	.9163	.9126	.9087	.9048	.9007	.8965	.8922	.8878
26	.9489	.9463	.9437	.9409	.9380	.9350	.9319	.9288	.9255	.9221
27	.9670	.9651	.9632	.9612	.9591	.9570	.9547	.9524	.9500	.9475

	Mean Arrival Rate λ									
	20.1	20.2	20.3	20.4	20.5	20.6	20.7	20.8	20.9	21.0
10	.0102	.0097	.0092	.0087	.0082	.0078	.0074	.0070	.0066	.0063
11	.0204	.0194	.0184	.0175	.0167	.0158	.0150	.0143	.0136	.0129
12	.0373	.0356	.0340	.0325	.0310	.0296	.0283	.0270	.0257	.0245
13	.0635	.0609	.0584	.0560	.0537	.0515	.0493	.0473	.0453	.0434
14	.1010	.0973	.0938	.0903	.0869	.0836	.0805	.0774	.0744	.0716
15	.1514	.1464	.1416	.1369	.1323	.1278	.1234	.1192	.1151	.1111
16	.2147	.2084	.2023	.1963	.1904	.1847	.1790	.1735	.1682	.1629
17	.2895	.2821	.2748	.2676	.2605	.2536	.2467	.2400	.2334	.2270
18	.3730	.3647	.3565	.3484	.3403	.3324	.3246	.3168	.3092	.3017
19	.4614	.4526	.4438	.4351	.4265	.4179	.4094	.4009	.3926	.3843
20	.5502	.5413	.5325	.5236	.5148	.5059	.4972	.4884	.4797	.4710
21	.6352	.6267	.6181	.6096	.6010	.5923	.5837	.5750	.5664	.5577
22	.7129	.7051	.6972	.6893	.6813	.6732	.6651	.6569	.6487	.6405
23	.7808	.7739	.7670	.7600	.7528	.7456	.7384	.7310	.7235	.7160
24	.8376	.8319	.8260	.8201	.8140	.8078	.8016	.7952	.7887	.7822
25	.8833	.8787	.8739	.8691	.8641	.8591	.8539	.8486	.8432	.8377
26	.9186	.9150	.9114	.9076	.9037	.8997	.8955	.8913	.8870	.8826
27	.9449	.9423	.9395	.9366	.9337	.9306	.9275	.9242	.9209	.9175

	Mean Arrival Rate λ									
	21.1	21.2	21.3	21.4	21.5	21.6	21.7	21.8	21.9	22.0
11	.0123	.0116	.0110	.0105	.0099	.0094	.0090	.0085	.0080	.0076
12	.0234	.0223	.0213	.0203	.0193	.0184	.0175	.0167	.0159	.0151
13	.0415	.0397	.0380	.0364	.0348	.0333	.0318	.0304	.0291	.0278
14	.0688	.0661	.0635	.0610	.0586	.0563	.0540	.0518	.0497	.0477
15	.1072	.1034	.0997	.0962	.0927	.0893	.0861	.0829	.0799	.0769
16	.1578	.1528	.1479	.1432	.1385	.1340	.1296	.1253	.1211	.1170
17	.2206	.2144	.2083	.2023	.1965	.1907	.1851	.1796	.1743	.1690
18	.2943	.2870	.2798	.2727	.2657	.2588	.2521	.2454	.2389	.2325
19	.3760	.3679	.3599	.3519	.3440	.3362	.3285	.3209	.3134	.3060
20	.4623	.4537	.4452	.4367	.4282	.4198	.4115	.4032	.3950	.3869
21	.5490	.5403	.5317	.5230	.5144	.5058	.4972	.4887	.4801	.4716
22	.6322	.6238	.6155	.6071	.5987	.5902	.5818	.5733	.5648	.5564
23	.7084	.7008	.6930	.6853	.6774	.6695	.6616	.6536	.6455	.6374
24	.7755	.7687	.7619	.7550	.7480	.7409	.7337	.7264	.7191	.7117
25	.8321	.8264	.8206	.8146	.8086	.8025	.7963	.7900	.7836	.7771
26	.8780	.8734	.8686	.8638	.8588	.8537	.8486	.8433	.8379	.8324
27	.9139	.9103	.9065	.9027	.8988	.8947	.8906	.8863	.8820	.8775

Table 7 Cutoff Points of the Chi-Square Distribution Function

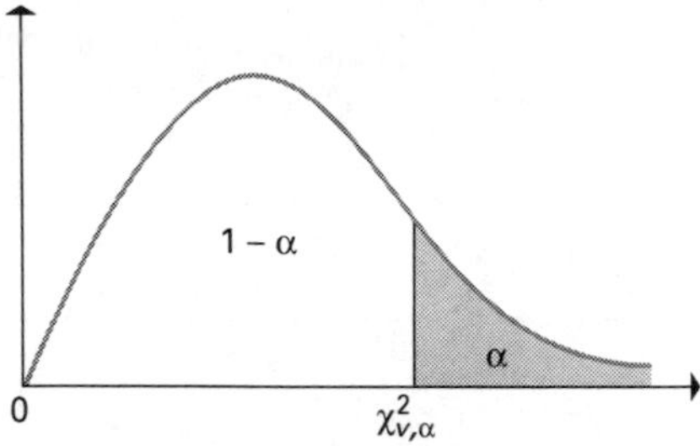

For selected probabilities α, the table shows the values $\chi^2_{v,\alpha}$ such that $P(\chi^2_v > \chi^2_{v,\alpha}) = \alpha$, where χ^2_v is a chi-square random variable with v degrees of freedom. For example, the probability is .100 that a chi-square random variable with 10 degrees of freedom is greater than 15.99.

v	α									
	.995	.990	.975	.950	.900	.100	.050	.025	.010	.005
1	0.0^4393	0.0^3157	0.0^3982	0.0^2393	0.0158	2.71	3.84	5.02	6.63	7.88
2	0.0100	0.0201	0.0506	0.103	0.211	4.61	5.99	7.38	9.21	10.60
3	0.072	0.115	0.216	0.352	0.584	6.25	7.81	9.35	11.34	12.84
4	0.207	0.297	0.484	0.711	1.064	7.78	9.49	11.14	13.28	14.86
5	0.412	0.554	0.831	1.145	1.61	9.24	11.07	12.83	15.09	16.75
6	0.676	0.872	1.24	1.64	2.20	10.64	12.59	14.45	16.81	18.55
7	0.989	1.24	1.69	2.17	2.83	12.02	14.07	16.01	18.48	20.28
8	1.34	1.65	2.18	2.73	3.49	13.36	15.51	17.53	20.09	21.96
9	1.73	2.09	2.70	3.33	4.17	14.68	16.92	19.02	21.67	23.59
10	2.16	2.56	3.25	3.94	4.87	15.99	18.31	20.48	23.21	25.19
11	2.60	3.05	3.82	4.57	5.58	17.28	19.68	21.92	24.73	26.76
12	3.07	3.57	4.40	5.23	6.30	18.55	21.03	23.34	26.22	28.30
13	3.57	4.11	5.01	5.89	7.04	19.81	22.36	24.74	27.69	29.82
14	4.07	4.66	5.63	6.57	7.79	21.06	23.68	26.12	29.14	31.32
15	4.60	5.23	6.26	7.26	8.55	22.31	25.00	27.49	30.58	32.80
16	5.14	5.81	6.91	7.96	9.31	23.54	26.30	28.85	32.00	34.27
17	5.70	6.41	7.56	8.67	10.09	24.77	27.59	30.19	33.41	35.72
18	6.26	7.01	8.23	9.39	10.86	25.99	28.87	31.53	34.81	37.16
19	6.84	7.63	8.91	10.12	11.65	27.20	30.14	32.85	36.19	38.58
20	7.43	8.26	9.59	10.85	12.44	28.41	31.41	34.17	37.57	40.00
21	8.03	8.90	10.28	11.59	13.24	29.62	32.67	35.48	38.93	41.40
22	8.64	9.54	10.98	12.34	14.04	30.81	33.92	36.78	40.29	42.80
23	9.26	10.20	11.69	13.09	14.85	32.01	35.17	38.08	41.64	44.18
24	9.89	10.86	12.40	13.85	15.66	33.20	36.42	39.36	42.98	45.56
25	10.52	11.52	13.12	14.61	16.47	34.38	37.65	40.65	44.31	46.93
26	11.16	12.20	13.84	15.38	17.29	35.56	38.89	41.92	45.64	48.29
27	11.81	12.88	14.57	16.15	18.11	36.74	40.11	43.19	46.96	49.64
28	12.46	13.56	15.31	16.93	18.94	37.92	41.34	44.46	48.28	50.99
29	13.12	14.26	16.05	17.71	19.77	39.09	42.56	45.72	49.59	52.34
30	13.79	14.95	16.79	18.49	20.60	40.26	43.77	46.98	50.89	53.67
40	20.71	22.16	24.43	26.51	29.05	51.81	55.76	59.34	63.69	66.77
50	27.99	29.71	32.36	34.76	37.69	63.17	67.50	71.42	76.15	79.49
60	35.53	37.48	40.48	43.19	46.46	74.40	79.08	83.30	88.38	91.95
70	43.28	45.44	48.76	51.74	55.33	85.53	90.53	95.02	100.4	104.2
80	51.17	53.54	57.15	60.39	64.28	96.58	101.9	106.6	112.3	116.3
90	59.20	61.75	65.65	69.13	73.29	107.6	113.1	118.1	124.1	128.3
100	67.33	70.06	74.22	77.93	82.36	118.5	124.3	129.6	135.8	140.2

Reproduced with permission from C. M. Thompson, "Tables of percentage points of the chi-square distribution," *Biometrika* 32 (1941).

Table 8 Cutoff Points for the Student's *t* Distribution

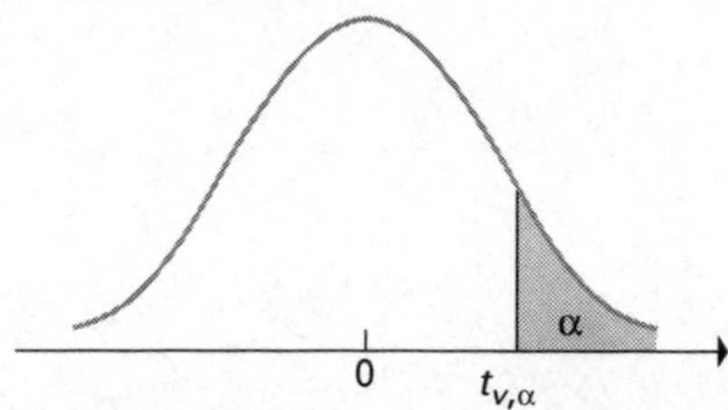

For selected probabilities, α, the table shows the values $t_{v,\alpha}$ such that $P(t_v > t_{v,\alpha}) = \alpha$, where t_v is a Student's *t* random variable with *v* degrees of freedom. For example, the probability is .10 that a Student's *t* random variable with 10 degrees of freedom exceeds 1.372.

v	α				
	0.100	0.050	0.025	0.010	0.005
1	3.078	6.314	12.706	31.821	63.657
2	1.886	2.920	4.303	6.965	9.925
3	1.638	2.353	3.182	4.541	5.841
4	1.533	2.132	2.776	3.747	4.604
5	1.476	2.015	2.571	3.365	4.032
6	1.440	1.943	2.447	3.143	3.707
7	1.415	1.895	2.365	2.998	3.499
8	1.397	1.860	2.306	2.896	3.355
9	1.383	1.833	2.262	2.821	3.250
10	1.372	1.812	2.228	2.764	3.169
11	1.363	1.796	2.201	2.718	3.106
12	1.356	1.782	2.179	2.681	3.055
13	1.350	1.771	2.160	2.650	3.012
14	1.345	1.761	2.145	2.624	2.977
15	1.341	1.753	2.131	2.602	2.947
16	1.337	1.746	2.120	2.583	2.921
17	1.333	1.740	2.110	2.567	2.898
18	1.330	1.734	2.101	2.552	2.878
19	1.328	1.729	2.093	2.539	2.861
20	1.325	1.725	2.086	2.528	2.845
21	1.323	1.721	2.080	2.518	2.831
22	1.321	1.717	2.074	2.508	2.819
23	1.319	1.714	2.069	2.500	2.807
24	1.318	1.711	2.064	2.492	2.797
25	1.316	1.708	2.060	2.485	2.787
26	1.315	1.706	2.056	2.479	2.779
27	1.314	1.703	2.052	2.473	2.771
28	1.313	1.701	2.048	2.467	2.763
29	1.311	1.699	2.045	2.462	2.756
30	1.310	1.697	2.042	2.457	2.750
40	1.303	1.684	2.021	2.423	2.704
60	1.296	1.671	2.000	2.390	2.660
∞	1.282	1.645	1.960	2.326	2.576

Table 9 Cutoff Points for the F Distribution

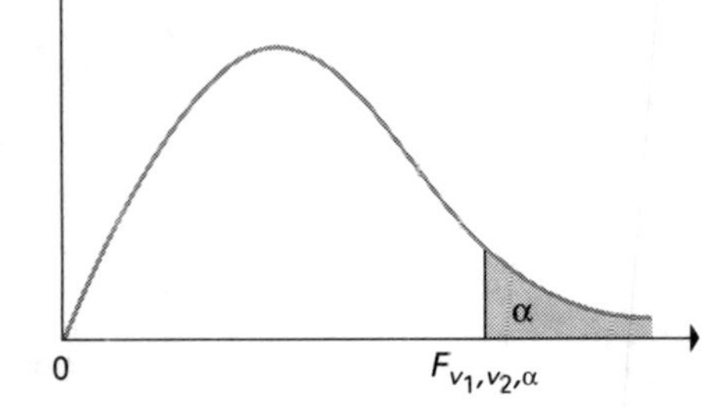

For probabilities $\alpha = 0.5$ and $\alpha = .01$, the tables show the values $F_{v_1, v_2, \alpha}$ such that $P(F_{v_1, v_2} > F_{v_1, v_2, \alpha}) = \alpha$, where F_{v_1, v_2} is an F random variable, with numerator degrees of freedom v_1 and denominator degrees of freedom v_2. For example, the probability is .05 that an $F_{3,7}$ random variable exceeds 4.35.

$\alpha = .05$

Denominator v_2	Numerator v_1																		
	1	2	3	4	5	6	7	8	9	10	12	15	20	24	30	40	60	120	∞
1	161.4	199.5	215.7	224.6	230.2	234.0	236.8	238.9	240.5	241.9	243.9	245.9	248.0	249.1	250.1	251.1	252.2	253.3	254.3
2	18.51	19.00	19.16	19.25	19.30	19.33	19.35	19.37	19.38	19.40	19.41	19.43	19.45	19.45	19.46	19.47	19.48	19.49	19.50
3	10.13	9.55	9.28	9.12	9.01	8.94	8.89	8.85	8.81	8.79	8.74	8.70	8.66	8.64	8.62	8.59	8.57	8.55	8.53
4	7.71	6.94	6.59	6.39	6.26	6.16	6.09	6.04	6.00	5.96	5.91	5.86	5.80	5.77	5.75	5.72	5.69	5.66	5.63
5	6.61	5.79	5.41	5.19	5.05	4.95	4.88	4.82	4.77	4.74	4.68	4.62	4.56	4.53	4.50	4.46	4.43	4.40	4.36
6	5.99	5.14	4.76	4.53	4.39	4.28	4.21	4.15	4.10	4.06	4.00	3.94	3.87	3.84	3.81	3.77	3.74	3.70	3.67
7	5.59	4.74	4.35	4.12	3.97	3.87	3.79	3.73	3.68	3.64	3.57	3.51	3.44	3.41	3.38	3.34	3.30	3.27	3.23
8	5.32	4.46	4.07	3.84	3.69	3.58	3.50	3.44	3.39	3.35	3.28	3.22	3.15	3.12	3.08	3.04	3.01	2.97	2.93
9	5.12	4.26	3.86	3.63	3.48	3.37	3.29	3.23	3.18	3.14	3.07	3.01	2.94	2.90	2.86	2.83	2.79	2.75	2.71
10	4.96	4.10	3.71	3.48	3.33	3.22	3.14	3.07	3.02	2.98	2.91	2.85	2.77	2.74	2.70	2.66	2.62	2.58	2.54
11	4.84	3.98	3.59	3.36	3.20	3.09	3.01	2.95	2.90	2.85	2.79	2.72	2.65	2.61	2.57	2.53	2.49	2.45	2.40
12	4.75	3.89	3.49	3.26	3.11	3.00	2.91	2.85	2.80	2.75	2.69	2.62	2.54	2.51	2.47	2.43	2.38	2.34	2.30
13	4.67	3.81	3.41	3.18	3.03	2.92	2.83	2.77	2.71	2.67	2.60	2.53	2.46	2.42	2.38	2.34	2.30	2.25	2.21
14	4.60	3.74	3.34	3.11	2.96	2.85	2.76	2.70	2.65	2.60	2.53	2.46	2.39	2.35	2.31	2.27	2.22	2.18	2.13
15	4.54	3.68	3.29	3.06	2.90	2.79	2.71	2.64	2.59	2.54	2.48	2.40	2.33	2.29	2.25	2.20	2.16	2.11	2.07
16	4.49	3.63	3.24	3.01	2.85	2.74	2.66	2.59	2.54	2.49	2.42	2.35	2.28	2.24	2.19	2.15	2.11	2.06	2.01
17	4.45	3.59	3.20	2.96	2.81	2.70	2.62	2.55	2.49	2.45	2.38	2.31	2.23	2.19	2.15	2.10	2.06	2.01	1.96
18	4.41	3.55	3.16	2.93	2.77	2.66	2.58	2.51	2.46	2.41	2.34	2.27	2.19	2.15	2.11	2.06	2.02	1.97	1.92
19	4.38	3.52	3.13	2.90	2.74	2.63	2.54	2.48	2.42	2.38	2.31	2.23	2.16	2.11	2.07	2.03	1.98	1.93	1.88

Table 9 Cutoff Points for the F Distribution Continued

	$\alpha = .05$																		
Denominator ν_2	Numerator ν_1																		
	1	2	3	4	5	6	7	8	9	10	12	15	20	24	30	40	60	120	∞
20	4.35	3.49	3.10	2.87	2.71	2.60	2.51	2.45	2.39	2.35	2.28	2.20	2.12	2.08	2.04	1.99	1.95	1.90	1.84
21	4.32	3.47	3.07	2.84	2.68	2.67	2.49	2.42	2.37	2.32	2.25	2.18	2.10	2.05	2.01	1.96	1.92	1.87	1.81
22	4.30	3.44	3.05	2.82	2.66	2.55	2.46	2.40	2.34	2.30	2.23	2.15	2.07	2.03	1.98	1.94	1.89	1.84	1.78
23	4.28	3.42	3.03	2.80	2.64	2.53	2.44	2.37	2.32	2.27	2.20	2.13	2.05	2.01	1.96	1.91	1.86	1.81	1.76
24	4.26	3.40	3.01	2.78	2.62	2.51	2.42	2.36	2.30	2.25	2.18	2.11	2.03	1.98	1.94	1.89	1.84	1.79	1.73
25	4.24	3.39	2.99	2.76	2.60	2.49	2.40	2.34	2.28	2.24	2.16	2.09	2.01	1.96	1.92	1.87	1.82	1.77	1.71
26	4.23	3.37	2.98	2.74	2.59	2.47	2.39	2.32	2.27	2.22	2.15	2.07	1.99	1.95	1.90	1.85	1.80	1.75	1.69
27	4.21	3.35	2.96	2.73	2.57	2.46	2.37	2.31	2.25	2.20	2.13	2.06	1.97	1.93	1.88	1.84	1.79	1.73	1.67
28	4.20	3.34	2.95	2.71	2.56	2.45	2.36	2.29	2.24	2.19	2.12	2.04	1.96	1.91	1.87	1.82	1.77	1.71	1.65
29	4.18	3.33	2.93	2.70	2.55	2.43	2.35	2.28	2.22	2.18	2.10	2.03	1.94	1.90	1.85	1.81	1.75	1.70	1.64
30	4.17	3.32	2.92	2.69	2.53	2.42	2.33	2.27	2.21	2.16	2.09	2.01	1.93	1.89	1.84	1.79	1.74	1.58	1.62
40	4.08	3.23	2.84	2.61	2.45	2.34	2.25	2.18	2.12	2.08	2.00	1.92	1.84	1.79	1.74	1.69	1.64	1.58	1.51
60	4.00	3.15	2.76	2.53	2.37	2.25	2.17	2.10	2.04	1.99	1.92	1.84	1.75	1.70	1.65	1.59	1.53	1.47	1.39
120	3.92	3.07	2.68	2.45	2.29	2.17	2.09	2.02	1.96	1.91	1.83	1.75	1.66	1.61	1.55	1.50	1.43	1.35	1.25
∞	3.84	3.00	2.60	2.37	2.21	2.10	2.01	1.94	1.88	1.83	1.75	1.67	1.57	1.52	1.46	1.39	1.32	1.22	1.00

Table 9 Cutoff Points for the F Distribution Continued

$\alpha = .01$

DENOMINATOR v_2	NUMERATOR v_1 1	2	3	4	5	6	7	8	9	10	12	15	20	24	30	40	60	120	∞
1	4052	4999.5	5403	5625	5764	5859	5928	5982	6022	6056	6106	6157	6209	6235	6261	6287	6313	6339	6366
2	98.50	99.00	99.17	99.25	99.30	99.33	99.36	99.37	99.39	99.40	99.42	99.43	99.45	99.46	99.47	99.47	99.48	99.48	99.50
3	34.12	30.82	29.46	28.71	28.24	27.91	27.67	27.49	27.35	27.23	27.05	26.87	26.69	26.60	26.50	26.41	26.32	26.22	26.13
4	21.20	18.00	16.69	15.98	15.52	15.21	14.98	14.80	14.66	14.55	14.37	14.20	14.02	13.93	13.84	13.75	13.65	13.56	13.46
5	16.26	13.27	12.06	11.39	10.97	10.67	10.46	10.29	10.16	10.05	9.89	9.72	9.55	9.47	9.38	9.29	9.20	9.11	9.02
6	13.75	10.92	9.78	9.15	8.75	8.47	8.26	8.10	7.98	7.87	7.72	7.56	7.40	7.31	7.23	7.14	7.06	6.97	6.88
7	12.25	9.55	8.45	7.85	7.46	7.19	6.99	6.84	6.72	6.62	6.47	6.31	6.16	6.07	5.99	5.91	5.82	5.74	5.65
8	11.26	8.65	7.59	7.01	6.63	6.37	6.18	6.03	5.91	5.81	5.67	5.52	5.36	5.28	5.20	5.12	5.03	4.95	4.86
9	10.56	8.02	6.99	6.42	6.06	5.80	5.61	5.47	5.35	5.26	5.11	4.96	4.81	4.73	4.65	4.57	4.48	4.40	4.31
10	10.04	7.56	6.55	5.99	5.64	5.39	5.30	5.06	4.94	4.85	4.71	4.56	4.41	4.33	4.25	4.17	4.08	4.00	3.91
11	9.65	7.21	6.22	5.67	5.32	5.07	4.89	4.74	4.63	4.54	4.40	4.25	4.10	4.02	3.94	3.86	3.78	3.69	3.60
12	9.33	6.93	5.95	5.41	5.06	4.82	4.64	4.50	4.39	4.30	4.16	4.01	3.86	3.78	3.70	3.62	3.54	3.45	3.36
13	9.07	6.70	5.74	5.21	4.86	4.62	4.44	4.30	4.19	4.10	3.96	3.82	3.66	3.59	3.51	3.43	3.34	3.25	3.17
14	8.86	6.51	5.56	5.04	4.69	4.46	4.28	4.14	4.03	3.94	3.80	3.66	3.51	3.43	3.35	3.27	3.18	3.09	3.00
15	8.68	6.36	5.42	4.89	4.56	4.32	4.14	4.00	3.89	3.80	3.67	3.52	3.37	3.29	3.21	3.13	3.05	2.96	2.87
16	8.53	6.23	5.29	4.77	4.44	4.20	4.03	3.89	3.78	3.69	3.55	3.41	3.26	3.18	3.10	3.02	2.93	2.84	2.75
17	8.40	6.11	5.18	4.67	4.34	4.10	3.93	3.79	3.68	3.59	3.46	3.31	3.16	3.08	3.00	2.92	2.83	2.75	2.65
18	8.29	6.01	5.09	4.58	4.25	4.01	3.84	3.71	3.60	3.51	3.37	3.23	3.08	3.00	2.92	2.84	2.75	2.66	2.57
19	8.18	5.93	5.01	4.50	4.17	3.94	3.77	3.63	3.52	3.43	3.30	3.15	3.00	2.92	2.84	2.76	2.67	2.58	2.49
20	8.10	5.85	4.94	4.43	4.10	3.87	3.70	3.56	3.46	3.37	3.23	3.09	2.94	2.86	2.78	2.69	2.61	2.52	2.42
21	8.02	5.78	4.87	4.37	4.04	3.81	3.64	3.51	3.40	3.31	3.17	3.03	2.88	2.80	2.72	2.64	2.55	2.46	2.36
22	7.95	5.72	4.82	4.31	3.99	3.76	3.59	3.45	3.35	3.26	3.12	2.98	2.83	2.75	2.67	2.58	2.50	2.40	2.31
23	7.88	5.66	4.76	4.26	3.94	3.71	3.54	3.41	3.30	3.21	3.07	3.93	2.78	2.70	2.62	2.54	2.45	2.35	2.26
24	7.82	5.61	4.72	4.22	3.90	3.67	3.50	3.36	3.26	2.17	3.03	2.89	2.74	2.66	2.58	2.49	2.40	2.31	2.21
25	7.77	5.57	4.68	4.18	3.85	3.63	3.46	3.32	3.22	3.13	2.99	2.85	2.70	2.62	2.54	2.45	2.36	2.27	2.17
26	7.72	5.53	4.64	4.14	3.82	3.59	3.42	3.29	3.18	3.09	2.96	2.81	2.66	2.58	2.50	2.42	2.33	2.23	2.13
27	7.68	5.49	4.60	4.11	3.78	3.56	3.39	3.26	3.15	3.06	2.93	2.78	2.63	2.55	2.47	2.38	2.29	2.20	2.10
28	7.64	5.45	4.57	4.07	3.75	3.53	3.36	3.23	3.12	3.03	2.90	2.75	2.60	2.52	2.44	2.35	2.26	2.17	2.06
29	7.60	5.42	4.54	4.04	3.73	3.50	3.33	3.20	3.09	3.00	2.87	2.73	2.57	2.49	2.41	2.33	2.23	2.14	2.03
30	7.56	5.39	4.51	4.02	3.70	3.47	3.30	3.17	3.07	2.98	2.84	2.70	2.55	2.47	2.39	2.30	2.21	2.11	2.01
40	7.31	5.18	4.31	3.83	3.51	3.29	3.12	2.99	2.89	2.80	2.66	2.52	2.37	2.29	2.20	2.11	2.02	1.92	1.80
60	7.08	4.98	4.13	3.65	3.34	3.12	2.95	2.82	2.72	2.63	2.50	2.35	2.20	2.12	2.03	1.94	1.84	1.73	1.60
120	6.85	4.79	3.95	3.48	3.17	2.96	2.79	2.66	2.56	2.47	2.34	2.19	2.03	1.95	1.86	1.76	1.66	1.53	1.38
∞	6.63	4.61	3.78	3.32	3.02	2.80	2.64	2.51	2.41	2.32	2.18	2.04	1.88	1.79	1.70	1.59	1.47	1.32	1.00

Reproduced, with permission of the trustees of Biometrika, from *Biometrika Tables for Statisticians*, vol. 1 (1966).

Table 10 Cutoff Points for the Distribution of the Wilcoxon Test Statistic

For sample size n, the table shows, for selected probabilities α, the numbers T_α such that $P(T \leq T_\alpha) = \alpha$, where the distribution of the random variable T is that of the Wilcoxon test statistic under the null hypothesis.

n	α				
	.005	.010	.025	.050	.100
4	0	0	0	0	1
5	0	0	0	1	3
6	0	0	1	3	4
7	0	1	3	4	6
8	1	2	4	6	9
9	2	4	6	9	11
10	4	6	9	11	15
11	6	8	11	14	18
12	8	10	14	18	22
13	10	13	18	22	27
14	13	16	22	26	32
15	16	20	26	31	37
16	20	24	30	36	43
17	24	28	35	42	49
18	28	33	41	48	56
19	33	38	47	54	63
20	38	44	53	61	70

Reproduced with permission from R. L. McCormack, "Extended tables of the Wilcoxon matched pairs signed rank statistics," *Journal of the American Statistical Association* 60 (1965).

Table 11 Cutoff Points for the Distribution of Spearman Rank Correlation Coefficient

For sample size n, the table shows, for selected probabilities α, the numbers $r_{s,\alpha}$ such that $P(r_s > r_{s,\alpha}) = \alpha$, where the distribution of the random variable r_s is that of Spearman rank correlation coefficient under the null hypothesis of no association.

n	α			
	.050	.025	.010	.005
5	.900	—	—	—
6	.829	.886	.943	—
7	.714	.786	.893	—
8	.643	.738	.833	.881
9	.600	.683	.783	.833
10	.564	.648	.745	.794
11	.523	.623	.736	.818
12	.497	.591	.703	.780
13	.475	.566	.673	.745
14	.457	.545	.646	.716
15	.441	.525	.623	.689
16	.425	.507	.601	.666
17	.412	.490	.582	.645
18	.399	.476	.564	.625
19	.388	.462	.549	.608
20	.377	.450	.534	.591
21	.368	.438	.521	.576
22	.359	.428	.508	.562
23	.351	.418	.496	.549
24	.343	.409	.485	.537
25	.336	.400	.475	.526
26	.329	.392	.465	.515
27	.323	.385	.456	.505
28	.317	.377	.448	.496
29	.311	.370	.440	.487
30	.305	.364	.432	.478

Reproduced with permission from E. G. Olds, "Distribution of sums of squares of rank differences for small samples," *Annals of Mathematical Statistics* 9 (1938).

Table 12 Cutoff Points for the Distribution of the Durbin-Watson Test Statistic

Let d_α be the number such that $P(d < d_\alpha) = \alpha$, where the random variable d has the distribution of the Durbin-Watson statistic under the null hypothesis of no autocorrelation in the regression errors. For probabilities $\alpha = .05$ and $\alpha = .01$, the tables show, for numbers of independent variables, K, values d_L and d_U such that $d_L \le d_\alpha \le d_U$, for numbers n of observations.

	$\alpha = .05$									
n	K									
	1		2		3		4		5	
	d_L	d_U	d_L	d_U	d_L	d_U	d_L	d_U	d_L	d_U
15	1.08	1.36	0.95	1.54	0.82	1.75	0.69	1.97	0.56	2.21
16	1.10	1.37	0.98	1.54	0.86	1.73	0.74	1.93	0.62	2.15
17	1.13	1.38	1.02	1.54	0.90	1.71	0.78	1.90	0.67	2.10
18	1.16	1.39	1.05	1.53	0.93	1.69	1.82	1.87	0.71	2.06
19	1.18	1.40	1.08	1.53	0.97	1.68	0.86	1.85	0.75	2.02
20	1.20	1.41	1.10	1.54	1.00	1.68	0.90	1.83	0.79	1.99
21	1.22	1.42	1.13	1.54	1.03	1.67	0.93	1.81	0.83	1.96
22	1.24	1.43	1.15	1.54	1.05	1.66	0.96	1.80	0.86	1.94
23	1.26	1.44	1.17	1.54	1.08	1.66	0.99	1.79	0.90	1.92
24	1.27	1.45	1.19	1.55	1.10	1.66	1.01	1.78	0.93	1.90
25	1.29	1.45	1.21	1.55	1.12	1.66	1.04	1.77	0.95	1.89
26	1.30	1.46	1.22	1.55	1.14	1.65	1.06	1.76	0.98	1.88
27	1.32	1.47	1.24	1.56	1.16	1.65	1.08	1.76	1.01	1.86
28	1.33	1.48	1.26	1.56	1.18	1.65	1.10	1.75	1.03	1.85
29	1.34	1.48	1.27	1.56	1.20	1.65	1.12	1.74	1.05	1.84
30	1.35	1.49	1.28	1.57	1.21	1.65	1.14	1.74	1.07	1.83
31	1.36	1.50	1.30	1.57	1.23	1.65	1.16	1.74	1.09	1.83
32	1.37	1.50	1.31	1.57	1.24	1.65	1.18	1.73	1.11	1.82
33	1.38	1.51	1.32	1.58	1.26	1.65	1.19	1.73	1.13	1.81
34	1.39	1.51	1.33	1.58	1.27	1.65	1.21	1.73	1.15	1.81
35	1.40	1.52	1.34	1.58	1.28	1.65	1.22	1.73	1.16	1.80
36	1.41	1.52	1.35	1.59	1.29	1.65	1.24	1.73	1.18	1.80
37	1.42	1.53	1.36	1.59	1.31	1.66	1.25	1.72	1.19	1.80
38	1.43	1.54	1.37	1.59	1.32	1.66	1.26	1.72	1.21	1.79
39	1.43	1.54	1.38	1.60	1.33	1.66	1.27	1.72	1.22	1.79
40	1.44	1.54	1.39	1.60	1.34	1.66	1.29	1.72	1.23	1.79
45	1.48	1.57	1.43	1.62	1.38	1.67	1.34	1.72	1.29	1.78
50	1.50	1.59	1.46	1.63	1.42	1.67	1.38	1.72	1.34	1.77
55	1.53	1.60	1.49	1.64	1.45	1.68	1.41	1.72	1.38	1.77
60	1.55	1.62	1.51	1.65	1.48	1.69	1.44	1.73	1.41	1.77
65	1.57	1.63	1.54	1.66	1.50	1.70	1.47	1.73	1.44	1.77
70	1.58	1.64	1.55	1.67	1.52	1.70	1.49	1.74	1.46	1.77
75	1.60	1.65	1.57	1.68	1.54	1.71	1.51	1.74	1.49	1.77
80	1.61	1.66	1.59	1.69	1.56	1.72	1.53	1.74	1.51	1.77
85	1.62	1.67	1.60	1.70	1.57	1.72	1.55	1.75	1.52	1.77
90	1.63	1.68	1.61	1.70	1.59	1.73	1.57	1.75	1.54	1.78
95	1.64	1.69	1.62	1.71	1.60	1.73	1.58	1.75	1.56	1.78
100	1.65	1.69	1.63	1.72	1.61	1.74	1.59	1.76	1.57	1.78

Table 12 Cutoff Points for the Distribution of the Durbin-Watson Test Statistic Continued

	α = .01									
n	K									
	1		2		3		4		5	
	d_L	d_U	d_L	d_U	d_L	d_U	d_L	d_U	d_L	d_U
15	0.81	1.07	0.70	1.25	0.59	1.46	0.49	1.70	0.39	1.96
16	0.84	1.09	0.74	1.25	0.63	1.44	0.53	1.66	0.44	1.90
17	0.87	1.10	0.77	1.25	0.67	1.43	0.57	1.63	0.48	1.85
18	0.90	1.12	0.80	1.26	0.71	1.42	0.61	1.60	0.52	1.80
19	0.93	1.13	0.83	1.26	0.74	1.41	0.65	1.58	0.56	1.77
20	0.95	1.15	0.86	1.27	0.77	1.41	0.68	1.57	0.60	1.74
21	0.97	1.16	0.89	1.27	0.80	1.41	0.72	1.55	0.63	1.71
22	1.00	1.17	0.91	1.28	0.83	1.40	0.75	1.54	0.66	1.69
23	1.02	1.19	0.94	1.29	0.86	1.40	0.77	1.53	0.70	1.67
24	1.04	1.20	0.96	1.30	0.88	1.41	0.80	1.53	0.72	1.66
25	1.05	1.21	0.98	1.30	0.90	1.41	0.83	1.52	0.75	1.65
26	1.07	1.22	1.00	1.31	0.93	1.41	0.85	1.52	0.78	1.64
27	1.09	1.23	1.02	1.32	0.95	1.41	0.88	1.51	0.81	1.63
28	1.10	1.24	1.04	1.32	0.97	1.41	0.90	1.51	0.83	1.62
29	1.12	1.25	1.05	1.33	0.99	1.42	0.92	1.51	0.85	1.61
30	1.13	1.26	1.07	1.34	1.01	1.42	0.94	1.51	0.88	1.61
31	1.15	1.27	1.08	1.34	1.02	1.42	0.96	1.51	0.90	1.60
32	1.16	1.28	1.10	1.35	1.04	1.43	0.98	1.51	0.92	1.60
33	1.17	1.29	1.11	1.36	1.05	1.43	1.00	1.51	0.94	1.59
34	1.18	1.30	1.13	1.36	1.07	1.43	1.01	1.51	0.95	1.59
35	1.19	1.31	1.14	1.37	1.08	1.44	1.03	1.51	0.97	1.59
36	1.21	1.32	1.15	1.38	1.10	1.44	1.04	1.51	0.99	1.59
37	1.22	1.32	1.16	1.38	1.11	1.45	1.06	1.51	1.00	1.59
38	1.23	1.33	1.18	1.39	1.12	1.45	1.07	1.52	1.02	1.58
39	1.24	1.34	1.19	1.39	1.14	1.45	1.09	1.52	1.03	1.58
40	1.25	1.34	1.20	1.40	1.15	1.46	1.10	1.52	1.05	1.58
45	1.29	1.38	1.24	1.42	1.20	1.48	1.16	1.53	1.11	1.58
50	1.32	1.40	1.28	1.45	1.24	1.49	1.20	1.54	1.16	1.59
55	1.36	1.43	1.32	1.47	1.28	1.51	1.25	1.55	1.21	1.59
60	1.38	1.45	1.35	1.48	1.32	1.52	1.28	1.56	1.25	1.60
65	1.41	1.47	1.38	1.50	1.35	1.53	1.31	1.57	1.28	1.61
70	1.43	1.49	1.40	1.52	1.37	1.55	1.34	1.58	1.31	1.61
75	1.45	1.50	1.42	1.53	1.39	1.56	1.37	1.59	1.34	1.62
80	1.47	1.52	1.44	1.54	1.42	1.57	1.39	1.60	1.36	1.62
85	1.48	1.53	1.46	1.55	1.43	1.58	1.41	1.60	1.39	1.63
90	1.50	1.54	1.47	1.56	1.45	1.59	1.43	1.61	1.41	1.64
95	1.51	1.55	1.49	1.57	1.47	1.60	1.45	1.62	1.42	1.64
100	1.52	1.56	1.50	1.58	1.48	1.60	1.46	1.63	1.44	1.65

Reproduced with permission from J. Durbin and G. S. Watson, "Testing for serial correlation in least squares regression, II," *Biometrika* 38 (1951).

Table 13 Factors for Control Charts

	$\bar{X}$-CHARTS				s-CHARTS				R-CHARTS					
n	A	A_2	A_3	c_4	B_3	B_4	B_5	B_6	d_2	d_3	D_1	D_2	D_3	D_4
2	2.121	1.880	2.659	0.7979	0	3.267	0	2.606	1.128	0.853	0	3.686	0	3.267
3	1.732	1.023	1.954	0.8862	0	2.568	0	2.276	1.693	0.888	0	4.358	0	2.574
4	1.500	0.729	1.628	0.9213	0	2.266	0	2.088	2.059	0.880	0	4.698	0	2.282
5	1.342	0.577	1.427	0.9400	0	2.089	0	1.964	2.326	0.864	0	4.918	0	2.114
6	1.225	0.483	1.287	0.9515	0.030	1.970	0.029	1.874	2.534	0.848	0	5.078	0	2.004
7	1.134	0.419	1.182	0.9594	0.118	1.882	0.113	1.806	2.704	0.833	0.204	5.204	0.076	1.924
8	1.061	0.373	1.099	0.9650	0.185	1.815	0.179	1.751	2.847	0.820	0.388	5.306	0.136	1.864
9	1.000	0.337	1.032	0.969	0.239	1.761	0.232	1.707	2.970	0.808	0.547	5.393	0.184	1.816
10	0.949	0.308	0.975	0.9727	0.284	1.716	0.276	1.669	3.078	0.797	0.687	5.469	0.223	1.777
11	0.905	0.285	0.927	0.9754	0.321	1.679	0.313	1.637	3.173	0.787	0.811	5.535	0.256	1.744
12	0.866	0.266	0.886	0.9776	0.354	1.646	0.346	1.610	3.258	0.778	0.922	5.594	0.283	1.717
13	0.832	0.249	0.850	0.9794	0.382	1.618	0.374	1.585	3.336	0.770	1.025	5.647	0.307	1.693
14	0.802	0.235	0.817	0.9810	0.406	1.594	0.399	1.563	3.407	0.763	1.118	5.696	0.328	1.672
15	0.775	0.223	0.789	0.9823	0.428	1.572	0.421	1.544	3.472	0.756	1.203	5.741	0.347	1.653
16	0.750	0.212	0.763	0.9835	0.448	1.552	0.440	1.526	3.532	0.750	1.282	5.782	0.363	1.637
17	0.728	0.203	0.739	0.9845	0.466	1.534	0.458	1.511	3.588	0.744	1.356	5.820	0.378	1.622
18	0.707	0.194	0.718	0.9854	0.482	1.518	0.475	1.496	3.640	0.739	1.424	5.856	0.391	1.608
19	0.688	0.187	0.698	0.9862	0.497	1.503	0.490	1.483	3.689	0.734	1.487	5.891	0.403	1.597
20	0.671	0.180	0.680	0.9869	0.510	1.490	0.504	1.470	3.735	0.729	1.549	5.921	0.415	1.585
21	0.655	0.173	0.663	0.9876	0.523	1.477	0.516	1.459	3.778	0.724	1.605	5.951	0.425	1.575
22	0.640	0.167	0.647	0.9882	0.534	1.466	0.528	1.448	3.819	0.720	1.659	5.979	0.434	1.566
23	0.626	0.162	0.633	0.9887	0.545	1.455	0.539	1.438	3.858	0.716	1.710	6.006	0.443	1.557
24	0.612	0.157	0.619	0.9892	0.555	1.445	0.549	1.429	3.895	0.712	1.759	6.031	0.451	1.548
25	0.600	0.153	0.606	0.9896	0.565	1.435	0.559	1.420	3.931	0.708	1.806	6.056	0.459	1.541

Source: Adapted from Table 27 of ASTM STP 15D ASTM *Manual on Presentation of Data and Control Chart Analysis.* ©1976 American Society for Testing and Materials, Philadelphia, PA.

Table 14 Cumulative Distribution Function of the Runs Test Statistic

For a given number n of observations, the table shows the probability, for a random time series, that the number of runs will not exceed K.

n	K																		
	2	3	4	5	6	7	8	9	10	11	12	13	14	15	16	17	18	19	20
6	.100	.300	.700	.900	1.000														
8	.029	.114	.371	.629	.886	.971	1.000												
10	.008	.040	.167	.357	.643	.833	.960	.992	1.000										
12	.002	.013	.067	.175	.392	.608	.825	.933	.987	.998	1.000								
14	.001	.004	.025	.078	.209	.383	.617	.791	.922	.975	.996	.999	1.000						
16	.000	.001	.009	.032	.100	.214	.405	.595	.786	.900	.968	.991	.999	1.000	1.000				
18	.000	.000	.003	.012	.044	.109	.238	.399	.601	.762	.891	.956	.988	.997	1.000	1.000	1.000		
20	.000	.000	.001	.004	.019	.051	.128	.242	.414	.586	.758	.872	.949	.981	.996	.999	1.000	1.000	1.000

Reproduced with permission from F. Swed and C. Eisenhart, "Tables for testing randomness of grouping in a sequence of alternatives," *Annals of Mathematical Statistics* 14 (1943).

Index

Tables